JOHN GAMBLE KIRKWOOD
COLLECTED WORKS

Selected Topics in Statistical Mechanics

Documents on Modern Physics

Edited by

ELLIOTT W. MONTROLL, Institute of Defense Analyses

GEORGE H. VINEYARD, Brookhaven National Laboratory

MAURICE LÉVY, Université de Paris

A. ABRAGAM, L'Effet Mössbauer
H. BACRY, Lectures on Group Theory
K. G. BUDDEN, Lectures on Magnetoionic Theory
J. W. CHAMBERLAIN, Motion of Charged Particles in the Earth's Magnetic Field
S. CHAPMAN, Solar Plasma and Geomagnetism and Aurora
H. CHIU, Neutrino Astrophysics
A. H. COTTRELL, Theory of Crystal Dislocations
R. H. DALITZ, The Quark Model for Elementary Particles
BRYCE S. DEWITT, Dynamical Theory of Groups and Fields
R. H. DICKE, The Theoretical Significance of Experimental Relativity
M. GOURDIN, Laws of Symmetry Theorem of T.C.P.
D. HESTENES, Space-Time Algebras
JOHN G. KIRKWOOD, Selected Topics in Statistical Mechanics
JOHN G. KIRKWOOD, Macromolecules
JOHN G. KIRKWOOD, Theory of Liquids
JOHN G. KIRKWOOD, Theory of Solutions
JOHN G. KIRKWOOD, Proteins
JOHN G. KIRKWOOD, Quantum Statistics and Cooperative Phenomena
JOHN G. KIRKWOOD, Shock Waves
JOHN G. KIRKWOOD, Dielectrics—Intermolecular Forces—Optical Rotation
V. KOURGANOFF, Stellar Nuclear Reactions and Internal Structure
ROBERT LATTÈS, Methods of Resolutions of Some Boundary Problems in Mathematical Physics
P. H. E. MEIJER, Quantum Statistical Mechanics
A. B. PIPPARD, The Dynamics of Conduction Electrons
H. REEVES, Stellar Evolution and Nucleosynthesis
L. SCHWARTZ, Applications of Distributions to the Theory of Elementary Particles in Quantum Mechanics
M. TINKHAM, Superconductivity

Additional volumes in preparation

JOHN GAMBLE KIRKWOOD
1907 – 1959

JOHN GAMBLE KIRKWOOD COLLECTED WORKS

General Editor

IRWIN OPPENHEIM

Professor of Chemistry
Massachusetts Institute of Technology

Selected Topics in Statistical Mechanics

Edited by

R. W. ZWANZIG

National Bureau of Standards
Washington, D.C.

GORDON AND BREACH

Science Publishers

New York · London · Paris

150 Fifth Avenue, New York, N.Y. 10011

For Great Britain and Europe:
Gordon and Breach Science Publishers, Ltd.
61 Carey Street, Chancery Lane, London, W.C.2, England

Library of Congress Catalog Card Number 65–16161

Distributed in France by:
Dunod Editeur
92 Rue Bonaparte, Paris 6, France

Distributed in Canada by:
The Ryerson Press
299 Queen Street West, Toronto 2B, Ontario

PRINTED IN ENGLAND BY W. S. COWELL LTD, IPSWICH

Documents on Modern Physics

Seventy years ago when the fraternity of physicists was smaller than the audience at a weekly physics colloquium in a major university a J. Willard Gibbs could, after ten years of thought, summarize his ideas on a subject in a few monumental papers or in a classic treatise. His competition did not intimidate him into a muddled correspondence with his favorite editor nor did it occur to his colleagues that their own progress was retarded by his leisurely publication schedule.

Today the dramatic phase of a new branch of physics spans less than a decade and subsides before the definitive treatise is published. Moreover modern physics is an extremely interconnected discipline and the busy practitioner of one of its branches must be kept aware of break-throughs in other areas. An expository literature which is clear and timely is needed to relieve him of the burden of wading through tentative and hastily written papers scattered in many journals.

To this end we have undertaken the editing of a new series, entitled *Documents on Modern Physics*, which will make available selected reviews, lecture notes, conference proceedings, and important collections of papers in branches of physics of special current interest. Complete coverage of a field will not be a primary aim. Rather, we will emphasize readability, speed of publication, and importance to students and research workers. The books will appear in low-cost paper-covered editions, as well as in cloth covers. The scope will be broad, the style informal.

From time to time, older branches of physics come alive again, and forgotten writings acquire relevance to recent developments. We expect to make a number of such works available by including them in this series along with new works.

ELLIOTT MONTROLL
GEORGE H. VINEYARD
MAURICE LÉVY

The Publishers wish to express their gratitude to the following organizations for permission to quote and reprint material from the journals and books mentioned:

The American Institute of Physics, for: *Journal of Chemical Physics*, 14, "The Statistical Mechanical Theory of Transport Processes. I. General Theory," pp. 180–201 (1946).

Journal of Chemical Physics, 15, "The Statistical Mechanical Theory of Transport Processes. II. Transport in Gases," pp. 72–76 (1947).

Journal of Chemical Physics, 17, "The Statistical Mechanical Theory of Transport Processes. III. The Coefficients of Shear and Bulk Viscosity of Liquids," pp. 988–994 (1949), with F. P. Buff and M. S. Green.

Journal of Chemical Physics, Vol. 19, No. 9, "The Statistical Mechanical Theory of Transport Processes. V. Quantum Hydrodynamics," pp. 1173–1180, September, 1951. J. H. Irving and Robert W. Zwanzig.

Journal of Chemical Physics, 56, "The Macroscopic Equations of Transport," p. 1048 (1952), with Bryce Crawford, Jr.

Journal of Chemical Physics, Vol. 21, No. 11, "The Statistical Mechanical Theory of Transport Processes. VI. A Calculation of the Coefficients of Shear and Bulk Viscosity of Liquids," pp. 2050–2055, November, 1953, with Robert W. Zwanzig, Kenneth Stripp and Irwin Oppenheim.

Journal of Chemical Physics, Vol. 22, No. 5, "Statistical Mechanical Theory of Transport Processes. VII. The Coefficient of Thermal Conductivity of Monatomic Liquids," pp. 783–790, May, 1954, with Robert W. Zwanzig, Irwin Oppenheim, Berni J. Alder.

Journal of Chemical Physics, Vol. 22, No. 6, "The Statistical Mechanical Theory of Transport Processes. VIII. Quantum Theory of Transport in Gases," pp. 1094–1103, June, 1954, with John Ross.

Journal of Chemical Physics, Vol. 24, No. 2, "Statistical Mechanical Theory of Transport Processes. IX. Contribution to the Theory of Brownian Motion," pp. 375–380, February, 1956, with John Ross.

Journal of Chemical Physics, Vol. 27, No. 2, "Characteristic Equations for Reactive Flow," p. 596, August, 1957, with W. W. Wood.

Journal of Chemical Physics, Vol. 28, No. 1, "Statistical Mechanics of Transport Processes. XI. Equations of Transport in Multicomponent Systems," pp. 136–145, January, 1958, with Richard J. Bearman.

Journal of Chemical Physics, Vol. 29, No. 4, "Statistical Mechanics of Irreversible Processes in Polymer Solutions," pp. 909–913, October, 1958, with Jerome J. Erpenbeck.

"The Statistical Mechanical Theory of Irreversible Processes in Solutions of Flexible Macromolecules," International Conference on Macromolecules in Amsterdam, September, 1949.

"The Statistical Mechanical Theory of Irreversible Processes," Nuovo Cimento, Supplement to Vol. VI, series IX, No. 2, p. 234 (1949).

Journal of Applied Physics, Vol. 28, No. 4, "Hydrodynamics of a Reacting and Relaxing Fluid," pp. 395–398, with William W. Wood.

"The Statistical Mechanical Basis of the Boltzmann Equation," with John Ross, Proceedings of the International Symposium on Transport Processes in Statistical Mechanics.

"The Statistical Mechanical Basis of the Enskog Theory of Transport in Dense Gases," Nuovo Cimento, N.1, Supplement Vol. 9, Serie X, with S. A. Rice.

Preface to the Kirkwood Papers

The following pages contain a reprinting of all the articles published by John Gamble Kirkwood and some of his reports to government agencies. Kirkwood's scientific work covered a wide variety of fields and for this reason it seemed suitable to publish his collected works in two formats. The first consists of a series of eight paper-back volumes each of which presents all of Kirkwood's work on a restricted topic. The papers in each of these volumes are, in general, arranged chronologically. The second format consists of two hard-cover volumes in which all of his work is arranged chronologically. The hard-cover volumes contain all of the papers in the paper-back volumes in addition to several miscellaneous papers which do not appear in any of the paper-back volumes.

Each of the paper-back volumes has been edited by a distinguished scientist who has been closely associated with that portion of Kirkwood's work covered in the particular volume. These editors have written introductions for the various volumes reviewing Kirkwood's work and placing it in historical perspective. These introductions also appear in the hard-cover volumes. Since all of the papers have been reset in type for these volumes, it has been possible to incorporate into them addenda and corrigenda that have appeared in the literature as well as those that have been supplied by co-authors of the various papers and by the editors. It has been the responsibility of the individual editors to incorporate this material and to proof-read the final manuscripts.

The contents and editors of the individual paper-back volumes are:

Dielectrics; Intermolecular Forces; Optical Rotation
Edited by R. B. Cole
Solution Theory: Non-Electrolytes and Electrolytes
Edited by J. C. Poirier and Z. W. Salsburg
Quantum Statistics; Cooperative Phenomena
Edited by F. H. Stillinger
Shock Waves Edited by W. W. Wood
Liquid Theory Edited by B. J. Alder
Proteins Edited by G. Scatchard
Transport Processes Edited by R. W. Zwanzig
Macromolecules Edited by P. L. Auer

A bibliography of Kirkwood's work is given in the hard-cover volumes.

Acknowledgments are due to the co-authors of many of the papers for supplying corrigenda and to the editors of the individual volumes without whom this work could not have been published. A special acknowledgment has to be made to Platonia K. Kirkwood for her help and advice in the preparation of this work.

IRWIN OPPENHEIM
Cambridge, Massachusetts

Contents

I. *The Statistical Mechanicai Theory of Transport Processes. I. General Theory* ... 1
- I. Introduction and General Theory ... 1
  - 1. Part A: Introductory Remarks ... 1
  - 2. Part B: Basic Concepts and Definitions ... 2
- II. The Theory of Brownian Motion ... 11
- III. The Distribution Functions ... 16
- IV. The Friction Constant ... 22
- V. Appendix: Remarks on the Mathematical Theory of the Operator ... 28

II. *Errata: Statistical Mechanics of Transport Processes. I. General Theory* ... 30

III. *The Statistical Mechanical Theory of Transport Processes. II. Transport in Gases* ... 31

IV. *Errata: Statistical Mechanics of Transport Processes. II. Transport in Gases* ... 37

V. *The Statistical Mechanical Theory of Transport Processes. III. The Coefficients of Shear and Bulk Viscosity of Liquids* ... 38
- I. ... 38
- II. ... 39
- III. ... 43
- IV. ... 46

VI. *Errata: The Statistical Mechanical Theory of Transport Processes. III. The Coefficients of Shear and Bulk Viscosity of Liquids* ... 51

VII. *The Statistical Mechanical Theory of Transport Processes. IV. The Equations of Hydrodynamics* ... 52
- I. Introduction ... 52
- I. The Phenomenological Theory ... 53
- II. Statistical Mechanical Theory—The Distribution Function and Expectation Values ... 55
- III. Statistical Mechanical Expressions for Densities ... 56
- IV. The Equation of Continuity ... 59
- V. The Hydrodynamical Equation of Motion (Momentum Transport) ... 59
- VI. The Energy Transport Equation ... 64
- VII. Compilation of Results ... 70
- VIII. Appendix ... 73

VIII. *The Statistical Mechanical Theory of Transport Processes. V. Quantum Hydrodynamics* ... 76
- I. Distribution Functions in Classical Statistical Mechanics ... 76
- II. Transition to Quantum Mechanics ... 77
- III. The Equations of Hydrodynamics ... 84
- IV. Conclusions ... 90
- V. Acknowledgement ... 90

IX. *The Statistical Mechanical Theory of Transport Processes. VI. A Calculation of the Coefficients of Shear and Bulk Viscosity of Liquids* 91
I. Introduction 91
II. Basic Equations 92
III. Bulk Viscosity 96
IV. Shear Viscosity 96
V. Final Results 98
VI. Appendix 1 98
VII. Appendix 2 99

X. *The Statistical Mechanical Theory of Transport Processes. VII. The Coefficient of Thermal Conductivity of Monatomic Liquids* 101
I. 101
II. 102
III. 105
IV. 106
V. 110

XI. *The Statistical Mechanical Theory of Transport Processes. VIII. Quantum Theory of Transport in Gases* 115
Appendix A 128
Appendix B 129
Appendix C 132

XII. *The Statistical Mechanical Theory of Transport Processes. IX. Contribution to the Theory of Brownian Motion* 134
Appendix A 142

XIII. *The Statistical Mechanical Theory of Transport Processes. X. The Heat of Transport in Binary Liquids Solutions* 143
I. Introduction 143
II. Phenomenological Theory 144
III. Statistical-Mechanical Expressions for the Densities and Fluxes 144
IV. The General Expression for the Heat of Transport 147
V. An Approximate Formula for the Heat of Transport 151

XIV. *The Statistical Mechanics of Transport Processes. XI. Equations of Transport in Multi-component Systems* 153
I. Introduction 153
II. The Phenomenological Theory 154
III. Statistical Mechanical Theory—The Distribution Function and Expressions for the Densities 157
IV. Equations of Transport 160
V. Further Development of the Equations of Motion and Heat Transport 165

XV. *The Statistical Mechanical Theory of Transport Processes. XII. Dense Rigid Sphere Fluids* 172
I. Introduction 172
II. Derivation of Transport Equation 173
III. The Dense Hard Sphere Fluid 176
IV. Coefficients of Viscosity and Heat Conduction of a Dense Fluid of Rigid Spheres 179
V. Discussion 183
VI. Acknowledgment 186

XVI. *The Statistical Mechanics of Transport Processes. XIV. Linear Relations in Multi-component Systems* 187
I. 188
II. 193
III. 194
IV. 196
V. 197
VI. 198

XVII. *The Statistical Mechanical Theory of Irreversible Processes in Solutions of Flexible Macromolecules* 201
I. Introduction 201
II. General Theory 201
III. Application to Visco-Elastic Behavior 207

XVIII. *The Statistical Mechanics of Irreversible Processes in Polymer Solutions* 211
I. Introduction 211
II. General Theory 212
III. Intrinsic Viscosity 216

XIX. *Erratum: The Statistical Mechanics of Irreversible Processes in Polymer Solutions* 221

XX. *On an Approximate Theory of Transport in Dense Media* 223
I. Introduction 223
II. The Coefficient of Self-Diffusion 224
III. The Stress Tensor 228
IV. Thermal Conductivity 231
V. Evaluation of Coefficients of Shear Viscosity and Thermal Conductivity for a Pure Fluid 232
VI. Discussion 234
VII. Acknowledgments 237

XXI. *On the Kinetic Theory of Dense Fluids. VIII. Some Comments on the Formal Computation of the Non-equilibrium Distribution Function of a Fluid* 238
I. Introduction 238
II. The Formal Cluster Expansion 240
III. Approximate Solutions for the Green's Functions 246

XXII. *The Statistical Mechanical Basis of the Enskog Theory of Transport in Dense Gases* 253
I. Interventi E Discussioni 254

XXIII. *The Statistical Mechanical Theory of Irreversible Processes* 255
I. 255
II. 256
III. 258

XXIV. *The Statistical Mechanical Basis of the Boltzmann Equation* 261

Preface

Kirkwood's work on non-equilibrium statistical mechanics is contained principally in a series of fourteen articles bearing the title "Statistical Mechanical Theory of Transport Processes". Articles in this series will be referred to by number in the following survey, as SMT-1, SMT-2, etc.

For completeness, seven other articles are included. Three of these are reports delivered at scientific conferences, and their content overlaps that of other articles in the SMT series to a considerable extent. Two papers deal with the theory of transport processes in polymer solutions. While this topic is covered comprehensively in another part of the Collected Works, we felt that these particular papers should be included here also, because of their fundamental character.

SMT-1: The first article of the SMT series was published in 1946. It is interesting to note that two other important developments in the theory of irreversible processes were published the same year, by Born and Green,[1] and by Bogolyubov.[2] These workers took substantially different points of view; but nevertheless they developed simultaneously and independently the so-called hierarchy method. This method is concerned with the recursive set of integral equations for phase space distribution functions of 1, 2, 3 . . . molecules in a fluid. (Hierarchy methods were actually introduced first, in 1935, by Kirkwood and by Yvon[3] in connection with problems in equilibrium statistical thermodynamics.) This set of integral equations is now commonly called the BBGKY hierarchy, for Bogolyubov, Born, Green, Kirkwood, and Yvon.

We propose to discuss the first article of the SMT series in some detail; partly because it is the foundation for later articles in the series, and partly because of its great influence on the historical development of non-equilibrium statistical mechanics.

The point of view taken by Kirkwood in this article was influenced substantially by previous work on transport processes in electrolyte solutions, notably by Debye, Falkenhagen, and Onsager and Fuoss. (References are given in SMT-1.) The characteristic feature of these investigations was a borrowing of concepts and mathematical methods from the theory of Brownian motion. In particular, these investigations were based on the possibility of separating forces on ions in solution into three physically distinct categories: Coulomb forces due to charges on other ions, Stokes' law frictional forces due to the viscosity of the solvent, and randomly fluctuating forces due to small scale molecular motions. In Brownian motion theory, the fluctuating force is related in a rather simple way to the frictional force, so that the important parameters of the system are the ionic charges and radii, their concentrations, and the viscosity and dielectric constant of the solvent. The theory that was constructed along these lines by Onsager and Fuoss is quantitatively successful in predicting ionic contributions to transport coefficients in dilute solutions.

---

[1] M. Born and H. S. Green, *Proc. Roy. Soc.* **A 188**, 10 (1946).

[2] N. N. Bogolyubov, *J. Phys. U.S.S.R.* **10**, 256, 265 (1946).

[3] J. Yvon, *Statistique des Fluides et L'Equation D'Etat,* Actualites Scientifique et Industrielles, No. 203. Hermann et Cie., Paris, 1935.

The success of these investigations is especially remarkable in view of the fact that Brownian motion theory was invented to describe random motions of particles that are very large compared with atoms, and that there was no reason to expect the theory to be valid for ions of atomic size. It is remarkable also that Stokes' law turns out to be approximately correct for ions; the principal uncertainty in its application lies in the proper choice of atomic radius (complicated by the question of ionic hydration).

Kirkwood was influenced also by the work of Chandrasekhar on dynamic friction in stellar clusters. (See Ref. 5 of SMT-1 for further references.) Stellar clusters and ionic solutions have only one feature in common: the important interactions vary inversely with distance. Among the many differences, a significant one is that there is no medium or solvent in a stellar cluster, so that there can be no Stokes' law friction. Nevertheless, Chandrasekhar successfully exploited Brownian motion ideas. Instead of postulating the necessary frictional force, he derived it from the gravitational attraction by means of statistical mechanical arguments. Essentially the same approach is now commonly used in plasma physics.

We remark here parenthetically that the *linear trajectory method* of calculating the friction constant, often referred to in the SMT series but never explained there, was modelled on similar calculations by Chandrasekhar. This method has been described in detail recently by Helfand.[4]

The publication in 1943 of Chandrasekhar's review article on stochastic processes in physics and astronomy also had a substantial influence on Kirkwood's work. This review article set forth, in an exceptionally comprehensive and lucid way, the assumptions and physical ideas that go into the theory of Brownian motion. Further, it called attention to Kramers' synthesis of the Liouville equation of classical statistical mechanics and the Fokker-Planck equation of Brownian motion theory, leading to a theory of random processes in phase space. One of the great achievements of SMT-1 was a derivation of Kramers' equation from the principles of statistical mechanics, without introducing *ad hoc* assumptions of randomness.

Kirkwood believed that the theory of irreversible processes had to be based on a particular theory of measurement. In SMT-1, macroscopic measurements are defined as involving three distinct operations. The first is a *sampling* of an individual system from a statistical ensemble. The second is time-averaging, or, more often, *time-smoothing* the property under observation over an interval of time that is long on a molecular time scale but short on a macroscopic (or hydrodynamic) time scale. The third operation is *coarse-graining*, i.e., averaging over a domain of configuration space that is molecularly large and macroscopically small. These operations are given a mathematical form in the first section of SMT-1, from Eq. (11) to Eq. (19).

Certain logical problems arise in connection with smoothing processes. Let us consider, for example, the time-smoothing operation as applied to the phase space distribution function $f(R^N, p^N; t)$ of the entire N molecule system. The time-smoothed distribution function, as defined by Kirkwood, is

$$\bar{f}(R^N, p^N; t) = \frac{1}{\tau}\int_0^{\tau} ds\, f(R^N, p^N; t+s).$$

It is easy to see that the smoothed function $\bar{f}$ obeys exactly the same Liouville

[4] E. Helfand, *Physics of Fluids* **4**, 681 (1961).

equation as the unsmoothed f. Also, if one knows the smoothed $\bar{f}$ as a function of time, then one can extract the unsmoothed f from this information. (The mathematics of unsmoothing or inverse smoothing have been discussed by van der Pol.[5])

For a smoothing operation to have an effect, some information must be discarded. This is not done by Kirkwood's definition of $\bar{f}$ as a floating time average. Kirkwood emphasized perhaps too much the formal and philosophical part of the smoothing operation, and did not call enough attention to certain associated operations which had the effect of discarding information. In reading SMT-1, it is important to remember that some of the approximations made in the course of derivations are best understood as the *discarding* part of time-smoothing.[6]

The two main topics of SMT-1 are the general theory of Brownian motion of a molecule in a fluid, and the development of mathematical techniques and notations that are put to use in subsequent articles.

Kirkwood's molecular Brownian motion theory follows in broad outline the phenomenological theory presented by Kramers and Chandrasekhar. In particular, Kirkwood makes the same basic Brownian motion approximation. Denote by $\Delta \boldsymbol{p}(\tau)$ the change in momentum of a specified molecule, during an interval τ (the time-smoothing interval) that is hydrodynamically short but molecularly long, as a result of interactions with other molecules of the fluid. The basic Brownian motion approximation is that certain quantities can be expanded in powers of $\Delta \boldsymbol{p}(\tau)$, and that only the first and second powers need to be kept. That is, $\Delta \boldsymbol{p}(\tau)$ is "small enough".

This assumption is familiar in conventional Brownian motion theory, and can be justified there by observing that Brownian particles are very heavy compared with the surrounding molecules, so that their momenta cannot change very much during collisions. Furthermore, this assumption has been justified, by Ross, in the limiting case where the interaction of the specified molecule with its surroundings is weak; the argument is given in SMT-9.

But this assumption cannot be correct for gases at low density. Here the change in momentum is due to binary collisions, and these are not necessarily weak. In fact, Kirkwood's assumption would have the effect of converting the correct Boltzmann equation into an incorrect Fokker–Planck equation. Kirkwood clearly recognized this difficulty, and consequently he approached the kinetic theory of gases in a different way (SMT-2).

It may be that this assumption is correct for liquids: one can suppose that very many small changes in momentum occur during the interval τ, and that they mostly cancel out so that $\Delta \boldsymbol{p}$ is small. But this must be regarded as conjecture. So far, there is no entirely convincing theoretical argument.

By means of this assumption, Kirkwood obtained the Langevin equation for the momentum of a molecule in a fluid, and also the Fokker-Planck equation for the time dependence of one- and two-particle distribution

---

[5] B. van der Pol, in *Probability and Related Topics in Physical Sciences*, by M. Kac. Interscience Publ. Inc., New York, 1959.

[6] Some years ago we analysed a special kind of Brownian motion using Kirkwood's ideas, but adding to them an explicit discarding operation—the dropping of high frequency components of time-dependent quantities. Once high frequency components are discarded, it is not possible to regain them, and inverse smoothing does not work. See R. Zwanzig, *Physics of Fluids* **2**, 12 (1959).

functions. The Fokker-Planck equations are used in SMT-3, 6, and 7 in the calculation of transport coefficients.

In connection with Brownian motion theory, SMT-1 introduced a molecular theory of the friction constant ζ. This quantity is the coefficient of proportionality in the relation between frictional force and velocity. Kirkwood derived a statistical mechanical expression for ζ, as the time integral of the time-correlation function of the fluctuating force on the molecule. This was the first transport coefficient to be given in such form; some years later, M. S. Green[7] used a generalization of Kirkwood's ideas to express a wide class of transport coefficients in terms of time-correlation functions.

The calculation of the friction coefficient poses serious difficulties. Throughout the SMT series, various estimates are mentioned; they are all in rough agreement with each other, and with experiment (self-diffusion), but none can be regarded as better than intelligent guesses. The calculation of time-correlation functions for liquids is still an important unsolved problem.

SMT-1 contains a preliminary announcement of statistical mechanical expressions for hydrodynamic quantities, in particular the stress tensor and heat current density. These expressions are derived in detail in SMT-4 (classical mechanics) and SMT-5 (quantum mechanics).

In concluding this survey of SMT-1, we mention that this article was the first in modern times in which Liouville operators are used in practical calculations. These operators were invented by Koopman, and applied extensively by von Neumann in providing a firm mathematical basis for ergodic theory. Kirkwood saw that they could be used also in a more practical way, just as the Hamiltonian operator is used in quantum mechanics. The present widespread use of Liouville operator methods in statistical mechanics, particularly by Prigogine and his co-workers, is due principally to the influence of SMT-1.

SMT-2, 8, 12, 13: In the first of these articles, Kirkwood applies the general theory of SMT-1 to a derivation of the Boltzmann equation of the kinetic theory of gases. It should be noted that there are many competing derivations; they all have different degrees of rigor and physical plausibility. Perhaps the most interesting feature of the derivation in SMT-2 is the treatment of pairs of molecules in periodic orbits. The conclusion is comforting: they play no role in the density range with which the Boltzmann equation is concerned.

Kirkwood's derivation makes use of time-smoothing. Its use, however, appears to be not so much a philosophical necessity as a mathematical convenience in integrating the Liouville equation for a pair of colliding particles. The smoothing time is taken to be longer than the duration of a collision, but shorter than the time between successive collisions of the same particle.

A later article, SMT-8, presents the quantum mechanical generalization of this work. The extra complications of particle statistics are also treated in this article.

SMT-12 uses much the same ideas in the derivation of the Enskog equation, which is concerned with the kinetic theory of rigid spheres at arbitrary density. Here, the smoothing time is taken to be infinitesimal—so that at most one binary collision can occur during this interval. Consequently, the derivation does not take account of what might be called pseudo-triple collisions, i.e., triplets of correlated successive binary collisions involving just three particles.

---

[7] M. S. Green, *J. Chem. Phys.* **20**, 1281 (1952); **22**, 398 (1954).

This departure from the original conception of time-smoothing as a necessary part of the measurement process shows clearly the importance of time-smoothing as a mathematical tool for the integration of the Liouville equation.

SMT-13 contains a detailed derivation of formulas for transport coefficients, starting from the Enskog equation obtained in SMT-12.

SMT-3, 6: These two articles are concerned with the theory of viscosity of a monatomic fluid. SMT-3 contains the general theory and a preliminary numerical calculation. The treatment of bulk viscosity given here is incorrect: SMT-6 gives the corrected theory.

The main difference between these two articles, with respect to numerical calculations and results, lies in the kind of radial distribution functions available at the time. It turns out that, at a crucial stage of the theory, one must solve a differential equation containing the equilibrium radial distribution function of the fluid. In 1949 little was known about radial distribution functions of real liquids (e.g., argon at its normal boiling point); so a rough approximation was made, having as its only virtue mathematical convenience in solving the differential equation. In 1953, integral equations for the radial distribution function of argon had been solved numerically; thus the same differential equation was solved again, this time by numerical methods. The results of the calculation are not especially encouraging.

SMT-3 contains the first published estimate of the friction constant. Because the idea underlying this estimate was not published there, we give an outline here. The starting point is Kirkwood's formula

$$\zeta = \frac{1}{3kT} \int_0^\tau \langle \mathbf{F}(0) \cdot \mathbf{F}(t) \rangle \, dt,$$

where $\mathbf{F}(t)$ is the total force on a given molecule at time t. We assume first that the time-correlation function of the force decays exponentially,

$$\langle \mathbf{F}(0) \cdot \mathbf{F}(t) \rangle = \langle \mathbf{F}(0) \cdot \mathbf{F}(0) \rangle \, e^{-t/\lambda}.$$

Then we assume that the time-smoothing interval τ is much longer than λ, so that

$$\zeta = \frac{1}{3kT} \langle \mathbf{F}(0) \cdot \mathbf{F}(0) \rangle \, \lambda.$$

Finally, we assume that the decay time λ is identical to the characteristic Brownian motion time m/ζ,

$$\lambda = m/\zeta;$$

The result is

$$\zeta^2 = \frac{m}{3kT} \langle \mathbf{F}(0) \cdot \mathbf{F}(0) \rangle$$

This can be transformed, by partial integrations, into Eq. (40) of SMT-3.

In SMT-6 the linear trajectory approximation to the friction constant was used instead. As we have mentioned, a detailed treatment was given by Helfand.[4]

The calculations presented in SMT-3 and 6 are based on a particular method of solution of the generalized Fokker-Planck equation. Alternative methods have been proposed by Lebowitz, Frisch, and Helfand.[8]

SMT-4, 5: In the statistical mechanical theory of transport processes, it is of the greatest importance to know what molecular quantities correspond to such macroscopic quantities as fluid velocity, stress tensor, heat current density, etc. These correspondences are established here, first using classical mechanics (SMT-4) and then using quantum mechanics (SMT-5).

A later treatment by Massignon[9] avoids certain expansions used in SMT-4 and 5, and presents a more careful discussion of the use of delta function techniques.

The quantum mechanical phase space distribution function invented by Wigner is used in the derivations in SMT-5. This topic has been reviewed recently in great detail by Mori, Oppenheim, and Ross.[10] We wish to mention here that the utility of the Wigner function method depends on the validity of the Weyl correspondence between classical quantities and quantum mechanical observables; and that the Weyl correspondence has been shown by Shewell[11] to have certain unsatisfactory features.

SMT-7: This article contains a calculation of the thermal conductivity of argon at its normal boiling point. It uses the same approach, and the same equilibrium radial distribution function and friction constant, as the viscosity calculation of SMT-6.

An interesting fact concerning this calculation (not recorded in the article) is that the final computed value for the thermal conductivity of argon was obtained several weeks before the publication of Uhlir's experimental value. The agreement between theory and experiment was much better than we had expected at that time.

SMT-9: As mentioned in the discussion of SMT-1, Kirkwood's Brownian motion method requires that the change in momentum of a specified molecule be small during the smoothing interval τ. This requirement was investigated in SMT-9 by means of a perturbation expansion. Ross found that the Brownian motion method is exact only in the limit of weak interactions. He found also that the linear trajectory approximation to the friction constant was exact in this limit.

Subsequent to this, similar results have been obtained by a variety of methods. We mention in particular the work of Prigogine and co-workers,[12] and Zwanzig.[13]

SMT-10, 11, 14: In these three articles the statistical mechanical theory of transport processes is extended to multi-component systems.

SMT-10 is concerned with an important special case, the theory of the heat of transport in a binary liquid mixture. SMT-11 contains a generalization of the work of Irving and Kirkwood (SMT-4) to multi-component systems; it contains also derivations of formulas for transport coefficients.

---

[8] J. Lebowitz, H. Frisch, and E. Helfand, *Physics of Fluids* **3**, 325 (1960).

[9] D. Massignon, *Mecanique Statistique des Fluids*, Dunod, Paris, 1957.

[10] H. Mori, I. Oppenheim, and J. Ross, in *Studies in Statistical Mechanics*, Vol. 1. Edited by J. DeBoer and G. E. Uhlenbeck. North Holland Publ. Co., Amsterdam, 1962.

[11] J. R. Shewell, *Am. J. of Physics* **27**, 16 (1959).

[12] I. Prigogine, *Non-Equilibrium Statistical Mechanics*, Interscience Publ. Inc., New York, 1962.

[13] R. Zwanzig, *J. Chem. Phys.* **33**, 1338 (1960); Lectures in Theor. Physics (Boulder) **3**, 106 (1960).

The general approach taken in these articles is rather different from earlier articles. In particular, the Brownian motion method, and its associated Fokker–Planck equations, are not used. Instead, irreversible effects are taken into account by means of the appropriate non-equilibrium distribution function; and this is constructed by finding the response of the system to external perturbations (external forces and heat reservoirs).

The resulting transport coefficients agree with those found by Green[7] using quite different methods.

This concludes our survey of the SMT series.

Polymers: Two articles on the statistical mechanics of irreversible processes in polymer solutions, one by Kirkwood (1949), and the other by Erpenbeck and Kirkwood (1958), are of particular interest because of their fundamental character.

The approach taken here involves a detailed analysis of Brownian motion in the space of the internal coordinates of the polymer chain (especially, the angles between various chemical bonds in the chain). A novel feature is the introduction of a non-Euclidean configuration space or "chain-space". The internal motions of the polymer chain, and the interactions of the chain with the velocity field of the solution, are described by a generalized Fokker-Planck equation involving the metric tensor of chain-space and a generalized diffusion tensor in this space. This remarkably elegant approach is much simpler than it appears at first; but one needs a slight acquaintance with the ideas and notation of tensor calculus to appreciate its beauty and power.

The Statistical Mechanical Theory of Transport Processes. I. General Theory

JOHN G. KIRKWOOD, *Baker Laboratory, Cornell University, Ithaca, New York*
(Received October 13, 1945)

Outlines are sketched for a general statistical mechanical theory of transport processes; e.g., diffusion, heat transfer, fluid flow, and response to time-dependent external force fields. In the case of gases the theory leads to the Maxwell-Boltzmann integro-differential equation of transport. In the case of liquids and solutions, it leads to a generalized theory of Brownian motion, in which the friction constant is explicitly related to the intermolecular forces acting in the system. Specific applications are postponed for treatment in later articles.

I. INTRODUCTION AND GENERAL THEORY

Part A: Introductory Remarks

The equilibrium theory of statistical mechanics has achieved a satisfactory general formulation at the hands of Gibbs and of later investigators. It provides a systematic interpretation from the molecular standpoint of the equilibrium behavior of thermodynamic systems. Of equal physico-chemical importance are the irreversible processes by which thermodynamic systems attain equilibrium in response to changes in external restraints. In addition to chemical reaction, the most common irreversible processes are the transport processes; diffusion, heat transfer, fluid flow, and response to external forces dependent upon time. Although much has been written on the interpretation of transport processes from the molecular standpoint, no systematic statistical mechanical theory has yet been formulated. In the present article, we shall suggest certain lines of thought on which we believe such a general theory of transport processes might be based. Since we shall formulate the theory within the frame of classical statistical mechanics, we shall not treat chemical reactions, which require the introduction of quantum-mechanical ideas and which are tolerably well described by the transition state theory of Eyring and Polanyi.[1] Quantum-mechanical generalization of the methods to be discussed will be postponed for later treatment.

Since the literature on transport processes is extensive and varied, we shall give here only a few key references and limit our preliminary remarks to a brief mention of the principal methods which have been used in investigating them. An exact and rigorous theory of transport exists for gases at sufficiently low density to be amenable to binary collision analysis. This theory is based upon the Maxwell-Boltzmann integro-differential equation, the consequences

---

[1] See Gladstone, Laidler, and Eyring, *Theory of Rate Processes* (McGraw-Hill Book Company, Inc., New York, 1941).

of which have been worked out in detail by Chapman and Enskog.[2] A satisfactory theory also exists for transport in dilute solutions, based upon the theory of Brownian motion, the foundations of which are due to Einstein.[3] The theory has been used very successfully in the treatment of irreversible processes in electrolyte solutions by Debye, Onsager, Falkenhagen, and others.[4] Recently Chandrasekar[5] has written an elegant review of the foundations and methods of the theory of Brownian motion, containing many new results, as well as an extensive bibliography. Although self-consistent, the theory of Brownian motion suffers from the defect that it contains an empirical friction constant related to inter-molecular forces and molecular structure in a manner not described by the theory. A semi-phenomenological discussion of the Thomson reciprocal relations in coupled transport processes has been given by Onsager[6] and is recommended for its perspectives on the general aspects of the problem of transport. Finally, there have been developed numerous model theories of transport processes, which are based upon simplified representations of the underlying elementary mechanisms. Significant results along these lines have been obtained in recent years by Eyring[1] and his co-workers using the transition state theory.

In the theoretical developments to be presented here, we shall attempt to integrate many of the ideas latent in the kinetic theory of gases and in the theory of Brownian motion into a systematic formulation. Although the notation is necessarily rather complicated, we have written from the physical rather than the mathematical standpoint. Although many mathematical problems are raised, the solution of which would require special and detailed investigation, none but relatively simple mathematical operations are employed in the development of the theory.

Part B: Basic Concepts and Definitions

The macroscopic state of a system of molecules is specified by a small number of molar variables, for example temperature, composition, and parameters of external force. Since its dynamical state is incompletely defined by the molar variables, the macroscopic behavior of the system requires interpretation from the standpoint of statistical mechanics, if a description in molecular terms is desired.

On the other hand, a phenomenological description of macroscopic behavior, without reference to the molecular structure of the system, is possible. Equilibrium behavior is described by thermodynamics. When the values of the molar variables are inconsistent with the conditions for thermodynamic equilibrium, transport processes occur, for example diffusion, heat transfer, and fluid flow. The most common transport processes are macroscopically described by the hydrodynamic equations of continuity, motion, and energy transport, supplemented by certain empirically established relations connecting the mass and heat currents and the stress tensor with the gradients of the molar variables or functions of those variables, for example, the chemical

[2] See Chapman and Cowling, *The Mathematical Theory of Non-Uniform Gases* (Cambridge University Press, New York, 1939).

[3] Einstein, *Ann. d. Physik* **17**, 549 (1905); **19**, 371 (1906).

[4] See L. Onsager and R. T. Fuoss, *J. Phys. Chem.* **36**, 2689 (1932).

[5] S. Chandrasekar, *Rev. Mod. Phys.* **15**, 1–89 (1943).

[6] L. Onsager ,*Phys. Rev.* **37**, 405 (1931); **38**, 2265 (1931).

potential gradients, temperature gradient, and rate of strain. The supplementary relations, constituting in their simplest form the laws of diffusion, heat conduction, and viscous fluid flow, contain certain material constants, the coefficients of diffusion, thermal conductivity, and viscosity, which depend upon the local macroscopic state of the system. The differential equations of transport, together with a specification of initial and boundary values of the molar variables, determine the macroscopic state as a function of time and position in the interior of the system.

The principal objectives of the statistical mechanical theory of transport are the formulation of the macroscopic differential equations of transport from the standpoint of molecular dynamics, the investigation of the limits of validity of the empirical laws of diffusion, heat conduction, and viscous flow, and the determination of the coefficients of diffusion, thermal conductivity, and viscosity, from the structure of the system on the molecular scale in terms of the forces acting between the molecules of which it is composed. A second important objective is the molecular interpretation of the linear stimulus-response theory[7] (based upon the concept of a relaxation time spectrum), describing departures from thermodynamic equilibrium, produced by time dependent external forces. This aspect of the theory is pertinent to such important problems as those of dielectric and mechanical loss.

As a preliminary step in the formulation of the theory of transport, it is necessary to examine the operation of measurement of a property in a system, the macroscopic state of which is changing with time. Since the dynamical state of a system of many degrees of freedom is incompletely defined by the small number of molar variables characterizing its macroscopic state, the first step in an operation of measurement consists in sampling a system at time t from an ensemble representing an initial distribution among accessible microscopic dynamical states. Although the initial distribution is arbitrary, we shall generally be concerned with distributions departing but slightly from statistical equilibrium, to be represented by the canonical or microcanonical ensembles of Gibbs, according to convenience. The second step in the operation or measurement consists in recording a time average of the property in question in the sample of the ensemble,[8] with specified dynamical state at time t, over an interval of time τ, macroscopically short, but microscopically long in a sense presently to be made more precise. If, as is customarily true for systems of many degrees of freedom, the fluctuation of the time averaged property in

---

[7] See, for example, Kármán and Biot, *Mathematical Methods in Engineering* (McGraw-Hill Book Company Inc., New York, 1940), Chap. X.

[8] From the logical point of view, we shall regard the class of macroscopic properties to be defined by the two operations described. That properties experimentally defined by thermodynamic measurements fall into this class, and involve the time as well as group average is fairly obvious. For example, instruments designed for the measurement of a representative property such as the pressure in a fluid in equilibrium automatically record a time average over an interval of the order of magnitude, say, of a second, a millisecond, or perhaps a microsecond. If the area of the surface on which the normal force is recorded is sufficiently small and the time resolution of the instrument sufficiently fine, fluctuations will of course be observed which are independent of the characteristics of the instrument. These fluctuations are, as is well known, responsible for the Brownian motion of colloidal particles. With sufficiently fine resolution, the force acting on unit area, therefore, ceases to be a macroscopic property in the sense in which we have defined this class. Thus, when we speak of pressure in a fluid as a macroscopic property, we mean the normal force per unit area averaged over a macroscopic interval of time of such a magnitude that the recorded average is not sensibly dependent on the magnitude of the interval.

the ensemble is sufficiently small, the complete operation of measurement yields a value differing by quantities of negligible order from a group average in the ensemble of the time average of the property over a microscopically long but macroscopically short interval τ. A third averaging operation is occasionally necessary, if the property in question is a point function in the three-dimensional configuration space of an individual molecule. This is an average over a macroscopically small domain of configuration space having a representative linear dimension large relative to the range of intermolecular force. The latter average is necessary in the formulation of the hydrodynamic equations of motion and energy transport and in the definition of such quantities as the stress tensor and the heat current.

Although we are forced to defer a detailed analysis of the time average and the magnitude of the interval τ until after the quantitative aspects of the theory have been developed, a few comments seem desirable at this point. To obtain an adequate macroscopic description of the secular variation of the observable properties of a system, it is necessary to select τ of sufficient magnitude to smooth out microscopic fluctuations in molecular distribution. For systems of suitable dynamical structure, the macroscopic description will then be independent of τ, as long as the periods of secular variation are long relative to τ. In the case of gases of such low density that molecular motion can be adequately analyzed in terms of binary collisions, the general theory leads to the Maxwell-Boltzmann integro-differential equation. Here is it obvious that τ must be long relative to the duration of a representative collision. In the case of liquids and liquid solutions where the collision analysis fails or becomes unduly complicated, the general theory may be cast in the form of the theory of Brownian motion, but extends this theory by explicitly relating the friction constant to the intermolecular forces acting in a system of molecules. Here it is found that τ must be long relative to the interval within which there is appreciable correlation between the total intermolecular force acting on a representative molecule at the beginning and end of that interval.

In classical statistical mechanics the dynamical states of a system of N molecules constitute a phase space and the ensemble representing a distribution in initial conditions, incompletely specified by the molar variables, is characterized by a probability density $f^{(N)}(\mathbf{p}, \mathbf{q}; t)$ in phase space, $\mathbf{p}$ representing the momentum coordinates and $\mathbf{q}$ the configuration coordinates of the system. In order to simplify our analysis somewhat, we shall suppose that the molecules possess only translatory degrees of freedom. The vector $\mathbf{p}$ is then defined in $3N$-dimensional momentum space and is composed of N vectors $\mathbf{p}_1 \cdots \mathbf{p}_N$, its projections on the 3-momentum spaces of the several molecules. Likewise $\mathbf{q}$ is a vector in $3N$-dimensional configuration space with components $\mathbf{R}_1, \cdots \mathbf{R}_N$ specifying the positions of the molecular centers of gravity in the 3-configuration spaces of the several molecules. The extension of the results which we shall obtain to molecules possessing internal degrees of freedom, for example rotational, will be obvious providing such internal degrees of freedom are of the low frequency type in the sense of van Vleck and are therefore amenable to classical statistics to an adequate degree of approximation.

We shall denote by $\mathbf{X}_i$, dependent only on the coordinates of that molecule, the external force acting on a molecule i of the system. If $\mathbf{X}_i$ is time dependent, we shall suppose that this dependence is secular, that is to say, $\mathbf{X}_i$ is not sensibly affected by an average over the microscopic interval τ. We shall denote by $\mathbf{F}_i$ the intermolecular force exerted on a specified molecule i by the other molecules of the system. Although many of our results will be independent of the assumption, we shall further assume that the potential of intermolecular force $V^{(N)}$ has the form

$$V^{(N)} = \sum_{k<l} V_{kl}(R_{kl}),$$
$$R_{kl} = |\mathbf{R}_l - \mathbf{R}_k|, \tag{1}$$

where V_{kl} depends only on the distance R_{kl} of the molecular pair consisting of molecules of types k and l. For the potential of Eq. (1), the intermolecular force is expressible in the form,

$$\mathbf{F}_i = \sum_{l=1\neq i}^{N} \mathbf{F}_{li},$$
$$\mathbf{F}_{li} = -\nabla_l V_{li} = (\mathbf{R}_{il}/R_{il})\frac{dV_{il}}{dR_{il}}, \tag{2}$$
$$\mathbf{R}_{il} = \mathbf{R}_l - \mathbf{R}_i.$$

By Liouville's theorem, embodying the equation of continuity in phase space and the laws of mechanics, it is well known that the probability distribution function, $f^{(N)}(\mathbf{p}, \mathbf{q}; t)$, satisfies the partial differential equation,

$$Lf^{(N)} + i\frac{\partial f^{(N)}}{\partial t} = 0,$$
$$L = i\sum_{l=1}^{N} \left\{\frac{\mathbf{p}_l}{m_l} \cdot \nabla_{R_l} + (\mathbf{X}_l + \mathbf{F}_l) \cdot \nabla_{\mathbf{p}_l}\right\}, \tag{3}$$

where m_l is the mass of molecule l. By introducing the factor i, the imaginary unit, the operator L is made self-adjoint when applied to a suitably restricted class of functions, a property to be used at a later stage of our discussion. Although $\mathbf{X}_l$ might be defined to include wall forces confining each molecule to a finite region of configuration space, say the interior of a containing vessel, we shall not include these forces in $\mathbf{X}_l$, but shall take them into account by requiring $f^{(N)}$ to vanish exterior to a region of volume v in the configuration space of each molecule, bounded by the walls of the container.

The characteristics of the partial differential Eq. (3) have the equations of motion of the dynamical system.

$$m_l(d\mathbf{R}_l/dt) = \mathbf{p}_l,$$
$$(d\mathbf{p}_l/dt) = \mathbf{X}_l + \mathbf{F}_l, \tag{4}$$
$$(d/dt) = (\partial/\partial t)_{\mathbf{p}_0\mathbf{q}_0},$$

where $\mathbf{p}_0$ and $\mathbf{q}_0$ are the coordinates of the system at an arbitrarily selected initial instant of time. If the ensemble is viewed from the hydrodynamical standpoint $\mathbf{p}_0$ and $\mathbf{q}_0$ may also be interpreted as the Lagrange coordinates of an element of the representative fluid in phase space.

The solutions of the partial differential Eq. (3) may be expressed in the form,

$$f^{(N)}(\mathbf{p}, \mathbf{q}; t+s) = f^{(N)}(\mathbf{p}_0, \mathbf{q}_0; t),$$
$$\mathbf{p} = \exp(-isL_0)\mathbf{p}_0, \tag{5}$$
$$\mathbf{q} = \exp(-isL_0)\mathbf{q}_0,$$

where the operator $\exp(-isL_0)$ is defined as follows.[9] If $\varphi(\mathbf{p}, \mathbf{q})$ is a function of $\mathbf{p}$ and $\mathbf{q}$ not explicitly dependent on time,

$$\psi(\mathbf{p}_0, \mathbf{q}_0; s) = \exp(-isL_0)\varphi(\mathbf{p}_0, \mathbf{q}_0), \tag{6}$$

is defined as the solution of the partial differential equation

$$i(\partial\psi/\partial s) = L_0\psi,$$
$$\psi(\mathbf{p}_0, \mathbf{q}_0; 0) = \varphi(\mathbf{p}_0, \mathbf{q}_0), \tag{7}$$

which satisfies the initial condition $\psi_0 = \varphi$. In domains of phase space free from singularities of L_0, the formal power series,

$$\exp(-isL_0) = \sum_{n=0}^{\infty} \frac{(-is)^n}{n!} L_0^n, \tag{8}$$

may frequently be employed to obtain useful results. We note also the property

$$\exp(-isL_0)\,\varphi(\mathbf{p}_0, \mathbf{q}_0) = \varphi(\mathbf{p}, \mathbf{q}),$$
$$\mathbf{p} = \exp(-isL_0)\mathbf{p}_0, \tag{9}$$
$$\mathbf{q} = \exp(-isL_0)\mathbf{q}_0.$$

The mathematical theory of the operator $\exp(-isL_0)$ may be formulated from a rigorous standpoint by the methods of spectral theory in Hilbert space.[10] In the analysis to follow, we shall find it sufficient to use the formal operator notation without reference to spectral theory. It should be remembered that explicit application of the operator $\exp(-isL_0)$ requires the construction of the solutions of the equations of motion, Eq. (4), and that the operation is merely a symbolic expression of the finite transformation, associated with the infinitesimal transformation L_0, implied in the solution of the equations of motion. An additional property, which will presently be used, is embodied in the well-known statement of Liouville's theorem that the transformation determinant or Jacobian for $\mathbf{p}_0 \rightarrow \mathbf{p}$; $\mathbf{q}_0 \rightarrow \mathbf{q}$ is unity

$$[\partial(\mathbf{p}, \mathbf{q})]/[\partial(\mathbf{p}_0, \mathbf{q}_0)] = 1, \tag{10}$$

which follows from the fact that $\exp(-isL_0)$ is a contact transformation.

---

[9] We note that the operator L of Eq. (3) is a function

$$L(\mathbf{p}, \mathbf{q}, \nabla_p, \nabla_q)$$

of $\mathbf{p}$, $\mathbf{q}$, ∇_q, and ∇_p. By L_0 we mean

$$L(\mathbf{p}_0, \mathbf{q}_0, \nabla_{p0}, \nabla_{q0})$$

where $\mathbf{p}_0$ and $\mathbf{q}_0$ are the Lagrange coordinates of the system at an arbitrary initial instant t preceding the interval s under discussion.

[10] von Neumann, *Proc. Nat. Acad. Sci.* **18**, 70 (1932); Koopman and von Neumann, *Proc. Nat. Acad. Sci.* **17**, 315 (1931).

We now proceed to formulate the averaging operations implied in a macroscopic measurement of a property, $\varphi(p, q)$ not explicitly dependent on time. The time average over the microscopic interval τ will be denoted by α_τ and is expressible in the form

$$\alpha_\tau \varphi = \frac{1}{\tau} \int_0^\tau \varphi(\exp(-isL_0)\mathbf{p}_0, \exp(-isL_0)\mathbf{q}_0) ds, \tag{11}$$

where $\mathbf{p}_0$ and $\mathbf{q}_0$ are the coordinates of the system at time t. The average in the ensemble from which the system is sampled for observation will be denoted by α_ϵ and is expressible in the form

$$\alpha_\epsilon \varphi = \int \int \varphi(\mathbf{p}_0, \mathbf{q}_0) f^{(N)}(\mathbf{p}_0, \mathbf{q}_0; t) d\mathbf{p}_0 d\mathbf{q}_0, \tag{12}$$

at time t, where $d\mathbf{p}_0$ and $d\mathbf{q}_0$ denote volume elements in momentum and configuration space. We identify the observed value $(\varphi)_{\text{obs}}$ with $\alpha_\epsilon \alpha_\tau \varphi$

$$\begin{gathered} (\varphi)_{\text{obs}} = \alpha_\epsilon \alpha_\tau \varphi, \\ \alpha_\epsilon \alpha_\tau \varphi = \frac{1}{\tau} \int \int \int_0^\tau \varphi[\exp(-isL_0)\mathbf{p}_0, \exp(-isL_0)\mathbf{q}_0] f^{(N)}(\mathbf{p}_0, \mathbf{q}_0; t) ds d\mathbf{p}_0 d\mathbf{q}_0 \end{gathered} \tag{13}$$

in accordance with our earlier analysis of the operation of macroscopic measurement. We now calculate $\alpha_\tau \alpha_\epsilon$ in which the averaging operations have been commuted.

$$\begin{gathered} \alpha_\tau \alpha_\epsilon \varphi = \int \int \varphi(\mathbf{p}_0, \mathbf{q}_0) \times \bar{f}^{(N)}(\mathbf{p}_0, \mathbf{q}_0; t) d\mathbf{p}_0 d\mathbf{q}_0, \\ \bar{f}^{(N)}(\mathbf{p}_0, \mathbf{q}_0; t) = \frac{1}{\tau} \int_0^\tau f^{(N)}(\mathbf{p}_0, \mathbf{q}_0; t + s) ds, \end{gathered} \tag{14}$$

where $\bar{f}^{(N)}$ is the time-smoothed probability density of the ensemble. Returning to Eq. (13), transforming the variables of integration, and using Eqs. (9) and (10), we obtain

$$\alpha_\epsilon \alpha_\tau \varphi = \int \int \varphi(\mathbf{p}, \mathbf{q}) \bar{f}^{(N)}(\mathbf{p}, \mathbf{q}; t) d\mathbf{p} d\mathbf{q}, \tag{15}$$

the right-hand side of which is identical with that of Eq. (14). We have therefore demonstrated that α_τ and α_ϵ commute and we may write,

$$\begin{gathered} (\varphi)_{\text{obs}} = \alpha_\epsilon \alpha_\tau \varphi = \alpha_\tau \alpha_\epsilon \varphi, \\ \alpha_\epsilon \alpha_\tau - \alpha_\tau \alpha_\epsilon = 0. \end{gathered} \tag{16}$$

In an ensemble representing statistical equilibrium, for example the canonical ensemble of Gibbs, for which the distribution function is

$${}^0 f^{(N)} = e^{\beta(A-H)}, \tag{17}$$

where H is the Hamiltonian function and β is equal to $1/kT$, we obtain from Eq. (15), since ${}^0 f^{(N)}$ is independent of time,

$$\alpha_\epsilon \alpha_\tau \varphi = \alpha_\epsilon \varphi, \quad (\varphi)_{\text{obs}} = \alpha_\epsilon \varphi. \tag{18}$$

Here the group average of the time average is equal to the group average, and $(\varphi)_{\text{obs}}$ is equal to the group average, the usual assumption of the equilibrium theory of statistical mechanics. The justification of Eqs. (16) and (18) as representations of a macroscopically observed property of course require a further step, the demonstration that the fluctuation in the ensemble of $\alpha_\tau\varphi$ is sufficiently small to reduce to a negligible value the expectation of an observation departing from $\alpha_\epsilon\alpha_\tau\varphi$ by an amount exceeding the precision of measurement.

It might be surmised that Eq. (18) would apply to observations in systems undergoing stationary transport processes, as well as in systems in thermodynamic equilibrium. Such a surmise would not in general be true, since stationary transport processes are stationary in the secular sense but not in the microscopic sense. That is to say, $\bar{f}^{(N)}$ may be independent of time although $f^{(N)}$ is not.

For brevity, we shall henceforth use the following notation

$$\begin{aligned} \alpha_\tau\varphi &= (\varphi)_\tau, \quad \alpha_\epsilon\varphi = \langle\varphi\rangle, \\ \alpha_\epsilon\alpha_\tau\varphi &= \langle(\varphi)_\tau\rangle, \\ \alpha_\tau\alpha_\epsilon\varphi &= (\langle\varphi\rangle)_\tau = \langle\varphi\rangle_{\text{Av}}, \end{aligned} \tag{19}$$

to represent the results of the several averaging operations. The commutability of α_τ and α_ϵ has been demonstrated when α_ϵ denotes an average over all degrees of freedom of the system. We shall presently find that α_τ and α_ϵ do not in general commute when α_ϵ represents a partial average over some but not all coordinates. This lack of commutability is closely associated with the dissipative mechanism by which, in the drift toward equilibrium, energy is distributed among the degrees of freedom in the system.

If we desire to determine the average value of a function $\varphi(\mathbf{p}, \mathbf{q})$ depending not on all coordinates in phase space, but only on these of a subset of n molecules, we may conveniently employ a distribution function of lower order. If we now let $\mathbf{p}$ and $\mathbf{q}$ denote the coordinates of the subset n alone and $\mathbf{P}$ and $\mathbf{Q}$ those of the set of $N-n$ molecules comprising the remainder of the system, the distribution function of order n is defined in the form

$$\begin{aligned} f^{(n)}(\mathbf{p}, \mathbf{q}; t) &= \int\int f^{(N)}(\mathbf{p}, \mathbf{q}, \mathbf{P}, \mathbf{Q}; t)d\mathbf{P}d\mathbf{Q}, \\ \bar{f}^{(n)}(\mathbf{p}, \mathbf{q}; t) &= \frac{1}{\tau}\int_0^\tau f^{(n)}(\mathbf{p}, \mathbf{q}; t+s)ds. \end{aligned} \tag{20}$$

By Eqs. (15) and (16), we obtain, after integration over those coordinates $\mathbf{P}$ and $\mathbf{Q}$ on which $\varphi(\mathbf{p}, \mathbf{q})$ does not depend,

$$(\langle\varphi\rangle)_\tau = \langle\varphi\rangle_{\text{Av}} = \int\int \varphi(\mathbf{p}, \mathbf{q})\bar{f}^{(n)}(\mathbf{p}, \mathbf{q}; t)d\mathbf{p}d\mathbf{q}. \tag{21}$$

If the system consists of several components, the molecular types represented in the set n will be represented by subscripts. Thus

$$f_{i\cdots l}{}^{(n)}(\mathbf{p}_1, \cdots \mathbf{p}_n, \mathbf{R}_1, \cdots \mathbf{R}_n; t)$$

denotes a distribution function of order n in a set comprising n specified molecules $1, \cdots n$ of respective types $i \cdots l$, the coordinates $(\mathbf{p}, \mathbf{q})$ of which have the components $\mathbf{p}_1 \cdots \mathbf{p}_n$, $\mathbf{R}_1 \cdots \mathbf{R}_n$ in the phases spaces of the individual molecules of the set.

The distribution functions $f^{(N)}$ and $f^{(n)}$ are related in the following way

$$f^{(N)}(\mathbf{p}, \mathbf{q}, \mathbf{P}, \mathbf{Q}; t) = f^{(n/N)}(\mathbf{p}, \mathbf{q}/\mathbf{P}, \mathbf{Q}; t) f^{(n)}(\mathbf{p}, \mathbf{q}; t), \tag{22}$$

to a third type of distribution function $f^{(n/N)}$ defining the relative probability density in the phase space of the set of $N - n$ molecules, if the set n is situated at a point $(\mathbf{p}, \mathbf{q})$ in its phase sub-space.

The distribution function $\bar{f}_i^{(1)}(\mathbf{R}, \mathbf{p}; t)$ represents the probability density of any specified molecule of type i, contained in the system, in the 6-dimensional phase space $(\mathbf{p}, \mathbf{R})$ of that molecule. The microscopic time average of the concentration of molecular species i at a point $\mathbf{R}$ in the vessel containing the system is

$$C_i(\mathbf{R}, t) = N_i \int \bar{f}_i^{(1)}(\mathbf{p}, \mathbf{R}; t) d\mathbf{p}, \tag{23}$$

where N_i is the total number of molecules of type i in the system. The mass current density of species i at point R is given by

$$\mathbf{j}_i = N_i \int \mathbf{p} \bar{f}_i^{(1)}(\mathbf{p}, \mathbf{R}; t) d\mathbf{p}. \tag{24}$$

The local temperature $T(\mathbf{R}, t)$ is defined in classical statistical mechanics by the relation

$$\begin{aligned} T(\mathbf{R}, t) &= [\langle \mathbf{p}^2 \rangle_{\mathrm{Av}} - \langle \mathbf{p} \rangle_{\mathrm{Av}}^2]/3mk, \\ \langle \mathbf{p}^2 \rangle_{\mathrm{Av}} &= (N/C) \int \mathbf{p}^2 \bar{f}^{(1)}(\mathbf{p}, \mathbf{R}; t) d\mathbf{p}, \qquad (25) \\ \langle \mathbf{p} \rangle_{\mathrm{Av}} &= (N/C) \int \mathbf{p} \bar{f}^{(1)}(\mathbf{p}, \mathbf{R}; t) d\mathbf{p}, \end{aligned}$$

where k is Boltzmann's constant. The temperature is thus determined by $\bar{f}^{(1)}$.

The distribution function $\bar{f}^{(2)}$ defines the probability density in the 12-dimensional phase space of a molecular pair. It may be regarded as a function of $\mathbf{R}_1$ and $\mathbf{R}_2$ or of $\mathbf{R}_1$ and $\mathbf{R}$, the position $\mathbf{R}_2 - \mathbf{R}_1$ of molecule 2 of the pair relative to molecule 1. Thus $\bar{f}_{il}^{(2)}(\mathbf{p}_1, \mathbf{p}_2, \mathbf{R}_1, \mathbf{R}; t)$ is the distribution function of order 2 for a pair of molecules of types i and 1, respectively. Its importance in the theory of transport will presently be made clear.

The central problem in the statistical mechanical theory of transport consists in the determination of the sequence of time averaged lower order distribution functions $\bar{f}^{(n)}(\mathbf{p}, \mathbf{q}; t)$, of which $\bar{f}^{(1)}$ and $\bar{f}^{(2)}$ play a role of particular importance. When the lower order distribution functions are known, pertinent average values of the properties of the system may be calculated by Eq. (21). In the investigation of mass transport by diffusion and convection, the mass current densities $\mathbf{j}_i$, related to the distribution functions $\bar{f}_i^{(1)}$ by Eq. (24), are of special importance.

In the investigation of fluid flow and the equation of motion of hydrodynamics from the molecular standpoint, the relation between the stress tensor $\boldsymbol{\sigma}$ and the potentials of intermolecular force is of special importance. For a system of one component composed of N molecules, with intermolecular forces of the type described by Eq. (1), contained in volume v, the stress tensor $\boldsymbol{\sigma}$ at a point $\mathbf{r}$ in the region v is found to be

$$\boldsymbol{\sigma} = -\frac{C}{m}[\langle \mathbf{pp} \rangle_{\mathrm{Av}} - \langle \mathbf{p} \rangle_{\mathrm{Av}} \langle \mathbf{p} \rangle_{\mathrm{Av}}] + \frac{C^2}{2}\int \frac{\mathbf{RR}}{R}\frac{dV}{dR}\bar{g}^{(2)}(\mathbf{r}, \mathbf{R}; t)d\mathbf{R},$$

$$\bar{g}^{(2)}(\mathbf{r}, \mathbf{R}; t) = \frac{N^2}{C^2}\int\int \bar{f}^{(2)}(\mathbf{p}_1, \mathbf{p}_2, \mathbf{r}, \mathbf{R}; t)d\mathbf{p}_1 d\mathbf{p}_2,$$

$$C(\mathbf{r}, t) = N\int \bar{f}^{(1)}(\mathbf{p}, \mathbf{r})d\mathbf{p}, \tag{26}$$

$$\langle \mathbf{pp} \rangle_{\mathrm{Av}} = \frac{N}{C}\int \mathbf{pp}\bar{f}^{(1)}(\mathbf{p}, \mathbf{r}; t)d\mathbf{p},$$

where $V(R)$ is the potential of intermolecular force for a molecular pair, m is the molecular mass, $\mathbf{r}$ the position of one molecule of the pair, held fixed in the averaging operation, and $\mathbf{R}$ is the position $\mathbf{R}_2 - \mathbf{R}_1$ of the second member of the pair relative to the first. The integral of the second term in $\boldsymbol{\sigma}$ extends over the relative coordinates of the pair. The stress tensor is thus determined by the distribution functions $\bar{f}^{(1)}$ and $\bar{f}^{(2)}$. The first term arising from momentum transport is identical with that customarily encountered in the kinetic theory of gases, for example in the Chapman-Enskog formulation. The second term, arising from intermolecular forces, becomes of dominant importance in liquids and solids.

In the investigation of heat transfer on the molecular scale, the relation between the heat current density $\mathbf{j}_q$ and the distribution functions and intermolecular forces is of primary significance. Again in a system of one component, this relation is found to be,

$$\mathbf{j}_q = \frac{C}{2m^2}\langle(\mathbf{p} - \langle \mathbf{p} \rangle_{\mathrm{Av}})(\mathbf{p} - \langle \mathbf{p} \rangle_{\mathrm{Av}})^2\rangle_{\mathrm{Av}}$$

$$-\frac{N^2}{2m}\int\int\int \{\mathbf{R}(\mathbf{p}_1 - \langle \mathbf{p} \rangle_{\mathrm{Av}}) \cdot \nabla V - V(\mathbf{p}_1 - \langle \mathbf{p} \rangle_{\mathrm{Av}})\}$$

$$\times \bar{f}^{(2)}(\mathbf{p}_1, \mathbf{p}_2, \mathbf{r}, \mathbf{R}; t)d\mathbf{p}_1 d\mathbf{p}_2 d\mathbf{R}. \tag{27}$$

The heat current thus depends upon the distribution functions $\bar{f}^{(1)}$ and $\bar{f}^{(2)}$. The first term, associated with kinetic energy transport, is the familiar term of the kinetic theory of gases. The second term, associated with energy transport by intermolecular forces, becomes of dominant importance in liquids and solids.

The macroscopic hydrodynamic equations of motion and energy transport will be treated from the molecular standpoint in separate articles on viscous fluid flow and heat transfer. In these articles, Eqs. (26) and (27) will be derived from fundamental principles and the ordinary laws of viscosity and thermal conduction will be shown to be valid under suitable conditions by expansion of the distribution functions $\bar{f}^{(1)}$ and $\bar{f}^{(2)}$ in the velocity and temperature gradients. The phenomenon of diffusion will also be treated in detail in a later article.

II. THE THEORY OF BROWNIAN MOTION

In liquids and other condensed systems, we shall find it convenient to use the concepts of the theory of Brownian motion in the formulation of the partial differential equations describing the behavior of the sequence of distribution functions $\bar{f}^{(n)}$. It is therefore desirable to examine the concepts of this theory from the molecular standpoint before proceeding to the problem of determining the distribution functions.

The theory of Brownian motion, which describes transport processes in dilute solution, is based upon the Langevin equation describing the motion of a molecule in an environment in statistical equilibrium. The Langevin equation has the form,

$$\frac{d\mathbf{p}_i}{dt} + \frac{\zeta_i^0}{m_i}\mathbf{p}_i = \mathbf{X}_i + \mathbf{G}_i, \tag{28}$$

where $\mathbf{p}_i$ is the momentum of a specified molecule i, m_i its mass, $\mathbf{X}_i$ the external force acting on it, and $\mathbf{G}_i$ a fluctuating intermolecular force, the time average of which vanishes over a macroscopically short interval τ, and which is uncorrelated in successive intervals of magnitude τ. In the dissipative term $\zeta_i^0\mathbf{p}_i/m_i$ the friction constant ζ_i^0 is a phenomenological constant, recognized to be determined by intermolecular forces, but the precise relationship between ζ_i^0 and the intermolecular forces in the system has not heretofore been established. Estimates of ζ_i^0 have therefore been limited to macromolecules dispersed in solvents of low molecular weight, where macroscopic hydrodynamics may reasonably be expected to apply. For a spherical molecule of radius a, in solvent of viscosity coefficient η, Stokes law yields the estimate $6\pi\eta a$ for the friction constant ζ_i^0.

We shall now attempt to show how the Langevin equation may be obtained from statistical mechanics and how the friction constant is related to the intermolecular forces. If $\mathbf{p}_i$ is the momentum of a specified molecule i in a system with completely specified coordinates $\mathbf{p}_{i0}$, $\mathbf{R}_{i0}$, $\mathbf{P}_0$, $\mathbf{Q}_0$, the latter being those of the remaining $N - 1$ molecules, at an arbitrary initial instant of time t, the equation of motion for the molecule in question is

$$\frac{d\mathbf{p}_i}{dt} = \left(\frac{\partial\mathbf{p}_i}{dt}\right)_{\mathbf{p}_{i0}\cdots Q_0} = \mathbf{X}_i + \mathbf{F}_i, \tag{29}$$

where $\mathbf{X}_i$ is the external force and $\mathbf{F}_i$ the intermolecular force acting on molecule i.

We now define $\mathbf{G}_i$ by the relation

$$\begin{aligned} \mathbf{G}_i &= \mathbf{F}_i - {}^i\langle(\mathbf{F}_i)_\tau\rangle, \\ {}^i\langle(\mathbf{F}_i)_\tau\rangle &= {}^i\alpha_\epsilon\alpha_\tau\mathbf{F}_i, \end{aligned} \tag{30}$$

where the left superscript i denotes an average in the ensemble, from which the system is sampled, with fixed initial coordinates $\mathbf{p}_{i0}$ and $\mathbf{R}_{i0}$ of molecule i. By the definitions of Part I, we have

$$^{i}\langle(\mathbf{F}_i)_\tau\rangle = \frac{1}{\tau}\int\int\int_0^\tau \mathbf{F}_i(t+s) f_i^{(1/N)}(\mathbf{p}_{i0}\mathbf{R}_{i0}/\mathbf{P}_0, \mathbf{Q}_0; t)\, ds\, d\mathbf{P}_0\, d\mathbf{Q}_0, \qquad (31)$$

where $\mathbf{F}_i(t+s)$ is used for brevity to denote $\mathbf{F}_i(R_i, Q)$ considered as a function of $\mathbf{R}_{i0}$, $\mathbf{Q}_0$, and s, and $f_i^{(1/N)}$ is the relative probability density in the ensemble at time t in the phase space of the $N-1$ molecules other than i, if i has the coordinates $\mathbf{p}_{i0}$ and $\mathbf{R}_{i0}$. We remark that $\mathbf{G}_i$ has the first property assigned to the fluctuating force in the Langevin equation, that is,

$$^{i}\alpha_\epsilon \alpha_\tau \mathbf{G}_i = 0, \qquad (32)$$

but in the somewhat extended sense that average in the ensemble of the time average of $\mathbf{G}_i$ vanishes. This extension is necessary to give precision to the concept of the fluctuating force. The second property, that of no correlation in successive τ intervals, will presently be discussed.

We now examine the average force $\langle(\mathbf{F}_i)_\tau\rangle$. If we make the hypothesis that the environment of molecule i is in statistical equilibrium, or can be regarded to be so to a sufficient degree of approximation, we may write Eq. (30) in the form

$$^{i}\langle(\mathbf{F}_i)_\tau\rangle = \frac{1}{\tau}\int\int\int_0^\tau \mathbf{F}_i(t+s)\, {}^0 f_i^{(1/N)}(\mathbf{p}_{i0}\mathbf{R}_{i0}/\mathbf{P}_0, \mathbf{Q}_0)\, ds\, d\mathbf{P}_0\, d\mathbf{Q}_0,$$

$$^0 f_i^{(1/N)} = \left(\frac{\beta}{2\pi m_i}\right)^{\frac{3}{2}} \frac{1}{v} \exp\left[\beta(A^N - H_0^N) + \beta p_{i0}^2/2m_i + \beta W_i^{(1)}(\mathbf{R}_{i0})\right], \qquad (33)$$

where ${}^0 f_i^{(1/N)}$ is the relative probability density in the canonical ensemble representing statistical equilibrium and defined by Eq. (22). The potential of the equilibrium average force[11] acting on molecule i is denoted by $W_i^{(1)}$. We next consider the average force $({}^i\langle\mathbf{F}_i\rangle)_\tau$ in which the order of the averaging operations α_τ and ${}^i\alpha_\epsilon$ is interchanged and we find,

$$({}^i\langle\mathbf{F}_i\rangle)_\tau = {}^i\langle\mathbf{F}_i\rangle^0 = \int\int F_i(\mathbf{R}_{i0}, \mathbf{Q})\, {}^0 f_i^{(1/N)}(\mathbf{p}_{i0}, \mathbf{R}_{i0}/\mathbf{P}, \mathbf{Q})\, d\mathbf{P}\, d\mathbf{Q}, \qquad (34)$$

if ${}^i\langle\mathbf{F}_i\rangle^0$, the equilibrium intermolecular force has only secular dependence on time so that it is not affected by an average over the microscopic interval τ. It will be shown in a later article on diffusion that in the equilibrium ensemble corresponding to specified composition gradients

$$^{i}\langle\mathbf{F}_i\rangle^0 = -\nabla\mu_i + kT\nabla \log C_i, \qquad (35)$$

where μ_i is the chemical potential of a molecule of type i and C_i is its concentration. Thus ${}^i\langle F_i\rangle^0$ will be secular for gradients appreciable only over distances of macroscopic magnitude and will in fact vanish if molecule i is a solute component of an ideal dilute solution. It also vanishes identically if the

[11] Note: For a discussion of equilibrium average forces and distribution functions, see J. G. Kirkwood, *J. Chem. Phys.* **3**, 300 (1935).

hypothesis of thermodynamic equilibrium is strictly fulfilled and there are no external forces $\mathbf{X}_i$ acting on the system.

If ${}^i\alpha_\epsilon$ and α_τ were commutable as are α_ϵ and α_τ, ${}^i\langle(\mathbf{F}_i)_\tau\rangle$ would be identical with ${}^i\langle\mathbf{F}_i\rangle^0$. This, however, is not the case. In order to establish the relation between ${}^i\langle(\mathbf{F}_i)_\tau\rangle$ and ${}^i\langle\mathbf{F}_i\rangle^0$, we rewrite Eq. (33) in the following form,

$$
\begin{aligned}
{}^i\langle(\mathbf{F}_i)_\tau\rangle = \frac{1}{\tau}\int_0^\tau \int\int\int\int \mathbf{F}_i(t+s)\delta(\mathbf{p}_{i0}' - \mathbf{p}_{i0})\delta(\mathbf{R}_{i0}' - \mathbf{R}_{i0}) \\
{}^0f_i{}^{(1/N)}\,(\mathbf{p}_{i0}', \mathbf{R}_{i0}'/\mathbf{P}_0, \mathbf{Q}_0)d\mathbf{p}_{i0}'d\mathbf{R}_{i0}'d\mathbf{P}_0 d\mathbf{Q}_0 ds, \quad (36)
\end{aligned}
$$

where the order of integration over time and phase space has been interchanged (this is permissible and has nothing to do with the commutation of ${}^i\alpha_\epsilon$ and α_τ), and the integration has extended over all of phase space at time t by introducing the delta functions $\delta(\mathbf{p}_{i0}' - \mathbf{p}_{i0})$ and $\delta(\mathbf{R}_{i0}' - \mathbf{R}_{i0})$, each the product of three delta functions for each component of the vector arguments. We next note the following properties of the functions appearing in the integrand of Eq. (36).

$$
\begin{aligned}
{}^0f_i{}^{(1/N)}(\mathbf{p}_{i0}', \mathbf{R}_{i0}'/\mathbf{P}_0, \mathbf{Q}_0) &= {}^0f_i{}^{(1/N)}(\mathbf{p}_i', \mathbf{R}_i'/\mathbf{P}, \mathbf{Q})\, {}^0f_i{}^{(1)}(\mathbf{p}_i', \mathbf{R}_i') \\
&\qquad /{}^0f^{(1)}\,(\mathbf{p}_{i0}', \mathbf{R}_{i0}'), \\
\frac{{}^0f_i{}^{(1)}(\mathbf{p}_i', \mathbf{R}_i')}{{}^0f_i{}^{(1)}(\mathbf{p}_{i0}', \mathbf{R}_{i0}')} &= \exp\{-\beta(p_i'^2 - p_{i0}'^2)/2m_i \\
&\qquad - \beta[W_i{}^{(1)}(\mathbf{R}_i') - W_i{}^{(1)}(\mathbf{R}_{i0}')]\}, \\
&= 1 - \frac{\beta\mathbf{p}_i'}{m_i}\cdot\Delta\mathbf{p}_i' + O[(\Delta\mathbf{p}_i')^2] + O(\Delta\mathbf{R}_i'), \quad (37)
\end{aligned}
$$

$$\Delta\mathbf{p}_i' = \mathbf{p}_i' - \mathbf{p}_{i0}' = \int_0^s \mathbf{F}_i(t+s')ds' + \mathbf{X}_i s,$$

$$\Delta\mathbf{R}_i' = \mathbf{R}_i' - \mathbf{R}_{i0}' = \int_0^s (\mathbf{p}_i'/m_i)ds'.$$

These relations follow at once from Eqs. (17), (20), (22), and (29) and the invariance of $H^{(N)}$ the complete Hamiltonian of the system under the transformation $(\mathbf{p}_{i0}', \mathbf{R}_{i0}', \mathbf{P}_0, \mathbf{Q}_0) \rightarrow (\mathbf{p}_i', \mathbf{R}_i', \mathbf{P}, \mathbf{Q})$ by the operator $\exp(-isL_0)$. We further note

$$
\begin{aligned}
\mathbf{F}_i(t+s) &= \mathbf{F}_i(R_i', Q), \\
\delta(\mathbf{p}_{i0}' - \mathbf{p}_{i0}) &= \delta(\mathbf{p}_i' - \mathbf{p}_{i0} - \Delta\mathbf{p}_i'), \\
&= \delta(\mathbf{p}_i' - p_{i0}) + \Delta\mathbf{p}_i'\cdot\nabla_{\mathbf{p}_{i0}}\delta(\mathbf{p}_i' - \mathbf{p}_{i0}) + O[(\Delta\mathbf{p}_i')^2], \quad (38) \\
\delta(\mathbf{R}_{i0}' - \mathbf{R}_{i0}) &= \delta(\mathbf{R}_i' - \mathbf{R}_{i0}) + O(\Delta\mathbf{R}_i').
\end{aligned}
$$

The expansions of the delta functions in power series in $\Delta\mathbf{p}_i'$ and $\Delta\mathbf{R}_i'$ are formal operations which can be justified by more tedious methods of calculation which circumvent their use. Substitution of the relations of Eqs. (37) and

(38) into the integral of Eq. (36) after transformation to the new variables $\mathbf{p}_i'$, $\mathbf{R}_i'$, $\mathbf{P}$, $\mathbf{Q}$ yields, after some calculation,

$$
{}^i\langle(\mathbf{F}_i)_\tau\rangle = {}^i\langle\mathbf{F}_i\rangle^0 - \boldsymbol{\zeta}_i \cdot \mathbf{p}_{i0}/m_i + kT\nabla_{\mathbf{p}_{i0}} \cdot \boldsymbol{\zeta}_i + O(\tau).
$$

$$
\boldsymbol{\zeta}_i = \frac{\beta}{\tau}\int\int\int_0^\tau\int_0^s \mathbf{F}_i(t+s)\mathbf{F}_i(t+s')\,{}^0f_i^{(1/N)}(\mathbf{p}_i, \mathbf{R}_i/\mathbf{P}, \mathbf{Q})ds'dsd\mathbf{P}d\mathbf{Q}, \tag{39}
$$

where in the expression for $\boldsymbol{\zeta}_i$, resulting from the calculation, $\mathbf{p}_{i0}$ and $\mathbf{R}_{i0}$ have been replaced by $\mathbf{p}_i$ and $\mathbf{R}_i$ and the remainder included in the term $O(\tau)$. If the tensor $\boldsymbol{\zeta}_i$ has a plateau value, not sensibly dependent on τ, for a microscopic interval τ of sufficient length, in a sense to be discussed presently, the remainder terms arising from the terms $O[(\Delta\mathbf{p}_i')^2]$ and $O[\Delta\mathbf{R}_i']$ in the integrand of Eq. (36) may be shown to be of order τ. In fluid systems such as liquids and liquid solutions, it is apparent that $\boldsymbol{\zeta}_i$ must be isotropic.

$$
\boldsymbol{\zeta}_i = \zeta_i\mathbf{1},
$$

$$
\zeta_i(\tau) = \frac{\beta}{3\tau}\int_0^\tau\int_{-s}^0\int\int \mathbf{F}_i(t+s)\cdot\mathbf{F}_i(t+s+s')\,{}^0f_i^{(1/N)}(\mathbf{p}_i, \mathbf{R}_i/\mathbf{P}, \mathbf{Q})d\mathbf{P}d\mathbf{Q}ds'ds, \tag{40}
$$

where a permissible change in the order of integration has been made and a change of time variable introduced.

If the structure of the dynamical system is such that in the equilibrium ensemble there exists a microscopic time interval τ_i, of sufficient length that the integral

$$
\frac{\beta}{3}\int_{-s}^0\int\int \mathbf{F}_i(t)\cdot\mathbf{F}_i(t+s')\,{}^0f_i^{(1/N)}(\mathbf{p}_{i0}, \mathbf{R}_{i0}/\mathbf{P}_0, \mathbf{Q}_0)d\mathbf{P}_0d\mathbf{Q}_0ds'
$$

possesses a plateau value ζ_i given by

$$
\zeta_i = \frac{\beta}{3}\int_{-\tau_i}^0\int\int \mathbf{F}_i(t)\mathbf{F}_i(t+s)\,{}^0f_i^{(1/N)}(\mathbf{p}_{i0}, \mathbf{R}_{i0}/\mathbf{P}_0, \mathbf{Q}_0)d\mathbf{P}_0d\mathbf{Q}_0ds, \tag{41}
$$

in the sense that for values of s greater than τ_i, but small on the macroscopic scale, the integral differs in absolute value from ζ_i by an amount less than the precision error of a macroscopic measurement of the quantity, then $\zeta_i(\tau)$ possesses the same plateau value ζ_i in the same sense for $\tau > \tau_i'$ where $\tau_i/\tau_i' \ll 1$. This may be expressed more precisely in the form,

$$
|\zeta_i(\tau) - \zeta_i| = O(\epsilon); \quad \tau_i' < \tau < \tau^* \tag{42}
$$

where ϵ is less than the precision error in the macroscopic measurement of ζ_i and τ^* is a macroscopic interval of time certainly of smaller magnitude than the representative period of the Poincaré cycles of the system. We have intentionally avoided identifying $\zeta_i(\tau)$, for sufficiently long τ, with its asymptotic value $\zeta_i(\infty)$, since the latter value may be shown to vanish for systems confined to a finite region of configuration space. The apparent paradox encountered here is precisely the paradox between dynamical reversibility and thermodynamic irreversibility. The dissipative processes appearing to operate in thermodynamic systems provide a valid description of macroscopic behavior only if the time over which the properties of the system are averaged in a macroscopic observation is long relative to the periods of microscopic fluctuation but short relative to the periods of Poincaré cycles,[12] within which secular changes in state may be spontaneously reversed. It is for these reasons that we are forced to speak of a plateau value for $\zeta_i(\tau)$ rather than of its asymptotic value at $\tau \to \infty$, in discussing macroscopic transport processes. Whether such a plateau value exists will depend upon the dynamical structure of the system, that is upon the particular form of its Hamiltonian.

We shall investigate the friction constant ζ_i in greater detail in Part IV. Anticipating a result to be obtained there, we remark that the integrand of Eq. (41) is found to be an even function of s.[13] This allows us to express ζ_i in the following form,

$$\zeta_i = \frac{1}{6kT}\int_{-\tau_i}^{+\tau_i} {}^i\langle \mathbf{F}_i \cdot e^{-is\mathrm{L}}\mathbf{F}_i\rangle^0 ds,$$

$${}^i\langle \mathbf{F}_i \cdot e^{-is\mathrm{L}}\mathbf{F}_i\rangle^0 = \int\int [\mathbf{F}_i(\mathbf{R}_i, \mathbf{Q}_i) \cdot e^{-is\mathrm{L}}\mathbf{F}_i(\mathbf{R}_i, \mathbf{Q}_i)] \; {}^0f_i^{(1/N)}(\mathbf{p}_i, \mathbf{R}_i/\mathbf{P}, \mathbf{Q})d\mathbf{P}d\mathbf{Q}. \tag{43}$$

Although it is apparent that in fluid systems ζ_i will not depend upon the position $\mathbf{R}_{i0}$ of the molecule in configuration space, ζ_i may depend upon the momentum $\mathbf{p}_{i0}$ of the molecule. It will be shown in Part IV that ζ_i does not sensibly depend upon momentum, if the mass of molecule i is large relative to those of the other molecules of the system, for example, when i is a macromolecule in a solvent of low molecular weight. Also, even when molecule i has a mass comparable with those of its environments, ζ_i may not depend sensibly on momentum in condensed systems such as liquids or liquid solutions. When ζ_i does depend upon momentum it is an even function of this variable.

Returning now to Eq. (29), introducing Eqs. (30), (39), and (40) and neglecting the terms of order τ in Eq. (39), after selecting τ of sufficient magnitude to achieve the plateau value of $\zeta_i(\tau)$, we obtain the equation of motion,

$$\frac{d\mathbf{p}_i}{dt} + \zeta_i^0\mathbf{p}_i/m_i = \mathbf{X}_i + \mathbf{G}_i, \quad \zeta_i^0 = \zeta_i - 2kT\frac{d\zeta_i}{dp_i^2}, \tag{44}$$

where we have suppressed ${}^i\langle \mathbf{F}_i\rangle^0$, shown to vanish for an ideal dilute solution, and have identified $\mathbf{p}_{i0}$ in Eq. (39) with $\mathbf{p}_i$, since the instant of time t, in the

[12] Poincaré has stated the theorem that in a system of particles in which the forces depend only upon the spatial coordinates, a given initial stage must recur to any specified degree of accuracy, an infinite number of times if the system is confined to a finite region of phase space. The term Poincaré cycle period is used to designate the time of recurrence of a given state to within a specified degree of accuracy in such "quasi-periodic" motion. For systems of molecules such periods are very long on the macroscopic time scale. It may therefore seem that we have placed undue emphasis on the rather obvious point that τ_i should be short relative to such periods. We have done so in order to call attention to the circumstance that the apparently innocent mathematical procedure of letting $\tau_i \to \infty$ in evaluating the friction constant leads to serious physical difficulties. For a more detailed discussion of these points, see S. Chandrasekar, *Rev. Mod. Phys.* **15**, 1–89 (1943), Appendix V.

[13] This may be regarded as a consequence of the principle of microscopic reversibility.

neighborhood of which the average ${}^{i}\langle(\mathbf{F}_i)_\tau\rangle$ is made is properly to be taken as identical with the instant t at which the acceleration $d\mathbf{p}_i/dt$ is to be calculated. If the plateau value ζ_i exists, it is evident that

$$^{i}\langle\mathbf{F}_i(t)\cdot\mathbf{F}_i(t+\tau)\rangle^0 = 0, \tag{45}$$

is valid to the same degree of approximation, that is τ exceeds the time interval during which there is sensible correlation between the total intermolecular force acting in molecule at instants of time separated by that interval. This implies that, with neglect of terms of order τ, there is no correlation between the force $\mathbf{G}_i$ acting on molecule i at successive instants t and $t + \tau$.

Equation (44) thus becomes identical with the Langevin equation, if ζ_i and therefore ζ_i^0 is independent of $\mathbf{p}_i$. When ζ_i depends upon $\mathbf{p}_i$, a generalized Langevin equation containing a friction constant dependent on the velocity of the molecule is obtained. We have by means of our analysis suggested the conditions under which the Langevin equation may be expected to be valid, and, what is more significant, have established a relation, Eq. (41), between the friction constant and the intermolecular forces acting in a system of molecules. Many mathematical points call for further investigation, particularly the specification of the properties of the class of systems for which a plateau value ζ_i exists, an investigation of the magnitude of the correlation time τ_i, and an examination of the magnitude of the neglected terms of order τ in Eq. (39). Some of these points will be discussed in Part IV.

Having established the Langevin equation, the details of the conventional theory of Brownian motion may be developed by the Markoff method or known alternative methods, which we do not need to discuss here.

III. THE DISTRIBUTION FUNCTIONS

We here return to the problem of determining the sequence of distribution functions $\bar{f}^{(n)}$ from which the average values characterizing macroscopic transport processes are to be calculated. We shall proceed from the Liouville differential equation, Eq. (3), and the definitions, Eq. (20), of the distribution functions $\bar{f}^{(n)}$. Our general method leads on the one hand to the Maxwell-Boltzmann integro-differential equation for gases of sufficiently low density to permit analysis by binary collisions, and, on the other hand to a generalized Fokker-Planck equation, by methods closely related to those of the theory of Brownian motion developed in Part II, for liquids and liquid solutions.

The Liouville equation and the definition of the distribution function $\bar{f}^{(n)}$ are conveniently summarized in the form

$$\sum_{l=1}^{N}\left\{\frac{\mathbf{p}_l}{m_l}\cdot\nabla_{R_l}f^{(N)} + (\mathbf{X}_l+\mathbf{F}_l)\cdot\nabla_{\mathbf{p}_l}f^{(N)}\right\} + \frac{\partial f^{(N)}}{\partial t} = 0,$$

$$f^{(n)}(\mathbf{p},\mathbf{q};t) = \int\int f^{(N)}(\mathbf{p},\mathbf{q},\mathbf{P},\mathbf{Q};t)d\mathbf{P}d\mathbf{Q}, \tag{46}$$

$$\bar{f}^{(n)}(\mathbf{p},\mathbf{q};t) = \frac{1}{\tau}\int_0^\tau f^{(n)}(\mathbf{p},\mathbf{q};t+s)ds,$$

where, as before, $\mathbf{p}$ and $\mathbf{q}$ denote the coordinates of the set of molecules n and $\mathbf{P}$ and $\mathbf{Q}$ those of the set $N - n$, constituting the other molecules of system. In our preliminary remarks, we shall repress subscripts indicating the molecule types comprised in the set n. Integrating the Liouville equation over the partial phase space (**P**, **Q**), and restricting our analysis to distributions $\bar{f}^{(N)}$ for which the surface integrals of the currents vanish on the boundary of the phase space accessible to the system, we obtain with use of Green's theorem,

$$\frac{\partial \bar{f}^{(n)}}{\partial t} + \frac{\mathbf{p}}{m} \cdot \nabla_{\mathbf{q}} \bar{f}^{(n)} + \mathbf{X} \cdot \nabla_{\mathbf{p}} \bar{f}^{(n)} = \nabla_{\mathbf{p}} \cdot \mathbf{\Omega}^{(n)},$$

$$\mathbf{\Omega}^{(n)} = -\frac{1}{\tau}\int_0^\tau \int \int \mathbf{F}(\mathbf{q}, \mathbf{Q}) f^{(N)}(\mathbf{p}, \mathbf{q}, \mathbf{P}, \mathbf{Q}; t+s) d\mathbf{P} d\mathbf{Q} ds, \tag{47}$$

where **X** denotes the total external and **F** the total intermolecular force, regarded as vectors in the n-configuration space of set n, and $\mathbf{p}/m$ represents a vector in the n-momentum space with projections $\mathbf{p}_1/m_1 \cdots \mathbf{p}_n/m_n$ on the 3-spaces of the several molecules of the set. If the intermolecular force has the form, Eq. (2), we may express the mean currents due to intermolecular forces as

$$\mathbf{\Omega}^{(n)} = -\sum_{i,k=1}^{n} \mathbf{F}_{ki} \bar{f}^{(n)} + \sum_{i=1}^{n} \sum_{l=n+1}^{N} \mathbf{\Omega}_{li}^{(n)},$$

$$\mathbf{\Omega}_{li}^{(n)} = -\int \int \mathbf{F}_{li}(R_{li}) \bar{f}^{(n+1)}(\mathbf{p}, \mathbf{q}, \mathbf{p}_l, \mathbf{R}_l; t) d\mathbf{p}_l d\mathbf{R}_l, \tag{48}$$

where $\mathbf{F}_{ki}$ and $\mathbf{\Omega}_{li}^{(n)}$ are to be treated as vectors in the 3-configuration space of molecule i of the set n (not as vectors in a common 3-space). Eqs. (47) and (48) provide a system of integro-differential equations for the sequence of distribution functions $\bar{f}^{(n)}$, in which the dissipative mechanism affecting their behavior is concealed in time-averaged function of highest order $\bar{f}^{(N)}$. It is therefore necessary to transform the terms $\mathbf{\Omega}_{li}^{(n)}$ with the aid of solutions, Eq. (5) of the Liouville equation for $f^{(N)}$ in order to obtain useful results.

To avoid undue complication, we shall now specialize the analysis to the distribution function $f_i^{(1)}$, the distribution function of order one for a molecule of type i. The extension of the method to distribution functions of higher order will be obvious. Eq. (47) now reduces to

$$\frac{\partial \bar{f}_i^{(1)}}{\partial t} + \frac{\mathbf{p}_i}{m_i} \cdot \nabla_{R_i} \bar{f}_i^{(1)} + \mathbf{X}_i \cdot \nabla_{\mathbf{p}_i} \bar{f}_i^{(1)} = \nabla_{\mathbf{p}_i} \cdot \mathbf{\Omega}_i^{(1)},$$

$$\mathbf{\Omega}_i^{(1)} = \sum_{l=1}^{\nu} N_l \mathbf{\Omega}_{li}^{(1)}, \tag{49}$$

$$\mathbf{\Omega}_{li}^{(1)} = -\frac{1}{\tau}\int_0^\tau \int \cdots \int \mathbf{F}_{li}(R_{il}) f^{(N)}(\mathbf{p}_i, \mathbf{R}_i, \mathbf{p}_l, \mathbf{R}_l, \mathbf{P}, \mathbf{Q}; t+s) \, d\mathbf{P} d\mathbf{Q} d\mathbf{p}_l d\mathbf{R}_l ds,$$

where **P** and **Q** here denote the coordinates of all molecules except those of a specified pair of molecules i and l of types i and l respectively (subscripts on coordinates denote specified molecules; on functions $\mathbf{\Omega}_{li}$, $\mathbf{F}_{li}$, etc., they denote molecular types). Using Eqs. (5) and (22) we may write

$$f^{(N)}(\mathbf{p}_i, \mathbf{R}_i, \mathbf{p}_l, \mathbf{R}_l, \mathbf{P}, \mathbf{Q}; t+s) = f^{(N)}(\mathbf{p}_{i0}, \mathbf{R}_{i0}, \mathbf{p}_{l0}, \mathbf{R}_{l0}, \mathbf{P}_0, \mathbf{Q}_0; t),$$

$$f^{(N)}(\mathbf{p}_{i0}, \mathbf{R}_{i0}, \mathbf{p}_{l0}, \mathbf{R}_{l0}, \mathbf{P}_0, \mathbf{Q}_0; t) = f_{il}^{(2/N)}(\mathbf{p}_{i0}, \mathbf{R}_{i0}, \mathbf{p}_{l0}, \mathbf{R}_{l0}, \mathbf{P}_0, \mathbf{Q}_0; t)$$
$$f_{il}^{(2)}(\mathbf{p}_{i0}, \mathbf{R}_{i0}, \mathbf{p}_{l0}, \mathbf{R}_{l0}; t), \tag{50}$$
$$f_{il}^{(2)}(\mathbf{p}_{i0}, \mathbf{R}_{i0}, \mathbf{p}_{l0}, \mathbf{R}_{l0}; t) = \varphi_{il}^{(2)}(\mathbf{p}_{i0}, \mathbf{R}_{i0}, \mathbf{p}_{l0}, \mathbf{R}_{l0}; t)$$
$$f_i^{(1)}(\mathbf{p}_{i0}, \mathbf{R}_{i0}; t) f_l^{(1)}(\mathbf{p}_{l0}, \mathbf{R}_{l0}; t),$$

where $f_{il}^{(2/N)}$ is the relative probability density in the partial phase space $(\mathbf{P}, \mathbf{Q})$ when a pair of molecules of type i and l have specified coordinates. The correlation function $\varphi_{il}^{(2)}$ is defined by the last of Eq. (50). In the last of Eq. (49) defining $\mathbf{Q}_{li}^{(1)}$ we extend the integration over all of phase space with the use of delta functions, transform the variables of integration from $\mathbf{p}_i \cdots \mathbf{Q}$ to $\mathbf{p}_{i0} \cdots \mathbf{Q}_0$, and introduce the relations of Eq. (50). We then obtain

$$\mathbf{\Omega}_{li}^{(1)} = \int \cdots \int \mathbf{K}_{li}(\mathbf{p}_{i0} \cdots \mathbf{R}_{l0}; t) f_l^{(1)}(\mathbf{p}_{l0}, \mathbf{R}_{l0}; t) f_i^{(1)}(\mathbf{p}_{i0}, \mathbf{R}_{i0}; t)$$
$$d\mathbf{p}_{l0} d\mathbf{R}_{l0} d\mathbf{p}_{i0} d\mathbf{R}_{i0},$$
$$\mathbf{K}_{li} = -\frac{1}{\tau}\int_0^\tau \int\int \mathbf{F}_{li}(t+s)\delta(\mathbf{p}_{i0} + \Delta\mathbf{p}_i - \mathbf{p}_i)\delta(\mathbf{R}_{i0} + \Delta\mathbf{R}_i - \mathbf{R}_i) \times$$
$$\varphi_{il}^{(2)}(\mathbf{p}_{i0} \cdots \mathbf{R}_{l0}; t)\; f^{(2/N)}(\mathbf{p}_{i0}, \mathbf{R}_{i0}, \mathbf{p}_{l0}, \mathbf{R}_{l0}/\mathbf{P}_0, \mathbf{Q}_0; t) d\mathbf{P}_0 d\mathbf{Q}_0 ds, \tag{51}$$
$$\mathbf{F}_{li}(t+s) = \mathbf{F}_{li}(R_{il}) = \mathbf{F}_{li}(p_{i0} \cdots Q_0; s),\ \Delta\mathbf{p}_i = \int_0^s \mathbf{F}_i ds' + \mathbf{X}_i s;$$
$$\Delta\mathbf{R}_i = \int_0^s \mathbf{p}_i/m_i ds'.$$

An integral of the type of $\mathbf{K}_{li}$ vanishes for sufficiently large τ if, in place of $\varphi_{il}^{(2)}$, the integrand contains a factor which is a short range function of the distance between molecules i and l, diminishing say with distance in the same order as $\mathbf{F}_{li}$. If we use the identity

$$\varphi_{il}^{(2)} = \exp(-\beta W_{il}^{(2)})[1 + (\varphi_{il}^{(2)} \exp(\beta W_{il}^{(2)}) - 1)], \tag{52}$$

where $W_{il}^{(2)}$ is equilibrium potential of mean force acting on the pair il and restrict our analysis to distributions for which $(\varphi_{il}^{(2)} \exp(\beta W_{il}^{(2)}) - 1)$ is a short range function of the intermolecular distance, we may express $\mathbf{K}_{li}$ in the form

$$\mathbf{K}_{li} = -\frac{1}{\tau}\int_0^\tau \int\int \mathbf{F}_{li}(t+s)\delta(\mathbf{p}_{i0} + \Delta\mathbf{p}_i - \mathbf{p}_i)\delta(\mathbf{R}_{i0} + \Delta\mathbf{R}_i - \mathbf{R}_i) \times$$
$$\exp(-\beta W_{il}^{(2)})\; f_{il}^{(2/N)}(\mathbf{p}_{i0}, \mathbf{R}_{i0}, \mathbf{p}_{l0}, \mathbf{R}_{l0}/\mathbf{P}_0, \mathbf{Q}_0; t) d\mathbf{P}_0 d\mathbf{Q}_0 ds, \tag{53}$$

where the factor $\exp(-\beta W_{il}^{(2)})$, although convenient for later use, is arbitrary to the extent that it might be replaced by unity or any function differing from unity by short range terms.

An analytical development of the Maxwell-Boltzmann integro-differential equation may be based on Eq. (53) and the assumption of binary molecular collisions, namely that for configurations in which $\mathbf{F}_{li}$ differs from zero, $d(\Delta\mathbf{p}_i)/dt = \mathbf{F}_{li}$. Since the derivation is somewhat complicated, we shall postpone it for special treatment in a later article. The derivation is worth while, since it clarifies certain important points left obscure by the usual physical argument used to establish the Maxwell-Boltzmann equation.

We shall here employ the methods of the theory of Brownian motion to evaluate $\mathbf{K}_{li}$, writing

$$\mathbf{K}_{li} = \mathbf{K}_{li}^0 + \Delta\mathbf{K}_{li}, \tag{54}$$

$$\mathbf{K}_{li}^0 = \frac{1}{\tau}\int_0^\tau \int\int \mathbf{F}_{li}(t+s)\delta(\mathbf{p}_{i0} + \Delta\mathbf{p}_i - \mathbf{p}_i)\delta(\mathbf{R}_{i0} + \Delta\mathbf{R}_i - \mathbf{R}_i) \times$$
$$\exp\left[-\beta W_{il}^{(2)}(R_{il})\right] {}^0f_{il}^{(2/N)}(\mathbf{p}_{i0}, \mathbf{R}_{i0}, \mathbf{p}_{l0}, \mathbf{R}_{l0}/\mathbf{P}_0, \mathbf{Q}_0)d\mathbf{P}_0 d\mathbf{Q}_0 ds,$$

$${}^0f_{il}^{(2/N)} = \left(\frac{\beta^2}{(2\pi)^2 m_i m_l}\right)^{\frac{3}{2}} \frac{1}{v^2} \exp\{\beta[A^N - H_0^N + p_{i0}^2/2m_i + p_{l0}^2/2m_l$$
$$+ W_{il}^{(2)}(R_{il0})]\},$$

where ${}^0f_{il}^{(2/N)}$ is the equilibrium distribution function in the phase space of the molecules constituting the environment of the molecular pair il, and $\Delta\mathbf{K}_{li}$ is the contribution to $\mathbf{K}_{li}$ arising from the departure of $f_{il}^{(2/N)}$ from the equilibrium distribution ${}^0f_{il}^{(2/N)}$. Introducing the following relations,

$$\exp\left[-\beta W_{il}^{(2)}(R_{il0})\right] {}^0f_{il}^{(2/N)}(\mathbf{p}_{i0}, \mathbf{R}_{i0}, \mathbf{p}_{l0}, \mathbf{R}_{l0}/\mathbf{P}_0, \mathbf{Q}_0)$$
$$= \exp\left[-\beta W_{il}^{(2)}(R_{il})\right] {}^0f_{il}^{(2/N)}(\mathbf{p}_i, \mathbf{R}_i, \mathbf{p}_l, \mathbf{R}_l/\mathbf{P}, \mathbf{Q})$$
$$\times \left\{1 - \frac{\beta\mathbf{p}_{i0}}{m_i}\cdot\Delta\mathbf{p}_i - \frac{\beta\mathbf{p}_{l0}}{m_l}\cdot\Delta\mathbf{p}_l + \cdots\right\}, \tag{55}$$

$$\delta(\mathbf{p}_{i0} + \Delta\mathbf{p}_i - \mathbf{p}_i) = \delta(\mathbf{p}_{i0} - \mathbf{p}_i) - \Delta\mathbf{p}_i \cdot \nabla_{\mathbf{p}_i}\delta(\mathbf{p}_{l0} - \mathbf{p}_i) + \cdots,$$
$$\delta(\mathbf{R}_{i0} + \Delta\mathbf{R}_i - \mathbf{R}_i) = \delta(\mathbf{R}_{i0} - \mathbf{R}_i) + \cdots,$$

based upon the invariance of H^N under the transformation $(\mathbf{p}_{0i}\cdots\mathbf{Q}_0)$ to $(\mathbf{p}_i\cdots\mathbf{Q})$, and expansion of the delta functions, we finally obtain for $\mathbf{\Omega}_{li}^{(1)}$,

$$\mathbf{\Omega}_{li}^{(1)} = {}^0\mathbf{\Omega}_{li}^{(1)} + \Delta\mathbf{\Omega}_{li}^{(1)},$$

$${}^0\mathbf{\Omega}_{li}^{(1)} = -({}^i\langle\mathbf{F}_{li}\rangle^0 + \zeta_l^i\mathbf{v}_l^*)f_i^{(1)}(\mathbf{p}_i, \mathbf{R}_i; t) + \zeta_i^l\{\mathbf{p}_i/m_i + kT\nabla_{\mathbf{p}_i}\}$$
$$f_i^{(1)}(\mathbf{p}_i, \mathbf{R}_i; t) + O(\tau),$$

$$\zeta_i^l = \frac{1}{6kT}\int_{-\tau_i}^{+\tau_i} {}^i\langle\mathbf{F}_{li}\cdot e^{-isL}\mathbf{F}_i\rangle^0 ds, \quad {}^i\langle\mathbf{F}_{li}\rangle^0 = \frac{1}{v}\int \mathbf{F}_{li}\exp(-\beta W_{il}^{(2)})d\mathbf{R}_l, \tag{56}$$

$$\mathbf{v}_l^* = (N_l/C_l)\int (\mathbf{p}_l/m_l)\chi_{il}f_l^{(1)}(\mathbf{p}_l, \mathbf{R}_l; t)d\mathbf{R}_l d\mathbf{p}_l,$$

$$\chi_{il} = \frac{\exp(-\beta W_{il}^{(2)})}{6kT\zeta_l^i}\int_{-\tau_i}^{+\tau_i} {}^{il}\langle\mathbf{F}_{li}\cdot e^{-isL}\mathbf{F}_l\rangle^0 ds,$$

where the methods of Part II have been used to simplify the plateau values of the partial friction constant $\zeta_i{}^l$, and departures of $f_l^{(1)}$ from ${}^0f_l^{(1)}$ have been ignored in the expressions for $\zeta_i{}^l$ and ${}^i\langle \mathbf{F}_{il}\rangle^0$, since we are interested here in obtaining relations valid only to the first order in parameters determining departures from equilibrium. Since the gradient of $f_l^{(1)}(\mathbf{p}_l, \mathbf{R}_l; t)$ in configuration space is supposed to be appreciable only over distances of macroscopic magnitude, and since χ_{il} is a short range function of the intermolecular distance R_{il}, we may write $f_l^{(1)}(\mathbf{p}_l, \mathbf{R}_i; t)$ in the integral defining $\mathbf{v}_l{}^*$. If χ_{il} is independent of $\mathbf{p}_l$, the integral $\int \chi_{il} d\mathbf{R}_l$ is unity and the velocity $\mathbf{v}_l{}^*$ reduces after time smoothing to the mean particle velocity, $\mathbf{v}_l$, of the molecular species l at point $\mathbf{R}_i$,

$$\mathbf{v}_l(\mathbf{R}_i, t) = (N_l/C_l) \int (\mathbf{p}_l/m_l) f_l^{(1)}(\mathbf{p}_l, \mathbf{R}_i; t) d\mathbf{p}_l. \tag{57}$$

The term $\Delta\mathbf{\Omega}_{li}{}^{(1)}$ represents the contribution to $\mathbf{\Omega}_{li}{}^{(1)}$ arising from the departure of the molecules of the environment of the pair il from statistical equilibrium. For convenience in notation, it will be convenient to define a supplementary force $\mathbf{F}_{li}{}^+$ by the relation

$$\Delta\mathbf{\Omega}_{li}{}^{(1)} = \mathbf{F}_{il}{}^+ f_i{}^{(1)}. \tag{58}$$

The calculation of $\mathbf{F}_{li}{}^+$ of course requires a knowledge of distribution functions of higher order than $f^{(1)}$. If we had calculated $\mathbf{\Omega}_{li}{}^{(1)}$ under the assumption not that the pair environment was in equilibrium, but in a lower order of approximation, that the environment of molecule i alone was in equilibrium, we would have obtained all terms in Eq. (56) except those involving the $\mathbf{v}_l{}^*$.

Introducing Eqs. (56) and (58) into Eq. (49), and neglecting terms of order τ, and performing a second time average over the interval τ on the terms of Eq. (56), which will not affect terms already smoothed and possessing only secular time dependence, we obtain the following partial differential equation for $\bar{f}_i{}^{(1)}$,

$$\frac{\partial \bar{f}_i{}^{(1)}}{\partial t} + \frac{\mathbf{p}_i}{m_i}\cdot\nabla_{\mathbf{R}_i} \bar{f}_i{}^{(1)} + \nabla_{\mathbf{p}_i}\cdot(\mathbf{F}_i{}^* + \mathbf{X}_i)\bar{f}_i{}^{(1)} = \nabla_{\mathbf{p}_i}\cdot\zeta_i\left\{\frac{\mathbf{p}_i}{m_i}\bar{f}_i{}^{(1)} + kT\nabla_{\mathbf{p}_i}\bar{f}_i{}^{(1)}\right\},$$

$$\mathbf{F}_i{}^* = {}^i\langle F_i\rangle^0 + \sum_{l=1}^{\nu} N_l \zeta_l{}^i \mathbf{v}_l{}^* + \mathbf{F}_i{}^+,$$

$$ {}^i\langle F_i\rangle^0 = \sum_{l=1}^{\nu} N_l\, {}^i\langle \mathbf{F}_{li}\rangle^0 = -\nabla\mu_i + kT\nabla\log C_i, \quad \mathbf{F}_i{}^+ = \sum_{l=1}^{\nu} N_l \mathbf{F}_{li}{}^+, \tag{59}$$

$$\zeta_i = \sum_{l=1}^{\nu} N_l \zeta_i{}^l = \frac{1}{6kT}\int_{-\tau_i}^{+\tau_i} {}^i\langle \mathbf{F}_i\cdot e^{-isL}\mathbf{F}_i\rangle^0 ds,$$

where, of course, $\mathbf{F}_i{}^+$ requires further analysis for its calculation. Equation (59) differs from the generalized Fokker-Planck equation of Chandrasekar[14] in the appearance of the force $\mathbf{F}_i{}^*$ and in the fact that we have related the friction constant to the intermolecular forces in an explicit manner. If the equation is formulated under the assumption that molecule i is a solute component of an ideal dilute solution with an environment in statistical equilibrium, $\mathbf{F}_i{}^*$ vanishes. In order to relate ζ_i to intermolecular forces, it is necessary to employ

---

[14] S. Chandrasekar, *Rev. Mod. Phys.* **15**, 1–89 (1943), Eq. (249).

statistical mechanics to construct the Brownian motion kernel of Chandrasekar's Eq. (241). This is, in effect, what we have attempted here, although we have made the Liouville equation our starting point rather than the formal integral equation, Chandrasekar (241).

The second group of terms, involving the $\mathbf{v}_l^*$, are of importance in the theory of diffusion. They give rise to macroscopic interactions by means of which a chemical potential gradient of one component of a solution may cause transport of another component. These questions will be treated in detail in a later article on diffusion.

The method employed in the formulation of Eq. (59) for the distribution function $\bar{f}^{(1)}$ may be applied to distribution functions of higher order $\bar{f}^{(n)}$, if the number of degrees of freedom of the set n is small relative to the total number of degrees of freedom of the entire system. Otherwise, it appears that the plateau values of the friction tensors will not in general exist. With slightly more tedious algebraic details, the method yields for the distribution function $\bar{f}_{i\cdots k}^{(n)}(\mathbf{p}, \mathbf{q}; t)$ in a set of n molecules of types $i \cdots k$, respectively,

$$\frac{\partial \bar{f}_{i\cdots k}^{(n)}}{\partial t} + \frac{\mathbf{p}}{m} \cdot \nabla_{\mathbf{q}} \bar{f}_{i\cdots k}^{(n)} + \nabla_{\mathbf{p}} \cdot (\mathbf{F}_{i\cdots k}^* + \mathbf{X}_{i\cdots k}) \bar{f}_{i\cdots k}^{(n)}$$

$$= \nabla_{\mathbf{p}} \cdot \zeta_{i\cdots k}^{(n)} \cdot \left\{ \frac{\mathbf{p}}{m} \bar{f}_{i\cdots k}^{(n)} + kT \nabla_{\mathbf{p}} \bar{f}_{i\cdots k}^{(n)} \right\},$$

$$\mathbf{F}_{ik\cdots}^* = {}^{i\cdots k}\langle \mathbf{F}_{i\cdots k} \rangle^0 + \sum_{l=1}^{\nu} N_l \int \zeta_l^{i\cdots k} \cdot \frac{\mathbf{p}_l}{m_l} \bar{f}_l^{(1)}(\mathbf{p}_l, \mathbf{R}_l; t) d\mathbf{R}_l d\mathbf{p}_l + \mathbf{F}_{i\cdots k}^+,$$

$$\zeta_l^{i\cdots k} = \frac{1}{2kT} \left\{ \sum_{\alpha=1}^{n} \int_{-\tau_{i\ldots k}}^{+\tau_{i\ldots k}} {}^{i\cdots kl}\langle \mathbf{F}_{\alpha l} e^{-isL} \mathbf{F}_l \rangle^0 ds \right\} \exp\left(-\beta W_{i\cdots kl}^{(n+1)}\right), \tag{60}$$

$$\zeta_{i\cdots k}^{(n)} = \frac{1}{2kT} \sum_{\alpha=1}^{n} \int_{-\tau_{i\ldots k}}^{+\tau_{i\ldots k}} {}^{i\cdots k}\langle \mathbf{F}_\alpha' e^{-isL} \mathbf{F}_\alpha' \rangle^0 ds,$$

$$\mathbf{F}_\alpha' = \sum_{l=n+1}^{N} \mathbf{F}_{l\alpha}, \quad {}^{i\cdots k}\langle \mathbf{F}_{i\ldots k} \rangle^0 = -\nabla_{\mathbf{q}} W_{i\cdots k}^{(u)},$$

where $W_{i\cdots k}^{(n)}$ is the equilibrium potential of average force in the set n, and $\mathbf{F}_{i\cdots k}^+$ is the average force due to the departure from equilibrium of the environment of the set of $n + 1$ molecules of types $i \cdots k$ and l. The friction tensor $\boldsymbol{\zeta}_{i\cdots k}^{(n)}$ is not in general isotropic in the momentum space of the set n as was $\boldsymbol{\zeta}_i^{(1)}$, which we denoted simply by $\zeta_i \mathbf{1}$, for fluid systems. Since ${}^{i\cdots k}\langle \mathbf{F}_{i\ldots k} \rangle^0$ may have gradients in configuration space which are appreciable over distances of molecular magnitude, Eq. (60) requires for its validity the additional conditions, not necessary in the case of $f_i^{(1)}$, that the correlation time $\tau_{i\ldots k}$, be sufficiently short that the changes in configuration of the set n, with representative velocities in the neighborhood of the equilibrium mean thermal velocities, are negligible in the interval $\tau_{i\ldots k}$, in comparison with the range of intermolecular force. Although this question requires more careful examination, we remark here that the condition is probably fulfilled to an adequate degree of approximation in condensed systems such as liquids and liquid solutions.

In a series of later articles treating specific transport processes, diffusion, heat conduction, and viscous fluid flow, we plan to suggest an approximation based upon the neglect of $\mathbf{F}_{ik}{}^{+}$ for pairs, namely the average force arising from the departure of the environment of sets of three molecules from equilibrium.

IV. THE FRICTION CONSTANT

The statistical mechanical theory of transport processes which we have outlined leads to a generalized theory of Brownian motion for small sets of n molecules forming a part of a large system of N molecules. The most significant result of the theory is the relation which it provides between the friction constant, entering into the Langevin equation and into the differential equations for the distribution functions of lower order, and the intermolecular forces acting in the system. We shall attempt here to transform the expression for the friction constant ζ_i into a form suitable for its calculation from the potential of intermolecular force. The method which we shall propose is to be regarded as tentative and the possibility that it may in the future have to be superseded by more refined methods should be kept in mind.

We repeat the expression, Eq. (43), for the friction constant ζ_i, introducing the canonical distribution for ${}^0f_i{}^{(1/N)}$

$$\zeta_i = \frac{1}{6kT}\int_{-\tau_i}^{+\tau_i} {}^i\langle \mathbf{F}_i \cdot e^{-isL}\mathbf{F}_i\rangle^0 ds,$$

$$ {}^l\langle \mathbf{F}_i \cdot e^{-isL}\mathbf{F}_i\rangle^0 = \int\int \{\mathbf{F}_i \cdot e^{-isL}\mathbf{F}_i\}\, ({}^0f_i{}^{(1)})^{-1} e^{\beta(A-H)} d\mathbf{P}d\mathbf{Q}, \tag{61}$$

$${}^0f_i{}^{(1)} = \left(\frac{\beta}{2\pi m_i}\right)^{\frac{3}{2}} \frac{1}{v} \exp\left[-\beta p_i{}^2/2m_i - \beta W_i{}^{(1)}\right],$$

$$L = i\sum_{l=1}^{N}\left\{\frac{\mathbf{p}_l}{m_l}\cdot\nabla_{\mathbf{R}_l} + \mathbf{F}_l\cdot\nabla_{\mathbf{p}_l}\right\},$$

where in the expression for the operator L, as also in the Hamiltonian H, we omit terms arising from the external forces $\mathbf{X}_l$, since the latter will contribute at most terms of the second order to the distribution functions, the external forces being assumed small, of the first order, in systems to which the theory is applicable. We recall that the friction constant may be a function $\zeta_i(\mathbf{R}_i, \mathbf{p}_i)$ of the coordinates of molecule i, although in fluid systems we would expect no sensible dependence on $\mathbf{R}_i$. It will be found to be convenient to introduce a friction constant $\langle\zeta_i\rangle_{\mathrm{Av}}$, the mean value of ζ in the phase space of molecule i.

$$\langle\zeta_i\rangle_{\mathrm{Av}} = \int\int \zeta_i(\mathbf{p}_i, \mathbf{R}_i)\,{}^0f_i{}^{(1)}(\mathbf{p}_i, \mathbf{R}_i)\,d\mathbf{p}_i d\mathbf{R}_i$$

$$= \frac{1}{6kT}\int_{-\tau_i}^{\tau_i} \langle \mathbf{F}_i \cdot e^{-isL}\mathbf{F}_i\rangle^0 ds, \tag{62}$$

$$\langle \mathbf{F}_i \cdot e^{-isL}\mathbf{F}_i\rangle^0 = \int\cdots\int \{\mathbf{F}_i \cdot e^{-isL}\mathbf{F}_i\}\, e^{\beta(A-H)} d\mathbf{p}_1 \cdots d\mathbf{R}_N.$$

If ζ_i is independent of $\mathbf{p}_i$ as well as $\mathbf{R}_i$, it is of course identical with $\langle\zeta_i\rangle_{\mathrm{Av}}$.

If we assume that the correlation $\langle \mathbf{F}_i \exp(-isL)\mathbf{F}_i \rangle^0$ between the intermolecular forces acting on molecule i at instants of time separated by the interval s is a monotone decreasing function of time in the neighborhood of $s = 0$, it is reasonable to try to represent the decay by a Gaussian factor determined by the second moment of the operator L. If we denote by $\mu_n^{(i)}$ the n'th moment of the operator L, defined as follows

$$\begin{aligned}
\mu_n^{(i)} &= \frac{1}{\Delta_{F_i}} \int \cdots \int \{\mathbf{F}_i \cdot L^n \mathbf{F}_i\} e^{\beta(A-H)} d\mathbf{p}_1 \cdots d\mathbf{R}_N, \\
\Delta_{F_i} &= \langle F_i^2 \rangle^0 = \int \cdots \int F_i^2 e^{\beta(A-H)} d\mathbf{p}_1 \cdots d\mathbf{R}_N, \\
\omega_i^2 &= \mu_2^{(i)},
\end{aligned} \tag{63}$$

where L^n denotes n successive applications of the operator L, we find that the $\mu_n^{(i)}$ are positive for even n and vanish for odd n. Using the formal power series, Eq. (8), for the operator $\exp(-isL)$ in the integrand of Eq. (62) defining $\langle \mathbf{F}_i \cdot e^{-isL}\mathbf{F}_i \rangle^0$ and factoring the function $\exp(-\omega_i^2 s^2/2)$ from the resulting power series, ω_i^2 being used in place of $\mu_1^{(i)}$, the second moment, we obtain,

$$\begin{aligned}
\langle \mathbf{F}_i \cdot e^{-isL}\mathbf{F}_i \rangle^0 &= \Delta_{F_i} \exp(-\omega_i^2 s^2/2) \sum_{n=0}^{\infty} \frac{\kappa_n^{(i)} (\omega_i^2 s^2)^n}{(2n)!}, \\
\kappa_n^{(i)} &= \sum_{r=0}^{n} \frac{(2n)!(-1)^r}{(2r)!(n-r)!2^{n-r}} \frac{\mu_{2r}^{(i)}}{\mu_2^{(i)r}}.
\end{aligned} \tag{64}$$

Substitution of the series (64) into the time integral of Eq. (62) yields the plateau value,

$$\langle \zeta_i \rangle_{\mathrm{Av}} = \frac{(2\pi)^{\frac{1}{2}} \Delta_{F_i}}{6kT\omega_i} \left\{ 1 + \sum_{n=2}^{\infty} \frac{\kappa_n^{(i)}}{2^n n!} \right\}, \tag{65}$$

with the neglect of terms of $O[\exp(-\omega_i^2 \tau_i^2/2)]$. Assuming the formal procedure leading to Eq. (65) to be valid, we are able to specify more precisely the magnitude of the microscopic time interval τ_i, over which the integral defining the friction constant $\langle \zeta_i \rangle_{\mathrm{Av}}$ must be extended in order to attain the plateau value. The correlation time is of the order of $1/\omega_i$ and τ_i must evidently be large relative to $1/\omega_i$.

We shall not here attempt to give a mathematical justification of the formal procedure leading to Eq. (65), but tentatively accept the result as plausible for systems of molecules with intermolecular forces of known types. Properly, the class of dynamical systems, for which the procedure is valid, should be characterized by suitable restrictions on their Hamiltonians. We should probably be prepared to find that, in cases of interest, the series of Eq. (65) is an asymptotic series and not a convergent series.

The variance or fluctuation of intermolecular force Δ_{F_i} may, for intermolecular forces of the type of Eq. (2), be expressed as follows

$$\Delta_{F_i} = \sum_{l=1}^{\nu} N_l \langle F_{li}^2 \rangle^0 + \sum_{l=1}^{\nu} \sum_{l'=1}^{\nu} N_l N_{l'} \langle \mathbf{F}_{li} \cdot \mathbf{F}_{l'i} \rangle^0, \tag{66}$$

where $\mathbf{F}_{li}$ is the force exerted on a molecule of type i by a molecule of type l. In the absence of long range forces, for example Coulomb forces acting between ions in solution, the average values of Eq. (66) may be transformed with the aid of Green's theorem to give,

$$\Delta_{F_i} = kT \sum_{l=1}^{\nu} c_l \Delta_{il}, \quad \Delta_{il} = N \int \nabla^2 V_{il}(R) \exp(-\beta W_{il}^{(2)}) dv, \tag{67}$$

where $W_{il}^{(2)}$ is equilibrium potential of average force between a pair of type il, V_{il} the potential of intermolecular force between the pair, and the integral is to be extended over all values of their relative coordinates; N is here Avogadro's number and c_l is the concentration of component l in moles per unit volume. The function $\exp(-\beta W_{il}^{(2)})$ is the radial distribution function for a pair il in the equilibrium ensemble.

The characteristic frequency ω_i^2 may be expressed in the following form,

$$\omega_i^2 = \frac{1}{\Delta_{F_i}} [\langle L^* \mathbf{F}_i \cdot L\mathbf{F}_i \rangle^0], \tag{68}$$

by virtue of the fact that L is self-adjoint. Integration over momentum space leads to the result

$$\omega_i^2 = \frac{kT}{\Delta_{F_i}} \sum_{l=1}^{N} (1/m_l) \langle (\nabla_l \mathbf{F}_i) : (\nabla_l \mathbf{F}_i) \rangle^0 \tag{69}$$

where $(\nabla_l \mathbf{F}_i):(\nabla_l \mathbf{F}_i)$ denotes the inner product of the dyadic $\nabla_l \mathbf{F}_i$, equal to the sum of the squares of its nine components. For intermolecular forces of the type of Eq. (2), a further reduction is possible, in the absence of long range Coulomb forces,

$$\omega_i^2 = \frac{kT}{\Delta_{F_i}} \left\{ \sum_{l=1}^{\nu} \left(\frac{1}{M_l} + \frac{1}{M_i} \right) C_l I_l^i + \frac{1}{M_i} \sum_{l=1}^{\nu} \sum_{l'=1}^{\nu} C_l C_{l'} I_{ll'}^i \right\},$$

$$I_l^i = N^2 \int \left\{ \left(\frac{d^2 V_{il}}{dR^2} \right)^2 + \frac{2}{R^2} \left(\frac{dV_{il}}{dR} \right)^2 \right\} \exp(-\beta W_{il}^{(2)}) dv,$$

$$I_{ll'}^i = N^3 \int \int \left\{ \cos^2 \gamma \frac{d^2 V_{il}}{dR^2} \frac{d^2 V_{il'}}{dR'^2} + \sin^2 \gamma \left[\frac{1}{R} \frac{dV_{il}}{dR} \frac{d^2 V_{il'}}{dR'^2} \right. \right.$$

$$\left. \left. + \frac{1}{R'} \frac{d^2 V_{il}}{dR^2} \frac{dV_{il'}}{dR'} \right] + \frac{3 - \cos^2 \gamma}{RR'} \frac{dV_{il}}{dR} \frac{dV_{il'}}{dR'} \right\} \exp(-\beta W_{ill'}^{(3)}) dv' dv, \tag{70}$$

$$\cos \gamma = (\mathbf{R}' \cdot \mathbf{R})/R'R,$$

where M_i and M_l are the molecular weights of components i and l respectively, and $V_{il}(R)$ and $V_{il'}(R')$ are the potentials of the force between pairs of types il

and il', respectively. The potential $W_{ill'}^{(3)}$ is the equilibrium potential of average force acting on molecules l' and l situated at points R' and R from the fixed molecule i. The average values in configuration space have been simplified for fluid systems in which $W_i^{(1)}$ the equilibrium potential of mean force on any molecule i is zero.

Returning to the friction constant ζ_i, which may depend upon $\mathbf{p}_i$ and thus differ from $\langle\zeta_i\rangle_{Av}$, we make the hypothesis that the time decay of the mean value ${}^i\langle\mathbf{F}_i \cdot e^{-isL}\mathbf{F}_i\rangle^0$ is also of the order of $\exp(-\omega_i^2 s^2/2)$ with the ω_i^2 of Eqs. (68)–(70). Using the power series, Eq. (8) for $\exp(-isL)$ in Eq. (61), again factoring $\exp(-\omega_i^2 s^2/2)$, and integrating with respect to time, we obtain the plateau value,

$$\zeta_i = \frac{(2\pi)^{\frac{1}{2}}\Delta_{F_i}}{6kT\omega_i}\left\{1 + \sum_{n=1}^{\infty}\frac{{}^i\kappa_n{}^{(i)}}{2^n n!}\right\}, \quad {}^i\kappa_n{}^{(i)} = \sum_{r=0}^{n}\frac{(2n)!(-1)^r}{(2r)!(n-r)!2^{n-r}}\frac{{}^i\mu_{2r}{}^{(i)}}{\mu_2{}^{(i)r}}, \tag{71}$$

$${}^i\mu_{2r}{}^{(i)} = (1/\Delta_{F_i})\,{}^i\langle\mathbf{F}_i \cdot L^{2r}\mathbf{F}_i\rangle^0,$$

where ${}^i\kappa_1{}^{(i)}$ depends upon $\mathbf{p}_i$ and does not vanish as did $\kappa_1{}^{(i)}$. The moments ${}^i\mu_n{}^{(i)}$ depend upon $\mathbf{p}_i$ and therefore differ from the $\mu_n{}^{(i)}$. The coefficients $\kappa_n{}^{(i)}$ and ${}^i\kappa_n{}^{(i)}$ can be expressed in terms of semi-invariants, frequently used in statistics, instead of directly in terms of the moments, if desired.

Assuming that moments of L higher than the second can be neglected and calculating the pertinent average values, we obtain the following approximation to the friction constant ζ_i.

$$\zeta_i = \frac{(2\pi)^{\frac{1}{2}}\Delta_{F_i}}{6kT\omega_i}[1 - \alpha_i(1 - \beta p_i^2/3m_i)], \quad \alpha_i = \frac{(kT)^2}{2M_i\Delta_{F_i}\omega_i^2}\sum_{l=1}^{\nu} C_l\alpha_l{}^i, \tag{72}$$

$$\alpha_l{}^i = N^2\int(\nabla^4 V_{il})\exp(-\beta W_{il}{}^{(2)})dv,$$

where Δ_{F_i} and ω_i are given by Eqs. (67) and (70). Green's theorem has again been used in calculating α_i under the restriction of short range intermolecular forces. We surmise and will later investigate by explicit calculation that in condensed systems such as liquids and liquid solutions, where the second group of terms of Eq. (70) involving the $I_{ll'}{}^i$ make the dominant contribution to ω_i^2, that α_i will be sufficiently small to neglect the dependence of ζ_i on p_i for values of p_i in the neighborhood of its equilibrium root mean square. In this case our approximation to the friction constant becomes

$$\zeta_i = \frac{(2\pi)^{\frac{1}{2}}\Delta_{F_i}}{6kT\omega_i}. \tag{73}$$

If molecule i is a macromolecule of high molecular weight M_i in a solvent of low molecular weight, we shall expect ζ_i to be effectively independent of p_i, since ω_i by Eq. (70) becomes independent of M_i and thus α_i diminishes with M_i, vanishing with the ratio of M_s/M_i, where M_i is the solvent molecular weight.

For a macromolecule in a solvent of low molecular weight we conclude from Eq. (73) and the asymptotic independence of ω_i on M_i that ζ_i will be also independent of M_i, depending only on the mass of the solvent molecules. The relation between Eq. (73) and the hydrodynamic estimate of ζ_i by Stokes law for macromolecules is connected with the boundary condition of no slip at an interface with a rigid surface, which is used in the hydrodynamics of viscous fluids. The resistance $\zeta_i \mathbf{p}_i/m_i$ experienced by a macroscopic sphere i, when determined by our method with the ζ_i of Eqs. (61) and (73), is due to a surface layer of molecules of solvent of thickness of the order of the range of intermolecular forces. If the hypothesis of no slip in this layer is made, the resistance $\zeta_i \mathbf{p}_i/m_i$ experienced by sphere will be equal to the hydrodynamic resistance $6\pi\eta \mathbf{p}_i/m_i$ exerted by the fluid on the surface layer. This argument might be made the basis for a molecular theory of the viscosity coefficient η, but it turns out not to be the most convenient or consequential approach to this problem.

A few further remarks concerning the dependence of the friction constant ζ_i on the mass of molecule i are of interest. Only when the mass of molecule i is large relative to those of the molecules of its environment will ζ_i be independent of M_i. In fact from Eqs. (70) and (73), one observes that if the mass of i is very small relative to those of its environment, ζ_i is proportional to $M_i^{\frac{1}{2}}$. This circumstance suggests, contrary to the conclusion to be drawn from the hydrodynamic estimate of ζ_i based on Stoke's law, that isotope separations by thermal diffusion or electrolysis might be practicable in liquids and liquid solutions, provided the solvent consists of molecules of mass not small relative to the masses of the molecules to be separated.

We remark that we have not proved the existence of a plateau value of the friction constant for systems of molecules interacting with intermolecular forces of the usual type. We have only outlined a method for estimating ζ_i which appears feasible if the plateau value exists. It is therefore of interest to examine two cases, the crystal with harmonic lattice vibrations and the gas with binary collisions, for which the integral Eq. (61), defining ζ_i, can be evaluated directly.

Although we shall not here reproduce the details of the analysis, we remark that the friction constant appears to have no plateau value for the crystal with harmonic lattice vibrations. This is evidently due to the fact that the motion is multiplied periodically. We do not conclude from this that no dissipative mechanism exists whereby a molecule moving in the lattice can exchange energy with the harmonic lattice vibrational modes, but only that anharmonic terms must be considered in describing the dissipative mechanism. Nor does this necessarily imply that Eqs. (67), (70), and (71), although they involve derivatives of the potentials of intermolecular force no higher than the second, do not provide an adequate approximation to the friction constant in crystals (of course, in crystals ζ_i is a function of $\mathbf{R}_i$ and requires a supplementary average over a domain of linear dimensions large relative to the lattice parameters before use in macroscopic transport theory). That is to say, the anharmonic terms may assure the approach to a plateau value, by affecting the wings of the force correlation, without sensibly affecting its value.

Although transport in gases of low density is most accurately described by the Maxwell-Boltzmann integro-differential equation, the theory developed here is applicable to a certain degree of approximation. Using binary collision analysis, we find that ζ_i does indeed have a plateau value for values of τ_i, long relative to the representative duration of a molecular collision. For simplicity, we give the result for a system of one component, easily generalized to an arbitrary number of components.

$$\begin{aligned}
\zeta &= \frac{N}{6vkT}\int\int \Phi\,(\mathbf{R}_0, \alpha, \epsilon)\left(\frac{dV}{dR_0}\right)\exp\,(-\,\beta V - \beta p_{20}{}^2/2m)d\mathbf{R}_0 d\mathbf{p}_{20}, \\
\Phi &= \frac{m}{2\alpha}\int_0^{\vartheta^*}\cos\,(\vartheta - \vartheta_0)\,R^2\frac{dV}{dR}\,d\vartheta, \\
\alpha &= |\mathbf{R}_0 \times \mathbf{p}_{12}{}^0|; \\
\vartheta^* &= 2\int_b^{\infty}\frac{(\alpha/r^2)dr}{[m(\epsilon - V(r) - \alpha^2/mr^2)]^{\frac{1}{2}}}, \\
\epsilon &= p_{12}{}^{02}/m + V(R_0),
\end{aligned} \tag{74}$$

where b is largest positive root of

$$\epsilon - V(b) - \alpha^2/mb^2 = 0,$$

and $\mathbf{p}_{12}{}^0$ and $\mathbf{R}_0$ are the relative momentum and position of a molecular pair, m the molecular mass, and V the potential of intermolecular force. In the integral defining Φ, R is to be evaluated as a function of ϑ, from the equation of the orbit,

$$\begin{aligned}
\vartheta &= \int_R^{\infty}\frac{(\alpha/r^2)dr}{[m(\epsilon - V - \alpha^2/mr^2)]^{\frac{1}{2}}}; \quad 0 \leqslant \vartheta \leqslant \vartheta^*/2, \\
\vartheta &= \vartheta^* - \int_R^{\infty}\frac{(\alpha/r^2)dr}{[m(\epsilon - V - \alpha^2/mr^2)]^{\frac{1}{2}}}; \quad \vartheta^*/2 < \vartheta \leqslant \vartheta^*
\end{aligned} \tag{75}$$

for a binary collision. A comparison of ζ evaluated by Eqs. (74) and (75) with the approximation, Eq. (71), would be desirable. However, it should be kept in mind in making such a comparison that the peak approximation, upon which Eq. (71) is based, is without doubt much better in liquids and liquid solutions than in gases.

We close our survey of the general theory by a remark about $\zeta_i(\infty)$, the asymptotic value of $\zeta_i(\tau)$ for $\zeta \to \infty$. In the case of gases, we would find that $\zeta_i(\infty)$ is vanishing or undeterminate, if we were so unwise as to let $\tau_i \to \infty$, since after a time of the order of the period of a Poincaré cycle, the contribution, Eq. (73), to ζ would be cancelled by that from a collision in which the orbit was traversed in the reverse sense. Using spectral theory (see Appendix I), we have convinced ourselves that in a system of molecules with arbitrary central forces, the only invariants of which are energy, total linear momentum, and total angular momentum, $\zeta_i(\infty)$ always vanishes. As we have already pointed out, this circumstance is related to the failure of thermodynamic dissipative mechanisms over very long periods comparable with those of Poincaré cycles.

Applications of the general theory, which we have presented here, to special transport processes will follow in later articles.

In conclusion, we wish to express our thanks to Professor Joseph E. Mayer for his kindness in reading this article in manuscript and for providing much illuminating criticism.

APPENDIX: REMARKS ON THE MATHEMATICAL THEORY OF THE OPERATOR

exp $(-isL)$

Although we shall not attempt an exhaustive justification of our manipulations of the operator exp $(-isL)$, we wish to call attention to the basic mathematical theory[15] underlying the use of this operator. We first consider the eigenvalue problem

$$L\psi_\lambda = \lambda\psi_\lambda, \tag{A1}$$

where the domain of the operator L is restricted to functions $g(p, q)$ in phase space which form a Hilbert space. Since L is self adjoint, the eigenvalues λ are real. The inner product (f, g) of two such functions is defined as

$$(f, g) = \int\int f^* g d\mathbf{p} d\mathbf{q}, \tag{A2}$$

where if f, g are vectors in phase space f^*g in the integrand is to be replaced by $f^* \cdot \mathbf{g}$. If $E(\lambda)$, the canonical resolution of the identity appropriate to L, is defined as the operator which projects any function g on the linear manifold in Hilbert space spanned by the eigenfunctions of L corresponding to eigenvalues less than λ, the operator exp $(-isL)$ may be represented by the Stieltjes integral,

$$e^{-isL} = \int_{-\infty}^{+\infty} e^{-i\lambda s} dE(\lambda). \tag{A3}$$

Using Eq. (A3) in Eq. (62) defining the mean friction constant $\langle\zeta_i\rangle_{\text{Av}}$, we have

$$\langle\zeta_i\rangle_{\text{Av}} = \frac{1}{6kT}\int_{-\tau_i}^{+\tau_i}\int_{-\infty}^{+\infty} e^{-i\lambda s} dz_i(\lambda) ds,$$

$$z_i(\lambda) = (E(\lambda)\mathbf{\Lambda}_i, \mathbf{\Lambda}_i), \tag{A4}$$

$$\mathbf{\Lambda}_i = \exp\left[\beta(A - H)/2\right]\mathbf{F}_i,$$

where the invariance of H under exp $(-isL)$ has been used to symmetrize the expression. The fluctuation of intermolecular force is evidently given by

$$\Delta_{F_i} = \int_{-\infty}^{+\infty} dz_i(\lambda) = (\mathbf{\Lambda}_i, \mathbf{\Lambda}_i), \tag{A5}$$

and the moments of L, with respect to $Z(\lambda)$, of Eq. (63) are expressible in the form,

$$\mu_n{}^{(i)} = \frac{1}{\Delta_{F_i}}\int_{-\infty}^{+\infty} \lambda^n dz_i(\lambda). \tag{A6}$$

The justification of the peak approximation,

$$\langle\zeta_i\rangle_{\text{Av}} = \frac{(2\pi)^{\frac{1}{2}}\Delta_{F_i}}{6kT\omega_i}, \quad \omega_i{}^2 = \mu_2{}^{(i)}, \tag{A7}$$

---

[15] See von Neumann, *Proc. Nat. Acad. Sci.* **18** (1932). Also *Quantenmechanik* (Verlagsbuchhandlung Julius Springer, Berlin, 1932); Stone, *Linear Transformations in Hilbert Space* (American Mathematical Society Publication, 1932).

employed in Part IV to represent $\langle\zeta_i\rangle_{Av}$, therefore must rest upon a study of the structure of the projection operator $E(\lambda)$ for the special dynamical system in question, and a verification that the integral,

$$\int_{-\infty}^{+\infty} e^{-is\lambda} dz_i(\lambda),$$

is adequately approximated by

$$\Delta_{F_i} \exp(-\omega_i^2 s^2/2)$$

in the neighborhood of $s = 0$ and for subsequent intervals of time of microscopic duration (small relative to the representative interval of macroscopic observation).

A brief discussion of the asymptotic value $\langle\zeta_i\rangle_{Av}(\infty)$ for $\tau_i \to \infty$ is of some interest here. Let us suppose that the spectrum of L is continuous in the neighborhood of $\lambda = 0$, and that the operator E_0' defined by

$$E_0' = \lim_{\lambda \to 0} \frac{E(\lambda) - E(-\lambda)}{2\lambda} \tag{A8}$$

exists. Then, commuting the order of integrations in Eq. (A4) and letting $\tau_i \to \infty$, we get

$$\zeta_i(\infty) = \frac{\pi}{6kT}(E_0'\mathbf{\Lambda}_i, E_0'\mathbf{\Lambda}_i), \tag{A9}$$

where $E_{0'}$ is the operator projecting a function in Hilbert space on the linear manifold spanned by the eigenfunctions of L per unit λ-interval in the vicinity of $\lambda = 0$. The functions spanning this manifold are functions of the invariants of L, that is the constants of the motion. For arbitrary central intermolecular forces, with energy, total linear momentum, and total angular momentum the only invariants, explicit calculation shows that $\langle\zeta_i\rangle_{Av}(\infty)$ vanishes, a fact to which attention has already been called.

Other uses of the spectral resolution of L may be mentioned. For example, the solution $\varphi(\mathbf{p}, \mathbf{q}; t)$ of the inhomogeneous equation,

$$L\varphi + i\frac{\partial \varphi}{\partial t} = A(\mathbf{p}, \mathbf{q}; t), \tag{A10}$$

$$\varphi(\mathbf{p}, \mathbf{q}; 0) = \varphi_0(\mathbf{p}, \mathbf{q}),$$

may be expressed in the form

$$\varphi(\mathbf{p}, \mathbf{q}; t) = \int_{-\infty}^{+\infty} e^{-i\lambda t} d(E(\lambda)\varphi_0) + \int_0^t \int_{-\infty}^{+\infty} e^{-i\lambda(t-s)} d(E(\lambda)A) ds \tag{A11}$$

which is useful in the treatment of time dependent external forces under certain circumstances.[16]

---

[16] This method is being studied by Dr. F. W. Boggs in connection with the general theory of dielectric loss.

Errata: Statistical Mechanics of Transport Processes
I. General Theory

[*J. Chem. Phys.* **14**, 180 (1946)]

JOHN G. KIRKWOOD, *Baker Laboratory, Cornell University*

In this article an important distinction was made between the distribution function $f^{(n)}(\mathbf{p}, \mathbf{q}; t)$ at time t and its time average $\bar{f}^{(n)}(\mathbf{p}, \mathbf{q}; t)$ over an interval τ subsequent to the instant t. The two functions are related in the following manner,

$$\bar{f}^{(n)}(\mathbf{p}, \mathbf{q}; t) = \frac{1}{\tau}\int_0^\tau f^{(n)}(\mathbf{p}, \mathbf{q}, t + s)ds.$$

Unfortunately, serious confusion was caused by a series of typographical errors introduced between galley and page proof, in which the bar was omitted at random from the functions $\bar{f}^{(n)}(\mathbf{p}, \mathbf{q}; t)$. These errors are to be corrected as follows:

1. $\bar{f}^{(N)}$ to replace $f^{(N)}$ on the left side of the second of Eqs. (14).

2. $\bar{f}^{(n)}$ to replace $f^{(n)}$:
   (a) On left side of second of Eqs. (20).
   (b) In integrand of Eq. (21).
   (c) On left side of the third of Eqs. (46).
   (d) On left side of the differential equation, Eq. (47).
   (e) On right side of the first of Eqs. (48).

3. $\bar{f}^{(1)}$ to replace $f^{(1)}$:
   (a) In the integrands on the right sides of Eqs. (23), (24), (25), (26), and the second of Eqs. (60).
   (b) On the left side of the differential equation, Eq. (49).
   (c) On both sides of the differential equation, Eq. (59).
   (d) First sentence, last paragraph, page 194.

Two additional errors of a minor character are also to be noted:

4. In the first of Eqs. (70), C_l, the concentrations in moles/cm³ should replace C_l, the concentrations in molecules/cm³.

5. The expression $6\pi\eta\mathbf{p}_i/m_i$ should replace $6\pi\eta m_i\mathbf{p}_i$ at the end of the eighteenth line from the bottom of the second column, page 198.

The Statistical Mechanical Theory of Transport Processes
II. Transport in Gases

JOHN G. KIRKWOOD, *Baker Laboratory, Cornell University, Ithaca, New York*
(Received October 28, 1946)

By means of the methods developed in the first paper of this series, SMTI, the Maxwell-Boltzmann integro-differential equation, underlying the well-developed Chapman-Enskog theory of transport phenomena in gases of low density, is derived from the principles of statistical mechanics. The derivation supplements and clarifies the usual physical argument employed to establish this important equation.

The molecular theory of transport in gases of low density is based upon the Maxwell-Boltzmann integro-differential equation, the consequences of which have been developed by Chapman, Enskog, and other investigators.[1] Rigorous mathematical methods, due principally to Enskog, applied to the solution of the Maxwell-Boltzmann equation, have yielded adequate and detailed theories of diffusion, viscous flow, heat conduction, and related phenomena in gases of sufficiently low density to be amenable to binary collision analysis. Little remains to be done along these lines.

The Maxwell-Boltzmann equation is customarily derived by means of a physical argument which, though plausible, leaves certain points rather obscure. The passage from "fine-grained" to "coarse-grained" distribution functions is glossed over and the role of multiply periodic states of motion is not clarified. In order to complete the molecular theory of transport in gases, an analytical derivation of the Maxwell-Boltzmann integro-differential equation from the principles of statistical mechanics is much to be desired. We shall here undertake such a derivation on the basis of the statistical mechanical theory of transport processes outlined in the first paper of this series,[2] SMTI.

We begin with Liouville's equation,

$$\frac{\partial f^{(N)}}{\partial t} + \sum_{l=1}^{N} \left\{ \frac{\mathbf{p}_l}{m_l} \cdot \nabla_{R_l} f^{(N)} + (\mathbf{X}_l + \mathbf{F}_l) \cdot \nabla_{p_l} f^{(N)} \right\} = 0,$$
$$\mathbf{F}_l = \sum_{i=1}^{N} \mathbf{F}_{il}, \tag{1}$$

for the distribution function $f^{(N)}$ in the phase space ($\mathbf{p}_1$, $\mathbf{p}_N$, $\mathbf{R}_1$, $\mathbf{R}_N$) of systems of N molecules. Here $\mathbf{X}_l$ is the external force acting on molecule l and $\mathbf{F}_l$, the total intermolecular force, assumed the sum of contributions $\mathbf{F}_{il}$, each

---

[1] See Chapman and Cowling, *Mathematical Theory of Non-Uniform Gases* (Cambridge University Press, 1939).

[2] J. G. Kirkwood, *J. Chem. Phys.* **14**, 180 (1946).

depending only on the relative configuration of molecules i and l. The distribution function $f_i^{(1)}$ in the 6-phase space of an individual molecule is given by

$$f_i^{(1)}(\mathbf{p}_i, \mathbf{R}_i; t) = \int\int f^{(N)}(\mathbf{p}_i, \mathbf{R}_i, \mathbf{P}, \mathbf{Q}; t) d\mathbf{P} d\mathbf{Q}, \tag{2}$$

where the integration extends over $(\mathbf{P}, \mathbf{Q})$ the residual phase space of the other $N - 1$ molecules of the system. The distribution function $\bar{f}_i^{(1)}$ averaged over an interval of time τ subsequent to the instant t is defined by the relation,

$$\bar{f}_i^{(1)}(\mathbf{p}_i, \mathbf{R}_i; t) = \frac{1}{\tau}\int_0^\tau f_i^{(1)}(\mathbf{p}_i, \mathbf{R}_i; t + s) ds. \tag{3}$$

It is this distribution function $\bar{f}_i^{(1)}$, "coarse-grained" in time, which we shall find to satisfy the Maxwell-Boltzmann equation when the influence of collisions involving more than two molecules is neglected and τ is selected as large relative to the duration of a representative collision. We surmise that an alternative description based upon a distribution function "coarse-grained" in phase space[3] might be constructed, but such a description is not necessary.

Integration of both sides of Eq. (1) over the residual phase space $(\mathbf{P}, \mathbf{Q})$ of all molecules except i and construction of the time average lead to the following equations, Eqs. (49) and (51) of SMTI, for the distribution function $\bar{f}_i^{(1)}$,

$$\frac{\partial \bar{f}_i^{(1)}}{\partial t} + \frac{\mathbf{p}_i}{m_i} \cdot \nabla_{R_i} \bar{f}_i^{(1)} + \mathbf{X}_i \cdot \nabla_{p_i} \bar{f}_i^{(1)} = \sum_{l=1}^{\nu} N_l \nabla_{p_i} \cdot \mathbf{\Omega}_{li}^{(1)},$$

$$\nabla_{p_i} \cdot \mathbf{\Omega}_{li}^{(1)} = \int \cdots \int (\nabla_{p_i} \cdot \mathbf{K}_{li}) f_i^{(1)}(\mathbf{p}_{i0}, \mathbf{R}_{i0}; t) f_l^{(1)}(\mathbf{p}_{l0}, \mathbf{R}_{l0}; t) \, d\mathbf{p}_{i0} d\mathbf{R}_{i0} d\mathbf{p}_{l0} d\mathbf{R}_{l0}, \tag{4}$$

$$\mathbf{K}_{li} = -\frac{1}{\tau}\int_0^\tau \int\int \mathbf{F}_{li}(t + s)\delta(\mathbf{p}_{i0} + \Delta\mathbf{p}_i - \mathbf{p}_i)\delta(\mathbf{R}_{i0} + \Delta\mathbf{R}_i - \mathbf{R}_i) \times (1 + \vartheta_{li}) f^{(2/N)}(\mathbf{p}_{i0} \cdots \mathbf{R}_{l0}/\mathbf{P}_0, \mathbf{Q}_0; t) d\mathbf{P}_0 d\mathbf{Q}_0 ds,$$

$$(1 + \vartheta_{li}) = \frac{f_{il}^{(2)}(\mathbf{p}_{i0} \cdots \mathbf{R}_{l0}; t)}{f_i^{(1)}(\mathbf{p}_{i0}, \mathbf{R}_{i0}; t) f_l^{(1)}(\mathbf{p}_{l0}, \mathbf{R}_{l0}; t)},$$

where the symbols have the same significance as in SMTI. $f^{(2/N)}(\mathbf{p}_{i0} \cdots \mathbf{R}_{l0}/\mathbf{P}_0, \mathbf{Q}_0; t)$ is the relative probability density in the residual phase space $(\mathbf{P}_0, \mathbf{Q}_0)$ of the remaining $N - 2$ molecules, if the specified pair, i and l, are situated at the point, $\mathbf{p}_{i0}, \mathbf{R}_{i0}, \mathbf{p}_{l0}, \mathbf{R}_{l0}$, in the phase space of that pair. The correlation function in pair space, $(1 + \vartheta_{li})$, was denoted by φ_{li} in STMI. If ϑ_{li} is a short range function of the intermolecular distance in a sense presently to be made more precise, that part of $\mathbf{K}_{li}$ arising from ϑ_{li} makes negligible contribution to $\mathbf{\Omega}_{li}^{(1)}$ for sufficiently large τ.

We shall assume that the force $\mathbf{F}_{li}$ exerted by molecule l on molecule i has a

[3] See Tolman, *Statistical Mechanics* (Oxford University Press, 1938), Chapter VI, Oxford VI.

finite range R_0, vanishing for intermolecular distances R_{il} greater than R_0. For short range intermolecular forces of the van der Walls type, this is not an essential limitation, since an R_0 of molecular order of magnitude may be chosen beyond which such intermolecular forces are of negligible magnitude. If for relative initial configurations of the pair *il*, for which $\mathbf{F}_{li}$ differs from zero in the subsequent interval τ, the probability of configurations of the remaining $N - 2$ molecules, for which their contribution to the force on *i* also differs from zero, is negligible, it is sufficient to use the *binary collision* approximation,

$$\partial(\Delta \mathbf{p}_i)/\partial s = \mathbf{F}_{li} \tag{5}$$

in the evaluation of the integrals $\mathbf{K}_{li}$ and $\nabla_{pi} \cdot \boldsymbol{\Omega}_{li}^{(1)}$. The condition for the validity of the approximation is that the ratio of the probability that three or more molecules are situated in region of 3-configuration space, of linear dimension of the order of magnitude of the range of intermolecular force R_0, to the probability that two molecules are situated in the region, be zero. For distributions departing but slightly from statistical equilibrium, this condition is normally fulfilled in the limit of zero density (the assumption of *molecular chaos*). If we make the additional assumption that $f_i^{(1)}$ and $f_l^{(1)}$ have only macroscopic dependence on $\mathbf{R}_i$ and $\mathbf{R}_l$,

$$|\nabla_{R_i} \log f_i{}^{(1)}| = 0(1/L_i), \quad |\nabla_{R_l} \log f_l{}^{(1)}| = 0(1/L_l), \tag{6}$$

where L_i and L_l are macroscopic lengths large relative to the range of intermolecule force, then to terms of order $0(R_0/L_i)$, we may replace $\delta(\mathbf{R}_{i0} + \Delta\mathbf{R} - \mathbf{R}_i)$ by $\delta(\mathbf{R}_{i0} - \mathbf{R}_i)$ in the integral defining $\mathbf{K}_{li}$ and $\mathbf{R}_{l0}$ by $\mathbf{R}_{i0}$ as the configurational argument of $f_l^{(1)}$ in the integral defining $\nabla_{p_i} \cdot \boldsymbol{\Omega}_{li}^{(1)}$, Eq. (4).

We now proceed to evaluate $\mathbf{K}_{li}$ and $\nabla_{p_i} \cdot \boldsymbol{\Omega}_{li}^{(1)}$ of Eq. (4) with the use of Eq. (5) and the other assumptions stated in the preceding paragraph. Changing configuration variables from $\mathbf{R}_{i0}$ and $\mathbf{R}_{l0}$ to $\mathbf{R}_{i0}$ and $\mathbf{R}_{il}{}^0$, the relative configuration of *i* and *l*, and using the properties of the delta functions $\delta(\mathbf{p}_{i0} + \Delta\mathbf{p}_i - \mathbf{p}_i)$ and $\delta(\mathbf{R}_{i0} - \mathbf{R}_i)$, we obtain from Eqs. (4) and (5),

$$\nabla_{p_i} \cdot \boldsymbol{\Omega}_{li}{}^{(1)} = \int\int\int \psi_{li} f_i{}^{(1)}(\mathbf{p}_{i0}, \mathbf{R}_i; t) f_l{}^{(1)}(\mathbf{p}_{l0}, \mathbf{R}_i; t) d\mathbf{p}_{i0} d\mathbf{p}_{l0} d\mathbf{R}_{il}{}^0/\tau,$$

$$\psi_{li} = (1 + \vartheta_{li}) \int_0^\tau \frac{\partial(\Delta\mathbf{p}_i)}{\partial s} \cdot \nabla_{\Delta p_i} \delta(\mathbf{p}_{i0} + \Delta\mathbf{p}_i - p_i) ds \tag{7}$$

$$= (1 + \vartheta_{li}) \{\delta(\mathbf{p}_{i0} + \Delta\mathbf{p}_i(\tau) - \mathbf{p}_i) - \delta(\mathbf{p}_{i0} - \mathbf{p}_i)\},$$

where the integration of $f^{(2/N)}$ over the residual configuration space $(\mathbf{P}_0, \mathbf{Q}_0)$ has been carried out to give unity, since, by Eq. (5), the other factors of the integrand of the expression defining $\mathbf{K}_{il}$ are independent of $\mathbf{P}_0$ and $\mathbf{Q}_0$, depending only on the Lagrange coordinates of the pair *il*, and $f^{(2/N)}$ is normalized to unity.

If the integral, $\int \vartheta_{li} d\mathbf{R}_{il}{}^0$, is bounded, it is possible to choose τ of sufficient magnitude to make contributions to $\nabla_{pi} \cdot \boldsymbol{\Omega}_{li}{}^{(1)}$, arising from the deviation ϑ_{li}, of the pair correlation function from unity, as small as desired, and we may write,

$$\nabla_{p_i} \cdot \boldsymbol{\Omega}_{li}^{(1)} = \int\int\int \{\delta(\mathbf{p}_i' - \mathbf{p}_i) - \delta(\mathbf{p}_{i0} - \mathbf{p}_i)\} f_i^{(1)}(\mathbf{p}_{i0}, \mathbf{R}_i; t) \tag{8}$$

$$f_l^{(1)}(\mathbf{p}_{l0}, \mathbf{R}_i; t) d\mathbf{p}_{i0} d\mathbf{p}_{l0} dR_{il}^0/\tau + 0(\tau_k/\tau),$$

$$\mathbf{p}_i' = \mathbf{p}_{i0} + \Delta\mathbf{p}_i(\tau)$$

where τ_k is a time interval of finite magnitude determined by the correlation integral, $\int \vartheta_{li} d\mathbf{R}_{il}^0$. Since the initial distribution is arbitrary there is no *a priori* reason for ϑ_{il} to be short range in the sense that the correlation integral is finite, but it may generally be expected to be so for distributions departing but slightly from statistical equilibrium. The requirement that it be so may be regarded as an auxiliary part of the assumption of *molecular chaos* which must be satisfied for the present analysis to be valid. We shall presently show that the volume in relative configuration space for which $\Delta\mathbf{p}_i(\tau)$ is non-vanishing becomes proportional to τ and that $\nabla_{p_i} \cdot \boldsymbol{\Omega}_{li}^{(1)}$ becomes independent of τ for sufficiently large τ.

We now need to consider in detail the solutions of Eq. (5), the equation of motion for a binary collision. Since these solutions are, of course, well known,[1] only the results will be summarized. The reduced mass m_{il} and the relative momentum $\mathbf{p}_{il}^0$ are defined as

$$1/m_{il} = 1/m_i + 1/m_l,$$

$$\mathbf{p}_{il} = \frac{m_{il}}{m_l}\mathbf{p}_l - \frac{m_{il}}{m_i}\mathbf{p}_i. \tag{9}$$

Pairs for which the initial Lagrange coordinate R_{il}^0 is greater than the range of intermolecular force occupy aperiodic orbits. The relative momentum remains constant and equal to $\mathbf{p}_{il}^0$ until a sphere of radius R_0 with origin, say in molecule *i*, is penetrated. If the initial configuration allows the penetration of this sphere, the collision is completed in a time τ_c, dependent on the collision parameters, the relative momentum receives a finite increment, $\Delta\mathbf{p}^*$, and subsequently remains constant and equal to $\mathbf{p}_{il}'$. The scalar magnitude p_{il}' is equal to p_{il}^0. By conservation of total linear momentum, $\mathbf{p}_{i0}$ and $\mathbf{p}_{l0}$ experience increments $-\Delta\mathbf{p}^*$ and $+\Delta\mathbf{p}^*$, respectively. Summarizing, we have

$$\Delta\mathbf{p}^* = \mathbf{p}_{il}' - \mathbf{p}_{il}^0, \quad \Delta\mathbf{p}_l = -\Delta\mathbf{p}_i = \Delta\mathbf{p}^*, \quad \Delta\mathbf{p}^* = 2p_{il}^0 \cos(\chi/2)\mathbf{e}, \tag{10}$$

$$\chi/2 = \int_a^\infty \frac{bp_{il}^0 dR/R^2}{[(1 - b^2/R^2)p_{il}^{02} - 2m_{il}V_{il}(R)]^{\frac{1}{2}}}, \quad bp_{il}^0 = |\mathbf{R}_{il}^0 \times \mathbf{p}_{il}^0|,$$

where a is the greatest positive root of the equation

$$(1 - b^2/a^2)p_{il}^{02} - 2m_{il}V_{il}(a) = 0.$$

V_{il} is the potential of the intermolecular force, $\mathbf{e}$ is a unit vector in the direction of the apse line drawn from molecule *i* to the orbit perihelion, and *b* is the impulse parameter.

For certain regions of the relative configuration space, the molecules occupy aperiodic orbits only partially traversed in the interval τ, or multiply periodic orbits with bounded $\Delta\mathbf{p}_{il}$. We now proceed to specify the several regions more precisely. To do this we select a cylindrical coordinate system in the relative Lagrange configuration space (z, b, ϵ) with origin in molecule i and z axis antiparallel to $\mathbf{p}_{il}^0$. The radial coordinate b is the impulse parameter and ϵ its azimuth. Unless the conditions,

$$(R_0^2 - b^2)^{\frac{1}{2}} \leqslant z \leqslant (p_{il}^0/m_{il})\tau + (R_0^2 - b^2)^{\frac{1}{2}}, \quad 0 \leqslant b \leqslant R_0, \tag{11}$$

are satisfied, the sphere R_0 is not penetrated in the interval τ, the momentum increment $\Delta\mathbf{p}_i$ remains zero, and the integrand, Eq. (8), vanishes. For those coordinates lying in filaments of volume,

$$(p_{il}^0/m_{il})(\tau - \tau_t)bdbd\epsilon,$$
$$(R_0^2 - b^2)^{\frac{1}{2}} \leqslant z \leqslant (p_{il}^0/m_{il})\,(\tau - \tau_c) + (R_0^2 - b^2)^{\frac{1}{2}}, \tag{12}$$

a complete collision is experienced in τ with momentum increments given by Eq. (10). In filaments of volume,

$$(p_{il}^0/m_{il})\tau_c bdbd\epsilon, \quad (p_{il}^0/m_{il})(\tau - \tau_c) + (R_0^2 - b^2)^{\frac{1}{2}} < z \leqslant (p_{il}^0/m_{il})\tau + (R_0^2 - b^2)^{\frac{1}{2}}, \tag{13}$$

partially completed collisions occur in the interval τ. In filaments of volume,

$$2(R_0^2 - b^2)^{\frac{1}{2}}bdbd\epsilon, \quad -(R_0^2 - b^2)^{\frac{1}{2}} \leqslant z < +\,(R_0^2 - b^2)^{\frac{1}{2}}, \tag{14}$$

within the sphere R_0, partially completed collisions may be completed or multiply periodic orbits may be traversed in the interval τ. Possible singular behavior being excluded, the integrand of Eq. (8) remains finite for the regions specified by Eqs. (13) and (14).

Carrying out the configurational integration in Eq. (8) with the aid of Eqs. (12), (13), and (14), we obtain,

$$\nabla_{p_i} \cdot \mathbf{\Omega}_{li}^{(1)} = \int \cdots \int \frac{p_{il}^0}{m_{il}} \{\delta(\mathbf{p}_i' - \mathbf{p}_i) - \delta(\mathbf{p}_{i0} - \mathbf{p}_i)\} f_i^{(1)}(\mathbf{p}_{i0}, \mathbf{R}_i; t)$$
$$f_l^{(1)}(\mathbf{p}_{l0}, \mathbf{R}_i; t)d\mathbf{p}_{i0}d\mathbf{p}_{l0}bdbd\epsilon + 0(\bar{\tau}_c/\tau),$$
$$\mathbf{p}_i' = \mathbf{p}_{i0} - \Delta\mathbf{p}^*, \tag{15}$$

where $\bar{\tau}_c$ is a finite time of the order of magnitude of the mean collision duration or of τ_k, whichever is the greater. Thus if τ is selected large relative to $\bar{\tau}_c$, only completed collisions in aperiodic orbits contribute to $\nabla_{p_i}\cdot\mathbf{\Omega}_{li}^{(1)}$. Since incomplete collisions and motion in multiply periodic orbits correspond to regions of relative configuration space of finite volume independent of τ, their contributions may be made as small as desired.

It should be remarked that τ cannot be allowed to approach infinity, since for systems confined to a finite domain of phase space, there will exist Poincaré cycle periods within which each orbit will be traversed in the reverse sense to any desired degree of accuracy, canceling its initial contribution to $\nabla_{p_i}\cdot\mathbf{\Omega}_{li}^{(1)}$. The thermodynamic irreversibility implied by the non-vanishing of the right-hand side of Eq. (15) would then fail.

In order to evaluate the right-hand side of Eq. (15), it is necessary to change variables in the term involving $\delta(\mathbf{p}_i' - \mathbf{p}_i)$ from $\mathbf{p}_{i0}$, $\mathbf{p}_{l0}$ to $\mathbf{p}_i'$ and $\mathbf{p}_l'$ where

$$\mathbf{p}_i' = \mathbf{p}_{i0} - \Delta\mathbf{p}^*, \quad \mathbf{p}_l' = \mathbf{p}_{l0} + \Delta\mathbf{p}^*. \tag{16}$$

The Jacobian of this transformation is easily shown to be unity. The second term of the integral may be evaluated at once. When the common symbol $\mathbf{p}_l$ is assigned to the remaining momentum variables of integration, $\mathbf{p}_l'$ and $\mathbf{p}_{l0}$, the two terms combine to yield,

$$\begin{aligned}\nabla_{p_i} \cdot \mathbf{\Omega}_{li}{}^{(1)} = \int_0^{2\pi}\int_0^{R_0}\int \frac{p_{il}}{m_{il}}\{&f_i{}^{(1)}(\mathbf{p}_i + \Delta\mathbf{p}^*, \mathbf{R}_i; t)f_l{}^{(1)}(\mathbf{p}_l - \Delta\mathbf{p}^*, \mathbf{R}_i; t) \\ &- f_i{}^{(1)}(\mathbf{p}_i, \mathbf{R}_i; t)f_l{}^{(1)}(\mathbf{p}_l, R_i; t)\}d\mathbf{p}_l b\,db\,d\epsilon, \end{aligned}\tag{17}$$

$$p_{il} = |\mathbf{p}_l/m_l - \mathbf{p}_i/m_i|m_{il},$$

with the neglect of terms, $0(\bar{\tau}_c/\tau)$. Substitution of the expressions, Eq. (17), into Eq. (4) and time averaging of both sides over the interval τ gives

$$\begin{aligned}&\frac{\partial \bar{f}_i{}^{(1)}}{\partial t} + \frac{\mathbf{p}_i}{m_i}\cdot \nabla_{R_i}\bar{f}_i{}^{(1)} + \mathbf{X}_i \cdot \nabla_{p_i}\bar{f}_i{}^{(1)} = \\ &\qquad \sum_{l=1}^{\nu} N_l \int_0^{2\pi}\int_0^{R_0}\int \frac{p_{il}}{m_{il}}\overline{\{f_i{}^{(1)*}f_l{}^{(1)*}} - \overline{f_i{}^{(1)}f_l{}^{(1)}\}}d\mathbf{p}_l b\,db\,d\epsilon,\end{aligned}$$

$$f_i{}^{(1)*} = f_i{}^{(1)}(\mathbf{p}_i + \Delta\mathbf{p}^*, \mathbf{R}_i; t), \quad f_l{}^{(1)*} = f_l{}^{(1)}(\mathbf{p}_l - \Delta\mathbf{p}^*, \mathbf{R}_i; t), \tag{18}$$

since the second time average does not affect the left-hand side of Eq. (4), all terms of which already have only secular dependence on time.

Equation (18) becomes identical with the Maxwell-Boltzmann integro-differential equation (in this equation the symbol f_i is customarily used to denote the molecular density, $N_i\bar{f}_i{}^{(1)}$, of species i) only if

$$\overline{f_i{}^{(1)}f_l{}^{(1)}} = \bar{f}_i{}^{(1)}\bar{f}_l{}^{(1)}. \tag{19}$$

Equation (19) is not necessarily true, but it is true to terms of the first order for distributions departing but slightly from equilibrium, represented by ${}^0f_i{}^{(1)}$ and ${}^0f_l{}^{(1)}$, both of which are independent of time. If

$$f_i{}^{(1)} = {}^0f_i{}^{(1)} + \varphi_i{}^{(1)}, \quad f_l{}^{(1)} = {}^0f_l{}^{(1)} + \varphi_l{}^{(1)},$$

$$\overline{f_i{}^{(1)}f_l{}^{(1)}} = \bar{f}_i{}^{(1)}\bar{f}_l{}^{(1)} = {}^0f_i{}^{(1)}\,{}^0f_l{}^{(1)} + {}^0f_i{}^{(1)}\bar{\varphi}_l{}^{(1)} + {}^0f_l{}^{(1)}\bar{\varphi}_i{}^{(1)} + 0(\overline{\varphi_i{}^{(1)}\varphi_l{}^{(1)}}). \tag{20}$$

Equations (18) and (20) are evidently identical with the Maxwell-Boltzmann equation to terms of the first order for small departures from statistical equilibrium. In all applications, solutions have been limited to terms of the first order. The proposed derivation of this equation from statistical mechanics is therefore complete.

Starting from Eq. (4), we should be able to develop a systematic scheme for taking into account collisions of higher order than binary and thus to obtain transport laws for gases of finite density instead of laws valid only in the limit of vanishing density. This problem is being considered. However, for this purpose, the Brownian motion approximations described in SMTI appear to offer the greatest promise.

Errata: Statistical Mechanics of Transport Processes II. Transport in Gases

[*J. Chem. Phys.* **15**, 72 (1947)]

JOHN G. KIRKWOOD, *Cornell University, Ithaca, New York*

February 7, 1947

The first line of Eq. (4) should read

$$\frac{\partial \bar{f}_i^{(1)}}{\partial t} + \frac{\mathbf{p}_i}{m_i} \cdot \nabla_{R_i} \bar{f}_i^{(1)} + \mathbf{X}_i \cdot \nabla_{p_i} \bar{f}_i^{(1)} = \sum_{l=1}^{\nu} N_l \nabla_{p_i} \cdot \mathbf{\Omega}_{li}^{(1)}$$

with the time-averaged distribution function $\bar{f}_i^{(1)}$ appearing instead of the unaveraged distribution function $f_i^{(1)}$.

The second line of Eq. (8) should read,

$$\mathbf{p}_i' = \mathbf{p}_{i0} + \Delta\mathbf{p}_i(\tau).$$

The last sentence of page 74 should read: "By conservation of total linear momentum $\mathbf{p}_{i0}$ and $\mathbf{p}_{l0}$ experience increments $-\Delta\mathbf{p}^*$ and $\Delta\mathbf{p}^*$, respectively."

The last term in the brackets of the integrand on the right-hand side of Eq. (18) should be $\overline{f_i^{(1)} f_l^{(1)}}$ instead of $\overline{f_l^{(1)} f_l^{(1)}}$.

[These corrections have been made in the text by the present editor.]

The Statistical Mechanical Theory of Transport Processes III. The Coefficients of Shear and Bulk Viscosity of Liquids*

JOHN G. KIRKWOOD, FRANK P. BUFF, AND MELVIN S. GREEN†
The Gates and Crellin Laboratories of Chemistry, California Institute of Technology, Pasadena, California

(Received March 17, 1949)

A molecular theory of the coefficients of shear and bulk viscosity of monatomic liquids is developed on the basis of the general theory of transport processes presented in the first article of this series. With the use of the Lennard-Jones potential and a reasonable analytic approximation to the experimental radial distribution function, calculations of the coefficients of shear and bulk viscosity of liquid argon at 89°K have been carried out. The theory leads explicitly to ratios of the coefficients to the friction constant of the theory of Brownian motion. With a preliminary estimate of the friction constant, a value of the shear viscosity of liquid argon in moderately good agreement with experiment is obtained.

I

The general statistical mechanical theory of transport processes, developed in the first article (SMTI) of this series,[1] has as an objective the determination of the coefficients of viscosity, diffusion and heat conductivity of fluids in terms of molecular variables. It is the purpose of the present article to present a detailed theory of the coefficients of shear and bulk viscosity of liquids based upon the general theory. The starting point is provided by the differential equations of the Chandrasekhar[2] type for the probability distribution functions in the phase space of sets of one, two, and three molecules of the liquid, which were derived from the molecular standpoint in SMTI. An alternative approach is provided by the kinetic theory of liquids of Born and Green.[3] While their theory parallels our own and duplicates many of its general results, it differs in the manner in which dissipative terms are introduced into the equations satisfied by the distribution functions. Although Born and Green have presented an interesting qualitative discussion of the coefficient of shear viscosity of liquids, they have not yet succeeded in constructing solutions of their equations for the distribution functions in sufficiently explicit form to yield concrete results.

---

* This work was carried out under Task Order XIII of Contract N6onr-244 between the Office of Naval Research and the California Institute of Technology.

† Present Address: Natural Sciences Staff, College of the University of Chicago, Chicago, Illinois.

[1] J. G. Kirkwood, *J. Chem. Phys.* **14**, 180 (1946).

[2] S. Chandrasekhar, *Rev. Mod. Phys.* **15**, 1 (1945). (Chandrasekhar's equations are derived from the phenomenological theory of Brownian motion.)

[3] M. Born and H. S. Green, *Proc. Roy. Soc.* **A188**, 10 (1946) and **190**, 455 (1947); H. S. Green, *Proc. Roy. Soc.* **A189**, 103 (1947).

The macroscopic hydrodynamics of viscous fluids is described by the equations of continuity and motion,

$$\nabla \cdot (\rho \mathbf{u}) + \partial \rho / \partial t = 0,$$

$$\rho (d\mathbf{u}/dt) = \mathbf{X} + \nabla \cdot \boldsymbol{\sigma},$$

where ρ is the density, $\mathbf{u}$ the particle velocity, $\mathbf{X}$ the external body force, and $\boldsymbol{\sigma}$ the stress tensor, supplemented by the Newtonian expression for the stress tensor,

$$\boldsymbol{\sigma} = - \{p + [(2\eta/3)] - \phi)\nabla \cdot \mathbf{u}\}\mathbf{1} + 2\eta\epsilon,$$

where p is the equilibrium pressure of the fluid, ϵ the rate of strain, and η and ϕ are the coefficients of shear and bulk viscosity. The stress tensor is determined by molecular distribution functions and intermolecular forces in the manner described by Eq. (26) of SMTI. There are two types of terms, one arising from momentum transport and one from the direct transmission of intermolecular forces, which is determined by the average density of molecular pairs. In thermodynamic equilibrium the stress reduces to a uniform normal pressure, the first term of which is the ideal gas contribution. The second term arising from intermolecular forces has no shear components, since the pair density, proportional to the radial distribution function of the theory of liquids, possesses spherical symmetry. Departure from equilibrium resulting from hydrodynamic flow leads to perturbations in the molecular distribution functions proportional to the components of the rate of strain. In liquids the momentum transport contribution to these terms is very small relative to the contribution from intermolecular forces. The latter contribution arises from the perturbation in the pair density. This perturbation consists of two parts, one spherically symmetric, which determines the bulk viscosity ϕ, and one having the symmetry of a surface harmonic of order two, which determines the shear viscosity.

By means of the general equations of SMTI, the perturbations in the pertinent molecular distribution functions have been constructed and the ratios η/ζ and ϕ/ζ of the two coefficients of viscosity to the Brownian motion friction constant ζ have been expressed in terms of definite integrals involving the potential of intermolecular force and the equilibrium radial distribution function. Calculations have been carried out for liquid argon at 89°K with the use of the Lennard-Jones potential of intermolecular force and the Eisenstein-Gingrich radial distribution function. The result of the calculation is

$$\eta/\zeta = 2.63 \times 10^{6} \text{ cm}^{-1}.$$

Although the theory of the friction constant ζ was presented in SMTI, it has not yet been possible to calculate it accurately. Our preliminary estimate, $\zeta = 4.84 \times 10^{-10}$ g sec.$^{-1}$, leads to a shear viscosity η of 1.27×10^{-3} poise, in fair agreement with the experimental value, 2.39×10^{-3} poise. Calculations relating to the bulk viscosity are postponed for treatment in a subsequent article.

II

In SMTI, the macroscopic observables of a system of N molecules were put into correspondence with average values determined by probability densities

$\bar{f}^{(n)}(\mathbf{p}, \mathbf{q}; t)$ in the phase space $(\mathbf{p}, \mathbf{q})$ of subsets of n molecules

$$\bar{f}^{(n)}(\mathbf{p}, \mathbf{q}; t) = \int\int \bar{f}^{(N)}(\mathbf{p}, \mathbf{q}, \mathbf{P}, \mathbf{Q}; t)\mathbf{dPdQ},$$

$$\bar{f}^{(N)}(\mathbf{p}, \mathbf{q}, \mathbf{P}, \mathbf{Q}; t) = \frac{1}{\tau}\int_0^\tau f^{(N)}(\mathbf{p}, \mathbf{q}, \mathbf{P}, \mathbf{Q}; t + s)ds, \tag{1}$$

where $(\mathbf{P}, \mathbf{Q})$ is the phase space of the residual set of $N - n$ molecules and $f^{(N)}(\mathbf{p}, \mathbf{q}, \mathbf{P}, \mathbf{Q}; t)$ is the probability density in the complete phase space of an example of the appropriate statistical ensemble, from which a system is sampled in the process of preparation at time t with specified values of the molar variables determining its macroscopic state. The interval τ is determined by the time resolution of the instruments employed in the measurement of the macroscopic observables. If the shortest period macroscopically resolved is long relative to the Brownian motion correlation time, it was made plausible that in liquids the macroscopic description would not sensibly depend upon the smoothing time τ, provided τ is long relative to the correlation time. For the representation of average values of functions of the configuration coordinates of small sets of n molecules, it is convenient to define number densities $\rho^{(n)}(\mathbf{q}; t)$ by the relation,

$$\rho^{(n)}(\mathbf{q}; t) = \frac{N!}{(N-n)!}\int \bar{f}^{(n)}(\mathbf{p}, \mathbf{q}; t)\mathbf{dp}. \tag{2}$$

The mass density ρ of hydrodynamic theory at a point $\mathbf{R}$ in a fluid and the particle velocity $\mathbf{u}$ are then determined by the relation,

$$\rho(\mathbf{R}) = m\rho^{(1)}(\mathbf{R}),$$

$$\rho\mathbf{u} = N\int \mathbf{p}\bar{f}^{(1)}(\mathbf{R}, \mathbf{p})d\mathbf{p}, \tag{3}$$

where m is the mass of a molecule. The distribution functions $\bar{f}^{(n)}$ were shown to satisfy partial differential equations, SMTI, Eq. (60), of the type derived by Chandrasekhar[2] on the basis of the phenomenological theory of Brownian motion. The use of these equations to determine the molecular distribution functions of a fluid in a state of stationary viscous flow will be presented in Section III.

In a system of molecules for which the potential of intermolecular force V_N can be represented in the form,

$$V^N = \sum_{i<k=1}^{N} V(R_{ik}), \tag{4}$$

where $V(R_{ik})$ is a function, say of the Lennard-Jones type, of the distance R_{ik} between the pair of molecules (ik), the stress tensor $\boldsymbol{\sigma}$ is given by SMTI, Eq. (26). In the notation of Eqs. (2) and (3), this equation becomes,

$$\boldsymbol{\sigma} = -\rho^{(1)}\left[\frac{\langle\mathbf{pp}\rangle_{\mathrm{Av}}}{m} - m\mathbf{uu}\right] + \tfrac{1}{2}\int \frac{\mathbf{R}_{12}\mathbf{R}_{12}}{R_{12}}\frac{dV}{dR_{12}}\rho^{(2)}(\mathbf{R}, \mathbf{R}_{12})dv_{12},$$

$$\rho^{(1)}\langle\mathbf{pp}\rangle_{\mathrm{Av}} = N\int \mathbf{pp}\bar{f}^{(1)}(\mathbf{p}, \mathbf{R})\mathbf{dp}, \tag{5}$$

where $\rho^{(2)}(\mathbf{R}, \mathbf{R}_{12})$ is the number density of pairs, one member of which is situated at point $\mathbf{R}$ and the other at point $\mathbf{R}_{12}$ relative to the position of the first. The integration in the second term of Eq. (5), the contribution of intermolecular forces to the stress tensor, extends over the relative configuration space $\mathbf{R}_{12}$ of the representative pair. The first term represents the momentum transfer contribution, important in gases, but almost negligible in liquids.

In a liquid in a state of stationary viscous flow, the distribution functions are perturbed in such a manner that the stress tensor takes on the extended Newtonian form. In Section III, it will be shown that with neglect of nonlinear terms in the rate of strain, $\dot{\epsilon}$,

$$-\rho^{(1)}\left[\frac{\langle \mathbf{pp}\rangle_{\mathrm{Av}}}{m} - m\mathbf{uu}\right]\rho^{(1)} = -\rho^{(1)}kT\mathbf{1} + \rho\frac{kT}{\zeta}\dot{\boldsymbol{\epsilon}},$$

$$\zeta = kT/D, \quad \dot{\boldsymbol{\epsilon}} = Sym\nabla\mathbf{u}, \tag{6}$$

where ζ is the Brownian motion friction constant and D is the coefficient of self-diffusion of the liquid. The pair density, $\rho^{(2)}$, determining the contribution of intermolecular forces to the stress tensor is conveniently written in the form,

$$\rho^{(2)}(\mathbf{R}, \mathbf{R}_{12}) = \rho^{(1)}(\mathbf{R})\rho^{(1)}(\mathbf{R} + \mathbf{R}_{12})g^{(2)}(\mathbf{R}, \mathbf{R}_{12}), \tag{7}$$

a relation defining the pair correlation function $g^{(2)}(\mathbf{R}, \mathbf{R}_{12})$. In Section III, it will be shown that $g^{(2)}$ can be expanded in the components of the rate of strain as,

$$g^{(2)} = g_0^{(2)}(R_{12})\left\{1 + \frac{\zeta}{2kT}\left[\frac{\mathbf{R}_{12}\cdot\dot{\boldsymbol{\epsilon}}\cdot\mathbf{R}_{12}}{R_{12}^2} - \tfrac{1}{3}\nabla\cdot\mathbf{u}\right]\psi_2(R_{12}) + \frac{\zeta}{6kT}(\nabla\cdot\mathbf{u})\psi_0(R_{12})\right\}, \tag{8}$$

where $g_0^{(2)}(R_{12})$ is the radial distribution function of the fluid in thermodynamic equilibrium and $\psi_0(R_{12})$ and $\psi_2(R_{12})$ satisfy certain ordinary differential equations, presently to be derived from the general theory of the probability densities, $\bar{f}^{(n)}$.

Substitution of the momentum contribution of Eq. (6) and the perturbed pair density of Eqs. (7) and (8) into Eq. (5) yields the stress tensor,

$$\boldsymbol{\sigma} = -[p + (2/3\eta - \phi)\nabla\cdot\mathbf{u}]\mathbf{1} + 2\eta\dot{\boldsymbol{\epsilon}},$$

$$p = \frac{NkT}{V} - \frac{2\pi N^2}{3V^2}\int_0^\infty R^3\frac{dV}{dR}g_0^{(2)}(R)dR, \tag{9}$$

where p is the equilibrium pressure of the liquid at the given temperature and uniform number density $\rho^{(1)}$, equal to the ratio of Avogadro's number N and the molal volume V. The coefficients of shear viscosity η and bulk viscosity ϕ are then given by the expressions

$$\eta = \rho\frac{kT}{2\zeta} + \frac{\pi\zeta}{15kT}\frac{N^2}{V^2}\int_0^\infty R^3\frac{dV}{dR}\psi_2(R)g_0^{(2)}(R)dR,$$

$$\phi = \rho\frac{kT}{3\zeta} + \frac{\pi\zeta}{9kT}\frac{N^2}{V^2}\int_0^\infty R^3\frac{dV}{dR}\psi_0(R)g_0^{(2)}(R)dR, \tag{10}$$

where, as subsequent calculations will show, the initial terms arising from momentum transport are of minor importance in liquids.

In order to evaluate the integrals of Eqs. (10), as well as to solve the differential equations determining the perturbation functions $\psi_0(R)$ and $\psi_2(R)$, it is necessary to know the equilibrium radial distribution function $g_0{}^{(2)}(R)$ and the potential of intermolecular force $V(R)$. The potential $V(R)$ is conveniently approximated by the Lennard-Jones expression,

$$V(R) = \epsilon\left(\frac{1}{x^n} - \frac{1}{x^6}\right), \qquad (11)$$

$$x = R/a_0.$$

In applications of the theory presently to be made to liquid argon, we shall use parameters, n, ϵ, and a_0, determined by Rushbrooke[4] and Corner.[5] The values are: $n = 11.4$; $\epsilon = 6.82 \times 10^{-14}$ erg; $a_0 = 3.43$A.

The radial distribution function $g_0{}^{(2)}(R)$ is of course determined by the potential of intermolecular force $V(R)$ and the thermodynamic variables.[6] It is also accessible to experimental measurement, since it determines the intensity of x-rays scattered by a liquid as a function of scattering angle. In the applications to follow, we shall make use of the radial distribution function data for argon of Eisenstein and Gingrich.[7] This function possesses a series of peaks with amplitude rapidly diminishing as R increases. Since it is found that the integrals of Eq. (10) are in the main determined by the first peak of the radial distribution function, the other factor being of very short range, we have constructed the following analytical approximation to $g_0{}^{(2)}(R)$,

$$\begin{aligned} g_0{}^{(2)}(R) &= (a_1/R)^s \exp\left\{\left(\frac{a_m}{a_1}\right)^t - \left(\frac{a_m}{R}\right)^t\right\};\ 0 \leq R \leq a_1, \\ &= 1; \quad R < a_1, \end{aligned} \qquad (12)$$

which represents quite well the first peaks of the Eisenstein-Gingrich curves. It has the important advantage of allowing the integration of the differential equations satisfied by the perturbation function ψ_0 and ψ_2, in terms of confluent hypergeometric functions. Two of the parameters $a_1 = 4.5$A and $t = 14$ are determined from the Eisenstein-Gingrich data to be relatively insensitive to temperature. For liquid argon 89°K and 1.2 atmos., the remaining parameters were determined with the use of the Lennard-Jones potential, Eq. (11), the theoretical equation of state, given by the second of Eq. (9), and the energy of vaporization,

$$E_v = -\frac{2\pi N^2}{V}\int_0^\infty R^2 V(R) g_0{}^{(2)}(R)dR. \qquad (13)$$

They were found to have the values, $a_m = 3.55$A and $s = 7.01$. This calibration was found to be necessary, since the Eisenstein-Gingrich functions fail to satisfy the equation of state, due to the extreme sensitivity of the cohesive

[4] G. S. Rushbrooke, *Proc. Roy. Soc.* (Edin.) **60**, 182 (1940).
[5] J. Corner, *Trans. Faraday Soc.* **35,** 711 (1939).
[6] J. G. Kirkwood and E. M. Boggs, *J. Chem. Phys.* **10**, 394 (1942).
[7] A. Eisenstein and N. S. Gingrich, *Phys. Rev.* **62**, 261 (1942).

pressure, arising from intermolecular forces, to the relative position of the first peak of $g_0^{(2)}(R)$ and the position of the minimum of the Lennard-Jones potential. With the adjusted parameters, the peak of the empirical function, Eq. (12), lies at 3.73A and corresponds to a coordination number of 8.1, both in good agreement with the experimental results of Eisenstein and Gingrich.

III

The determination of the perturbations from equilibrium of the distribution functions, $\bar{f}^{(1)}(\mathbf{p}, \mathbf{R})$ and $\rho^{(2)}(\mathbf{R}, \mathbf{R}_{12})$ in a liquid in a state of stationary viscous flow is based upon the use of the Chandrasekhar equations, SMTI, Eq. (59) and Eq. (60), derived from the standpoint of molecular dynamics in the first paper of this series. In order to determine the momentum contribution to the stress tensor, we employ the equation [SMTI (59)]

$$\frac{\partial \bar{f}^{(1)}}{\partial t} + \frac{\mathbf{p}}{m} \cdot \nabla_R \bar{f}^{(1)} + \nabla_\mathbf{p} \cdot \mathbf{F}^{(1)} \bar{f}^{(1)} = \zeta \nabla_\mathbf{p} \cdot \left\{ \left(\frac{\mathbf{p}}{m} - \mathbf{u} \right) \bar{f}^{(1)} + kT \nabla_\mathbf{p} \bar{f}^{(1)} \right\},$$

$$\mathbf{F}^{(1)} = {}^{(1)}\langle \mathbf{F} \rangle_{\mathrm{Av}}{}^0 + {}^{(1)}\mathbf{F}^+, \tag{14}$$

where ζ is the friction constant of the theory of Brownian motion, ${}^{(1)}\langle \mathbf{F} \rangle_{\mathrm{Av}}{}^0$ is the average in the equilibrium ensemble of the total intermolecular force acting on a molecule situated at point $\mathbf{R}$, and ${}^{(1)}\mathbf{F}^+$ is the perturbation arising from the departure of $\rho^{(2)}$ from equilibrium. Upon multiplication of both sides of Eq. (14) by $(\mathbf{p}/m - \mathbf{u})(\mathbf{p}/m - \mathbf{u})$ and integration over momentum space, we find with the use of Green's theorem that

$$\langle \mathbf{\Pi\Pi} \rangle_{\mathrm{Av}} - mkT\mathbf{1} = -\frac{m}{2\zeta} \left\{ \langle \mathbf{\Pi\Pi} \rangle_{\mathrm{Av}} \cdot \nabla \mathbf{u} + \langle \mathbf{\Pi} \cdot \nabla \mathbf{u} \mathbf{\Pi} \rangle_{\mathrm{Av}} \right.$$

$$\left. + \mathbf{u} \cdot \nabla \langle \mathbf{\Pi\Pi} \rangle_{\mathrm{Av}} + \frac{\partial \langle \mathbf{\Pi\Pi} \rangle_{\mathrm{Av}}}{\partial t} \right\}, \tag{15}$$

$$\mathbf{\Pi} = \mathbf{p} - m\mathbf{u},$$

with the neglect of non-linear terms in all perturbations from equilibrium. In the stationary case, Eq. (15) leads at once to Eq. (6), in the linear approximation, and the momentum transfer contribution to the stress tensor is evaluated.

In order to determine the pair density $\rho^{(2)}$, from which the intermolecular force contribution to the stress tensor is to be calculated, we employ Eq. (60) of SMTI in the form appropriate to $\bar{f}^{(2)}(\mathbf{p}_1, \mathbf{R}_1, \mathbf{p}_2, \mathbf{R}_2; t)$ in the phase space of molecular pairs,

$$\frac{\partial \bar{f}^{(2)}}{\partial t} + \frac{\mathbf{p}_1}{m} \cdot \nabla_{\mathbf{p}_1} \bar{f}^{(2)} + \frac{\mathbf{p}_2}{m} \cdot \nabla_{\mathbf{R}_2} \bar{f}^{(2)} + \nabla_{\mathbf{p}_1} \cdot \mathbf{F}_1^{(2)} \bar{f}^{(2)} + \nabla_{\mathbf{p}_2} \cdot \mathbf{F}_2^{(2)} \bar{f}^{(2)}$$

$$= \nabla_{\mathbf{p}_1} \cdot \zeta_1^{(2)} \cdot \left\{ \left(\frac{\mathbf{p}_1}{m} - \mathbf{u}_1 \right) \bar{f}^{(2)} + kT \nabla_{\mathbf{p}_1} \bar{f}^{(2)} \right\} \tag{16}$$

$$+ \nabla_{\mathbf{p}_2} \cdot \zeta_2^{(2)} \cdot \left\{ \left(\frac{\mathbf{p}_2}{m} - \mathbf{u}_2 \right) \bar{f}^{(2)} + kT \nabla_{\mathbf{p}_2} \bar{f}^{(2)} \right\};$$

$$\mathbf{F}_1^{(2)} = {}^{(2)}\langle \mathbf{F}_1 \rangle_{\mathrm{Av}}{}^0 + {}^{(2)}\mathbf{F}_1^+; \quad \mathbf{F}_2^{(2)} = {}^{(2)}\langle \mathbf{F}_2 \rangle_{\mathrm{Av}}{}^0 + {}^{(2)}\mathbf{F}_2^+,$$

where ${}^{(2)}\langle \mathbf{F}_1 \rangle_{\mathrm{Av}}{}^0$ is the mean force acting on the first molecule of the pair in the unperturbed equilibrium ensemble, subject to the condition that the configuration $(\mathbf{R}_1, \mathbf{R}_2)$ of the pair is fixed, and ${}^{(2)}\mathbf{F}_1{}^+$ is the perturbation arising from the departure of $\rho^{(3)}$, the density in triplet configuration space from equilibrium. The friction tensor $\boldsymbol{\zeta}^{(2)}$ is a second rank tensor in the six-dimensional configuration space of the pair, related to intermolecular forces in the manner prescribed in SMTI. The vectors $\mathbf{u}_1$ and $\mathbf{u}_2$ are the particle velocities of three-dimensional hydrodynamics, defined by Eq. (3), at the respective positions $\mathbf{R}_1$ and $\mathbf{R}_2$ of the pair. Integration of both sides of Eq. (16) over the momentum space of both molecules leads to the equation of continuity in pair configuration space,

$$\frac{\partial \rho^{(2)}}{\partial t} + \nabla_{\mathbf{R}_1} \cdot \mathbf{j}_1{}^{(2)} + \nabla_{\mathbf{R}_2} \cdot \mathbf{j}_2{}^{(2)} = 0,$$

$$\mathbf{j}_\alpha{}^{(2)} = \frac{N(N-1)}{m} \int \int \mathbf{p}_\alpha \bar{f}^{(2)}(\mathbf{p}_1, \mathbf{p}_2, \mathbf{R}_1, \mathbf{R}_2; t) d\mathbf{p}_1 d\mathbf{p}_2, \tag{17}$$

with $\mathbf{j}_\alpha{}^{(2)}$ the number current density in pair space projected on the 3-space of molecule α. Multiplication of both sides of Eq. (16) by $\mathbf{p}_1$ and $\mathbf{p}_2$ respectively, followed by integration over momentum space, yields the equations,

$$\begin{aligned} m\frac{\partial \mathbf{j}_1{}^{(2)}}{\partial t} &= -kT\nabla_{\mathbf{R}_1}\rho^{(2)} + \mathbf{F}_1{}^{(2)}\rho^{(2)} - \boldsymbol{\zeta}_1{}^{(2)} \cdot [\mathbf{j}_1{}^{(2)} - \mathbf{u}_1\rho^{(2)}], \\ m\frac{\partial \mathbf{j}_2{}^{(2)}}{\partial t} &= -kT\nabla_{\mathbf{R}_2}\rho^{(2)} + \mathbf{F}_2{}^{(2)}\rho^{(2)} - \boldsymbol{\zeta}_2{}^{(2)} \cdot [\mathbf{j}_2{}^{(2)} - \mathbf{u}_2\rho^{(2)}], \end{aligned} \tag{18}$$

with the neglect of non-linear terms in $\mathbf{u}_1$ and $\mathbf{u}_2$ and of terms of the order of $1/\zeta$ in the departure of the non-diagonal terms in $\langle \mathbf{p}_\alpha \mathbf{p}_\alpha \rangle_{\mathrm{Av}}{}^{(2)}/m$ from their vanishing equilibrium values. Similar equations are obtained by the same procedure from Eq. (14),

$$\begin{aligned} m\frac{\partial \mathbf{j}_\alpha{}^{(1)}}{\partial t} &= -kT\nabla_{\mathbf{R}\alpha}\rho^{(1)}(\mathbf{R}_\alpha) + \mathbf{F}_\alpha{}^{(1)}\rho^{(1)}(\mathbf{R}_\alpha), \\ \frac{\partial \rho^{(1)}(\mathbf{R}_\alpha)}{\partial t} &+ \nabla_{\mathbf{R}\alpha} \cdot \mathbf{j}_\alpha{}^{(1)} = 0, \quad \alpha = 1, 2, \\ \mathbf{j}_\alpha{}^{(1)} &= \rho^{(1)}(\mathbf{R}_\alpha)\mathbf{u}(\mathbf{R}_\alpha). \end{aligned} \tag{19}$$

We now introduce the simplifications,

$$\begin{aligned} \boldsymbol{\zeta}_1{}^{(2)} &= \boldsymbol{\zeta}_2{}^{(2)} = \zeta \mathbf{1}, \\ \mathbf{F}_\alpha{}^{(2)} - \mathbf{F}_\alpha{}^{(1)} &= kT\nabla_{\mathbf{R}\alpha} \log g_0{}^{(2)}(R_{12}); \quad \alpha = 1, 2, \end{aligned} \tag{20}$$

where ζ is the singlet friction constant of Eq. (14) and $g_0{}^{(2)}$ is the equilibrium radial distribution function. The first of Eqs. (20) implies the neglect of the dependence of the friction tensor $\boldsymbol{\zeta}^{(2)}$ on the relative configuration of the pair, and the second approximates the mean intermolecular force difference by its equilibrium value.[8] Thus it is a well-known result of equilibrium statistical mechanics that

$$g_0^{(2)} = \exp(-(W^{(2)} - W_1^{(1)} - W_2^{(1)})/kT),$$

$$^0\langle \mathbf{F}_\alpha \rangle_{\mathrm{Av}}^{(2)} = -\nabla_{R\alpha} W^{(2)}(R_{12}), \quad \alpha = 1, 2, \tag{21}$$

$$^0\langle \mathbf{F}_\alpha \rangle_{\mathrm{Av}}^{(1)} = -\nabla_{R\alpha} W^{(1)}(R_\alpha),$$

where $W^{(1)}$ and $W^{(2)}$ are the potentials of mean force in singlet space and pair space, respectively.

Introduction of Eq. (7) into Eqs. (17) and (18) and elimination of $\rho^{(1)}(\mathbf{R}_1)$ and $\rho^{(2)}(\mathbf{R}_2)$ by means of Eqs. (19) leads, with neglect of the inertial terms, to the following equation for the correlation function,

$$\nabla_R \cdot \{\nabla_R g^{(2)} - (\nabla_R \log g_0^{(2)}) g^{(2)}\} - \frac{\zeta}{2kT}\frac{\partial g^{(2)}}{\partial t} = \frac{\zeta}{2kT} \mathbf{R} \cdot \dot{\boldsymbol{\epsilon}} \cdot \nabla_R g^{(2)},$$

$$\mathbf{j}_{12}^{(2)} = -\frac{2kT}{\zeta}\{\nabla_R g^{(2)} - (\nabla_R \log g_0^{(2)}) g^{(2)}\}, \tag{22}$$

$$\rho^{(1)}(\mathbf{R}_1)\rho^{(1)}(\mathbf{R}_2)\mathbf{j}_{12}^{(2)} = [\mathbf{j}_2^{(2)} - \rho^{(2)}\mathbf{u}_2] - [\mathbf{j}_1^{(2)} - \rho^{(2)}\mathbf{u}_1],$$

$$g^{(2)}(\mathbf{R}_1, \mathbf{R}) = g^{(2)}(\mathbf{R}); \quad \mathbf{R} = \mathbf{R}_2 - \mathbf{R}_1; \quad \mathbf{u}_2 - \mathbf{u}_1 = \mathbf{R} \cdot \nabla \mathbf{u},$$

where $\mathbf{j}_{12}^{(2)}$ is the excess probability current density in relative pair space, vanishing at $R \to \infty$ by definition and is conditioned by the absence of sources or sinks in the pair density distribution.

Introduction of Eq. (8) into Eq. (22) and linearization with respect to the components of the rate of strain $\dot{\boldsymbol{\epsilon}}$ leads, in the stationary case, to the following ordinary differential equation for the functions $\psi_2(R)$ and $\psi_0(R)$,

$$\frac{d}{dR}\left(R^2 g_0^{(2)} \frac{d\psi_2}{dR} - 6 g_0^{(2)} \psi_2 = R^3 \frac{dg_0^{(2)}}{dR},\right.$$

$$\frac{d}{dR}\left(R^2 g_0^{(2)} \frac{d\psi_0}{dR}\right) = R^3 \frac{dg_0^{(2)}}{dR}. \tag{23}$$

In coordinate representation $\psi_2(R)$ is the coefficient of surface harmonics of order two, arising from the shear component of the rate of strain, and $\psi_0(R)$ is the coefficient of the surface harmonic of order zero, arising from the dilatational component. The excess probability current density in the relative pair space is given by

$$\mathbf{j}_{12}^{(2)} = -g_0^{(2)}\left\{\nabla_R \left[\frac{\mathbf{R} \cdot \dot{\boldsymbol{\epsilon}} \cdot \mathbf{R}}{R^2} - \tfrac{1}{3}\nabla \cdot \mathbf{u}\right] \psi_2(R) + \tfrac{1}{3}(\nabla \cdot \mathbf{u})\psi_0(R)\right\}. \tag{24}$$

The requirement that $\mathbf{j}_{12}^{(2)}$ vanish at $R = \infty$ and that there be no sources or sinks in pair space leads to the boundary conditions,

[8] See J. G. Kirkwood, *J. Chem. Phys.* **3**, 300 (1935).

$$\lim_{R\to\infty} \psi_2(R) = 0, \tag{25a}$$

$$\lim_{R\to 0} R^2 g_0{}^{(2)} \frac{d\psi_2(R)}{dR} = 0, \tag{25b}$$

$$\lim_{R\to\infty} \frac{d\psi_0(R)}{dR} = 0, \tag{25c}$$

$$\lim_{R\to 0} R^2 g_0{}^{(2)} \frac{d\psi_0(R)}{dR} = 0, \tag{25d}$$

subject to which Eqs. (23) are to be solved. In addition, ψ_2, $d\psi_2/dR$, and $d\psi_0/dR$ must be continuous for all $0 \leq R \leq \infty$, a condition which must be applied at the cut-off point, $R = a_1$, of the approximate radial distribution function, Eq. (12), in order to ensure continuity of the pair current at this point.

IV

The solution of the ψ_2 Eq. (23a) is based on use of the approximate representation of $g_0{}^{(2)}$ given in Eq. (12). Since $R^2/2$ is a particular solution, we only have to investigate the homogeneous equation

$$x^2 \frac{d^2\psi_2}{dx^2} + \left\{2 + x\frac{d \log g_0{}^{(2)}}{dx}\right\} x \frac{d\psi_2}{dx} - 6\psi_2 = 0; \quad x = \frac{R}{a_0}. \tag{26}$$

For $x_1 < x$, Eq. (26) reduces to Euler's equation so that the solution satisfying the boundary condition at infinity, Eq. (25a), is given by

$$\psi_2 = K_2/x^3; \quad x_1 < x. \tag{27}$$

Substitution of the first peak approximation in Eq. (26) leads to the following differential equation for $0 \leq x \leq x_1$

$$\begin{gathered} z^2 \frac{d^2\psi_2}{dz^2} + (2k - z)z\frac{d\psi_2}{dz} + (k + m - \tfrac{1}{2})(k - m - \tfrac{1}{2})\psi_2 = 0, \\ k = \tfrac{1}{2} + \frac{s-1}{2t}; \quad m = \frac{1}{t}\left(\left(\frac{s-1}{2}\right)^2 + 6\right)^{\frac{1}{2}}; \quad z = \left(\frac{x_m}{x}\right)^t. \end{gathered} \tag{28}$$

Two linearly independent solutions of this equation are found to be $e^{z/2}z^{-k}W_{k,m}(z)$ and $e^{z/2}z^{-k}W_{-k,m}(-z)$, where $W_{k,m}(z)$ is the Whittaker confluent hypergeometric function.[9] We note that the generalized hypergeometric function is given by

$$\begin{gathered} {}_pF_q(\alpha_1, \alpha_2, \cdots \alpha_p; \rho_1, \rho_2, \cdots \rho_q; z) = \\ \sum_{n=0}^{\infty} \frac{\Gamma(\alpha_1 + n)\Gamma(\alpha_2 + n) \cdots \Gamma(\alpha_p + n)\Gamma(\rho_1)\Gamma(\rho_2) \cdots \Gamma(\rho_q)z^n}{\Gamma(\alpha_1)\Gamma(\alpha_2) \cdots \Gamma(\alpha_p)\Gamma(\rho_1 + n)\Gamma(\rho_2 + n) \cdots \Gamma(\rho_q + n)n!}. \end{gathered} \tag{29}$$

---

[9] For discussion of this function, see Whittaker and Watson, *Modern Analysis* (The Macmillan Company, New York, 1943).

In order to satisfy the boundary condition at the origin, Eq. (25b), it is seen from the asymptotic expansion of $W_{k,m}(z)$

$$W_{k,m}(z) \sim e^{-z/2} z^k \, {}_2F_0(\tfrac{1}{2} - m - k, \tfrac{1}{2} + m - k; -z^{-1}) \tag{30}$$

$$|\arg z| < 3\pi/2$$

that $e^{z/2}z^{-k}W_{-k,m}(-z)$ is not an admissible solution. Thus for $0 \leq x \leq x_1$, with

$$y_1(z) = e^{z/2} z^{-k} W_{k,m}(z), \tag{31}$$

$$\psi_2 = (a_0{}^2 x^2/2) + K_1 y_1(z).$$

The derivative of $y_1(z)$ is readily obtained from the Mellin-Barnes type contour integral representation of $W_{k,m}(z)$

$$W_{k,m}(z) = \frac{e^{-z/2} z^k}{2\pi i}$$

$$\times \int_{-\infty i}^{+\infty i} \frac{\Gamma(v)\Gamma(-v-k+m+\tfrac{1}{2})\Gamma(-v-k-m+\tfrac{1}{2}) z^v dv}{\Gamma(-k-m+\tfrac{1}{2})\Gamma(-k+m+\tfrac{1}{2})}, \tag{32}$$

with the result

$$\frac{dy_1(z)}{dx} = \frac{6}{tx} z^{-k} e^{z/2} W_{k-1,m}(z). \tag{33}$$

The constants K_1 and K_2 are determined by the requirement that ψ_2 and $d\psi_2/dx$ be continuous at x_1. With use of Eq. (33) we find after some elementary calculations that

$$K_1 = -a_0{}^2 x_1{}^2 K_3 = -\frac{a_0{}^2 x_1{}^2 (5/2) z_1{}^k e^{-z_1}}{3W_{k,m}(z_1) + \dfrac{6}{t} W_{k-1,m}(z_1)},$$

$$K_2 = -a_0{}^2 x_1{}^5 K_4 \tag{34}$$

$$= -\frac{a_0{}^2 x_1{}^5 \left\{ W_{k,m}(z_1) - \dfrac{3}{t} W_{k-1,m}(z_1) \right\}}{3W_{k,m}(z_1) + \dfrac{6}{t} W_{k-1,m}(z_1)},$$

$$z_1 = \left(\frac{x_m}{x_1}\right)^t.$$

Since in our numerical example $z_1 = 3.67 \times 10^{-2}$, $W_{k,m}(z_1)$ is easily computed by means of the relation

$$W_{k,m}(z) = z^{(1/2)+m} e^{-z/2} \frac{\Gamma(-2m)}{\Gamma(\tfrac{1}{2} - m - k)} \times {}_1F_1(\tfrac{1}{2} + m - k; 1 + 2m; z)$$

$$+ z^{(1/2)-m} e^{-z/2} \frac{\Gamma(2m)}{\Gamma(\tfrac{1}{2} + m - k)} \times {}_1F_1(\tfrac{1}{2} - m - k; 1 - 2m; z), \tag{35}$$

only a few terms in the power series being required.

Substitution of ψ_2 given by Eqs. (27) and (31) into Eq. (10) and use of the potential $V(x)$, Eq. (11), leads to the following result for the coefficient of shear viscosity,

$$\eta = \frac{\zeta \pi N^2 a_0{}^5}{15kTv^2}\left[\frac{1}{2}\int_0^{x1} x^5 g_0{}^{(2)}(x)\frac{dV(x)}{dx}dx + K_4 x_1{}^5 V(x_1) + K_3\frac{\epsilon x_1{}^{2+s}e^{z1}}{tx_m{}^{3+s}}\left\{\frac{nI_{n-3}}{x_m{}^{n-6}} - 6I_3\right\}\right] + \frac{NmkT}{2v\zeta}, \tag{36}$$

$$I_\alpha = I_\alpha(\infty) - I(z_1),$$

$$I(z) = \int_0^z y_1(z)e^{-z}z^{(\alpha+s/t)-1}dz.$$

The value of $I_\alpha(\infty)$ is conveniently calculated with use of Eq. (32) and Barnes lemma (reference 9, p. 289).

$$I_\alpha(\infty) = \frac{1}{2\pi i}\int_{-\infty i}^{+\infty i}\frac{\Gamma(v)\Gamma(-v-k-m+\frac{1}{2})\Gamma(-v-k+m+\frac{1}{2})\Gamma\left(v+\frac{\alpha+s}{t}\right)dv}{\Gamma(-k-m+\frac{1}{2})\Gamma(-k+m+\frac{1}{2})}$$

$$= \frac{\Gamma\left(\frac{\alpha+s}{t}-k-m+\frac{1}{2}\right)\Gamma\left(\frac{\alpha+s}{t}-k+m+\frac{1}{2}\right)}{\Gamma\left(\frac{\alpha+s}{t}+1-2k\right)}; \quad t > n-2. \tag{37}$$

Use of Eq. (35) and Kummer's formula

$$e^{-z}{}_1F_1(\tfrac{1}{2}+m-k;1+2m;z) = {}_1F_1(\tfrac{1}{2}+m+k;1+2m;-z), \tag{38}$$

immediately leads to the result

$$I_\alpha(z_1) = I_\alpha{}^m(z_1) + I_\alpha{}^{-m}(z_1), \tag{39}$$

where

$$I_\alpha{}^\beta(z_1) = \frac{\Gamma(-2\beta)}{\Gamma(\frac{1}{2}-\beta-k)}\frac{z_1{}^{(\alpha+s/t)-k+1/2+\beta}}{\left(\frac{\alpha+s}{t}-k+\frac{1}{2}+\beta\right)}\,{}_2F_2\left(\tfrac{1}{2}+\beta+k, \frac{\alpha+s}{t}-k+\tfrac{1}{2}+\beta; 1+2\beta, \frac{\alpha+s}{t}-k+\tfrac{3}{2}+\beta; -z_1\right).$$

We have carried out the numerical calculation of η for liquid argon at 89°K

$$\eta = 2.63 \times 10^6\zeta + \frac{8.53 \times 10^{-15}}{\zeta}\text{ poise}$$

the second term arising from momentum transport being negligible in comparison with the first. It is of interest to note that by defining an effective radius by the relationship $\zeta = 6\pi\eta R_{\text{eff}}$, $R_{\text{eff}} = 2.0$A at 89°K, while the actual radius, taken to be one-half the distance between nearest neighbours is 1.9A.

In order to check our theory with experiment it is necessary to calculate the friction constant. As a preliminary estimate we find that

$$\zeta^2 = \frac{4\pi a_0 \rho}{3} \int_0^\infty x^2 \left(\frac{d^2 V}{dx^2} + \frac{2}{x}\frac{dV}{dx} \right) g_0{}^{(2)} dx, \tag{40}$$

which for liquid argon at 89°K, using Eqs. (11) and (12) leads to $\zeta = 4.84 \times 10^{-10}$ g sec.$^{-1}$. With this value of the friction constant, the calculated coefficient of shear viscosity for liquid argon at 89°K is 1.27×10^{-3} poise which is in moderately good agreement with the extrapolated experimental determination of 2.39×10^{-3} poise.[10]

The solution of the ψ_0 Eq. (23b), subject to the boundary condition at the origin, Eq. (25d), is given by

$$\begin{aligned} \psi_0 &= a_0{}^2 \int_\infty^x \frac{d\xi}{\xi^2 g_0{}^{(2)}} \int_0^\xi \frac{dg_0{}^{(2)}}{dw} w^3 dw + \psi_0(\infty), \\ \psi_0 &\sim \frac{c}{x} + \psi_0(\infty) \quad \text{for } x \text{ large.} \end{aligned} \tag{41}$$

In order to evaluate $\psi_0(\infty)$ we consider Eq. (22) for the case of a periodic dilation of frequency ω. For large x, we obtain

$$\frac{d}{dx}\left(x^2 \frac{d\psi_0}{dx} \right) - \frac{i\omega\zeta a_0{}^2}{2kT} x^2 \psi_0 = 0, \tag{42}$$

with the solution

$$\psi_0 \sim \frac{A(\omega)}{x} \exp\left(- \left[\frac{a_0}{2}\left(\frac{\omega\zeta}{kT}\right)^{\frac{1}{2}} x(1+i) \right] \right)$$

$$\frac{B(\omega)}{x} \exp\left(\left[\frac{a_0}{2}\left(\frac{\omega\zeta}{kT}\right)^{\frac{1}{2}} x(1+i) \right] \right). \tag{43}$$

The boundary condition at infinity Eq. (25c) requires that $B(\omega) = 0$. For the case of zero frequency of dilation

$$\psi_0 \sim \lim_{\omega \to 0} \frac{A(\omega)}{x} \exp\left\{ - \left[\frac{a_0}{2}\left(\frac{\omega\zeta}{kT}\right)^{\frac{1}{2}} x(1+i) \right] \right\} = \frac{C}{x}. \tag{44}$$

Comparison of (41) and (44) shows that ψ_0 vanishes at infinity. We thus obtain the following expression for the coefficient of bulk viscosity

$$\phi = \frac{NmkT}{3v\zeta} + \frac{\zeta\pi a_0{}^5 N^2}{9kT} \int_0^\infty x^3 \frac{dV}{dx} g_0{}^{(2)} dx \times \int_\infty^x \frac{d\xi}{\xi^2 g_0{}^{(2)}} \int_0^\xi w^3 \frac{dg_0{}^{(2)}}{dw} dw. \tag{45}$$

---

[10] N. S. Rudenko and L. W. Schubnikow, *Physik. Zeits. Sowjetunion* **6**, 470 (1934).

Numerical calculations of the coefficient of bulk viscosity are postponed for later treatment, since the result appears to be extraordinary sensitive to the equilibrium radial distribution function and it is believed that a better approximation than that of Eq. (12) is required. For the same reason, our numerical estimate of the shear viscosity is to be considered preliminary and subject to revision. From recent ultrasonic absorption measurements of Galt,[11] an upper bound to the ratio ϕ/η is estimated to be $\frac{1}{3}$ for liquid argon at 85°K. However, in the absence of an experimental value of the heat conductivity, the calculation of the absolute value of ϕ is not possible.

[11] J. G. Galt, *J. Chem. Phys.* **16**, 505 (1948).

Errata: The Statistical Mechanical Theory of Transport Processes.

III. The Coefficients of Shear and Bulk Viscosity of Liquids

[*J. Chem. Phys.* **17**, 988 (1949)]

JOHN G. KIRKWOOD, FRANK P. BUFF, AND MELVIN S. GREEN
The Gates and Crellin Laboratories of Chemistry, California Institute of Technology, Pasadena 4, California

Equation (6) should read

$$\left[\frac{\langle \mathbf{PP}\rangle_{\mathsf{Av}}}{m} - m\mathbf{uu}\right]\rho^{(1)} = \rho^{(1)}kT\mathbf{1} - \frac{\rho^{(1)}kT}{\zeta}\left[\dot{\boldsymbol{\epsilon}} - \mathbf{1}\frac{\nabla\cdot\mathbf{u}}{3}\right],$$

where $\mathbf{1}$ is the unit tensor. The first term $\rho^{(1)}kT/3\zeta$ in the second of Eqs. (10) defining bulk viscosity should be omitted. Likewise, the first term $NmkT/3v\zeta$ of Eq. (45) should be omitted. In the first line of Eq. (16), ∇_{P_1} should be changed to ∇_{R_1}. In the last line of Eq. (36), $I(z)$ should read $I_\alpha(z)$. In the first line of reference 2, the date should be changed from 1945 to 1943.

The change in Eq. (6) removes kinetic energy transport terms from the bulk viscosity, which in any event are negligible in liquids, for which the theory is designed. The intermolecular force contribution to bulk viscosity remains unaffected by the change.

The change in Eq. (6) is necessitated by the definition of temperature in the non-equilibrium case

$$\langle \Pi^2\rangle_{\mathsf{Av}} = 3mkT$$

and the retention of ${}^{(1)}\mathbf{F}\dagger$, as yet undetermined by our theory, in Eq. (15), which should read

$$\langle \mathbf{\Pi\Pi}\rangle_{\mathsf{Av}} - mkT\mathbf{1} = \frac{m}{2\zeta}\Big[\langle \mathbf{\Pi\Pi}\rangle_{\mathsf{Av}}\cdot\nabla\mathbf{u} + \langle \mathbf{\Pi}\cdot\nabla\mathbf{u}\mathbf{\Pi}\rangle_{\mathsf{Av}} + \mathbf{u}\cdot\nabla\langle \mathbf{\Pi\Pi}\rangle_{\mathsf{Av}} + \frac{\partial\langle \mathbf{\Pi\Pi}\rangle_{\mathsf{Av}}}{\partial t} - \langle {}^{(1)}\mathbf{F}\dagger\mathbf{\Pi}\rangle_{\mathsf{Av}} - \langle \mathbf{\Pi}\,{}^{(1)}\mathbf{F}\dagger\rangle_{\mathsf{Av}}\Big]$$

$$\rho^{(1)}\langle {}^{(1)}\mathbf{F}\dagger\mathbf{\Pi}\rangle_{\mathsf{Av}} = N\int^{(1)} \mathbf{F}\dagger\mathbf{\Pi}\bar{f}^{(1)}d\mathbf{p}.$$

By taking the trace of both sides of the corrected form of Eq. (15), we obtain

$$\frac{\partial T}{\partial t} + \mathbf{u}\cdot\nabla T + \frac{2}{3}T\nabla\cdot\mathbf{u} - \frac{2}{3mk}\mathrm{Tr}\langle {}^{(1)}\mathbf{F}\dagger\mathbf{\Pi}\rangle_{\mathsf{Av}} = 0$$

and are led to the corrected form of Eq. (6).

Thus, as in the kinetic theory of gases, there is no momentum transport contribution to the bulk viscosity in view of the non-equilibrium definition of temperature. The intermolecular force term is therefore not only dominant but the only contribution to bulk viscosity.

[These corrections have *not* been entered in the text.]

The Statistical Mechanical Theory of Transport Processes. IV. The Equations of Hydrodynamics*

J. H. IRVING AND JOHN G. KIRKWOOD, *Gates and Crellin Laboratories of Chemistry No. 1343, Pasadena, California*

(Received November 21, 1949)

The equations of hydrodynamics—continuity equation, equation of motion, and equation of energy transport—are derived by means of the classical statistical mechanics. Thereby, expressions are obtained for the stress tensor and heat current density in terms of molecular variables. In addition to the familiar terms occurring in the kinetic theory of gases, there are terms depending upon intermolecular force. The contributions of intermolecular force to the stress tensor and heat current density are expressed, respectively, as quadratures of the density and current density in the configuration space of a pair of molecules.

INTRODUCTION

This paper will be concerned with a derivation of the equations of hydrodynamics from the principles of the classical statistical mechanics. In particular, the equation of continuity, the equation of motion, and the equation of energy transport will be derived. By so doing, the stress tensor and heat current density can be expressed in terms of molecular variables. The stress tensor consists of a kinetic part (which occurs in the kinetic theory of gases) and another term (dominant for a liquid) which will be expressed as a quadrature involving the potential of intermolecular force and the density of pairs of molecules. The heat current density is the sum of the familiar kinetic part and a quadrature involving the potential of intermolecular force and the density and current density in the configuration space of a pair of molecules. The results were previously stated in the first article of this series,[1] when this derivation was promised.

To obtain explicit expressions for the pair probability density and probability current density one would in principle need to solve the Liouville equation [Eq. (2.2)] for the probability distribution in Gibbs phase space and then perform repeated integrations. Since this program is untenable for a liquid, various attempts have been made to obtain a closed equation satisfied approximately by the probability distribution function in the phase space of a pair of molecules. One such equation has been derived by Born and Green[2] using a generalized "superposition" assumption. Another, a generalization of the well-known Fokker-Planck equation of stochastic theory, has been derived by Kirkwood[1] by introducing the concepts of time smoothing and a friction

* This work was supported by the U.S. ONR under Contract N6onr-244 with the California Institute of Technology.

[1] J. G. Kirkwood, *J. Chem. Phys.* **14**, 180 (1946).

[2] M. Born and H. S. Green, *Proc. Roy. Soc.* **A188**, 10 (1946).

constant. This latter equation has been applied to obtain an expression for the stress tensor linear in gradients of fluid velocity and, thereby, expressions (in terms of molecular variables) for coefficients of shear and volume viscosity.[3] The same equation generalized to non-uniform temperatures, after linearizing in the temperature gradient, leads to an explicit expression for the heat current and thereby to an expression for the coefficient of thermal conductivity.[4] We shall assume, for purposes of mathematical simplicity, a single component, single-phase fluid system consisting of molecules which interact under central forces only. It is not difficult to generalize the treatment to a multiple component or multiple phase system or to include molecular interaction depending upon rotational or internal degrees of freedom. Before entering upon the statistical mechanical theory, we shall first review the phenomenological theory of the hydrodynamical equations.

I. THE PHENOMENOLOGICAL THEORY

We imagine a continuous fluid consisting of a single chemical component with mass density $\rho(\mathbf{r}; t)$ and local velocity $\mathbf{u}(\mathbf{r}; t)$ at the point $\mathbf{r}$ and at the time t. We now imagine ω to be a fixed region somewhere in the interior of the fluid. The mass of the fluid within ω is given by

$$\int_\omega \rho(\mathbf{r}; t) d\omega.$$

Its rate of change, since ω is fixed (not moving with the fluid), is

$$\int_\omega \frac{\partial}{\partial t} \rho(\mathbf{r}; t) d\omega.$$

This increase of mass must be entirely due to influx of fluid through the boundary S of ω, i.e.,

$$\int_\omega \frac{\partial}{\partial t} \rho d\omega = - \int_S \rho \mathbf{u} \cdot d\mathbf{S} = - \int_\omega \nabla_{\mathbf{r}} \cdot [\rho \mathbf{u}] d\omega$$

where the surface integral has been converted to a volume integral by Gauss' theorem. Since ω is quite arbitrary, upon equating integrands, we get the continuity equation

$$\frac{\partial}{\partial t} \rho(\mathbf{r}; t) = - \nabla_{\mathbf{r}} \cdot [\rho(\mathbf{r}; t) \mathbf{u}(\mathbf{r}; t)]. \tag{1.1}$$

The hydrodynamical equation of motion may be derived by equating the rate of change of momentum within ω,

$$\int_\omega \frac{\partial}{\partial t} [\rho(\mathbf{r}; t) \mathbf{u}(\mathbf{r}; t)] d\omega$$

---

[3] Kirkwood, Buff, and Green, *J. Chem. Phys.* **17**, 988 (1949).

[4] Kirkwood, Standart, and Irving (in preparation). The numerical evaluation awaits a more precise computation of the theoretical radial distribution function.

plus the rate of flow of momentum out through the surface of ω,

$$\int_S \rho(\mathbf{r};t)\mathbf{u}(\mathbf{r};t)\mathbf{u}(\mathbf{r};t)\cdot d\mathbf{S} = \int_\omega \nabla_\mathbf{r}\cdot[\rho\mathbf{u}\mathbf{u}]d\omega$$

to the sum of the forces acting on the fluid within ω. These forces are the body force

$$\int_\omega \mathbf{X}(\mathbf{r};t)d\omega,$$

where $\mathbf{X}$ is the force per unit volume due to external sources, and the surface force

$$\int_S \boldsymbol{\sigma}(\mathbf{r};t)\cdot d\mathbf{S} = \int_\omega \nabla_\mathbf{r}\cdot\boldsymbol{\sigma}d\omega,$$

where $\boldsymbol{\sigma}$ is the symmetric stress tensor.

Since ω is arbitrary, the resulting differential equation is

$$\frac{\partial}{\partial t}[\rho\mathbf{u}] + \nabla_\mathbf{r}\cdot[\rho\mathbf{u}\mathbf{u}] = \mathbf{X} + \nabla_\mathbf{r}\cdot\boldsymbol{\sigma}. \tag{1.2}$$

We now introduce the internal energy density, $E(\mathbf{r};t)$, consisting of three parts—the interaction potential energy density, $E_V(\mathbf{r};t)$, due to interactions between fluid particles; the kinetic energy density, $E_K(\mathbf{r};t)$; and the potential energy density, $E_\psi(\mathbf{r};t)$, due to external sources, assumed to be conservative.

$$E = E_V + E_E + E_\psi. \tag{1.3}$$

The rate of change of internal energy within ω is

$$\int_\omega \frac{\partial}{\partial t}E(\mathbf{r};t)d\omega.$$

The rate of flux of energy from ω is

$$\int_S [E(\mathbf{r};t)\mathbf{u}(\mathbf{r};t) + \mathbf{q}(\mathbf{r};t)]\cdot d\mathbf{S} = \int_\omega \nabla_\mathbf{r}\cdot[E\mathbf{u}+\mathbf{q}]d\omega$$

where $E\mathbf{u}$ is the convective energy current and $\mathbf{q}$ is the conductive heat current. The work done per unit time by the fluid within ω on the rest of the system is

$$-\int_\omega \mathbf{u}\cdot\boldsymbol{\sigma}\cdot d\mathbf{S} = -\int_S \nabla_\mathbf{r}\cdot(\mathbf{u}\cdot\boldsymbol{\sigma})d\omega.$$

According to the law of conservation of energy, the sum of these three rates must vanish. Since ω is arbitrary, the sum of the integrands must also vanish, giving the energy transport equation

$$(\partial/\partial t)E + \nabla_\mathbf{r}\cdot[E\mathbf{u} + \mathbf{q} - \mathbf{u}\cdot\boldsymbol{\sigma}] = 0. \tag{1.4}$$

II. STATISTICAL MECHANICAL THEORY—THE DISTRIBUTION FUNCTION AND EXPECTATION VALUES

In the statistical mechanical theory we no longer consider a continuous fluid, but rather we treat a system consisting of N molecules, each having three degrees of translational freedom (but for the sake of simplicity, no other degrees of freedom). We denote the positions of these molecules by the sequence of three-vectors $\mathbf{R}_1, \mathbf{R}_2, \cdots, \mathbf{R}_N$, and their momenta by $\mathbf{p}_1, \mathbf{p}_2, \cdots, \mathbf{p}_N$. According to Gibbs, the instantaneous state of the system may be represented by a point in the $6N$-dimensional phase space representing the $3N$ coordinates and $3N$ momenta of the system. We may consider our representative system as drawn randomly from an ensemble of similar systems, the state of each being confined to that portion of phase space consistent with the macroscopic restraints imposed in the preparation of the system.[5]

The probability distribution function (relative density of representative points in phase space) we denote by

$$f(\mathbf{R}_1, \cdots, \mathbf{R}_N; \mathbf{p}_1, \cdots, \mathbf{p}_N; t),$$

satisfying the normalization condition

$$\underbrace{\int \cdots \int}_{6N \text{ fold}} f d\mathbf{R}_1 \cdots d\mathbf{R}_N d\mathbf{p}_1 \cdots d\mathbf{p}_N = 1 \tag{2.1}$$

where $d\mathbf{R}_k$ stands for a volume element in the configuration space and $d\mathbf{p}_k$ a volume element in the momentum space of the kth molecule. f changes in time according to the well-known Liouville equation

$$\frac{\partial f}{\partial t} = \sum_{k=1}^{N} \left[-\frac{\mathbf{p}_k}{m_k} \cdot \nabla_{\mathbf{R}_k} f + \nabla_{\mathbf{R}_k} U \cdot \nabla_{\mathbf{p}_k} f \right] \tag{2.2}$$

where U is the potential energy of the entire system.

Any dynamical variable, $\alpha(\mathbf{R}_1, \cdots, \mathbf{R}_N; \mathbf{p}_1, \cdots, \mathbf{p}_N)$, has an expectation value given at time t by

$$\langle \alpha; f \rangle = \underbrace{\int \cdots \int}_{6N \text{ fold}} \alpha(\mathbf{R}_1, \cdots, \mathbf{p}_1 \cdots) f(\mathbf{R}_1, \cdots \mathbf{p}_1, \cdots; t) \times d\mathbf{R}_1 \cdots d\mathbf{R}_N d\mathbf{p}_1 \cdots d\mathbf{p}_N. \tag{2.3}$$

We thus denote by $\langle \alpha; f \rangle$ the expectation value of α for a distribution function f. (It is merely the inner product of α and f taken over phase space.)

Providing α does not depend on time explicitly, the rate of change of the expectation value of α is given by

$$\frac{\partial}{\partial t} \langle \alpha; f \rangle = \left\langle \alpha; \frac{\partial f}{\partial t} \right\rangle = \sum_{k=1}^{N} \left[\left\langle \alpha; -\frac{\mathbf{p}_k}{m_k} \cdot \nabla_{\mathbf{R}_k} f \right\rangle + \langle \alpha; \nabla_{\mathbf{R}_k} U \cdot \nabla_{\mathbf{p}_k} f \rangle \right]. \tag{2.4}$$

[5] See reference 1 for a discussion of the process of measurement.

By Green's theorem applied in the space of $\mathbf{R}_k$

$$\left\langle \alpha; -\frac{\mathbf{p}_k}{m_k} \cdot \nabla_{\mathbf{R}_k} f \right\rangle = \left\langle \frac{\mathbf{p}_k}{m_k} \cdot \nabla_{\mathbf{R}_k} \alpha ; f \right\rangle \tag{2.5}$$

providing the integrated part vanishes; i.e., providing the system is bounded or f falls off sufficiently rapidly as $\mathbf{R}_k \to \infty$. Likewise, since $\nabla_{\mathbf{R}_k} U$ is independent of momentum $\mathbf{p}_k$, and since f falls off rapidly as $\mathbf{p}_k \to \infty$, use of Green's theorem in the momentum space of $\mathbf{p}_k$ yields

$$\langle \alpha; \nabla_{\mathbf{R}_k} U \cdot \nabla_{\mathbf{p}_k} f \rangle = -\langle \nabla_{\mathbf{R}_k} U \cdot \nabla_{\mathbf{p}_k} \alpha ; f \rangle. \tag{2.6}$$

Thus, (2.4) becomes

$$\frac{\partial}{\partial t} \langle \alpha ; f \rangle = \sum_{k=1}^{N} \left\langle \frac{\mathbf{p}_k}{m_k} \cdot \nabla_{\mathbf{R}_k} \alpha - \nabla_{\mathbf{R}_k} U \cdot \nabla_{\mathbf{p}_k} \alpha ; f \right\rangle \tag{2.7}$$

giving the rate of change of the expectation value of α as the expectation value of the dynamical variable

$$\sum_{k=1}^{N} \left[\frac{\mathbf{p}_k}{m_k} \cdot \nabla_{\mathbf{R}_k} \alpha - \nabla_{\mathbf{R}_k} U \cdot \nabla_{\mathbf{p}_k} \alpha \right].$$

We shall use (2.7) to derive the equations of hydrodynamics.

III. STATISTICAL MECHANICAL EXPRESSIONS FOR DENSITIES

The equations of hydrodynamics (1.1), (1.2), and (1.4) are concerned with densities in ordinary 3-space, e.g., mass density, momentum density, and energy density. We shall now express these as the expectation values of dynamical variables over an ensemble having distribution function f.

The probability per unit volume that the kth molecules be at $\mathbf{R}_k$ is

$$\underbrace{\int \cdots \int}_{6N\text{-}3 \text{ fold}} f(\mathbf{R}_1, \cdots \mathbf{p}_1, \cdots ; t) d\mathbf{R}_1 \cdots \times d\mathbf{R}_{k-1} d\mathbf{R}_{k+1} \cdots d\mathbf{R}_N d\mathbf{p}_1 \cdots d\mathbf{p}_N$$

where the integration is over all position vectors except $\mathbf{R}_k$ and over all momenta vectors. Introducing Dirac's δ-function, the probability per unit volume that the kth molecule be at $\mathbf{r}$ at time t is

$$\langle \delta(\mathbf{R}_k - \mathbf{r}) ; f \rangle$$

$$= \underbrace{\int \cdots \int}_{6N \text{ fold}} \delta(\mathbf{R}_k - \mathbf{r}) f(\mathbf{R}_1, \cdots ; \mathbf{p}_1, \cdots ; t) d\mathbf{R}_1 \cdots d\mathbf{p}_N.$$

The total mass density at $\mathbf{r}$ due to all molecules is thus given at time t by

$$\rho(\mathbf{r}; t) = \sum_{k=1}^{N} m_k \langle \delta(\mathbf{R}_k - \mathbf{r}) ; f \rangle. \tag{3.1}$$

The mean momentum of the kth molecule, providing it is at $\mathbf{r}$ and the locations of the others are unspecified, is given by the ratio

$$\frac{\underset{6N\text{ fold}}{\int \cdots \int} \mathbf{p}_k \delta(\mathbf{R}_k - \mathbf{r}) f(\mathbf{R}_1, \cdots; \mathbf{p}_1 \cdots; t) d\mathbf{R}_1 \cdots d\mathbf{p}_N}{\underset{6N\text{ fold}}{\int \cdots \int} \delta(\mathbf{R}_k - \mathbf{r}) f(\mathbf{R}_1, \cdots; \mathbf{p}_1, \cdots; t) d\mathbf{R}_1 \cdots d\mathbf{p}_N} = \frac{\langle \mathbf{p}_k \delta(\mathbf{R}_k - \mathbf{r}); f \rangle}{\langle \delta(\mathbf{R}_k - \mathbf{r}); f \rangle}.$$

Consequently, $\langle \mathbf{p}_k \delta(\mathbf{R}_k - \mathbf{r}); f \rangle$ is the product of this mean momentum by the probability per unit volume that the kth molecule be at $\mathbf{r}$; i.e., it is the contribution of the kth molecule to the momentum per unit volume (mass current density). The total momentum density at $\mathbf{r}$ is thus given at time t by

$$\rho(\mathbf{r}; t)\mathbf{u}(\mathbf{r}; t) = \sum_{k=1}^{N} \langle \mathbf{p}_k \delta(\mathbf{R}_k - \mathbf{r}); f \rangle, \tag{3.2}$$

where $\mathbf{u}(\mathbf{r}; t)$, thus defined, is the mean fluid velocity at $\mathbf{r}$.

There is no difficulty encountered in defining mass density or momentum density since the mass or momentum of any molecule may be considered as localized at that molecule. This is also true of kinetic energy density. Since the kinetic energy of the kth molecules is $p_k^2/2m_k$ (where p_k is the magnitude of the vector $\mathbf{p}_k$), its contribution to the kinetic energy density at $\mathbf{r}$ is $\langle (p_k^2/2m_k) \delta(\mathbf{R}_k - \mathbf{r}); f \rangle$, and the entire kinetic energy density at $\mathbf{r}$ is given at the time t by

$$E_K(\mathbf{r}; t) = \sum_{k=1}^{N} \left\langle \frac{p_k^2}{2m_k} \delta(\mathbf{R}_k - \mathbf{r}); f \right\rangle. \tag{3.3}$$

The potential energy, U, of the system we shall assume to be of the form

$$U = \sum_{k=1}^{N} \psi_k(\mathbf{R}_k) + \tfrac{1}{2} \sum_{j \neq k} \sum V_{jk} \tag{3.4}$$

where $\psi_k(\mathbf{R}_k)$ is the potential energy of the kth molecule in an external field of force, and V_{jk} is the mutual potential between the jth and kth molecules.

The potential energy $\psi_k(\mathbf{R}_k)$ may quite naturally be considered localized at $\mathbf{R}_k$, the location of the kth molecule. Thus, the total potential energy density at $\mathbf{r}$ associated with the interaction of molecules with the external field is

$$\begin{aligned} E_\psi(\mathbf{r}; t) &= \sum_{k=1}^{N} \langle \psi_k(\mathbf{R}_k) \delta(\mathbf{R}_k - \mathbf{r}); f \rangle \\ &= \sum_{k=1}^{N} \psi_k(\mathbf{r}) \langle \delta(\mathbf{R}_k - \mathbf{r}); f \rangle. \end{aligned} \tag{3.5}$$

Similarly the force on the kth molecule due to external sources is $-\nabla_{\mathbf{R}_k} \psi_k (\mathbf{R}_k)$, and the external force (body force) per unit volume at $\mathbf{r}$ is

$$\begin{aligned} X(\mathbf{r}; t) &= -\sum_{k=1}^{N} \langle [\nabla_{\mathbf{R}_k} \psi_k(\mathbf{R}_k)] \delta(\mathbf{R}_k - \mathbf{r}); f \rangle \\ &= -\sum_{k=1}^{N} [\nabla_{\mathbf{r}} \psi_k(\mathbf{r})] \langle \delta(\mathbf{R}_k - \mathbf{r}); f \rangle. \end{aligned} \tag{3.6}$$

The potential V_{jk}, depending on the location of both the jth and the kth molecule, is not so naturally localizable; it may only be considered as localized at a point in the six-dimensional configuration space of the pair. It is necessary, however, to define interaction potential energy density in 3-space, for this concept is required to give meaning to the internal energy density of the energy transport equation. For most systems of interest the potential V_{jk} is a short-range function of the molecular separation, R_{jk}, and consequently contributes negligibly to the potential energy unless molecules j and k are close, in which case, if the interaction potential energy be considered as distributed in any manner in the vicinity of the pair, it is sufficiently localized for macroscopic applications. This localization may be made quite precise (though arbitrary) by saying that half of the energy V_{jk} resides in each molecule of the pair. By this formal definition the total interaction potential energy residing in the kth molecule is

$$\frac{1}{2}\sum_{\substack{j=1\\ \neq k}}^{N} V_{jk}$$

and the total interaction potential energy density at $\mathbf{r}$ is

$$E_V(\mathbf{r};t) = \frac{1}{2}\sum_{j\neq k}\sum \langle V_{jk}\delta(\mathbf{R}_k - \mathbf{r}); f\rangle. \tag{3.7}$$

As mentioned previously, the stress tensor and heat current density will be expressed as quadratures involving the pair density of molecules and the current density in pair space, respectively.

The pair density, $\rho^{(2)}(\mathbf{r}, \mathbf{r}'; t)$ is the probability per (unit volume)^2 that one molecule (any molecule) will be at $\mathbf{r}$ and another will be at $\mathbf{r}'$. It is given by

$$\rho^{(2)}(\mathbf{r}, \mathbf{r}'; t) = \sum_{j\neq k}\sum \langle \delta(\mathbf{R}_j - \mathbf{r})\delta(\mathbf{R}_k - \mathbf{r}'); f\rangle. \tag{3.8}$$

The pair density is a symmetric function of its two arguments, $\mathbf{r}$ and $\mathbf{r}'$.

The particle current density in pair space is given by the six-component vector

$$\mathbf{j}^{(2)}(\mathbf{r}, \mathbf{r}'; t) = \sum_{k\neq i}\sum \left\langle \left(\frac{\mathbf{p}_k}{m_k} \oplus \frac{\mathbf{p}_i}{m_i}\right) \times \delta(\mathbf{R}_k - \mathbf{r})\delta(\mathbf{R}_i - \mathbf{r}'); f\right\rangle. \tag{3.9}$$

In this equation $(\mathbf{p}_k/m_k) \oplus (\mathbf{p}_i/m_i)$ is also a six-component vector, the velocity in the pair space of the kth and ith molecules. It is the direct sum of $\mathbf{p}_k/m_k$, lying entirely in the three-dimensional subspace of the kth molecule, and $\mathbf{p}_i/m_i$, lying in the subspace of the ith molecule. The six components of $\mathbf{j}^{(2)}$ may be labeled as the corresponding components of $\mathbf{r} \oplus \mathbf{r}'$. The first three components, i.e., the projection of $\mathbf{j}^{(2)}$ onto the space of its first argument, $\mathbf{r}$, is

$$\mathbf{j}_1^{(2)}(\mathbf{r}, \mathbf{r}'; t) = \sum_{k\neq i}\sum \left\langle \frac{\mathbf{p}_k}{m_k}\delta(\mathbf{R}_k - \mathbf{r})\delta(\mathbf{R}_i - \mathbf{r}'); f\right\rangle. \tag{3.10}$$

It is this quantity which will arise in the expression for heat current. $\mathbf{j}_1^{(2)}(\mathbf{r}, \mathbf{r}'; t)$ may be interpreted as the particle current density at $\mathbf{r}$ (in ordinary physical space), if another particle is at $\mathbf{r}'$, multiplied by the particle density at $\mathbf{r}'$. In contrast to the pair density, $\mathbf{j}_1^{(2)}(\mathbf{r}, \mathbf{r}'; t)$ is not a symmetrical function of $\mathbf{r}$ and $\mathbf{r}'$.

The densities which have been defined in this section are point functions. They are all ensemble averages of dynamical variables. It should be emphasized, however, that the conventional hydrodynamics is concerned with macroscopic observables. In measuring these observables one not only takes a statistical average over the systems of an ensemble (by repeating the observations many times) but two additional averages as well. The first is a spatial average over a microscopically large though macroscopically small domain, determined by the resolving power of one's measuring instruments. The second is a time average over an interval determined by the relaxation time of one's measuring instruments. The equation of hydrodynamics are thus relations among these measured averages, found to hold empirically.

In addition to the point function densities defined above, we shall later give a point function definition for stress tensor and heat current. It is interesting that these point functions, though averaged neither over space nor time, satisfy equations that are identical in form to the equations of hydrodynamics (at least to those hydrodynamical equations for a single component, single phase system, derived in Section I). In the following sections we shall derive the hydrodynamical-like equations satisfied by these point functions. To obtain the hydrodynamical equations themselves it is merely necessary to perform the appropriate space and time averages.

It will be noted that in defining the densities, heretofore, we have made no reference to the similarity of molecules. Nor are the derivations of the statistical mechanical expressions for the time rate of change of these densities facilitated by imposing the restriction of similar molecules. It is only when we are ready to define the point function stress tensor and heat current density that we must impose this restriction; for these functions are defined so as to satisfy the hydrodynamical equations of Section I, which are only valid for a single component, single phase system.

IV. THE EQUATION OF CONTINUITY

We now apply Eq. (2.7) to the derivation of the equation of continuity. To this end we take α to be

$$\alpha \equiv \sum_{j=1}^{N} m_j \delta(\mathbf{R}_j - \mathbf{r}). \tag{4.1}$$

Then, as required for (2.7),

$$\frac{\mathbf{p}_k}{m_k} \cdot \nabla_{\mathbf{R}_k} \alpha - \nabla_{\mathbf{R}_k} U \cdot \nabla_{\mathbf{p}_k} \alpha = \mathbf{p}_k \cdot \nabla_{\mathbf{R}_k} \delta(\mathbf{R}_k - \mathbf{r}) = -\nabla_{\mathbf{r}} \cdot [\mathbf{p}_k \delta(\mathbf{R}_k - \mathbf{r})]. \tag{4.2}$$

From the definition (3.1), Eqs. (4.1), (2.7), and (4.2), and finally the definition (3.2)

$$\frac{\partial}{\partial t} \rho(\mathbf{r}; t) = \frac{\partial}{\partial t} \langle \alpha; f \rangle = \sum_{k=1}^{N} \langle -\nabla_{\mathbf{r}} \cdot [\mathbf{p}_k \delta(\mathbf{R}_k - \mathbf{r})]; f \rangle = -\nabla_{\mathbf{r}} \cdot [\rho(\mathbf{r}; t) \mathbf{u}(\mathbf{r}; t)]$$

which is the equation of continuity, (1.1).

V. THE HYDRODYNAMICAL EQUATION OF MOTION (MOMENTUM TRANSPORT)

Before deriving the hydrodynamical equation of motion we wish to alter (2.7) to give the rate of change of the expectation value of a vector $\boldsymbol{\alpha}$ having components α_ν. According to (2.7), for $\nu = 1, 2, 3$,

$$\frac{\partial}{\partial t}\langle \alpha_\nu; f\rangle = \sum_{k=1}^{N} \left\langle \frac{\mathbf{p}_k}{m_k} \cdot \nabla_{\mathbf{R}_k}\alpha_\nu - \nabla_{\mathbf{R}_k} U \cdot \nabla_{\mathbf{p}_k}\alpha_\nu; f \right\rangle.$$

These three equations ($\nu = 1, 2, 3$) may be written in diadic notation as

$$\frac{\partial}{\partial t}\langle \boldsymbol{\alpha}; f\rangle = \sum_{k=1}^{N} \left\langle \left(\frac{\mathbf{p}_k}{m_k} \cdot \nabla_{\mathbf{R}_k}\right)\boldsymbol{\alpha} - (\nabla_{\mathbf{R}_k} U \cdot \nabla_{\mathbf{p}_k})\boldsymbol{\alpha}; f \right\rangle. \tag{5.1}$$

We now take $\boldsymbol{\alpha}$ to be

$$\boldsymbol{\alpha} = \sum_{j=1}^{N} \mathbf{p}_j \delta(\mathbf{R}_j - \mathbf{r}). \tag{5.2}$$

Then

$$\left(\frac{\mathbf{p}_k}{m_k} \cdot \nabla_{\mathbf{R}_k}\right)\boldsymbol{\alpha} - (\nabla_{\mathbf{R}_k} U \cdot \nabla_{\mathbf{p}_k})\boldsymbol{\alpha} = \left(\frac{\mathbf{p}_k}{m_k} \cdot \nabla_{\mathbf{R}_k}\right)\mathbf{p}_k\delta(\mathbf{R}_k - \mathbf{r})$$
$$- (\nabla_{\mathbf{R}_k} U \cdot \nabla_{\mathbf{p}_k})\mathbf{p}_k\delta(\mathbf{R}_k - \mathbf{r}) = - \nabla_{\mathbf{r}} \cdot \left[\frac{\mathbf{p}_k\mathbf{p}_k}{m_k}\delta(\mathbf{R}_k - \mathbf{r})\right]$$
$$- (\nabla_{\mathbf{R}_k} U)\delta(\mathbf{R}_k - \mathbf{r}). \tag{5.3}$$

From (3.4)

$$\nabla_{\mathbf{R}_k} U = \nabla_{\mathbf{R}_k}\psi_k(\mathbf{R}_k) + \sum_{\substack{j=1\\ \neq k}}^{N} \nabla_{\mathbf{R}_k} V_{jk}. \tag{5.4}$$

From (5.2) and the definition of momentum density, (3.2), we have

$$\langle \boldsymbol{\alpha}; f\rangle = \rho(\mathbf{r}; t)\mathbf{u}(\mathbf{r}; t). \tag{5.5}$$

Substituting (5.5) and (5.3) into (5.1) and replacing $\nabla_{\mathbf{R}_k} U$ by its equivalent given in (5.4), we obtain, upon introducing $\mathbf{X}$, the body force defined in (3.6),

$$\frac{\partial}{\partial t}[\rho(\mathbf{r}; t)\mathbf{u}(\mathbf{r}; t)] = - \nabla_{\mathbf{r}} \cdot \sum_{k=1}^{N} \left\langle \frac{\mathbf{p}_k\mathbf{p}_k}{m_k}\delta(\mathbf{R}_k - \mathbf{r}); f \right\rangle$$
$$+ \mathbf{X}(\mathbf{r}; t) - \sum_{j \neq k}\sum \langle (\nabla_{\mathbf{R}_k} V_{jk})\delta(\mathbf{R}_k - \mathbf{r}); f\rangle. \tag{5.6}$$

The first term on the right in Eq. (5.6) may be modified by noting that

$$\sum_{k=1}^{N} m_k \left\langle \left(\frac{\mathbf{p}_k}{m_k} - \mathbf{u}\right)\left(\frac{\mathbf{p}_k}{m_k} - \mathbf{u}\right)\delta(\mathbf{R}_k - \mathbf{r}); f \right\rangle$$
$$= \sum_{k=1}^{N} \left\langle \frac{\mathbf{p}_k\mathbf{p}_k}{m_k}\delta(\mathbf{R}_k - \mathbf{r}); f \right\rangle - \mathbf{u}\sum_{k=1}^{N} \langle \mathbf{p}_k\delta(\mathbf{R}_k - \mathbf{r}); f\rangle$$
$$- \sum_{k=1}^{N} \langle \mathbf{p}_k\delta(\mathbf{R}_k - \mathbf{r}); f\rangle\mathbf{u} + \mathbf{u}\mathbf{u}\sum_{k=1}^{N} m_k\langle \delta(\mathbf{R}_k - \mathbf{r}); f\rangle$$
$$= \sum_{k=1}^{N} \left\langle \frac{\mathbf{p}_k\mathbf{p}_k}{m_k}\delta(\mathbf{R}_k - \mathbf{r}); f \right\rangle - \rho\mathbf{u}\mathbf{u} \tag{5.7}$$

where we have used (3.1) and (3.2).

The last term in (5.6) may be cast in a more convenient form by symmetrizing with respect to the dummy indices j and k.

$$
\begin{aligned}
-\sum_{j\neq k}\sum &\langle(\nabla_{\mathbf{R}_k}V_{jk})\delta(\mathbf{R}_k-\mathbf{r});f\rangle \\
&= -\frac{1}{2}\sum_{j\neq k}\sum\langle(\nabla_{\mathbf{R}_k}V_{jk})\delta(\mathbf{R}_k-\mathbf{r})+(\nabla_{\mathbf{R}_j}V_{kj})\delta(\mathbf{R}_j-\mathbf{r});f\rangle \\
&= -\frac{1}{2}\sum_{j\neq k}\sum\langle(\nabla_{\mathbf{R}_k}V_{jk})\times[\delta(\mathbf{R}_k-\mathbf{r})-\delta(\mathbf{R}_j-\mathbf{r})];f\rangle. \qquad (5.8)
\end{aligned}
$$

where we have used Newton's third law:

$$\nabla_{\mathbf{R}_j}V_{kj} = -\nabla_{\mathbf{R}_k}V_{jk}.$$

The difference of the δ-functions may be expanded formally as a Taylor's series in the vector separation, $\mathbf{R}_{jk} = \mathbf{R}_k - \mathbf{R}_j$.

$$
\begin{aligned}
\delta(\mathbf{R}_k&-\mathbf{r})-\delta(\mathbf{R}_j-\mathbf{r}) \\
&= -\mathbf{R}_{jk}\cdot\nabla_{\mathbf{r}}\delta(\mathbf{R}_j-\mathbf{r})+\tfrac{1}{2}(\mathbf{R}_{jk}\cdot\nabla_{\mathbf{r}})^2\delta(\mathbf{R}_j-\mathbf{r})-\cdots \\
&\qquad +\frac{1}{n!}(-\mathbf{R}_{jk}\cdot\nabla_{\mathbf{r}})^n\delta(\mathbf{R}_j-\mathbf{r})+\cdots \\
&= -\nabla_{\mathbf{r}}\cdot\Bigg[\mathbf{R}_{jk}\Bigg\{1-\frac{1}{2}\mathbf{R}_{jk}\cdot\nabla_{\mathbf{r}}+\cdots \\
&\qquad +\frac{1}{n!}(-\mathbf{R}_{jk}\cdot\nabla_{\mathbf{r}})^{n-1}+\cdots\Bigg\}\delta(\mathbf{R}_j-\mathbf{r})\Bigg]. \qquad (5.9)
\end{aligned}
$$

Substituting (5.9) into (5.8) gives, after commuting $\nabla_{\mathbf{r}}$ with the integration over phase space:

$$
\begin{aligned}
-\sum_{j\neq k}\sum &\langle(\nabla_{\mathbf{R}_k}V_{jk})\delta(\mathbf{R}_k-\mathbf{r});f\rangle \\
&= \nabla_{\mathbf{r}}\cdot\Bigg[\frac{1}{2}\sum_{j\neq k}\sum\Bigg\langle(\nabla_{\mathbf{R}_k}V_{jk})\mathbf{R}_{jk}\Bigg\{1-\frac{1}{2}\mathbf{R}_{jk}\cdot\nabla_{\mathbf{r}} \\
&\qquad +\cdots+\frac{1}{n!}(-\mathbf{R}_{jk}\cdot\nabla_{\mathbf{r}})^{n-1}+\cdots\Bigg\}\delta(\mathbf{R}_j-\mathbf{r});f\Bigg\rangle\Bigg]. \qquad (5.10)
\end{aligned}
$$

Substituting (5.7) and (5.10) into (5.6), we obtain

$$
\begin{aligned}
(\partial/\partial t)&[\rho\mathbf{u}]+\nabla_{\mathbf{r}}\cdot[\rho\mathbf{u}\mathbf{u}] \\
&= \mathbf{X}+\nabla_{\mathbf{r}}\cdot\Bigg[-\sum_{k=1}^{N}m_k\Bigg\langle\left(\frac{\mathbf{p}_k}{m_k}-\mathbf{u}\right)\left(\frac{\mathbf{p}_k}{m_k}-\mathbf{u}\right)\delta(\mathbf{R}_k-\mathbf{r});f\Bigg\rangle \\
&+\frac{1}{2}\sum_{j\neq k}\sum\Bigg(\Bigg\langle\nabla_{\mathbf{R}_k}V_{jk}\Bigg)\mathbf{R}_{jk}\Bigg\{1-\frac{1}{2}\mathbf{R}_{jk}\cdot\nabla_{\mathbf{r}}+\cdots+\frac{1}{n!}(-\mathbf{R}_{jk}\cdot\nabla_{\mathbf{r}})^{n-1} \\
&\qquad +\cdots\Bigg\}\delta(\mathbf{R}_i-\mathbf{r});f\Bigg\rangle\Bigg]. \qquad (5.11)
\end{aligned}
$$

Equation (5.11) has been derived without referring to the restriction of a single component, single phase system. In fact, the equation holds as well when there are non-central forces depending upon rotational or other internal degrees of freedom.[6]

We now wish to compare (5.11) with (1.2), the hydrodynamical equation for a single component, single phase system. Consequently we must consider (5.11) when all particles are identical. We shall also limit the subsequent treatment to central forces depending on range only. Hence,

$$V_{jk} = V(R_{jk})$$

and

$$\nabla_{\mathbf{R}_k} V_{jk} = \frac{\mathbf{R}_{jk}}{R_{jk}} V'(R_{jk}).$$

We are now ready to define a point function stress tensor, $\boldsymbol{\sigma}$.

$$\boldsymbol{\sigma}(\mathbf{r}; t) = \boldsymbol{\sigma}_k(\mathbf{r}; t) + \boldsymbol{\sigma}_V(\mathbf{r}; t) \tag{5.12}$$

$$\boldsymbol{\sigma}_k(\mathbf{r}; t) = -\sum_{k=1}^{N} m \left\langle \left(\frac{\mathbf{p}_k}{m} - \mathbf{u}\right)\left(\frac{\mathbf{p}_k}{m} - \mathbf{u}\right) \delta(\mathbf{R}_k - \mathbf{r}); f \right\rangle \tag{5.13}$$

$$\boldsymbol{\sigma}_V(\mathbf{r}; t) = \frac{1}{2} \sum_{j \neq k}\sum \left\langle \frac{\mathbf{R}_{jk}\mathbf{R}_{jk}}{R_{jk}} V'(R_{jk}) \left\{ 1 - \frac{1}{2} \mathbf{R}_{jk} \cdot \nabla_{\mathbf{r}} + \cdots \right.\right.$$

$$\left.\left. + \frac{1}{n!} (-\mathbf{R}_{jk} \cdot \nabla_{\mathbf{r}})^{n-1} + \cdots \right\} \delta(\mathbf{R}_j - \mathbf{r}); f \right\rangle \cdot \tag{5.14}$$

With this definition Eq. (5.11) becomes identical in form to the hydrodynamical equation of motion, (1.2). It is an equation relating point function densities and the point function stress tensor. When appropriate space and time averages are taken, it becomes the hydrodynamical equation itself.

Since only the divergence of $\boldsymbol{\sigma}$ enters into the hydrodynamical equation of motion, $\boldsymbol{\sigma}$ itself is undetermined (so far as this equation goes) up to an arbitrary tensor of vanishing divergence. The stress tensor we have defined in

---

[6] In the event that there are other degrees of freedom ξ_i having conjugate momenta η_i, then f is a distribution function in a phase space of higher dimensions, and the expectation value of a dynamical variable α is $\langle \alpha; f \rangle$, where the brackets now indicate integration over this entire phase space. The Liouville equation, (2.2), must be amended by adding to the right

$$\sum_i \left[-\frac{\partial H}{\partial \eta_i}\frac{\partial f}{\partial \xi_i} + \frac{\partial \mathrm{H}}{\partial \xi_i}\frac{\partial f}{\partial \eta_i} \right],$$

where H is the Hamiltonian of the system. This changes the expression for $(\partial/\partial t)\langle \alpha; f \rangle$ by

$$\sum_i \left\langle \alpha; -\frac{\partial H}{\partial \eta_i}\frac{\partial f}{\partial \xi_i} + \frac{\partial H}{\partial \xi_i}\frac{\partial f}{\partial \eta_i} \right\rangle.$$

Providing α is independent of all ξ_i and η_i, this vanishes upon integrating the first term by parts with respect to ξ_i, and the second term with respect to η_i, assuming that the integrated parts also vanish (e.g., if ξ_i is cyclic and $f \to 0$ rapidly as $\eta_i \to \pm\infty$). Consequently, the expression for the rate of change of the expectation value of a dynamical variable independent of internal degrees of freedom is unchanged by the existence of these internal degrees of freedom. Thus, the derivation of (5.11) is equally valid for central or non-central forces depending upon rotational or other internal degrees of freedom.

Eqs. (5.12)–(5.14) is not only the most apparent choice to reduce (5.11) to the hydrodynamical equation of motion but also is the only choice in accord with the physical definition of the stress tensor as the force transmitted per unit area.

$\boldsymbol{\sigma}_k$ is the kinetic contribution to the stress tensor. $\boldsymbol{\sigma}_k \cdot d\mathbf{S}$, viewed from a coordinate system moving with the local velocity $\mathbf{u}$, is the momentum transferred per unit time across the area dS due to the macroscopically imperceptible spread of the fluid velocities about the mean fluid velocity. $\boldsymbol{\sigma}_k$ is the familiar expression for the stress tensor which arises in the kinetic theory of gases, when the intermolecular force can be neglected. It is dominated by $\boldsymbol{\sigma}_V$ in liquids.

$\boldsymbol{\sigma}_V$ is the contribution of intermolecular forces to the stress tensor. $\boldsymbol{\sigma}_V \cdot d\mathbf{S}$ represents the force acting across dS due to the interaction of molecules on opposite sides of dS. This fact is demonstrated in the Appendix.

We now set out to express $\boldsymbol{\sigma}_V$ as a quadrature involving the pair density defined in (3.8). First we introduce into (5.14) a new δ-function, $\delta(\mathbf{R}_{jk} - \mathbf{R})$, and integration over the new variable, $\mathbf{R}$.

$$\boldsymbol{\sigma}_V(\mathbf{r};t) = \frac{1}{2}\sum_{j\neq k}\sum \left\langle \int_{3\text{ fold}} \delta(\mathbf{R}_{jk} - \mathbf{R})\,\frac{\mathbf{RR}}{R}\,V'(R)\left\{1 - \frac{1}{2}\,\mathbf{R}\cdot\nabla_{\mathbf{r}} + \cdots + \frac{1}{n!}\,(-\mathbf{R}\cdot\nabla_{\mathbf{r}})^{n-1} + \cdots\right\}\delta(\mathbf{R}_j - \mathbf{r})d\mathbf{R}; f\right\rangle.$$

We now commute the integration over $\mathbf{R}$ with the integration over phase and with the summation, and we factor out of the brackets and out of the sum all quantities which do not depend on the particle coordinates nor the indices j and k.

$$\boldsymbol{\sigma}_V(\mathbf{r};t) = \frac{1}{2}\int_{3\text{ fold}} \frac{\mathbf{RR}}{R}\,V'(R)\times\left\{1 - \frac{1}{2}\mathbf{R}\cdot\nabla_{\mathbf{r}} + \cdots + \frac{1}{n!}(-\mathbf{R}\cdot\nabla_{\mathbf{r}})^{n-1} + \cdots\right\} \times \sum_{j\neq k}\sum \langle\delta(\mathbf{R}_{jk} - \mathbf{R})\delta(\mathbf{R}_j - \mathbf{r}); f\rangle d\mathbf{R}.$$

The product $\delta(\mathbf{R}_{jk} - \mathbf{R})\delta(\mathbf{R}_j - \mathbf{r})$ is equivalent to the product $\delta(\mathbf{R}_j - \mathbf{r})$ $\delta(\mathbf{R}_k - \mathbf{r} - \mathbf{R})$; consequently the sum may be identified as the pair density defined in (3.8). This gives

$$\boldsymbol{\sigma}_V(\mathbf{r};t) = \frac{1}{2}\int_{3\text{ fold}} \frac{\mathbf{RR}}{R}\,V'(R)\left\{1 - \frac{1}{2}\mathbf{R}\cdot\nabla_{\mathbf{r}} + \cdots + \frac{1}{n!}(-\mathbf{R}\cdot\nabla_{\mathbf{r}})^{n-1} + \cdots\right\}\rho^{(2)}(\mathbf{r}, \mathbf{r} + \mathbf{R}; t)d\mathbf{R}. \tag{5.15}$$

For a liquid, the pair density, $\rho^{(2)}(\mathbf{r}, \mathbf{r} + \mathbf{R})$, considered as a function of the two independent coordinates $\mathbf{r}$ and $\mathbf{R}$, is a slow function of $\mathbf{r}$, although a sensitive function of the relative coordinate, $\mathbf{R}$. Since the change in the pair density due to changing the independent variable $\mathbf{r}$ by an amount $\mathbf{R}$, $\mathbf{R}\cdot\nabla_{\mathbf{r}}\rho^{(2)}(\mathbf{r}, \mathbf{r} + \mathbf{R})$ is negligible with respect to $\rho^{(2)}(\mathbf{r}, \mathbf{r} + \mathbf{R})$ for $\mathbf{R}$ of the order of the "range" of intermolecular force [range of $V'(R)$], all terms beyond the first in the brace of (5.15) may be neglected. Only at a boundary or interface is $\rho^{(2)}(\mathbf{r}, \mathbf{r} + \mathbf{R})$ also sensitive to $\mathbf{r}$, in which case neglecting terms beyond the first may not be justified.

For a fluid with identical particles it is convenient to express the pair density as a product of singlet particle densities, $\rho(\mathbf{r}; t)/m$ and $\rho(\mathbf{r} + \mathbf{R}; t)/m$, and a correlation function, $g^{(2)}$.

$$\rho^{(2)}(\mathbf{r}, \mathbf{r} + \mathbf{R}; t) = \frac{1}{m^2} \rho(\mathbf{r}; t)\rho(\mathbf{r} + \mathbf{R}; t)g^{(2)}(\mathbf{r}; \mathbf{R}; t). \tag{5.16}$$

$g^{(2)}$ is expressed as a function of $\mathbf{r}$, the coordinate of the first of the pair (to which it is insensitive) and $\mathbf{R}$, the relative coordinate (to which it is sensitive).

When (5.16) is substituted into (5.15), neglecting all terms beyond the first in the brace and replacing the slowly varying mass density $\rho(\mathbf{r} + \mathbf{R}; t)$ by $\rho(\mathbf{r}; t)$, we obtain the approximation (very accurate for a bulk fluid phase).

$$\boldsymbol{\sigma}_V(\mathbf{r}; t) = \frac{[\rho(\mathbf{r}; t)]^2}{2m^2} \int_{3\text{ fold}} \frac{\mathbf{RR}}{R} V'(R)g^{(2)}(\mathbf{r}; \mathbf{R}; t)d\mathbf{R}. \tag{5.17}$$

The intermolecular force contribution to the macroscopic stress tensor may be obtained by taking the appropriate space and time averages of (5.17). The equation is invariant under averaging except that $g^{(2)}$ must be replaced by its average.

The pressure may be obtained by taking the diagonal sum of the stress tensor

$$P = -\tfrac{1}{3} \text{ Trace } \boldsymbol{\sigma}. \tag{5.18}$$

From (5.13)

$$-\frac{1}{3} \text{Trace } \boldsymbol{\sigma}_K = \frac{2}{3} \sum_{k=1}^{N} \left\langle \frac{m}{2} \left| \frac{\mathbf{p}_k}{m} - \mathbf{u} \right|^2 \delta(\mathbf{R}_k - \mathbf{r}); f \right\rangle \tag{5.19}$$

and from (5.17)

$$-\frac{1}{3} \text{Trace } \boldsymbol{\sigma}_V = -\frac{[\rho(\mathbf{r}; t)]^2}{6m^2} \int_{3\text{ fold}} R V'(R)g^{(2)}(\mathbf{r}; \mathbf{R}; t)d\mathbf{R}. \tag{5.20}$$

The sum occurring in (5.19) is [according to (3.3)] the kinetic energy density at $\mathbf{r}$ measured from a frame of reference moving with the mean velocity, $\mathbf{u}$. In equilibrium this is given by $(3/2)kT \times \rho/m$, the kinetic energy per molecule times the particle density. In an equilibrium state, $g^{(2)}$ and ρ are independent of $\mathbf{r}$ and $g^{(2)}$ is isotropic with respect to the relative coordinate, $\mathbf{R}$; i.e., $g^{(2)}$ is a function of the distance R only. Equations (5.18)–(5.20) thus give for the equilibrium pressure

$$P_{\text{eq}} = \frac{\rho}{m} kT - \frac{2\pi}{3} \left(\frac{\rho}{m}\right)^2 \int R^3 V'(R)g^{(2)}(R)dR. \tag{5.21}$$

This is the "equation of state" for a fluid which may be derived without regard to hydrodynamics by using the virial theorem.

VI. THE ENERGY TRANSPORT EQUATION

The derivation of the energy transport equation follows the lines of the preceding section. However, since the equations involved have more terms, confusion can be avoided by deriving separate expressions for the rate of change of the several parts of the energy density.

First we shall apply Eq. (2.7) taking

$$\alpha = \sum_{j=1}^{N} \frac{p_j^2}{2m_j} \delta(\mathbf{R}_j - \mathbf{r}). \tag{6.1}$$

The kinetic energy density, (3.3), is

$$E_K(\mathbf{r}; t) = \langle \alpha; f \rangle. \tag{6.2}$$

As required by (2.7)

$$\begin{aligned}
&\frac{\mathbf{p}_k}{m_k} \cdot \nabla_{\mathbf{R}_k} \alpha - (\nabla_{\mathbf{R}_k} U) \cdot \nabla_{\mathbf{p}_k} \alpha \\
&\quad = -\frac{\mathbf{p}_k^2}{2m_k} \frac{\mathbf{p}_k}{m_k} \cdot \nabla_{\mathbf{r}} \delta(\mathbf{R}_k - \mathbf{r}) - (\nabla_{\mathbf{R}_k} U) \cdot \frac{\mathbf{p}_k}{m_k} \delta(\mathbf{R}_k - \mathbf{r}) \\
&\quad = -\nabla_{\mathbf{r}} \cdot \left[\frac{p_k^2}{2m_k} \frac{\mathbf{p}_k}{m_k} \delta(\mathbf{R}_k - \mathbf{r}) \right] \\
&\qquad\qquad - \left[\nabla_{\mathbf{R}_k} \psi_k(\mathbf{R}_k) + \sum_{\substack{j=1 \\ \neq k}}^{N} \nabla_{\mathbf{R}_k} V_{jk} \right] \cdot \frac{\mathbf{p}_k}{m_k} \delta(\mathbf{R}_k - \mathbf{r}),
\end{aligned} \tag{6.3}$$

where we have used (5.4). When (6.2) and (6.3) are substituted into (2.7), we obtain

$$\begin{aligned}
\frac{\partial}{\partial t} E_K(\mathbf{r}; t) = &- \nabla_{\mathbf{r}} \cdot \sum_{k=1}^{N} \left\langle \frac{p_k^2}{2m_k} \frac{\mathbf{p}_k}{m_k} \delta(\mathbf{R}_k - \mathbf{r}); f \right\rangle \\
&- \sum_{k=1}^{N} [\nabla_{\mathbf{r}} \psi_k(\mathbf{r})] \cdot \left\langle \frac{\mathbf{p}_k}{m_k} \delta(\mathbf{R}_k - \mathbf{r}); f \right\rangle \\
&- \sum_{j \neq k} \sum \left\langle (\nabla_{\mathbf{R}_k} V_{jk}) \cdot \frac{\mathbf{p}_k}{m_k} \delta(\mathbf{R}_k - \mathbf{r}); f \right\rangle \cdot
\end{aligned} \tag{6.4}$$

Next we apply (2.7) using

$$\alpha = \sum_{j=1}^{N} \psi_j(\mathbf{r}) \delta(\mathbf{R}_j - \mathbf{r}). \tag{6.5}$$

Then, according to (3.5), the energy density due to external fields is

$$E_\psi(\mathbf{r}; t) = \langle \alpha; f \rangle \tag{6.6}$$

and

$$\begin{aligned}
&(\mathbf{p}_k/m_k) \cdot \nabla_{\mathbf{R}_k} \alpha - (\nabla_{\mathbf{R}_k} U) \cdot \nabla_{\mathbf{p}_k} \alpha \\
&\qquad = \psi_k(\mathbf{r}) (\mathbf{p}_k/m_k) \cdot \nabla_{\mathbf{R}_k} \delta(\mathbf{R}_k - \mathbf{r}) \\
&\qquad = -\psi_k(\mathbf{r}) \nabla_{\mathbf{r}} \cdot [(\mathbf{p}_k/m_k) \delta(\mathbf{R}_k - \mathbf{r})].
\end{aligned} \tag{6.7}$$

Substituting (6.6) and (6.7) into (2.7) gives

$$\frac{\partial}{\partial t} E_\psi(\mathbf{r}; t) = -\sum_{k=1}^{N} \psi_k(\mathbf{r}) \nabla_{\mathbf{r}} \cdot \left\langle \frac{\mathbf{p}_k}{m_k} \delta(\mathbf{R}_k - \mathbf{r}); f \right\rangle \cdot \tag{6.8}$$

Finally, we shall apply (2.7) using

$$\alpha = \frac{1}{2} \sum_{i \neq j}\sum V_{ij}\delta(\mathbf{R}_j - \mathbf{r}). \tag{6.9}$$

The potential energy density due to molecular interaction is then, according to (3.7),

$$E_V(\mathbf{r}; t) = \langle \alpha; f \rangle \tag{6.10}$$

and

$$\begin{aligned}
&(\mathbf{p}_k/m_k) \cdot \nabla_{\mathbf{R}_k}\alpha - (\nabla_{\mathbf{R}_k} U) \cdot \nabla_{\mathbf{p}_k}\alpha \\
&= \frac{\mathbf{p}_k}{2m_k} \cdot \Bigg[\sum_{\substack{j=1\\ \neq k}}^{N} (\nabla_{\mathbf{R}_k} V_{kj})\delta(\mathbf{R}_j - \mathbf{r}) + \sum_{\substack{i=1\\ \neq k}}^{N} (\nabla_{\mathbf{R}_k} V_{ik})\delta(\mathbf{R}_k - \mathbf{r}) \\
&\qquad + \sum_{\substack{i=1\\ \neq k}}^{N} V_{ik}\nabla_{\mathbf{R}_k}\delta(\mathbf{R}_k - \mathbf{r}) \Bigg] \\
&= \frac{\mathbf{p}_k}{2m_k} \cdot \sum_{\substack{j=1\\ \neq k}}^{N} (\nabla_{\mathbf{R}_k} V_{jk})[\delta(\mathbf{R}_j - \mathbf{r}) + \delta(\mathbf{R}_k - \mathbf{r})] \\
&\qquad - \frac{1}{2}\nabla_{\mathbf{r}} \cdot \Bigg[\sum_{\substack{j=1\\ \neq k}}^{N} V_{jk} \frac{\mathbf{p}_k}{m_k} \delta(\mathbf{R}_k - \mathbf{r}) \Bigg] \cdot
\end{aligned} \tag{6.11}$$

When (6.10) and (6.11) are substituted into (2.7), we obtain

$$\begin{aligned}
\frac{\partial}{\partial t} E_V(\mathbf{r}; t) &= \frac{1}{2} \sum_{j \neq k}\sum \left\langle (\nabla_{\mathbf{R}_k} V_{jk}) \cdot \frac{\mathbf{p}_k}{m_k} [\delta(\mathbf{R}_j - \mathbf{r}) + \delta(\mathbf{R}_k - \mathbf{r})]; f \right\rangle \\
&\qquad - \frac{1}{2}\nabla_{\mathbf{r}} \left[\sum_{j \neq k}\sum \left\langle V_{jk} \frac{\mathbf{p}_k}{m_k} \delta(\mathbf{R}_k - \mathbf{r}); f \right\rangle \right] \cdot
\end{aligned} \tag{6.12}$$

Adding up the rates given in (6.4), (6.8), and (6.12), we obtain the rate of change of the total internal energy density.

$$\begin{aligned}
\frac{\partial}{\partial t} E(\mathbf{r}; t) &= -\nabla_{\mathbf{r}} \cdot \Bigg[\sum_{k=1}^{N} \left\langle \frac{p_k^2}{2m_k} \frac{\mathbf{p}_k}{m_k} \delta(\mathbf{R}_k - \mathbf{r}); f \right\rangle \\
&\quad + \sum_{k=1}^{N} \psi_k(\mathbf{r}) \left\langle \frac{\mathbf{p}_k}{m_k} \delta(\mathbf{R}_k - \mathbf{r}); f \right\rangle + \frac{1}{2} \sum_{j \neq k}\sum \left\langle V_{jk} \frac{\mathbf{p}_k}{m_k} \delta(\mathbf{R}_k - \mathbf{r}); f \right\rangle \Bigg] \\
&\quad + \frac{1}{2} \sum_{j \neq k}\sum \left\langle (\nabla_{\mathbf{R}_k} V_{jk}) \cdot \frac{\mathbf{p}_k}{m_k} [\delta(\mathbf{R}_j - \mathbf{r}) - \delta(\mathbf{R}_k - \mathbf{r})]; f \right\rangle \cdot
\end{aligned} \tag{6.13}$$

From the definitions of the several parts of the energy density

$$\begin{aligned}
\nabla_{\mathbf{r}} \cdot (E\mathbf{u}) &= \nabla_{\mathbf{r}} \cdot \Bigg[\sum_{k=1}^{N} \left\langle \frac{p_k^2}{2m_k} \mathbf{u}\delta(\mathbf{R}_k - \mathbf{r}); f \right\rangle \\
&\quad + \sum_{k=1}^{N} \psi_k(\mathbf{r}) \langle \mathbf{u}\delta(\mathbf{R}_k - \mathbf{r}); f \rangle + \frac{1}{2} \sum_{j \neq k}\sum \langle V_{jk}\mathbf{u}\delta(\mathbf{R}_k - \mathbf{r}); f \rangle \Bigg] \cdot
\end{aligned} \tag{6.14}$$

Adding (6.14) to (6.13), we obtain

$$\frac{\partial}{\partial t} E(\mathbf{r}; t) + \nabla_{\mathbf{r}} \cdot (E\mathbf{u}) = - \nabla_{\mathbf{r}} \cdot \Bigg[\sum_{k=1}^{N} \left\langle \frac{p_k^2}{2m_k} \left(\frac{\mathbf{p}_k}{m_k} - \mathbf{u} \right) \delta(\mathbf{R}_k - \mathbf{r}); f \right\rangle$$

$$+ \sum_{k=1}^{N} \psi_k(\mathbf{r}) \left\langle \left(\frac{\mathbf{p}_k}{m_k} - \mathbf{u} \right) \delta(\mathbf{R}_k - \mathbf{r}); f \right\rangle$$

$$+ \frac{1}{2} \sum_{j \neq k} \sum \left\langle V_{jk} \left(\frac{\mathbf{p}_k}{m_k} - \mathbf{u} \right) \delta(\mathbf{R}_k - \mathbf{r}); f \right\rangle \Bigg]$$

$$+ \frac{1}{2} \sum_{j \neq k} \sum \left\langle (\nabla_{\mathbf{R}_k} V_{jk}) \cdot \frac{\mathbf{p}_k}{m_k} [\delta(\mathbf{R}_j - \mathbf{r}) - \delta(\mathbf{R}_k - \mathbf{r})]; f \right\rangle \cdot \qquad (6.15)$$

Equation (6.15) has been derived without any reference to the assumption of a single component, single phase system. The derivation is equally valid for central or non-central forces depending upon rotational or other internal degrees of freedom.

In order to reduce (6.15) to the point function counterpart of the hydrodynamical equation of energy transport for a single component, single phase system, (1.4), we must assume all molecules identical. We shall further impose the restriction that the intermolecular force shall be central, depending upon range only.

Under the assumption of identical molecules, the second term on the right of (6.15) vanishes, for it becomes

$$\frac{\psi(\mathbf{r})}{m} \left[\sum_{k=1}^{N} \langle \mathbf{p}_k \delta(\mathbf{R}_k - \mathbf{r}); f \rangle - \mathbf{u} \sum_{k=1}^{N} m \langle \delta(\mathbf{R}_k - \mathbf{r}); f \rangle \right] = 0$$

by the definition (3.1) and (3.2).

To reduce (6.15) to the form of (1.4) it is necessary to define a point function heat current density, $\mathbf{q}(\mathbf{r}; t)$, satisfying the equation:

$$\nabla_{\mathbf{r}} \cdot (\mathbf{q} - \mathbf{u} \cdot \boldsymbol{\sigma}) = \nabla_{\mathbf{r}} \cdot \Bigg[\sum_{k=1}^{N} \left\langle \frac{p_k^2}{2m} \left(\frac{\mathbf{p}_k}{m} - \mathbf{u} \right) \delta(\mathbf{R}_k - \mathbf{r}); f \right\rangle$$

$$+ \frac{1}{2} \sum_{j \neq k} \sum \left\langle V(R_{kj}) \left(\frac{\mathbf{p}_k}{m} - \mathbf{u} \right) \delta(\mathbf{R}_k - \mathbf{r}); f \right\rangle \Bigg]$$

$$+ \frac{1}{2} \sum_{j \neq k} \sum \left\langle \frac{V'(R_{kj})}{R_{kj}} \mathbf{R}_{kj} \cdot \frac{\mathbf{p}_k}{m} [\delta(\mathbf{R}_j - \mathbf{r}) - \delta(\mathbf{R}_k - \mathbf{r})]; f \right\rangle \qquad (6.16)$$

where $\boldsymbol{\sigma}$ is the point function stress tensor defined in (5.12). We have used the relations:

$$V_{jk} = V(R_{kj})$$

$$\nabla_{\mathbf{R}_k} V_{jk} = \frac{\mathbf{R}_{jk}}{R_{jk}} V'(R_{jk}) = - \frac{\mathbf{R}_{kj}}{R_{kj}} V'(R_{kj}).$$

Equation (6.16) merely specifies the divergence of the heat current, and leaves $\mathbf{q}$ itself undetermined up to the curl of an arbitrary vector field. We shall now find a particular solution of (6.16), and then we shall demonstrate that this solution agrees with the physical definition of the heat current density.

The last term of (6.16) may be converted into a divergence by replacing the difference of the δ-functions by the Taylor's series expansion given in (5.9), interchanging the roles of j and k.

$$\frac{1}{2}\sum_{j\neq k}\sum\left\langle\frac{V'(R_{kj})}{R_{kj}}\mathbf{R}_{kj}\cdot\frac{\mathbf{p}_k}{m}[\delta(\mathbf{R}_j-\mathbf{r})-\delta(\mathbf{R}_k-\mathbf{r})];f\right\rangle$$

$$=-\nabla_{\mathbf{r}}\cdot\left[\frac{1}{2}\sum_{j\neq k}\sum\left\langle\frac{V'(R_{kj})}{R_{kj}}\mathbf{R}_{kj}\mathbf{R}_{kj}\cdot\frac{\mathbf{p}_k}{m}\left\{1-\frac{1}{2}\mathbf{R}_{kj}\cdot\nabla_{\mathbf{r}}\right.\right.\right.$$

$$\left.\left.\left.+\cdots+\frac{1}{n!}(-\mathbf{R}_{kj}\cdot\nabla_{\mathbf{r}})^{n-1}+\cdots\right\}\delta(\mathbf{R}_k-\mathbf{r});f\right\rangle\right]\cdot \quad (6.17)$$

From the definition of $\boldsymbol{\sigma}_k$ in (5.13),

$$\nabla_{\mathbf{r}}\cdot(\mathbf{u}\cdot\boldsymbol{\sigma}_K)$$

$$=\nabla_{\mathbf{r}}\cdot\left[\sum_{k=1}^{N}\left\langle\frac{m}{2}\left(-2\frac{\mathbf{p}_k}{m}\cdot\mathbf{u}+2u^2\right)\left(\frac{\mathbf{p}_k}{m}-\mathbf{u}\right)\delta(\mathbf{R}_k-\mathbf{r});f\right\rangle\right]$$

$$=\nabla_{\mathbf{r}}\cdot\left[\sum_{k=1}^{N}\left\langle\frac{m}{2}\left(-2\frac{\mathbf{p}_k}{m}\cdot\mathbf{u}+u^2\right)\left(\frac{\mathbf{p}_k}{m}-\mathbf{u}\right)\delta(\mathbf{R}_k-\mathbf{r});f\right\rangle\right] \quad (6.18)$$

since

$$\sum_{k=1}^{N}\left\langle\frac{m}{2}u^2\left(\frac{\mathbf{p}_k}{m}-\mathbf{u}\right)\delta(\mathbf{R}_k-\mathbf{r});f\right\rangle$$

$$=\frac{u^2}{2}\left[\sum_{k=1}^{N}\langle\mathbf{p}_k\delta(\mathbf{R}_k-\mathbf{r});f\rangle-\mathbf{u}\sum_{k=1}^{N}m\langle\delta(\mathbf{R}_k-\mathbf{r});f\rangle\right]=0$$

by (3.1) and (3.2).

When (6.17) is substituted into (6.16) and (6.18) added to this equation, we obtain

$$\nabla_{\mathbf{r}}\cdot(\mathbf{q}-\mathbf{u}\cdot\boldsymbol{\sigma}_V)=\nabla_{\mathbf{r}}\cdot\left[\sum_{k=1}^{N}\left\langle\frac{m}{2}\left|\frac{\mathbf{p}_k}{m}-\mathbf{u}\right|^2\left(\frac{\mathbf{p}_k}{m}-\mathbf{u}\right)\delta(\mathbf{R}_k-\mathbf{r});f\right\rangle\right.$$

$$+\frac{1}{2}\sum_{j\neq k}\sum\left\langle V(R_{kj})\left(\frac{\mathbf{p}_k}{m}-\mathbf{u}\right)\delta(\mathbf{R}_k-\mathbf{r});f\right\rangle$$

$$-\frac{1}{2}\sum_{j\neq k}\sum\left\langle\frac{V'(R_{kj})}{R_{kj}}\mathbf{R}_{kj}\mathbf{R}_{kj}\cdot\frac{\mathbf{p}_k}{m}\left\{1-\frac{1}{2}\mathbf{R}_{kj}\cdot\nabla_{\mathbf{r}}+\cdots\right.\right.$$

$$\left.\left.\left.+\frac{1}{n!}(-\mathbf{R}_{kj}\cdot\nabla_{\mathbf{r}})^{n-1}+\cdots\right\}\delta(\mathbf{R}_k-\mathbf{r});f\right\rangle\right], \quad (6.19)$$

where $|(\mathbf{p}_k/m)-\mathbf{u}|$ is the magnitude of the vector $(\mathbf{p}_k/m)-\mathbf{u}$.

We shall now define the point function heat current density, the most apparent solution of (6.19), as

$$\mathbf{q}(\mathbf{r};t) = \mathbf{q}_K(\mathbf{r};t) + \mathbf{q}_V(\mathbf{r};t) \tag{6.20}$$

$$\mathbf{q}_K(\mathbf{r};t) = \sum_{k=1}^{N} \left\langle \frac{m}{2}\left|\frac{\mathbf{p}_k}{m} - \mathbf{u}\right|^2 \left(\frac{\mathbf{p}_k}{m} - \mathbf{u}\right)\delta(\mathbf{R}_k - \mathbf{r}); f \right\rangle \tag{6.21}$$

$$\begin{aligned}\mathbf{q}_V(\mathbf{r};t) = \mathbf{u}\cdot\left[\boldsymbol{\sigma}_V - \frac{1}{2}\sum_{j\neq k}\sum \langle V(R_{kj})\mathbf{1}\delta(\mathbf{R}_k - \mathbf{r}); f\rangle\right] \\ + \frac{1}{2}\sum_{j\neq k}\sum \left\langle \left[V(R_{kj})\mathbf{1} - \frac{V'(R_{kj})}{R_{kj}}\mathbf{R}_{kj}\mathbf{R}_{kj}\left\{1 + \cdots \right.\right.\right. \\ \left.\left.\left. + \frac{1}{n!}(-\mathbf{R}_{kj}\cdot\nabla_{\mathbf{r}})^{n-1} + \cdots\right\}\right]\cdot\frac{\mathbf{p}_k}{m}\delta(\mathbf{R}_k - \mathbf{r}); f\right\rangle\end{aligned} \tag{6.22}$$

where $\mathbf{1}$ is the unit tensor of the second rank.

$\mathbf{q}_V$ may be expressed in terms of the pair density and particle current density in pair space by introducing into (6.22) a new δ-function $\delta(\mathbf{R}_{kj} - \mathbf{R})$, and integrating over $\mathbf{R}$.

$$\begin{aligned}\mathbf{q}_V(\mathbf{r};t) = \mathbf{u}\cdot\left[\boldsymbol{\sigma}_V - \frac{1}{2}\sum_{j\neq k}\sum\left\langle \int_{3\text{ fold}} \delta(\mathbf{R}_{kj} - \mathbf{R})\right.\right. \\ \left.\left. \times V(R)\mathbf{1}\delta(\mathbf{R}_k - \mathbf{r})d\mathbf{R}; f\right\rangle\right] + \frac{1}{2}\sum_{j\neq k}\sum\left\langle\int_{3\text{ fold}}\delta(\mathbf{R}_{kj} - \mathbf{R})\right. \\ \times\left[V(R)\mathbf{1} - \frac{V'(R)}{R}\mathbf{R}\mathbf{R}\left\{1 + \cdots\right.\right. \\ \left.\left.\left. + \frac{1}{n!}(-\mathbf{R}\cdot\nabla_{\mathbf{r}})^{n-1} + \cdots\right\}\right]\cdot\frac{\mathbf{p}_k}{m}\delta(\mathbf{R}_k - \mathbf{r})d\mathbf{R}; f\right\rangle.\end{aligned}$$

Commuting the integrations over $\mathbf{R}$ with the phase integrals and the summations we obtain

$$\begin{aligned}\mathbf{q}_V(\mathbf{r};t) = \mathbf{u}\cdot\left[\boldsymbol{\sigma}_V - \frac{1}{2}\int_{3\text{ fold}} V(R)\mathbf{1}\sum_{j\neq k}\sum\langle\delta(\mathbf{R}_{kj} - \mathbf{R})\right. \\ \left. \times\,\delta(\mathbf{R}_k - \mathbf{r}); f\rangle d\mathbf{R}\right] + \frac{1}{2}\int_{3\text{ fold}}\left[V(R)\mathbf{1} - \frac{\mathbf{R}\mathbf{R}}{R}V'(R)\right. \\ \left.\times\left\{1 - \frac{1}{2}\mathbf{R}\cdot\nabla_{\mathbf{r}} + \cdots\frac{1}{n!}(-\mathbf{R}\cdot\nabla_{\mathbf{r}})^{n-1} + \cdots\right\}\right] \\ \cdot\left[\sum_{j\neq k}\sum\frac{\mathbf{p}_k}{m}\delta(\mathbf{R}_{kj} - \mathbf{R})\delta(\mathbf{R}_k - \mathbf{r}); f\right\rangle\right]d\mathbf{R}.\end{aligned}$$

The product $\delta(\mathbf{R}_{kj} - \mathbf{R})\delta(\mathbf{R}_k - \mathbf{r})$ is equivalent to the product $\delta(\mathbf{R}_k - \mathbf{r})$ $\delta(\mathbf{R}_j - \mathbf{r} - \mathbf{R})$. Consequently, referring to the definitions (3.8) and (3.10) and replacing $\boldsymbol{\sigma}_V$ by its value given in (5.15), the above equation becomes

$$\mathbf{q}_V(\mathbf{r}; t) = -\frac{1}{2}\mathbf{u}(\mathbf{r}; t) \cdot \int_{3\text{ fold}} \left[V(R)\mathbf{1} - \frac{\mathbf{RR}}{R} V'(R) \left\{ 1 - \frac{1}{2}\mathbf{R} \cdot \nabla_{\mathbf{r}} \right.\right.$$

$$\left.\left. + \cdots + \frac{1}{n!}(-\mathbf{R} \cdot \nabla_{\mathbf{r}})^{n-1} + \cdots \right\} \right] \rho^{(2)}(\mathbf{r}, \mathbf{r} + \mathbf{R}; t) d\mathbf{R}$$

$$+ \frac{1}{2} \int_{3\text{ fold}} \left[V(R)\mathbf{1} - \frac{\mathbf{RR}}{R} V'(R) \left\{ 1 - \frac{1}{2}\mathbf{R} \cdot \nabla_{\mathbf{r}} + \cdots \right.\right.$$

$$\left.\left. + \frac{1}{n!}(-\mathbf{R} \cdot \nabla_{\mathbf{r}})^{n-1} + \cdots \right\} \right] \cdot \mathbf{j}_1^{(2)}(\mathbf{r}, \mathbf{r} + \mathbf{R}); t) d\mathbf{R}. \tag{6.23}$$

In the interior of a fluid $\rho^{(2)}$ and $\mathbf{j}_1^{(2)}$ are very slow functions of $\mathbf{r}$; consequently, as explained in the preceding section, all terms in the brace beyond the first may be neglected. Equation (6.23) then reduces to

$$\mathbf{q}_V(\mathbf{r}; t) = \frac{1}{2} \int_{3\text{ fold}} \left[V(R)\mathbf{1} - \frac{\mathbf{RR}}{R} V'(R) \right]$$

$$\cdot [\mathbf{j}_1^{(2)}(\mathbf{r}, \mathbf{r} + \mathbf{R}; t) - \mathbf{u}(\mathbf{r}; t)\rho^{(2)}(\mathbf{r}, \mathbf{r} + \mathbf{R}; t)] d\mathbf{R}. \tag{6.24}$$

What are the physical interpretations of the various terms comprising $\mathbf{q}$? The interpretation is somewhat easier viewed from a coordinate frame moving with the local velocity $\mathbf{u}$. $\mathbf{q}_k$ represents the current density of kinetic energy due to the macroscopically imperceptible random molecular motion. It is this term which occurs in the kinetic theory of gases. The terms in $\mathbf{q}_V$ involving $V(R)$ (but not its derivative) represent the current density of potential energy due to this same random motion. The terms in $\mathbf{q}_V$ involving $V'(R)$, when dotted into an element of area $d\mathbf{S}$, represent the work per unit time done on molecules on one side of dS by molecules on the other. Work is done on the former as they move (due to their macroscopically imperceptible random motion) through the force field of the latter.

COMPILATION OF RESULTS

The equations of phenomenological hydrodynamics for a single component, single phase system are relations among certain macroscopic observables—mass density, fluid velocity, body force density, energy density, stress tensor, and heat current density. Using classical statistical mechanics, we have found that it is possible to define the corresponding microscopic observables and that equations identical in form to the hydrodynamical equations relate these quantities. The macroscopic equations may be obtained from the microscopic (or point function) equations by averaging over a microscopically large though macroscopically small space domain determined by the resolution of one's measurements and averaging over a time interval of the order of the relaxation time of one's measuring instruments.

The microscopically correct hydrodynamical equations are the continuity equation:

$$\frac{\partial}{\partial t}\rho(\mathbf{r};t) = -\nabla_{\mathbf{r}}\cdot[\rho(\mathbf{r};t)\mathbf{u}(\mathbf{r};t)], \tag{1.1}$$

the equation of motion (momentum transport equation):

$$\frac{\partial}{\partial t}[\rho\mathbf{u}] + \nabla_{\mathbf{r}}\cdot[\rho\mathbf{u}\mathbf{u}] = \mathbf{X} + \nabla_{\mathbf{r}}\cdot\boldsymbol{\sigma}, \tag{1.2}$$

and the energy transport equation

$$\frac{\partial E}{\partial t} + \nabla_{\mathbf{r}}\cdot[E\mathbf{u} + \mathbf{q} - \mathbf{u}\cdot\boldsymbol{\sigma}]. \tag{1.4}$$

The quantities appearing in the above equations are defined as follows:[7]

$$\rho\mathbf{r};t) = \sum_{k=1}^{N} m_k\langle\delta(\mathbf{R}_k - \mathbf{r});f\rangle \tag{3.1}$$

= mass density at **r**.

$$\mathbf{u}(\mathbf{r};t) = \frac{1}{\rho(\mathbf{r};t)}\sum_{k=1}^{N}\langle\mathbf{p}_k\delta(\mathbf{R}_k - \mathbf{r});f\rangle \tag{3.2}$$

= mean molecular velocity (fluid velocity) at **r**.

$$\mathbf{X}(\mathbf{r};t) = -\sum_{k=1}^{N}[\nabla_{\mathbf{r}}\psi_k(\mathbf{r})]\langle\delta(\mathbf{R}_k - \mathbf{r});f\rangle \tag{3.6}$$

= body force per unit volume due to external fields at **r**.

$$E(\mathbf{r};t) = E_K + E_\psi + E_V \tag{1.3}$$

= internal energy density at **r**, where

$$E_K(\mathbf{r};t) = \sum_{k=1}^{N}\left\langle\frac{p_k^2}{2m_k}\delta(\mathbf{R}_k - \mathbf{r});f\right\rangle \tag{3.3}$$

= kinetic energy density,

$$E_\psi(\mathbf{r};t) = \sum_{k=1}^{N}\psi_k(\mathbf{r})\langle\delta(\mathbf{R}_k - \mathbf{r});f\rangle \tag{3.5}$$

= potential energy density associated with external fields, and

$$E_V(\mathbf{r};t) = \frac{1}{2}\sum_{j\neq k}\sum\langle V_{jk}\delta(\mathbf{R}_k - \mathbf{r});f\rangle \tag{3.7}$$

= potential energy density due to molecular interaction. (In defining E_V it is assumed that the potential energy of interaction between two molecules is localized half at each molecule.)

[7] The bracket notation $\langle\ ;f\rangle$ means the expectation value of the quantity appearing to the left of the semicolon over an ensemble having a probability distribution function, $f(\mathbf{R}_1, \cdots, \mathbf{R}_N; \mathbf{p}_1, \cdots \mathbf{p}_N; t)$.

These definitions are completely general. The other quantities, however, appearing in the above hydrodynamical equations, $\boldsymbol{\sigma}$ and $\mathbf{q}$, have been defined only for a single component, single phase system in which the intermolecular force is central, depending on range only. Their definitions follow.

$$\boldsymbol{\sigma}(\mathbf{r}; t) = \boldsymbol{\sigma}_K + \boldsymbol{\sigma}_V \tag{5.12}$$

= stress tensor at $\mathbf{r}$, where

$$\boldsymbol{\sigma}_K = -\sum_{k=1}^{N} m \left\langle \left(\frac{\mathbf{p}_k}{m} - \mathbf{u}\right)\left(\frac{\mathbf{p}_k}{m} - \mathbf{u}\right) \delta(\mathbf{R}_k - \mathbf{r}); f \right\rangle \tag{5.13}$$

= kinetic contribution to stress tensor. (This is the dominant term for gases, but relatively unimportant for liquids.) And

$$\boldsymbol{\sigma}_V(\mathbf{r}; t) = \frac{1}{2} \int_{3\text{ fold}} \frac{\mathbf{RR}}{R} V'(R) \left\{ 1 - \frac{1}{2} \mathbf{R} \cdot \nabla_{\mathbf{r}} + \cdots \right.$$

$$\left. \frac{1}{n!} (-\mathbf{R} \cdot \nabla_{\mathbf{r}})^{n-1} + \cdots \right\} \rho^{(2)}(\mathbf{r}, \mathbf{r} + \mathbf{R}; t) d\mathbf{R} \tag{5.15}$$

= intermolecular force contribution to stress tensor. (This is the dominant term for liquids.)

$$\mathbf{q}(\mathbf{r}; t) = \mathbf{q}_K + \mathbf{q}_V \tag{6.20}$$

= heat current density at $\mathbf{r}$, where

$$\mathbf{q}_K(\mathbf{r}; t) = \sum_{k=1}^{N} \left\langle \frac{m}{2} \left| \frac{\mathbf{p}_k}{m} - \mathbf{u} \right|^2 \left(\frac{\mathbf{p}_k}{m} - \mathbf{u}\right) \delta(\mathbf{R}_k - \mathbf{r}); f \right\rangle \tag{6.21}$$

= heat current due to transport of thermal kinetic energy, and

$$\mathbf{q}_V(\mathbf{r}; t) = -\frac{1}{2} \mathbf{u}(\mathbf{r}; t) \cdot \int_{3\text{ fold}} \left[V(R)\mathbf{1} - \frac{\mathbf{RR}}{R} V'(R) \right.$$

$$\left. \times \left\{ 1 - \frac{1}{2} \mathbf{R} \cdot \nabla_{\mathbf{r}} + \cdots + \frac{1}{n!} (-\mathbf{R} \cdot \nabla_{\mathbf{r}})^{n-1} + \cdots \right\} \right]$$

$$\times \rho^{(2)}(\mathbf{r}; \mathbf{r} + \mathbf{R}; t) d\mathbf{R} + \frac{1}{2} \int_{3\text{ fold}} \left[V(R)\mathbf{1} - \frac{\mathbf{RR}}{R} V'(R) \right.$$

$$\left. \times \left\{ 1 - \frac{1}{2} \mathbf{R} \cdot \nabla_{\mathbf{r}} + \cdots + \frac{1}{n!} (-\mathbf{R} \cdot \nabla_{\mathbf{r}})^{n-1} + \cdots \right\} \right]$$

$$\cdot \mathbf{j}_1^{(2)}(\mathbf{r}; \mathbf{r} + \mathbf{R}; t) d\mathbf{R} \tag{6.23}$$

= contribution to heat current density by molecular interaction.

In the definitions of $\boldsymbol{\sigma}_V$ and $\mathbf{q}_V$ the following quantities appear.

$$\rho^{(2)}(\mathbf{r}, \mathbf{r}'; t) = \sum_{j \neq k}\sum \langle \delta(\mathbf{R}_j - \mathbf{r})\delta(\mathbf{R}_k - \mathbf{r}'); f \rangle \tag{3.8}$$

= pair density at $\mathbf{r}$ and $\mathbf{r}'$, the probability per (unit volume)^2 that one particle (any particle) will be at $\mathbf{r}$ and another at $\mathbf{r}'$.

$$\mathbf{j}_1^{(2)}(\mathbf{r}, \mathbf{r}'; t) = \sum_{k \neq i}\sum \left\langle \frac{\mathbf{p}_k}{m_k} \delta(\mathbf{R}_k - \mathbf{r})\delta(\mathbf{R}_i - \mathbf{r}'); f \right\rangle \tag{3.10}$$

= projection onto the space of $\mathbf{r}$ of the particle current density at $\mathbf{r}$, $\mathbf{r}'$ in pair space, = particle current density at $\mathbf{r}$ if another particle is at $\mathbf{r}'$ multiplied by the particle density at $\mathbf{r}'$.

The differential operator, $\nabla_\mathbf{r}$, occurring in the definitions of $\boldsymbol{\sigma}_V$ and $\mathbf{q}_V$ operate on $\rho^{(2)}(\mathbf{r}, \mathbf{r} + \mathbf{R}; t)$ and $\mathbf{j}_1^{(2)}(\mathbf{r}, \mathbf{r} + \mathbf{R}; t)$ with $\mathbf{R}$ held fixed. Since in the interior of a fluid $\rho^{(2)}$ and $\mathbf{j}_1^{(2)}$ are slow functions of $\mathbf{r}$ (holding $\mathbf{R}$ fixed), changing negligibly for $\mathbf{r}$ varying by a displacement whose length is of the order of the "range" of intermolecular forces, all terms beyond the first may be neglected in the brace appearing in the definitions of $\boldsymbol{\sigma}_V$ and $\mathbf{q}_V$. This yields the simplified expressions:

$$\mathbf{q}_V(\mathbf{r}; t) = \frac{1}{2} \int_{3\text{ fold}} \left[V(R)\mathbf{1} - \frac{\mathbf{RR}}{R} V'(R) \right]$$

$$\cdot [\mathbf{j}_1^{(2)}(\mathbf{r}, \mathbf{r} + \mathbf{R}; t) - \mathbf{u}(\mathbf{r}; t)\rho^{(2)}(\mathbf{r}, \mathbf{r} + \mathbf{R}; t)]d\mathbf{R} \tag{6.24}$$

$$\boldsymbol{\sigma}_V(\mathbf{r}; t) = \frac{1}{2m^2} [\rho(\mathbf{r}; t)]^2 \int_{3\text{ fold}} \frac{\mathbf{RR}}{R} V'(R) g^{(2)}(\mathbf{r}; \mathbf{R}; t) d\mathbf{R} \tag{5.17}$$

where the correlation function $g^{(2)}$ is defined by

$$\rho^{(2)}(\mathbf{r}; \mathbf{r} + \mathbf{R}; t) = \frac{1}{m^2} \rho(\mathbf{r}; t)\rho(\mathbf{r} + \mathbf{R}; t) g^{(2)}(\mathbf{r}; \mathbf{R}; t). \tag{5.16}$$

The pressure is defined by

$$P(\mathbf{r}; t) = -\tfrac{1}{3} \operatorname{Trace} \boldsymbol{\sigma}(\mathbf{r}; t). \tag{5.18}$$

In an ensemble which is in equilibrium with a temperature T, the pressure is

$$P_{\text{eq}} = \frac{\rho}{m} kT - \frac{2\pi}{3} \left(\frac{\rho}{m}\right)^2 \int R^3 V'(R) g^{(2)}(R) dR. \tag{5.21}$$

This is the equation of state, obtainable by other methods as well.

APPENDIX

The part of the stress tensor at the point $\mathbf{r}$ due to intermolecular forces is defined so that

$$\boldsymbol{\sigma}_V(\mathbf{r}; t) \cdot d\mathbf{S} = \text{"the force acting across } dS\text{."} \tag{A.1}$$

First we imagine a plane tangent to dS at $\mathbf{r}$. This plane divides the fluid into two parts. That portion into which the vector $d\mathbf{S}$ points we shall refer to as "outside of dS;" the other portion is "inside of dS."

The interaction forces acting on the fluid are all between pairs of molecules. Let us say that the force between a pair of molecules "acts across dS" if the line of centers between these molecules intersects dS between the molecules.[8] This can only happen (for infinitesimal dS) if one molecule of the pair is "inside dS" and the other is "outside." By convention, the "force acting across dS" is the force acting on the molecule inside dS.

If a molecule is located at $\mathbf{r}'$ inside dS, and another at $\mathbf{r}' + \mathbf{R}$ outside of dS, then the force acting on the molecule at $\mathbf{r}'$ is

$$(\mathbf{R}/R)V'(R). \tag{A.2}$$

This force "acts across dS" only if $\mathbf{r}' + \alpha\mathbf{R}$ terminates on dS for some α between 0 and 1.

Keeping $\mathbf{R}$ fixed, the volume of the element at $\mathbf{r}'$, over which $\mathbf{r}' + \alpha\mathbf{R}$ terminates on dS for α between α_0 and $\alpha_0 + d\alpha$, is $d\mathbf{S} \cdot \mathbf{R}d\alpha$.

The probability of finding a molecule (any molecule) in this volume and another at $\mathbf{r}' + \mathbf{R}$ with the relative displacement $\mathbf{R}$ ranging over a volume $d\mathbf{R}$ is

$$\rho^{(2)}(\mathbf{r}', \mathbf{r}' + \mathbf{R})(d\mathbf{S} \cdot \mathbf{R}d\alpha)d\mathbf{R} = \rho^{(2)}(\mathbf{r} - \alpha\mathbf{R}; \mathbf{r} - \alpha\mathbf{R} + \mathbf{R})(d\mathbf{S} \cdot \mathbf{R}d\alpha)d\mathbf{R}. \tag{A.3}$$

The error in replacing $\mathbf{r}'$ by $\mathbf{r} - \alpha\mathbf{R}$ is an infinitesimal of a higher order, since the difference between $\mathbf{r}'$ and $\mathbf{r} - \alpha\mathbf{R}$ is an infinitesimal (the vector from $\mathbf{r}$ to some other point on dS).

The total force acting across dS is, therefore, the integral of the product of (A.2) and (A.3).

"The force acting across dS"

$$= d\mathbf{S} \cdot \int \left\{ \int_0^1 \frac{\mathbf{RR}}{R} V'(R)\rho^{(2)}(\mathbf{r} - \alpha\mathbf{R}, \mathbf{r} - \alpha\mathbf{R} + \mathbf{R})d\alpha \right\} d\mathbf{R} \tag{A.4}$$

where $\mathbf{R}$ ranges over those values only for which $\mathbf{R} \cdot d\mathbf{S}$ is positive (i.e., $\mathbf{R}$ from the inside toward the outside).

Making the change of variable, $\gamma = 1 - \alpha$, the brace in Eq. (A.4) becomes

$$\{\ \} = \int_0^1 \frac{\mathbf{RR}}{R} V'(R)\rho^{(2)}(\mathbf{r} + \gamma\mathbf{R} - \mathbf{R}; \mathbf{r} + \gamma\mathbf{R})d\gamma$$

$$= \int_0^1 \frac{\mathbf{RR}}{R} V'(R)\rho^{(2)}(\mathbf{r} + \gamma\mathbf{R}; \mathbf{r} + \gamma\mathbf{R} - \mathbf{R})d\gamma,$$

where we have used the symmetry of $\rho^{(2)}$ with respect to its two arguments.

---

[8] This definition of the force "acting across dS" is quite arbitrary, and with another definition we would obtain a different expression for the point function stress tensor. But all definitions must have this in common—that the stress between a pair of molecules be concentrated near the line of centers. When averaging over a domain large compared with the range of intermolecular force, these differences are washed out, and the ambiguity remaining in the macroscopic stress tensor is of negligible order.

Changing the name of the integration variable γ back to α one notes that the brace is an even function of the vector **R**. Consequently, (A.4) may be written: "The force acting across dS"

$$= d\mathbf{S} \cdot \frac{1}{2} \int_{3\text{ fold}} \frac{\mathbf{RR}}{R} V'(R) \left[\int_0^1 \rho^{(2)}(\mathbf{r} - \alpha\mathbf{R}; \mathbf{r} - \alpha\mathbf{R} + \mathbf{R}) d\alpha \right] dR \quad \text{(A.5)}$$

where the integration over **R** now extends over all space. Since dS was arbitrarily chosen through **r**, we obtain on comparing (A.1) and (A.5)

$$\boldsymbol{\sigma}_V(\mathbf{r}; t) = \frac{1}{2} \int_{3\text{ fold}} \frac{\mathbf{RR}}{R} V'(R) \left[\int_0^1 \rho^{(2)}(\mathbf{r} - \alpha\mathbf{R}, \mathbf{r} - \alpha\mathbf{R} + \mathbf{R}; t) d\alpha \right] d\mathbf{R}. \quad \text{(A.6)}$$

$\rho^{(2)}$, appearing in (A.6), may be expanded in a Taylor's series in α.

$$\rho^{(2)}(\mathbf{r} - \alpha\mathbf{R}; \mathbf{r} - \alpha\mathbf{R} + \mathbf{R}) = \Big\{ 1 - \alpha\mathbf{R} \cdot \nabla_{\mathbf{r}} + \frac{\alpha^2}{2} (\mathbf{R} \cdot \nabla_{\mathbf{r}})^2 + \cdots$$

$$+ \frac{\alpha^{n-1}}{(n-1)!} (-\mathbf{R} \cdot \nabla_{\mathbf{r}})^{n-1} + \cdots \Big\} \rho^{(2)}(\mathbf{r}, \mathbf{r} + \mathbf{R}) \quad \text{(A.7)}$$

where it is understood that **R** is to be held constant when operating with $\nabla_{\mathbf{r}}$.
Substituting (A.7) into (A.6) and integrating over α from 0 to 1, we obtain:

$$\boldsymbol{\sigma}_V(\mathbf{r}; t) = \frac{1}{2} \int_{3\text{ fold}} \frac{\mathbf{RR}}{R} V'(R) \Big\{ 1 - \frac{1}{2} \mathbf{R} \cdot \nabla_{\mathbf{r}} + \cdots$$

$$+ \frac{1}{n!} (-\mathbf{R} \cdot \nabla_{\mathbf{r}})^{n-1} + \cdots \Big\} \rho^{(2)}(\mathbf{r}, \mathbf{r} + \mathbf{R}; t) d\mathbf{R}. \quad \text{(A.8)}$$

This is identical to the expression given in Eq. (5.15).

The Statistical Mechanical Theory of Transport Processes. V. Quantum Hydrodynamics*

J. H. IRVING† AND ROBERT W. ZWANZIG, *Gates and Crellin Laboratories of Chemistry, California Institute of Technology, Pasadena, California*

(Received June 1, 1951)

This paper is concerned with certain extensions of a formal technique devised by Wigner for handling problems in quantum-statistical mechanics, especially to problems in quantum-mechanical transport processes. The approach is to find the closest possible analogy between classical and quantum-statistical mechanics, so that the extensive work in classical statistical mechanics can be utilized. This analogy is attained with the Wigner distribution function, with which averages of dynamical variables in quantum mechanics may be calculated by integrations in phase space. We will first state some basic properties of distribution functions in classical statistical mechanics, and then state the corresponding properties of the density matrix in quantum mechanics. We will define and discuss the Wigner distribution function, show that it has the desired averaging properties, and obtain the analog of the Liouville equation satisfied by this function. We will derive the analog of the Liouville equation in reduced phase space, and then obtain the equations of hydrodynamics from quantum-statistical mechanics.

I. DISTRIBUTION FUNCTIONS IN CLASSICAL STATISTICAL MECHANICS

Gibbsian statistical mechanics is based on the concept of a distribution of systems in phase space. His "density-in-phase" is now usually called the distribution function. (Hereafter, we will abbreviate this to d.f.) When normalized over the entire volume accessible to the system, it becomes the probability d.f., and gives the probability that the coordinates and momenta of a system of N particles will have the values $\mathbf{R}_1, \mathbf{R}_2, \cdots \mathbf{R}_N$, and $\mathbf{p}_1, \mathbf{p}_2, \cdots \mathbf{p}_N$. (When no confusion will result, we will refer to the sets of coordinates and momenta with single symbols $\mathbf{R}, \mathbf{p}$.) In equilibrium, for a canonical ensemble, the probability d.f. has the form,

$$f^{(N)}(\mathbf{R}, \mathbf{p}) = \exp [\beta(A - H^{(N)})], \tag{1.1}$$

where A is the free energy of the system, and $H^{(N)}$ is the Hamiltonian function,

$$H^{(N)} = \sum_{k=1}^{N} \frac{p_k^2}{2m_k} + U(\mathbf{R}_1, \mathbf{R}_2, \cdots \mathbf{R}_N). \tag{1.2}$$

---

* This work was supported by the ONR under Contract N6onr-244 with the California Institute of Technology. The paper is one of a series of articles on the statistical mechanical theory of transport processes by John G. Kirkwood and collaborators.

† Present address, Hughes Aircraft Company, Culver City, California.

In a nonequilibrium state, the time behavior of the d.f. is given by Liouville's equation,

$$\frac{\partial f^{(N)}}{\partial t} + \sum_{k=1}^{N} \frac{\mathbf{p}_k}{m_k} \cdot \nabla_{\mathbf{R}_k} f^{(N)} + \sum_{k=1}^{N} (\nabla_{\mathbf{R}_k} U) \cdot \nabla_{\mathbf{p}_k} f^{(N)} = 0. \qquad (1.3)$$

Usually the potential is simplified to a sum of terms which refer to interactions between single particles and an external field, and other terms which refer to interactions between pairs of particles:

$$U(\mathbf{R}_1, \cdots \mathbf{R}_N) = \sum_{k=1}^{N} \phi_k(\mathbf{R}_k) + \tfrac{1}{2} \sum_{j \neq k}^{N} \sum^{N} V_{jk}(\mathbf{R}_j, \mathbf{R}_k). \qquad (1.4)$$

When this is done, reduced d.f.'s, and in particular the singlet and pair d.f. become useful. The reduced d.f.'s are defined by

$$f^{(m)}(\mathbf{R}_1, \cdots \mathbf{R}_m, \mathbf{p}_1, \cdots \mathbf{p}_m; t) = \int \cdots \int f^{(N)} \prod_{m+1}^{N} d\mathbf{R}_k d\mathbf{p}_k \qquad (1.5)$$

and are called specific d.f.'s because they refer to the precise specification of each particle. Also used are the generic d.f.'s, which refer to the probability of finding any particle of the required type at a point in phase space. With the assumption of pair potentials many thermodynamic and transport properties of fluids can be expressed in terms of the singlet and pair d.f. alone. An excellent discussion on the use of these d.f.'s in equilibrium statistical mechanics may be found in an article by DeBoer.[1]

II. TRANSITION TO QUANTUM MECHANICS

It is not immediately clear how one should go about setting up the quantum-mechanical analog of classical Gibbsian statistical mechanics. The difficulty lies in the fact that the uncertainty principle prohibits the precise specification of the location of a system in phase space. Several approaches are possible in defining quantum mechanical d.f.'s. One of them is to use instead of the phase space technique, the matrix formulation of quantum mechanics, in which the analog of the d.f. is the density matrix. A second possibility is to construct a d.f. which has no simple interpretation in terms of probability concepts, but which can be used for calculating averages over phase space in a way which is formally identical with the classical one. This is the procedure that was followed by Wigner and which will be utilized later in this paper.[2]

The density matrix method can be developed in a very general way;[3] however, it is usually used in the "coordinate" representation. This has been

[1] J. DeBoer, *Reports on Progress in Physics* **XII**, 1948–9, pp. 305–374.

[2] Another possibility may be to use some kind of coarse-graining in phase space, so that one may talk about the probability of finding a system in a certain cell, possibly of volume h^{3N}, in phase space. This approach has not yet been used successfully.

[3] J. Von Neumann, *Mathematische Grundlage der Quantenmechanik* (Dover Publications, New York, 1943).

studied in great detail by Husimi[4] and by Born and Green.[5] The density matrix is defined for a pure state as

$$\rho(\mathbf{R}, \mathbf{R}'; t) = \Psi^*(\mathbf{R}'; t)\Psi(\mathbf{R}; t), \tag{2.1}$$

where $\Psi(\mathbf{R}; t)$ is the wave function for the state of the system. When we deal with an ensemble of systems, or a mixed state, the density matrix has the form,

$$\rho(\mathbf{R}, \mathbf{R}'; t) = \sum A_j \Psi_j^*(\mathbf{R}'; t)\Psi_j(\mathbf{R}; t), \tag{2.2}$$

where Ψ_j is the wave function and A_j is the statistical weight of the j'th state in the ensemble. The space d.f. is given by $\rho(\mathbf{R}, \mathbf{R}; t)$ and reduced d.f.'s are defined in the usual way. Averages of dynamical variables are calculated as traces of matrix products: if $\alpha(\mathbf{R}, \mathbf{R}')$ is the matrix associated with the variable α, then the average value of α is the trace of the matrix product of α and ρ,

$$\langle\alpha\rangle_{\mathrm{Av}} = \int\int \alpha(\mathbf{R}, \mathbf{R}')\rho(\mathbf{R}', \mathbf{R})d\mathbf{R}'d\mathbf{R}. \tag{2.3}$$

This is the average over a state, if the system is in a pure state; or it is the ensemble average of the pure state averages, if the system is in a mixed state. Matrices are assigned to the basic variables in the following way—

coordinates:

$$\alpha(\mathbf{R}_1, \cdots \mathbf{R}_N) \to \alpha(\mathbf{R}_1, \cdots \mathbf{R}_N) \prod_k \delta(\mathbf{R}_k - \mathbf{R}_k')$$

momenta:

$$\mathbf{p}_j \to -i\hbar\nabla_{\mathbf{R}_j} \cdots \prod_k \delta(\mathbf{R}_k - \mathbf{R}_k'). \tag{2.4}$$

For example, the Hamiltonian operator is

$$H^{(N)}(\mathbf{R}, \mathbf{R}') = \left\{ -\sum_j \frac{\hbar^2}{2m_j} \nabla_{\mathbf{R}_j}{}^2 + U(\mathbf{R}) \right\} \prod_k \delta(\mathbf{R}_k - \mathbf{R}_k') \tag{2.5}$$

and Schrödinger's time dependent equation is

$$\frac{\partial\rho^{(N)}}{\partial t} = -\frac{i}{\hbar}\left\{ \sum_k \frac{-\hbar^2}{2m_k} \nabla_{\mathbf{R}_k}{}^2\rho^{(N)} + \sum_k \frac{\hbar^2}{2m_k} \nabla_{\mathbf{R}'_k}{}^2\rho^{(N)} + U(\mathbf{R})\rho^{(N)} - U(\mathbf{R}')\rho^{(N)} \right\}. \tag{2.6}$$

(The superscript on ρ refers to the number of particles in the system.) This equation is the quantum-mechanical analog of the classical Liouville equation in the density matrix formalism. Born and Green[5] have made use of this in their method for setting up a quantum-mechanical theory of transport processes.

---

[4] K. Husimi, *Proc. Phys.-Math. Soc.* Japan **22**, 264 (1940).

[5] M. Born and H. S. Green, *A General Kinetic Theory of Liquids* (Cambridge University Press, London, 1949).

In 1932, Wigner[6] showed how a phase space d.f. could be constructed and used for simple evaluations of averages. This function is defined most conveniently in terms of the density matrix,

$$f^{(N)}(\mathbf{R}, \mathbf{p}; t) = \left(\frac{1}{\pi\hbar}\right)^{3N} \int \cdots \int_{-\infty}^{+\infty} \exp\left(\frac{2i}{\hbar}\, \mathbf{p} \cdot \mathbf{Y}\right)$$

$$\times\, \rho^{(N)}(\mathbf{R} - \mathbf{Y}; \mathbf{R} + \mathbf{Y}; t)\, d\mathbf{Y}. \tag{2.7}$$

Some of the more important properties of the Wigner d.f. are as follows:

(1) $f^{(N)}$ is everywhere real, although not necessarily positive.

(2)
$$\int f^{(N)} d\mathbf{p} = \rho^{(N)}(\mathbf{R}, \mathbf{R}; t) \tag{2.8}$$

so that the integral of the d.f. over momentum space *does* give the probability density in configuration space.

(3)
$$\int f^{(N)} d\mathbf{R} = \sigma^{(N)}(\mathbf{p}, \mathbf{p}; t), \tag{2.9}$$

where $\boldsymbol{\sigma}^{(N)}$ $(\mathbf{p}, \mathbf{p}'; t)$ is the momentum representation of the density matrix.[7] Therefore, the integral of the d.f. over configuration space gives the probability density in momentum space.

(4)
$$\frac{1}{m_j} \int \mathbf{p}_j f^{(N)} d\mathbf{p} = \frac{\hbar}{2im_j} \{\Psi^* \nabla_{\mathbf{R}_j} \Psi - \Psi \nabla_{\mathbf{R}_j} \Psi^*\} \tag{2.10}$$

when $f^{(N)}$ represents the pure state Ψ. The right side is recognized as the standard expression for the probability current density in configuration space.

(5) $f^{(N)}(\mathbf{R}, \mathbf{p}; t)$

$$= \left(\frac{1}{\pi\hbar}\right)^{3N} \int \cdots \int_{-\infty}^{+\infty} \exp\left[-\frac{2i}{\hbar}\, \mathbf{R} \cdot \mathbf{p}'\right] \times \sigma^{(N)}(\mathbf{p} - \mathbf{p}', \mathbf{p} + \mathbf{p}'; t)\, d\mathbf{p}', \tag{2.11}$$

which is an expression for $f^{(N)}$ dual to Eq. (2.7) where the roles of coordinates and momenta are changed, and i is replaced by $-i$.

(6) Since the Wigner d.f. is a bilinear form in Ψ, it is symmetric for both symmetric and antisymmetric wave functions. However, it is possible to determine whether any particular d.f. corresponds to a Bose-Einstein or a Fermi-Dirac system in this way: take the inverse Fourier transform of $f^{(N)}$ to obtain $\rho^{(N)}(\mathbf{R}, \mathbf{R}')$ and then examine the symmetry of this function by interchanging either the primed or the unprimed quantities, but not both.

---

[6] E. Wigner, *Phys. Rev.* **40**, 749 (1932¹.

[7] $\sigma^{(N)}$ is not independent of $\rho^{(N)}$ because of the Fourier transform relation between coordinate and momentum representations of the wave function. This is a point of major difference between quantum mechanics and classical mechanics, where the probability densities in configuration and momentum space may be specified independently. This independence permits, for example, a factorization of the classical d.f. for a canonical ensemble.

(7) The great values of the Wigner d.f. is that it is possible to calculate averages of dynamical variables by direct integration over phase space, without using operator technique. Although Wigner showed this only for some special kinds of variables, it gives the correct average for any function of coordinates and momenta, if the Weyl correspondence[8,9] for quantum mechanical operators is used. This assignment of operators is made in the following way: if $g(\mathbf{p}, \mathbf{q})$ is the classical variable whose operator is desired, we obtain its Fourier expansion ξ,

$$g(\mathbf{p}, \mathbf{q}) = \int\int \exp\left[i(\boldsymbol{\sigma} \cdot \mathbf{p} + \boldsymbol{\tau} \cdot \mathbf{q})\right]\xi(\boldsymbol{\sigma}, \boldsymbol{\tau})d\boldsymbol{\sigma}d\boldsymbol{\tau}. \tag{2.12}$$

Then, the quantum-mechanical operator is defined as

$$G(\mathbf{x}, \mathbf{x}') = \int\int \exp\left[i(\boldsymbol{\sigma} \cdot \mathbf{P} + \boldsymbol{\tau} \cdot \mathbf{Q})\right]\xi(\boldsymbol{\sigma}, \boldsymbol{\tau})d\boldsymbol{\sigma}d\boldsymbol{\tau}, \tag{2.13}$$

where $\mathbf{P}(\mathbf{x}, \mathbf{x}')$ and $\mathbf{Q}(\mathbf{x}, \mathbf{x}')$ are the operators corresponding to momentum and position. We will now derive this averaging property of the Wigner d.f., using the coordinate representation of the density matrix. For simplicity in notation, only one dimension will be considered—the generalization is obvious. The operators P and Q are now

$$P = i\hbar\frac{d}{dx}\delta(x - x'); \quad P^n = \left(-i\hbar\frac{d}{dx}\right)^n \delta(x - x')$$

$$Q = x\delta(x - x'); \qquad Q^n = x^n\delta(x - x')$$

and the average value of g is

$$\langle g\rangle_{\text{Av}} = \int\int\left\{\int G(x, x')\rho(x', x'')dx'\right\}\delta(x - x'')dxdx''.$$

Substitute the expression for g into the integral, and use the following property[7] of the exponential operator

$$e^{i(\sigma P + \tau Q)} = \exp\left(i\frac{\sigma\hbar}{2}\tau\right)e^{i\tau Q}e^{i\sigma P}$$

to get

$$\langle g\rangle_{\text{Av}} = \int\left[\exp\left(i\frac{\sigma\hbar}{2}\tau\right)e^{i\tau Q}e^{i\sigma P}\rho(x', x'')\right] \times \xi(\sigma, \boldsymbol{\tau})\delta(x - x'')dxdx'dx''d\sigma d\tau.$$

Then, the Taylor's series expansion property

$$e^{i\sigma P(x, x')}\rho(x', x'') = \rho(x' + \sigma h, x'')\delta(x - x')$$

leads to

$$\langle g\rangle_{\text{Av}} = \int\left[\exp\left(i\frac{\sigma\hbar}{2}\tau\right)e^{i\tau Q(x,x')}\rho(x' + \sigma\hbar, x'')\right]\xi(\sigma, \tau)$$

$$\times\ \delta(x - x')\delta(x - x'')dxdx'dx''d\sigma d\tau$$

[8] H. Weyl, *The Theory of Groups and Quantum Mechanics* (London), p. 274.
[9] N. H. McCoy, *Proc. Nat. Acad. Sci.* **18**, 674 (1932).

and integration over x' and x'' gives

$$\langle g\rangle_{Av} = \int \exp\left(i\frac{\sigma\hbar}{2}\tau\right) e^{i\tau x}\rho(x + \sigma\hbar, x)\xi(\sigma, \tau)dxd\sigma d\tau.$$

Now replace $\xi(\sigma, \tau)$ by its expansion $g(p, q)$:

$$\langle g\rangle_{Av} = \left(\frac{1}{2\pi}\right)^2 \int \exp\left(i\frac{\sigma\hbar}{2}\tau\right) e^{i\tau x}\rho(x + \sigma h, x)$$
$$\times\, g(p, q)e^{-i(\sigma p + \tau p)}dxd\sigma d\tau dpdq.$$

Integrate over τ and then over x, using the Fourier theorem to get

$$\langle g\rangle_{Av} = \frac{1}{2\pi}\int e^{-i\sigma p}g(p, q)\rho\left(q + \frac{\hbar\sigma}{2},\ q - \frac{\hbar\sigma}{2}\right)d\sigma dpdq.$$

Now, take $\hbar\sigma/2 = -Y$, and

$$\langle g\rangle_{Av} = \frac{1}{\hbar\pi}\int \exp\left(\frac{2i}{\hbar}pY\right) g(p, q)\rho(q - Y, q + Y)dpdqdY \qquad (2.14)$$

or

$$\langle g\rangle_{Av} = \int g(p, q)f(p, q)dpdq$$
$$f(p, q) = \frac{1}{\hbar\pi}\int \exp\left(\frac{2i}{\hbar}pY\right)\rho(q - Y, q + Y)dY, \qquad (2.15)$$

where f is the Wigner d.f. for one dimension.

With this theorem, it should be possible to carry large parts of classical statistical mechanics into quantum-mechanical language merely by changing the definition of the d.f. This will be illustrated in this paper by deriving the equations of hydrodynamics.

The starting point for a statistical mechanical theory of transport processes in quantum mechanics is the analog of the Liouville equation. The quantum-mechanical equation of motion has already been given in the density matrix formalism, and can be used to get the equation of motion for Wigner's d.f. Although this is described in detail by Wigner[6] we will outline the derivation here. We replace $\mathbf{R}$ by $\mathbf{R} - \mathbf{Y}$ and $\mathbf{R}'$ by $\mathbf{R} + \mathbf{Y}$ in Eq. (2.6), multiply through by $(1/h\pi)^{3N} \exp(2i\mathbf{p}\cdot\mathbf{Y}/h)$ and integrate over $\mathbf{Y}$: This gives

$$\frac{\partial f^{(N)}}{\partial t} = -\frac{i}{\hbar}\left(\frac{1}{\hbar\pi}\right)^{3N}\sum_{k=1}^{N}\frac{\hbar^2}{2m_k}\int \exp\left(\frac{2i\mathbf{p}\cdot\mathbf{Y}}{\hbar}\right)$$
$$\times\,[\nabla_{\mathbf{R}_k+\mathbf{Y}_k}{}^2\rho^{(N)}(\mathbf{R} - \mathbf{Y}, \mathbf{R} + \mathbf{Y})$$
$$-\,\nabla_{\mathbf{R}_k-\mathbf{Y}_k}{}^2\rho^{(N)}(\mathbf{R} - \mathbf{Y}, \mathbf{R} + \mathbf{Y})]d\mathbf{Y}$$
$$-\frac{i}{\hbar}\left(\frac{1}{\hbar\pi}\right)^{3N}\int \exp\left(\frac{2i\mathbf{p}\cdot\mathbf{Y}}{\hbar}\right)$$
$$\times\,[U(\mathbf{R} - \mathbf{Y}) - U(\mathbf{R} + \mathbf{Y})]\rho^{(N)}(\mathbf{R} - \mathbf{Y}, \mathbf{R} + \mathbf{Y})d\mathbf{Y}.$$

The kinetic energy contributions can be integrated by parts,

$$\sum_{k=1}^{N} \frac{\hbar^2}{2m_k} \frac{i}{\hbar} \left(\frac{1}{\hbar\pi}\right)^{3N} \int \exp\left(\frac{2i\mathbf{p}\cdot\mathbf{Y}}{\hbar}\right)$$
$$\times [\nabla_{\mathbf{R}_k+\mathbf{Y}_k}{}^2 \rho^{(N)}(\mathbf{R}-\mathbf{Y}, \mathbf{R}+\mathbf{Y}; t)$$
$$- \nabla_{\mathbf{R}_k-\mathbf{Y}_k}{}^2 \rho^{(N)}(\mathbf{R}-\mathbf{Y}, \mathbf{R}+\mathbf{Y}; t)]d\mathbf{Y}$$
$$= \sum_{k=1}^{N} \frac{\mathbf{p}_k}{m_k} \cdot \nabla_{\mathbf{R}_k} f^{(N)}(\mathbf{R}, \mathbf{p}; t), \tag{2.16}$$

which is identical in form with the classical result. The potential energy contribution is

$$\boldsymbol{\theta} \cdot f^{(N)} = \frac{i}{\hbar}\left(\frac{1}{\hbar\pi}\right)^{3N} \int [U(\mathbf{R}-\mathbf{Y}) - U(\mathbf{R}+\mathbf{Y})]$$
$$\times \exp\left(\frac{2i}{\hbar}\mathbf{p}\cdot\mathbf{Y}\right) \rho^{(N)}(\mathbf{R}-\mathbf{Y}, \mathbf{R}+\mathbf{Y})d\mathbf{Y}, \tag{2.17}$$

and the equation of motion can be written

$$\frac{\partial f^{(N)}}{\partial t} + \sum_{k=1}^{N} \frac{\mathbf{p}_k}{m_k} \cdot \nabla_{\mathbf{R}_k} f^{(N)} + \boldsymbol{\theta} \cdot f^{(N)} = 0. \tag{2.18}$$

The potential dependent term can be put into several different forms, involving integral or differential operators. If we define the kernel

$$K(\mathbf{R}, \mathbf{p}-\mathbf{p}') = \frac{i}{\hbar}\left(\frac{1}{\hbar\pi}\right)^{3N} \times \int_{-\infty}^{+\infty} [U(\mathbf{R}-\mathbf{x}) - U(\mathbf{R}+\mathbf{x})]$$
$$\times \exp\left[\frac{2i}{\hbar}(\mathbf{p}-\mathbf{p}')\cdot\mathbf{x}\right]d\mathbf{x} \tag{2.19}$$

then this term is

$$\boldsymbol{\theta} \cdot f^{(N)} = \int_{-\infty}^{+\infty} K(\mathbf{R}, \mathbf{p}-\mathbf{p}') f^{(N)}(\mathbf{R}, \mathbf{p}')d\mathbf{p}'. \tag{2.20}$$

Another possible form is

$$\boldsymbol{\theta} \cdot f^{(N)} = \frac{i}{\hbar}\left(\frac{1}{\hbar\pi}\right)^{3N} \times \int\int [f^{(N)}(\mathbf{R}, \mathbf{p}-\mathbf{p}') - f^{(N)}(\mathbf{R}, \mathbf{p}+\mathbf{p}')]$$
$$\times \exp\left[\frac{2i}{\hbar}(\mathbf{R}-\mathbf{x})\cdot\mathbf{p}'\right] U(\mathbf{x})d\mathbf{x}d\mathbf{p}'. \tag{2.21}$$

The corresponding differential operator forms are

$$\boldsymbol{\theta} \cdot f^{(N)} = \frac{i}{\hbar}\left[U\left(\mathbf{R} - \frac{\hbar}{2i}\nabla_{\mathbf{p}}\right) - U\left(\mathbf{R} + \frac{\hbar}{2i}\nabla_{\mathbf{p}}\right)\right] f^{(N)}(\mathbf{R}, \mathbf{p}), \tag{2.22}$$

$$\boldsymbol{\theta} \cdot f^{(N)} = \frac{i}{\hbar}\left[f^{(N)}\left(\mathbf{R}, \mathbf{p} - \frac{\hbar}{2i}\nabla_{\mathbf{R}}\right) - f^{(N)}\left(\mathbf{R}, \mathbf{p} + \frac{\hbar}{2i}\nabla_{\mathbf{R}}\right)\right] U(\mathbf{R}), \tag{2.23}$$

and may be summarized in a convenient formal way:

$$\boldsymbol{\theta} \cdot f^{(N)} = -\frac{2}{\hbar} \sin\left[\frac{\hbar}{2} \nabla_{\mathbf{R}} \nabla_{\mathbf{p}}\right] U(\mathbf{R}) f^{(N)}(\mathbf{R}, \mathbf{p}), \tag{2.24}$$

where $\nabla_{\mathbf{R}}$ must operate on the potential only. The series expansion of this is the form that Wigner obtained originally. It shows that the quantum-mechanical equation of motion differs from the classical one only in second and higher powers of $\hbar$. For a system of harmonic oscillators the quantum-mechanical and classical equations are identical.

If the potential can be expressed as a sum of pair potentials and an external part,

$$U = \sum_{i=1}^{N} \phi_i(\mathbf{R}_i) + \tfrac{1}{2} \sum_{i \neq j}^{N} \sum^{N} V_{ij}(\mathbf{R}_i, \mathbf{R}_j) \tag{1.4}$$

then the operator forms can be written in the same way,

$$\boldsymbol{\theta} \cdot f^{(N)} = \sum_i \boldsymbol{\theta}_i^{(e)} \cdot f^{(N)} + \tfrac{1}{2} \sum_{i \neq j} \sum \boldsymbol{\theta}_{ij} \cdot f^{(N)}, \tag{2.25}$$

where $\boldsymbol{\theta}_i^{(e)}$ is the operator corresponding to the i'th part of the external potential and $\boldsymbol{\theta}_{ij}$ is the operator corresponding to the pair potential, V_{ij}.

The reduced equations of motion are analogous to the classical ones, with the correspondence of $\boldsymbol{\theta}_i$ in quantum mechanics to $-(\nabla_{\mathbf{R}_i} U) \cdot \nabla_{\mathbf{p}_i}$ in the classical case. The equation of motion for the set of particles **n** is obtained by integrating the equation of motion for the entire set **N** over the coordinates and momenta of the set **N** — **n**. We restrict the discussion to the distributions for which the surface integrals of the currents vanish on the boundary of the phase space accessible to the system, so that Green's theorem may be used:

$$f^{(n)}(\mathbf{r}, \mathbf{p}) = \int\int f^{(N)}(\mathbf{r}, \mathbf{p}; \mathbf{R}, \mathbf{P}) d\mathbf{R} d\mathbf{P}$$

$$\frac{\partial f^{(n)}}{\partial t} + \sum_{i=1}^{n} \frac{\mathbf{p}_i}{m_i} \cdot \nabla_{\mathbf{r}_i} f^{(n)} + \sum_{i=1}^{n} \boldsymbol{\theta}_i^{(e)} \cdot f^{(n)} = -X^{(n)} \tag{2.26}$$

$$X^{(n)} = \int\int \left\{ \sum_{i=n+1}^{N} \boldsymbol{\theta}_i^{(e)} \cdot f^{(N)} + \tfrac{1}{2} \sum_{i \neq j}^{N} \sum^{N} \boldsymbol{\theta}_{ij} \cdot f^{(N)} \right\} d\mathbf{R} d\mathbf{P},$$

where **r**, **p** refer to the set **n** and **R**, **P** refer to the set **N** — **n**. The first part of the integral vanishes by integration over **P**. The second part can be split up into three groups of terms, one containing terms referring to pair interactions for which both particles are in the set **n**, another in which one particle is in set **n** and the other is in set **N** — **n**, and the third in which both particles are in set **N** — **n**:

$$X^{(n)} = \tfrac{1}{2} \sum_{i=1}^{n} \sum_{\substack{j=1 \\ i \neq j}}^{n} \int\int \boldsymbol{\theta}_{ij} \cdot f^{(N)} d\mathbf{R} d\mathbf{P} + \sum_{i=1}^{n} \sum_{j=n+1}^{N} \int\int \boldsymbol{\theta}_{ij} \cdot f^{(N)} d\mathbf{R} d\mathbf{P}$$

$$+ \tfrac{1}{2} \sum_{i=n+1}^{N} \sum_{\substack{j=n+1 \\ i \neq j}}^{N} \int\int \boldsymbol{\theta}_{ij} \cdot f^{(N)} d\mathbf{R} d\mathbf{P}.$$

The third group of terms vanish by integration over **P**, the first group integrates obviously, and the second group leads to integrals involving $f^{(n+1)}$:

$$X^{(n)} = \tfrac{1}{2} \sum_{\substack{i=1 \\ i \neq j}}^{n} \sum_{j=1}^{n} \boldsymbol{\theta}_{ij} \cdot f^{(n)} + \sum_{i=1}^{n} \sum_{j=n+1}^{N} X_{ij}{}^{(n)},$$

$$X_{ij}{}^{(n)} = \int \int \boldsymbol{\theta}_{ij} \cdot f^{(n+1)}(\mathbf{r}, \mathbf{p}; \mathbf{R}_j, \mathbf{P}_j) d\mathbf{R}_j d\mathbf{P}_j. \tag{2.27}$$

Equations (2.26) and (2.27) contain the reduced Liouville equation in quantum-statistical mechanics. The specialization to the equation for the singlet d.f. is given here as an illustration:

$$\frac{\partial f^{(1)}}{\partial t} + \frac{\mathbf{p}_1}{m_1} \cdot \nabla_{\mathbf{R}_1} f^{(1)} + \boldsymbol{\theta}_1{}^{(e)} \cdot f^{(1)}$$

$$= - \sum_{j=2}^{N} \int \int \boldsymbol{\theta}_{1j} \cdot f^{(2)}(\mathbf{R}_1, \mathbf{R}_j, p_1, p_j; t) d\mathbf{R}_j d\mathbf{p}_j. \tag{2.28}$$

III. THE EQUATIONS OF HYDRODYNAMICS

In this section, we will show how the equations of hydrodynamics can be derived in quantum-statistical mechanics. In particular, we will show that the derivations and results are formally identical with those obtained by Irving and Kirkwood.[10] Their derivations have been given in great detail, and there is no need to duplicate them here. The goal of the following discussion is a statement of the equations of hydrodynamics in a form which involves all N particles in the system. The remainder of the derivation consists in reducing these equations to a form which involves singlet and pair d.f.'s, and may be found in the paper of Irving and Kirkwood. The notation used here will be the same as their's.

The equations of hydrodynamics are obtained by calculating the time derivatives at a point of the fluid of the mass density, the momentum density, and the energy density. For this purpose, the following results are useful. If $\alpha(\mathbf{R}, \mathbf{p})$ is a dynamical variable, the average of α is

$$\langle \alpha \rangle_{\mathrm{Av}} \equiv \langle \alpha(\mathbf{R}, \mathbf{p}); f^{(N)}(\mathbf{R}, \mathbf{p}; t) \rangle = \int \int \alpha(\mathbf{R}, \mathbf{p}) f^{(N)}(\mathbf{R}, \mathbf{p}; t) d\mathbf{R} d\mathbf{p} \tag{3.1}$$

and if α is not an explicit function of the time,

$$\frac{\partial \langle \alpha \rangle_{\mathrm{Av}}}{\partial t} = \left\langle \alpha(\mathbf{R}, \mathbf{p}); \frac{\partial f^{(N)}(\mathbf{R}, \mathbf{p}; t)}{\partial t} \right\rangle. \tag{3.2}$$

When we use the analog of Liouville's theorem in this expression, we get

$$\frac{\partial \langle \alpha \rangle_{\mathrm{Av}}}{\partial t} = - \left\langle \alpha; \sum_{k=1}^{N} \frac{\mathbf{p}_k}{m_k} \cdot \nabla_{\mathbf{R}_k} f^{(N)} \right\rangle - \langle \alpha; \boldsymbol{\theta} \cdot f^{(N)} \rangle. \tag{3.3}$$

[10] J. H. Irving and J. G. Kirkwood, *J. Chem. Phys.* **18**, 817 (1950).

The first term is identical with the classical one, and can be transformed with Green's theorem to

$$\left\langle \alpha; -\sum_{k=1}^{N} \frac{\mathbf{p}_k}{m_k} \cdot \nabla_{\mathbf{R}_k} f^{(N)} \right\rangle = \left\langle \sum_{k=1}^{N} \frac{\mathbf{p}_k}{m_k} \cdot \nabla_{\mathbf{R}_k} \alpha; f^{(N)} \right\rangle. \tag{3.4}$$

The other term is (using Eq. (2.21))

$$\langle \alpha; \boldsymbol{\theta} \cdot f^{(N)} \rangle = \frac{i}{\hbar}\left(\frac{1}{\hbar\pi}\right)^{3N} \times \int\int \alpha(\mathbf{R}, \mathbf{p})\{f^{(N)}(\mathbf{R}, \mathbf{p} - \mathbf{p}') - f^{(N)}(\mathbf{R}, \mathbf{p} + \mathbf{p}')\}$$
$$\times \exp\left[\frac{2i}{\hbar}(\mathbf{R} - \mathbf{R}') \cdot \mathbf{p}'\right] U(\mathbf{R}')d\mathbf{R}'d\mathbf{p}'d\mathbf{R}d\mathbf{p},$$

and when $\mathbf{p} - \mathbf{p}'$ is replaced by $\mathbf{p}$ in the first term of the integral, and $\mathbf{p} + \mathbf{p}'$ is replaced by $\mathbf{p}$ in the second term (the limits remaining from minus infinity to plus infinity), we get

$$\langle \alpha; \boldsymbol{\theta} \cdot f^{(N)} \rangle = \langle A; f^{(N)} \rangle \tag{3.5}$$

$$A = \frac{i}{\hbar}\left(\frac{1}{\hbar\pi}\right)^{3N} \int\int \{\alpha(\mathbf{R}, \mathbf{p} + \mathbf{p}') - \alpha(\mathbf{R}, \mathbf{p} - \mathbf{p}')\}$$
$$\times \exp\left[\frac{2i}{\hbar}(\mathbf{R} - \mathbf{R}') \cdot \mathbf{p}'\right] U(\mathbf{R}')d\mathbf{R}'d\mathbf{p}'.$$

This can also be put into operator form,

$$A = \frac{i}{\hbar}\left\{\alpha\left(\mathbf{R}, \mathbf{p} + \frac{\hbar}{2i}\nabla_{\mathbf{R}}\right) - \alpha\left(\mathbf{R}, \mathbf{p} - \frac{\hbar}{2i}\nabla_{\mathbf{R}}\right)\right\} U(\mathbf{R}). \tag{3.6}$$

If we expand this as a series in $\hbar$ and take the limit as $\hbar$ approaches zero, the classical result is obtained. A more useful result is this: if α is of the form,

$$\alpha = \alpha_1(\mathbf{R}) + \sum_{k=1}^{N} \alpha_{2k}(\mathbf{R})\mathbf{p}_k + \sum_{j=1}^{N}\sum_{k=1}^{N} \alpha_{3jk}(\mathbf{R})\mathbf{p}_j \cdot \mathbf{p}_k, \tag{3.7}$$

this leads by a simple substitution to the equation for the rate of change of the average value of this special α:

$$\frac{\partial\langle\alpha\rangle_{\mathrm{Av}}}{\partial t} = \sum_{1=k}^{N}\left\langle \frac{\mathbf{p}_k}{m_k} \cdot \nabla_{\mathbf{R}_k}\alpha_1; f^{(N)} \right\rangle$$
$$+ \sum_{j=1}^{N}\sum_{k=1}^{N}\left\langle \frac{\mathbf{p}_j\mathbf{p}_k}{m_k} \cdot \nabla_{\mathbf{R}_k}\alpha_{2j}; f^{(N)} \right\rangle$$
$$+ \sum_{k=1}^{N} \langle \alpha_{2k}(\nabla_{\mathbf{R}_k} U); f^{(N)} \rangle \tag{3.7'}$$
$$+ \sum_i\sum_j\sum_k \left\langle \mathbf{p}_i \cdot \mathbf{p}_j \frac{\mathbf{p}_k}{m_k} \cdot \nabla_{\mathbf{R}_k}\alpha_{3ij}; f^{(N)} \right\rangle$$
$$+ \sum_j\sum_k \langle \alpha_{3jk}(\mathbf{p}_j \cdot \nabla_{\mathbf{R}_k} U + \mathbf{p}_k \cdot \nabla_{\mathbf{R}_j} U); f^{(N)} \rangle,$$

which differs from the corresponding classical equation only in the definition of the d.f. It can also be shown that higher terms in the expansion of α in powers of $\mathbf{p}$ will lead to expressions differing in form from the classical ones.

As a special case of this theorem, take the following values of α

$$\alpha_d = \sum_{k=1}^{N} m_k \delta(\mathbf{R}_k - \mathbf{r})$$

$$\boldsymbol{\alpha}_m = \sum_{k=1}^{N} \mathbf{p}_k \delta(\mathbf{R}_k - \mathbf{r}) \tag{3.8}$$

$$\alpha_E = \sum_{k=1}^{N} \left\{ \frac{p_k^2}{2m_k} + \phi_k(\mathbf{R}_k) + \tfrac{1}{2} \sum_{\substack{i=1 \\ \neq k}}^{N} V_{ik}(\mathbf{R}_i, \mathbf{R}_k) \right\} \delta(\mathbf{R}_k - \mathbf{r}).$$

These quantities define the mass density, the momentum density, and the energy density:

$$\rho(\mathbf{r}; t) = \langle \alpha_d; f^{(N)} \rangle \tag{3.9}$$

$$\rho(\mathbf{r}; t)\mathbf{u}(\mathbf{r}; t) = \langle \boldsymbol{\alpha}_m; f^{(N)} \rangle \tag{3.10}$$

$$E(\mathbf{r}; t) = \langle \alpha_E; f^{(N)} \rangle \tag{3.11}$$

and lead to the equations of continuity, momentum transport, and energy transport, respectively:

$$\frac{\partial \rho(\mathbf{r}; t)}{\partial t} = -\nabla_{\mathbf{r}} \cdot [\rho(\mathbf{r}; t)\mathbf{u}(\mathbf{r}; t)] \tag{3.12}$$

$$\begin{aligned} \frac{\partial[\rho(\mathbf{r}; t)\mathbf{u}(\mathbf{r}; t)]}{\partial t} = &-\nabla_{\mathbf{r}} \cdot \sum_{k=1}^{N} \left\langle \frac{\mathbf{p}_k \mathbf{p}_k}{m_k} \delta(\mathbf{R}_k - \mathbf{r}); f^{(N)} \right\rangle \\ &- \sum_{j \neq k}^{N} \sum^{N} \langle (\nabla_{\mathbf{R}_k} V_{jk}) \delta(\mathbf{R}_k - \mathbf{r}); f^{(N)} \rangle \\ &- \sum_{k=1}^{N} [\nabla_{\mathbf{r}} \phi_k(\mathbf{r})] \langle \delta(\mathbf{R}_k - \mathbf{r}); f^{(N)} \rangle \end{aligned} \tag{3.13}$$

$$\begin{aligned} \frac{\partial E(\mathbf{r}; t)}{\partial t} = &-\nabla_{\mathbf{r}} \cdot \Bigg[\sum_{k=1}^{N} \left\langle \frac{p_k^2}{2m_k} \frac{\mathbf{p}_k}{m_k} \delta(\mathbf{R}_k - \mathbf{r}); f^{(N)} \right\rangle \\ &+ \sum_{k=1}^{N} \phi_k(\mathbf{r}) \left\langle \frac{\mathbf{p}_k}{m_k} \delta(\mathbf{R}_k - \mathbf{r}); f^{(N)} \right\rangle \\ &+ \tfrac{1}{2} \sum_{j \neq k}^{N} \sum^{N} \left\langle V_{jk} \frac{\mathbf{p}_k}{m_k} \delta(\mathbf{R}_k - \mathbf{r}); f^{(N)} \right\rangle \Bigg] \\ &+ \tfrac{1}{2} \sum_{j \neq k}^{N} \sum^{N} \Bigg\langle (\nabla_{\mathbf{R}_k} V_{jk}) \cdot \frac{\mathbf{p}_k}{m_k} \\ &\times [\delta(\mathbf{R}_j - \mathbf{r}) - \delta(\mathbf{R}_k - \mathbf{r})]; f^{(N)} \Bigg\rangle. \end{aligned} \tag{3.14}$$

These results have the same form as the classical ones, as obtained by Irving and Kirkwood, although the d.f. is of course determined by the laws of quantum mechanics. The remainder of their derivation consists in transforming these equations into the form in which the stress tensor and heat current density are given in terms of singlet and pair d.f.'s and the potential of intermolecular force. Since these transformations are identical with those of the classical case, they will not be repeated here. We will now state the results of these calculations. The microscopically correct hydrodynamical equations are the continuity equation:

$$\frac{\partial}{\partial t}\rho \mathbf{r}; t) = -\nabla_{\mathbf{r}} \cdot [\rho(\mathbf{r}; t)\mathbf{u}(\mathbf{r}; t)] \tag{3.12}$$

the equation of motion (momentum transport equation):

$$\frac{\partial}{\partial t}[\rho\mathbf{u}] + \nabla_{\mathbf{r}} \cdot [\rho\mathbf{u}\mathbf{u}] = \mathbf{X} + \nabla_{\mathbf{r}} \cdot \boldsymbol{\sigma} \tag{3.13$'$}$$

and the energy transport equation,

$$\frac{\partial E}{\partial t} + \nabla_{\mathbf{r}} \cdot [E\mathbf{u} + \mathbf{q} - \mathbf{u} \cdot \boldsymbol{\sigma}] = 0. \tag{3.14$'$}$$

The quantities appearing in the above equations are defined as follows:[11]

$$\rho(\mathbf{r}; t) = \sum_{k=1}^{N} \langle m_k \delta(\mathbf{R}_k - \mathbf{r}); f^{(N)} \rangle \tag{3.9}$$

= mass density at **r**.

$$\mathbf{u}(\mathbf{r}; t) = \frac{1}{\rho(\mathbf{r}; t)} \sum_{k=1}^{N} \langle \mathbf{p}_k \delta(\mathbf{R}_k - \mathbf{r}); f^{(N)} \rangle \tag{3.10}$$

= mean molecular velocity (fluid velocity) at **r**.

$$\mathbf{X}(\mathbf{r}; t) = -\sum_{k=1}^{N} [\nabla_{\mathbf{r}}\phi_k(\mathbf{r})] \langle \delta(\mathbf{R}_k - \mathbf{r}); f^{(N)} \rangle \tag{3.15}$$

= body force per unit volume due to external fields at **r**.

$$E(\mathbf{r}; t) = E_K + E_\phi + E_V \tag{3.16}$$

= internal energy density at **r**, where

$$E_K(\mathbf{r}; t) = \sum_{k=1}^{N} \left\langle \frac{p_k^2}{2m_k} \delta(\mathbf{R}_k - \mathbf{r}); f^{(N)} \right\rangle \tag{3.17}$$

= kinetic energy density,

[11] The bracket notation $\langle\, ; f \rangle$ means the expectation value of the quantity appearing to the left of the semicolon over an ensemble having a probability distribution function, $f(\mathbf{R}_1, \cdots, \mathbf{R}_N; \mathbf{p}_1, \cdots \mathbf{p}_N; t)$.

$$E_\phi(\mathbf{r};t) = \sum_{k=1}^{N} \phi_k(\mathbf{r})\langle\delta(\mathbf{R}_k - \mathbf{r}); f^{(N)}\rangle \tag{3.18}$$

= potential energy density associated with external fields, and

$$E_V(\mathbf{r};t) = \tfrac{1}{2}\sum_{j\neq k}\sum \langle V_{jk}\delta(\mathbf{R}_k - \mathbf{r}); f^{(N)}\rangle \tag{3.19}$$

= potential energy density caused by molecular interaction. (In defining E_V it is assumed that the potential energy of interaction between two molecules is localized half at each molecule.)

These definitions are completely general. The other quantities, however, appearing in the above hydrodynamical equations, $\boldsymbol{\sigma}$ and $\mathbf{q}$, have been defined only for a single component, single phase system in which the intermolecular force is central, depending on range only. Their definitions follow.

$$\boldsymbol{\sigma}(\mathbf{r};t) = \boldsymbol{\sigma}_K + \boldsymbol{\sigma}_V \tag{3.20}$$

= stress tensor at $\mathbf{r}$, where

$$\boldsymbol{\sigma}_K = -\sum_{k=1}^{N} m\left\langle\left(\frac{\mathbf{p}_k}{m} - \mathbf{u}\right)\left(\frac{\mathbf{p}_k}{m} - \mathbf{u}\right)\delta(\mathbf{R}_k - \mathbf{r}); f^{(N)}\right\rangle \tag{3.21}$$

= kinetic contribution to stress tensor.

$$\boldsymbol{\sigma}_V(\mathbf{r};t) = \frac{1}{2}\int \frac{\mathbf{R}\mathbf{R}}{R}V'(R)\left\{1 - \tfrac{1}{2}\mathbf{R}\cdot\nabla_{\mathbf{r}} + \cdots + \frac{1}{n!}(-\mathbf{R}\cdot\nabla_{\mathbf{r}})^{n-1} + \cdots\right\}\rho^{(2)}(\mathbf{r}, \mathbf{r}+\mathbf{R}; t)d\mathbf{R} \tag{3.22}$$

= intermolecular force contribution to stress tensor.

$$\mathbf{q}(\mathbf{r};t) = \mathbf{q}_K + \mathbf{q}_V \tag{3.23}$$

= heat current density at $\mathbf{r}$, where

$$\mathbf{q}_K(\mathbf{r};t) = \sum_{k=1}^{N}\left\langle\frac{m}{2}\left|\frac{\mathbf{p}_k}{m} - \mathbf{u}\right|^2 \times \left(\frac{\mathbf{p}_k}{m} - \mathbf{u}\right)\delta(\mathbf{R}_k - \mathbf{r}); f^{(N)}\right\rangle \tag{3.24}$$

= heat current due to transport of thermal kinetic energy, and

$$\begin{aligned}\mathbf{q}_V(\mathbf{r};t) = &-\tfrac{1}{2}\mathbf{u}(\mathbf{r};t)\cdot\int\Big[V(R)\mathbf{1} - \frac{\mathbf{R}\mathbf{R}}{R}V'(R) \\ &\times\{1 - \tfrac{1}{2}\mathbf{R}\cdot\nabla_{\mathbf{r}} + \cdots\}\Big]\times\rho^{(2)}(\mathbf{r}, \mathbf{r}+\mathbf{R}; t)d\mathbf{R} \\ &+\frac{1}{2}\int\Big[V(R)\mathbf{1} - \frac{\mathbf{R}\mathbf{R}}{R}V'(R)\times\{1 - \tfrac{1}{2}\mathbf{R}\cdot\nabla_{\mathbf{r}} + \cdots\}\Big] \\ &\cdot\mathbf{j}_1^{(2)}(\mathbf{r}, \mathbf{r}+\mathbf{R}; t)d\mathbf{R}\end{aligned} \tag{3.25}$$

= contribution to heat current density by molecular interaction.

In the definitions of $\boldsymbol{\sigma}_V$ and $\mathbf{q}_V$ the following quantities appear,

$$\rho^{(2)}(\mathbf{r}, \mathbf{r}'; t) = \sum_{j \neq k}\sum \langle \delta(\mathbf{R}_j - \mathbf{r})\delta(\mathbf{R}_k - \mathbf{r}'); f^{(N)} \rangle \tag{3.26}$$

= pair density at $\mathbf{r}$ and $\mathbf{r}'$, the probability per (unit volume)^2 that one particle (any particle) will be at $\mathbf{r}$ and another at $\mathbf{r}'$.

$$\mathbf{j}_1{}^{(2)}(\mathbf{r}, \mathbf{r}'; t) = \sum_{j \neq k}\sum \left\langle \frac{\mathbf{p}_k}{m_k} \delta(\mathbf{R}_k - \mathbf{r})\delta(\mathbf{R}_j - \mathbf{r}'); f^{(N)} \right\rangle \tag{3.27}$$

= projection onto the space of $\mathbf{r}$ of the particle current density at $\mathbf{r}$, $\mathbf{r}'$ in pair space, = particle current density at $\mathbf{r}$ if another particle is at $\mathbf{r}'$ multiplied by the particle density at $\mathbf{r}'$.

The differential operator, $\nabla_{\mathbf{r}}$, occurring in the definitions of $\boldsymbol{\sigma}_V$ and $\mathbf{q}_V$ operate on $\rho^{(2)}(\mathbf{r}, \mathbf{r} + \mathbf{R}; t)$ and $\mathbf{j}_1{}^{(2)}(\mathbf{r}, \mathbf{r} + \mathbf{R}; t)$ with $\mathbf{R}$ held fixed. Since in the interior of a fluid $\rho^{(2)}$ and $\mathbf{j}_1{}^{(2)}$ are slow functions of $\mathbf{r}$ (holding $\mathbf{R}$ fixed), changing negligibly for $\mathbf{r}$ varying by a displacement whose length is of the order of the "range" of intermolecular forces, all terms beyond the first may be neglected in the brace appearing in the definitions of $\boldsymbol{\sigma}_V$ and $\mathbf{q}_V$. This yields the simplified expressions:

$$\boldsymbol{\sigma}_V(\mathbf{r}; t) = \frac{1}{2m^2}[\rho(\mathbf{r}; t)]^2 \times \int \frac{\mathbf{R}\mathbf{R}}{R} V'(R) g^{(2)}(\mathbf{r}, \mathbf{R}; t) d\mathbf{R} \tag{3.28}$$

$$\mathbf{q}_V(\mathbf{r}; t) = \frac{1}{2}\int \left[V(R)\mathbf{1} - \frac{\mathbf{R}\mathbf{R}}{R} V'(R) \right]$$

$$\cdot [\mathbf{j}_1{}^{(2)}(\mathbf{r}, \mathbf{r} + \mathbf{R}; t) - \mathbf{u}(\mathbf{r}; t)\rho^{(2)}(\mathbf{r}, \mathbf{R} + \mathbf{r}; t)] d\mathbf{R} \tag{3.29}$$

where the correlation function $g^{(2)}$ is defined by

$$\rho^{(2)}(\mathbf{r}, \mathbf{r} + \mathbf{R}; t) = (1/m^2)\rho(\mathbf{r}; t)\rho(\mathbf{r} + \mathbf{R}; t) g^{(2)}(\mathbf{r}, \mathbf{R}; t). \tag{3.30}$$

The pressure is defined by

$$P(\mathbf{r}; t) = -\tfrac{1}{3}\,\mathrm{Trace}\,\boldsymbol{\sigma}(\mathbf{r}; t). \tag{3.31}$$

In an ensemble which is in equilibrium, the pressure is

$$P = \tfrac{2}{3}\sum_{k=1}^{N} \left\langle \frac{p_k{}^2}{2m} \delta(\mathbf{R}_k - \mathbf{r}); f^{(N)} \right\rangle - \frac{2\pi}{3}\left(\frac{\rho}{m}\right)^2 \int_0^\infty R^3 V'(R) g^{(2)}(R) dR. \tag{3.32}$$

(In deriving the stress tensor, it is assumed that $\mathbf{R} \cdot \nabla_{\mathbf{R}}\rho^{(2)}$ is negligible. In the absence of external forces, and with the neglect of surface effects, this assumption is justified.) We cannot replace the average kinetic energy by $3kT/2$, because this is now a quantum-mechanical system. Thus, the temperature enters into the equation in an implicit way. This is the quantum-mechanical equation of state that has been obtained by Born and Green[5] using the virial theorem and by DeBoer[1] using statistical thermodynamics. There is some ambiguity in the derivation presented here, for the following reason: the stress tensor obtained by this method is undetermined up to an arbitrary tensor of vanishing divergence. This arbitrary tensor may not necessarily have a vanishing trace, and may therefore contribute to the pressure. In the classical case, Irving and Kirkwood showed that the definition used here in terms of the d.f. is consistent with the physical picture involving the force "acting across" a unit area. This definition may be used in the quantum-mechanical case, but is still arbitrary.

CONCLUSIONS

The equations of hydrodynamics have been derived from quantum-statistical mechanics, and contain microscopically correct expressions for the stress tensor and heat current density of a quantum fluid. These expressions are identical with the classical ones, except in the specification of the d.f., which must be obtained using some quantum-mechanical theory. Born and Green have obtained similar expressions in the density matrix formalism. Their efforts to apply these expressions to the problem of liquid helium II have not been entirely successful. What is needed is a logical procedure for terminating the chain of reduced equations of motion, so that $f^{(2)}$ can be evaluated with fair accuracy. This may take the form of a quantum-mechanical analog of the theory of Brownian motion developed by Kirkwood, or some other way of introducing the irreversibility of hydrodynamic effects. When such a theory is available, it should be possible to construct a rigorous molecular theory of quantum superfluids.

ACKNOWLEDGMENT

The authors are grateful to Professor J. G. Kirkwood and to Professor E. Wigner for suggesting various aspects of the problem and for many helpful discussions.

Note added in proof: E. Moyal [*Proc. Cambridge Phil. Soc.* **45**, 99 (1949)] has made a similar discussion of some of the properties of the Wigner d.f., and H. S. Green [*J. Chem. Phys.* **19**, 955 (1951)] has shown how an approximate Wigner d.f. may be obtained using quantum corrections to the classical d.f.

The Statistical Mechanical Theory of Transport Processes. VI. A Calculation of the Coefficients of Shear and Bulk Viscosity of Liquids*

ROBERT W. ZWANZIG, JOHN G. KIRKWOOD, KENNETH F. STRIPP, AND IRWIN OPPENHEIM
The Sterling Chemistry Laboratory, Yale University, New Haven, Connecticut

(Received March 11, 1953)

The theory of the coefficients of shear and bulk viscosity of liquids developed in the third article of this series is applied to the calculation of the coefficients of viscosity of liquid argon at its normal boiling point. The theory of the bulk viscosity, including a previously omitted term due to the rate of dilatation, is presented. With the use of the Lennard-Jones potential, a radial distribution function which is a much better approximation than the previously used one, and a new approximation to the friction constant, values are obtained for the coefficients of viscosity.

I. INTRODUCTION

In the third article of this series[1] (SMT III) Kirkwood, Buff, and Green presented a statistical mechanical theory of the coefficients of bulk and shear viscosity of liquids, and reported a calculation of the coefficient of shear viscosity of liquid argon at its normal boiling point. Their calculation was performed with a special approximation to the equilibrium radial distribution function, chosen to represent the experimentally observed shape of its first peak, and containing parameters which were adjusted to give correct calculated values for the equilibrium pressure and internal energy. Since then, more accurate equilibrium radial distribution functions have been obtained by solving the appropriate integral equations[2,3] in the superposition approximation. In the present article, the coefficients of bulk and shear viscosity are calculated using the new radial distribution functions. The special analytic form of the peak approximation used in SMT III permitted exact solution of the differential equations for the perturbation to the equilibrium radial distribution function due to fluid flow. With the new distribution functions, the differential equations must be solved numerically. The method of solution used here is described in appendices I and II.

The theory of the coefficient of bulk viscosity given in SMT III was incomplete. In Sec. II, the complete theory, including an omitted term due to the rate of dilatation, is presented.

The friction constant used in SMT III was obtained by a very rough

* This work was carried out under contract Nonr-410(00) with the U.S. Office of Naval Research.

[1] Kirkwood, Buff, and Green, *J. Chem. Phys.* **17**, 988 (1949).
[2] Kirkwood, Lewinson, and Alder, *J. Chem. Phys.* **20**, 929 (1952).
[3] Zwanzig, Kirkwood, Stripp, and Oppenheim, *J. Chem. Phys.* (to be published).

approximation. The friction constant used here was obtained by the more detailed linear trajectory analysis, which will be described in a later paper.

The numerical value obtained for the coefficient of shear viscosity η of liquid argon at its normal boiling point is $\eta = 0.73 \times 10^{-3}$ poise. This differs from the result $\eta = 1.27 \times 10^{-3}$ poise given in SMT III, and is smaller than the experimental value $\eta = 2.39 \times 10^{-3}$ poise by a factor of about three. The friction constant is $\zeta = 2.85 \times 10^{-10}$ g/sec which is also smaller than the value $\zeta = 4.84 \times 10^{-10}$ g/sec used in SMT III. The sensitivity of the friction constant and the coefficients of bulk and shear viscosity to the shape of the equilibrium radial distribution function is investigated. The friction constant and the coefficient of shear viscosity are insensitive, but the bulk viscosity φ is quite sensitive. The result $\varphi = 0.36 \times 10^{-3}$ poise is less reliable than the calculated shear viscosity.

II. BASIC EQUATIONS

The equations of continuity and motion of a viscous fluid are

$$\frac{\partial \rho}{\partial t} + \nabla_R \cdot \rho \mathbf{u} = 0,$$

$$\frac{\partial}{\partial t} \rho \mathbf{u} = \mathbf{X} + \nabla_R \cdot \boldsymbol{\sigma}, \tag{1}$$

where ρ is the mass density of the fluid, $\mathbf{u}$ is the fluid velocity, $\mathbf{X}$ represents external body forces, and $\boldsymbol{\sigma}$ is the stress tensor of the fluid. The Newtonian stress tensor depends on pressure P, rate of strain $\dot{\boldsymbol{\epsilon}}$, and divergence of velocity $\nabla \cdot \mathbf{u}$ in this way,

$$\boldsymbol{\sigma} = -\left\{P + \left[\frac{2\eta}{3} - \varphi\right] \nabla \cdot \mathbf{u}\right\} \mathbf{1} + 2\eta \dot{\boldsymbol{\epsilon}}, \tag{2}$$

where $\mathbf{1}$ is the unit dyad and η and φ are the coefficients of shear and bulk viscosity. In the statistical mechanical theory of transport processes, the stress tensor may be expressed in terms of molecular variables,

$$\boldsymbol{\sigma} = -\rho^{(1)}\left[\frac{\langle \mathbf{pp} \rangle_{\text{Av}}}{m} - m\mathbf{uu}\right] + \tfrac{1}{2}\int \frac{\mathbf{R}_{12}\mathbf{R}_{12}}{R_{12}} \frac{dV(R_{12})}{dR_{12}} \rho^{(2)}(\mathbf{R}, \mathbf{R}_{12}) d^3 R_{12}$$

$$\rho^{(1)}\langle \mathbf{pp} \rangle_{\text{Av}} = N \int \mathbf{pp} f^{(1)}(\mathbf{R}, \mathbf{p}) d\mathbf{p}, \tag{3}$$

where m is the mass of an individual molecule, N is Avogadro's number, $V(R_{12})$ is the potential of intermolecular force of a pair of molecules separated by the distance R_{12}, $\rho^{(1)}(\mathbf{R})$ is the average number density of molecules at $\mathbf{R}$, $\rho^{(2)}(\mathbf{R}, \mathbf{R}_{12})$ is the average number density of pairs of molecules when one is at $\mathbf{R}$ and the other is at $\mathbf{R} + \mathbf{R}_{12}$, and $\bar{f}^{(1)}(\mathbf{R}, \mathbf{p})$ is the probability that a given molecule has momentum $\mathbf{p}$ and is at position $\mathbf{R}$. To convert this expression for the stress tensor to the Newtonian form, it is necessary to expand $\bar{f}^{(1)}$ and $\rho^{(2)}$ in $\nabla \cdot \mathbf{u}$ and $\dot{\boldsymbol{\epsilon}}$. When this is done, the momentum transport contribution becomes

$$\rho^{(1)}\left[\frac{\langle \mathbf{pp} \rangle_{\text{Av}}}{m} - m\mathbf{uu}\right] = \rho^{(1)} kT\mathbf{1} - \frac{\rho^{(1)} kT}{\zeta}\left[\dot{\boldsymbol{\epsilon}} - \frac{\nabla \cdot \mathbf{u}}{3}\mathbf{1}\right], \tag{4}$$

where ζ is the Brownian motion friction constant. With the definition of the pair correlation function,

$$g^{(2)}(\mathbf{R}, \mathbf{R}_{12}) = \rho^{(2)}(\mathbf{R}, \mathbf{R}_{12})/\rho^{(1)}(\mathbf{R})\rho^{(1)}(\mathbf{R} + \mathbf{R}_{12}), \tag{5}$$

and the expansion in spherical harmonics,

$$g^{(2)}(\mathbf{R}_{12}) = g_0^{(2)}(R_{12})\left\{1 + \frac{\zeta}{kT} \times \left[\frac{\mathbf{R}_{12} \cdot \dot{\boldsymbol{\epsilon}} \cdot \mathbf{R}_{12}}{R_{12}^2} - \tfrac{1}{3}\nabla \cdot \mathbf{u}\right]\psi_2(R_{12}) + \frac{\zeta}{6kT}(\nabla \cdot \mathbf{u})\psi_0(R_{12})\right\}, \tag{6}$$

expressions for the pressure and coefficients of shear and bulk viscosity are

$$P = \rho^{(1)}kT - \frac{2\pi}{3}[\rho^{(1)}]^2 \int_0^\infty R^3 \frac{dV}{dR} g_0^{(2)}(R)dR, \tag{7}$$

$$\eta = \frac{\rho^{(1)}kT}{2m\zeta} + \frac{\pi\zeta}{15kT}[\rho^{(1)}]^2 \int_0^\infty R^3 \frac{dV}{dR} g_0^{(2)}(R)\psi_2(R)dR, \tag{8}$$

$$\varphi = \frac{\pi\zeta}{9kT}[\rho^{(1)}]^2 \int_0^\infty R^3 \frac{dV}{dR} g_0^{(2)}(R)\psi_0(R)dR. \tag{9}$$

The function $g_0^{(2)}(R_{12})$ is the equilibrium radial distribution function of the fluid, and $\psi_0(R_{12})$ and $\psi_2(R_{12})$ describe the perturbation of $g^{(2)}$ caused by fluid flow.

The perturbed $g^{(2)}$ satisfies the differential equation

$$\nabla_R \cdot \{\nabla_R g^{(2)} - g^{(2)}\nabla_R \log g_0^{(2)}\} - \frac{\zeta}{kT}\frac{\partial g^{(2)}}{\partial t} = \frac{\zeta}{2kT}\mathbf{R} \cdot \dot{\boldsymbol{\epsilon}}\, \nabla_R g^{(2)}, \tag{10}$$

together with boundary conditions resulting from requirements imposed on the excess current density in pair configuration space. When $g^{(2)}$ is expanded in spherical harmonics (Eq. 6), the equation is linearized with respect to the rate of strain $\dot{\boldsymbol{\epsilon}}$, and only the stationary state is considered, differential equations are obtained for $\psi_0(R)$ and $\psi_2(R)$. The equation for ψ_2 is

$$\frac{d}{dR}\left(R^2 g_0^{(2)}(R)\frac{d\psi_2(R)}{dR}\right) - 6g_0^{(2)}(R)\psi_2(R) = R^3 \frac{dg_0^{(2)}(R)}{dR}$$

$$\lim_{R\to 0} R^2 g_0^{(2)}(R)\frac{d\psi_2(R)}{dR} = 0, \tag{11}$$

$$\lim_{R\to\infty} \psi_2(R) = 0.$$

The differential equation given in SMT III for $\psi_0(R)$ is not complete:[4] the

[4] The authors are indebted to Professor F. P. Buff for pointing this out to them.

H

correct form is

$$\frac{d}{dR}\left(R^2 g_0^{(2)}(R)\,\frac{d\psi_0(R)}{dR}\right) = R^3\,\frac{dg_0^{(2)}(R)}{dR} - 3R^2\,\frac{\partial g_0^{(2)}(R)}{\partial \log \rho^{(1)}},$$

$$\lim_{R\to 0} R^2 g_0^{(2)}(R)\,\frac{d\psi_0(R)}{dR} = 0, \tag{12}$$

$$\lim_{R\to\infty} \frac{d\psi_0(R)}{dR} = 0.$$

In SMT III, the second term on the right-hand side of the differential equation does not appear. This correction is due to the physical impossibility of having a stationary state of dilatation, so that $\partial g^{(2)}/\partial t$ must not be neglected. Actually,

$$\frac{\partial g^{(2)}}{\partial t} = \frac{\partial g^{(2)}}{\partial \rho^{(1)}}\frac{\partial \rho^{(1)}}{\partial t} = \left(\frac{\partial g^{(2)}}{\partial \log \rho^{(1)}}\right)_T \nabla\cdot \mathbf{u}, \tag{13}$$

when the equation of continuity is used. The boundary conditions are not affected by this correction.

In this article, the Lennard-Jones intermolecular potential,

$$V(R) = \epsilon\gamma_L(x),$$

$$x = R/a, \tag{14}$$

$$\gamma_L = 4\left(\frac{1}{x^{12}} - \frac{1}{x^6}\right),$$

will be used. With the parameters a and ϵ one may construct a dimensionless or reduced pressure P^*, volume v^*, and temperature T^*,

$$P = P^*(\epsilon/a^3)$$

$$v = v^*(Na^3) \tag{15}$$

$$T = T^*(\epsilon/k).$$

Dimensionless quantities will be denoted by asterisks throughout this article. The differential equations are transformed by the substitution $x = R/a$ to

$$\frac{d}{dx}\left(x^2 g_0^{(2)}(x)\,\frac{d\psi_0^*(x)}{dx}\right) = x^3\,\frac{dg_0^{(2)}(x)}{dx} + 3v^*x^2\,\frac{\partial g_0^{(2)}(x)}{dv^*}, \tag{16}$$

$$\frac{d}{dx}\left(x^2 g_0^{(2)}(x)\,\frac{d\psi_2^*(x)}{dx}\right) - 6g_0^{(2)}(x)\psi_2^*(x) = x^3\,\frac{dg_0^{(2)}(x)}{dx}, \tag{17}$$

where

$$\psi_0^*(x) = \frac{1}{a^2}\,\psi_0(x), \tag{18}$$

$$\psi_2^*(x) = \frac{1}{a^2}\,\psi_2(x). \tag{19}$$

These equations are now dimensionless. In terms of reduced variables, the coefficients of bulk and shear viscosity are

$$\varphi = \left(\frac{\zeta}{a}\right) I_0^*, \tag{20}$$

$$\eta = \left(\frac{\zeta}{a}\right) I_2^*, \tag{21}$$

where

$$I_0^* = \frac{\pi}{9T^*v^{*2}} \int^{\infty} x^3 \gamma_L'(x) g_0^{(2)}(x) \psi_0^*(x) dx, \tag{22}$$

$$I_2^* = \frac{\pi}{15T^*v^{*2}} \int_0^{\infty} x^3 \gamma_L'(x) g_0^{(2)}(x) \psi_2^*(x) dx. \tag{23}$$

The momentum contribution to η will be neglected, since it is numerically dominated by the potential contribution in the liquid state.[1] The bulk viscosity does not contain a momentum contribution. Values of a and ϵ were determined for argon by Michels[5] from second virial coefficient data. They are

$$a = 3.405 \times 10^{-8} \text{ cm},$$

$$\epsilon = 1.653 \times 10^{-14} \text{ erg}.$$

The numerical value of the friction constant will be presented in Sec. V.

The equilibrium radial distribution function $g_L(cx)$ used in these calculations was described in detail in a recent publication.[3] This function was obtained by solving the appropriate integral equation with the Lennard-Jones potential. In the present article, the viscosity coefficients will be calculated at the boiling point of argon under atmospheric pressure, where the reduced variables of state are $T^* = 0.7454$ and $v^* = 1.223$. The parameter c is introduced into the radial distribution function $g_L(x)$ in order to obtain better agreement between calculated and experimental thermodynamic properties. In particular, the equilibrium pressure of the fluid is calculated by substituting $g_L(cx)$ for $g_0^{(2)}$ in Eq. (7), and the value of c is determined which leads to the experimental pressure. This value is $c = 1.026$ at the normal boiling point. In SMT III, a similar procedure was carried out, with two adjustable parameters, and the experimental pressure and internal energy were used to determine the parameters. In the present article, a much better initial approximation to $g_0^{(2)}$ is used, and only one parameter is adjusted.

When $g_L(cx)$ is substituted for $g_0^{(2)}(x)$ in the differential equation for $\psi_0^*(x)$ and $\psi_2^*(x)$, a simple transformation leads to

$$\psi_0^*(x; \text{with } g_L(cx)) = (1/c^2)\psi_0^*(cx; \text{with } g_L(x)) \tag{24}$$

and an exactly similar expression for ψ_2^*. Therefore it is necessary to solve the differential equations only with $g_L(x)$, or $c = 1$. Then, the appropriate substitutions lead to,

$$I_0^*(c) = cI_0^*(1) - \frac{16\pi}{3T^*v^{*2}}(c^6 - 1)c \times \int_0^{\infty} x^{-10} g_L(x) \psi_0^*(x) dx, \tag{25}$$

[5] Michels, Wijker, and Wijker, *Physica* **15**, 627 (1949).

$$I_2^*(c) = cI_2^*(1) - \frac{16\pi}{5T^*v^{*2}}(c^6 - 1)c \times \int_0^\infty x^{-10} g_L(x)\psi_2^*(x)dx, \qquad (26)$$

where $I_0^*(c)$ and $I_2^*(c)$ are the values of these functions obtained using $g_L(cx)$ throughout, $I_0^*(1)$ and $I_2^*(1)$ are the values obtained using $g_L(x)$ throughout, and $\psi_0^*(x)$ and $\psi_2^*(x)$ are the functions obtained by solving the differential equations with $g_L(x)$.

III. BULK VISCOSITY

The differential equation (Eq. (16)) for $\psi_0^*(x)$ may be integrated directly. For convenience, $\psi_0^*(x)$ is split into two parts,

$$\psi_0^*(x) = C_1(x) + C_2(x), \qquad (27)$$

where

$$C_1(x) = -\int_x^\infty \frac{ds}{s^2 g_0^{(2)}(s)} \int_0^s u^3 \frac{dg_0^{(2)}(u)}{du} du, \qquad (28)$$

and

$$C_2(x) = -3v^* \int_x^\infty \frac{ds}{s^2 g_0^{(2)}(s)} \int_0^s u^2 \left(\frac{\partial g_0^{(2)}(u)}{\partial v^*}\right)_T du. \qquad (29)$$

These integrals were evaluated numerically, using the radial distribution function $g_L(x)$. The details of this computation are presented in Appendix I. The contributions of $C_1(x)$ and $C_2(x)$ to the integral I_0^* are

$$I_0^* = 0.187 + 0.360 = 0.547.$$

The effect on I_0^* of the correction to the differential equation for ψ_0 is considerable.

In order to calculate $I_0^*(c)$ as a function of the scale factor c, the integral

$$\int_0^\infty x^{-10} g_L(x)\psi_0^*(x)dx = 0.204$$

is needed. Table I, which contains $I_0^*(c)$ as a function of c, was constructed using these values in Eq. (25). The results show that $I_0^*(c) = a\varphi/\zeta$ is quite sensitive to the value of c and therefore to the shape of the radial distribution function. At $c = 1.026$, $I_0^*(c) = 0.038$. For a slightly higher value of c, $I_0^*(c)$ becomes negative.

In section V, numerical values for ζ and a will be introduced, and the calculation of φ will be completed.

IV. SHEAR VISCOSITY

The differential equation (Eq. 17) for $\psi_2^*(x)$ may be converted into an integral equation,

$$\psi_2^*(x) = C_1(x) - 3k(0)G(x) + 6G(x) \int_x^\infty g_0^{(2)}(s)\psi_2^*(s)ds$$
$$- 6 \int_x^\infty G(s) g_0^{(2)}(s)\psi_2^*(s)ds, \qquad (30)$$

where $C_1(x)$ is part of $\psi_0^*(x)$, defined in Sec. III,

$$k(0) = \int_0^\infty x^2[g_0^{(2)}(x) - 1]dx \tag{31}$$

TABLE I.

c	$I_0^*(c)$	$I_2^*(c)$	$\varphi(c)/\eta(c)$
1.000	0.547	0.0696	7.9
1.010	0.362	0.0729	5.0
1.020	0.163	0.0763	2.1
1.026	0.038	0.0784	0.5
1.030	−0.073	0.0799	−0.9
peak	...	0.090	...

and

$$G(x) = \int_x^\infty \frac{1}{u^2 g_0^{(2)}(u)} du. \tag{32}$$

This equation was solved numerically with the radial distribution function $g_L(x)$. The method of solution is described in detail in Appendix II. The function $\psi_2^*(x)$ leads to numerical values

$$I_2^*(1) = 0.06964,$$

$$\int_0^\infty x^{-10} g_L(x) \psi_2^*(x) dx = -0.00451.$$

The column labeled $I_2^*(c)$ in Table I was constructed by substituting these numerical values into Eq. (26). This function is less sensitive to c than $I_0^*(c)$. The peak approximation of SMT III leads to a value I_2^* (labeled "peak" in Table I) which is close to the value obtained using $g_L(cx)$ with $c \approx 1.06$.

The ratio

$$\varphi(c)/\eta(c) = I_0^*(c)/I_2^*(c) \tag{33}$$

is independent of the friction constant, and depends only on the reduced parameters of state v^* and T^*. It is given as a function of c in Table I. The

TABLE II

c	$\zeta(c) \times 10^{10}$ g/sec	$\varphi(c) \times 10^3$ poise	$\eta(c) \times 10^3$ poise
1.00	3.53	6.34	0.81
1.01	3.27	3.89	0.78
1.02	3.01	1.61	0.75
1.026	2.85	0.36	0.73
1.03	2.74	−0.66	0.72
peak	...	...	0.84
expt	...	...	2.39

ratio varies considerably with c: at $c = 1.026$ it has the value $\varphi/\eta \approx 0.5$. There are no reliable experimental results with which to compare this.

In Sec. V, numerical values of ζ, a, and ϵ will be introduced and the calculation of the shear viscosity will be completed.

V. FINAL RESULTS

In Secs. III and IV, computations of the quantities $a\varphi/\zeta$ and $a\eta/\zeta$ were described. In order to complete the calculation of the coefficients of bulk and shear viscosity, the friction constant ζ must be known. The value $\zeta = 4.84 \times 10^{-10}$ g/sec used in SMT III was obtained from an approximate expression for the friction constant using the peak approximation for the radial distribution function. In a forthcoming article, another calculation of the friction constant, by the method of linear trajectories, will be described. This value is

$$\zeta = \left(\frac{m\epsilon}{a^2}\right)^{\frac{1}{2}} \zeta^*, \tag{34}$$

$$\zeta^* = \begin{cases} 11.49; & c = 1 \\ 9.27; & c = 1.026, \end{cases}$$

where ζ^* is the friction constant in dimensionless form, at the normal boiling point. This calculation was performed with $g_L(cx)$, for scale factors $c = 1$ and $c = 1.026$: $\zeta(c)$ is obtained by linear interpolation. In Table II, $\zeta(c)$, $\varphi(c)$, and $\eta(c)$ are tabulated. The coefficient of shear viscosity obtained using this friction constant (with $c = 1.026$) and the integrals $I_2{}^*$ computed with the peak approximation of SMT III is also given in this table. The calculated coefficients of shear viscosity are all too small by a factor of about three. The calculated coefficients of bulk viscosity depend strongly on the value chosen for c.

APPENDIX I

The procedure used in the calculation of $I_0{}^*(c)$ will be described in detail. Equation (28) was rearranged and integrated by parts to yield

$$C_1(x) = \int_x^\infty \left[\frac{u}{g_0{}^{(2)}(u)} - u\right] du + 3G(x)[k(0) - k(x)] + 3h(x); \tag{35}$$

where

$$G(x) = \int_x^\infty \frac{du}{u^2 g_0{}^{(2)}(u)},$$

$$k(x) = \int_x^\infty u^2[g_0{}^{(2)}(u) - 1]du, \tag{36}$$

$$h(x) = \int_0^\infty G(u)u^2[g_0{}^{(2)}(u) - 1]du.$$

The integrals were calculated, and tabulated separately, and then added. For all the numerical integrations, the trapezoidal rule was used, with the intervals 0.01 for $1.00 \leqslant x \leqslant 1.12$, 0.02 for $1.12 \leqslant x \leqslant 1.28$, and 0.04 for $1.28 \leqslant x \leqslant 8.80$. For $x \geqslant 8.80$, $g_L(x)$ is uniformly unity and the integrals were therefore evaluated analytically. The values of $g_L(x)$ at 0.01 and 0.02 intervals were obtained by a numerical interpolation on the values at 0.04 intervals.

Although this method may be used to calculate $C_1(x)$ for $x < 1$, it was found to be more practical to use the alternative expression

$$C_1(x) = C_1(1) - \int_x^1 \frac{du}{u^2 g_0{}^{(2)}(u)} \int_0^u v^3 \frac{dg_0{}^{(2)}(v)}{dv} dv, \tag{37}$$

or, after integrating by parts,

$$C_1(x) = C_1(1) + \frac{x^2 - 1}{2} + 3\int_x^1 \frac{du}{u^2 g_0^{(2)}(u)} \int_0^u v^2 g_0^{(2)}(v)dv. \tag{38}$$

The integral was evaluated numerically, using the trapezoidal rule and an 0.01 interval, for $x < 1$.

In order to calculate $C_2(x)$, it is necessary to evaluate the derivative $\partial g_0^{(2)}(x)/\partial v^*$. Since the radial distribution function $g_L(x)$, which was obtained for only four unequally spaced values of v^*, is to be used, the differentiation was performed using Lagrange's interpolation formula. Due to numerical inaccuracies in $g_L(x)$, the resulting derivative is not a smooth function. To remove this roughness, Spencer's analytic smoothing formula[6] was used. For the integrations leading to $C_2(x)$, the trapezoidal rule was used with the same intervals as in the calculation of $C_1(x)$.

APPENDIX II

Equation (17), together with its boundary conditions, is equivalent to the integral equation

$$\psi_2^*(x) = -6\int_x^\infty \frac{dt}{t^2 g_0^{(2)}(t)} \int_0^t g_0^{(2)}(s)\psi_2^*(s)ds$$

$$-\int_x^\infty \frac{dt}{t^2 g_0^{(2)}(t)} \int_0^t s^3 \frac{dg_0^{(2)}(s)}{ds} ds. \tag{39}$$

When $\int_0^t$ is replaced by $\int_0^\infty - \int_t^\infty$ in the first term of the right-hand side, and the order of integration is changed, this equation is transformed to

$$\psi_2^*(x) = C_1(x) - 3k(0)G(x) + 6G(x)\int_x^\infty g_0^{(2)}(s)\psi_2^*(s)ds$$

$$-6\int_x^\infty G(s)g_0^{(2)}(s)\psi_2^*(s)ds, \tag{40}$$

where $C_1(x)$, $G(x)$, and $k(0)$ were defined in Appendix I. In solving this integral equation, the integrals were replaced by sums, using the trapezoidal rule. When the interval is 0.04, the equation becomes

$$\psi_2^*(x) = C_1(x) - 3k(0)G(x) + 0.24\{G(x)\sum_{x+.04}^{\infty} g_0^{(2)}(s)\psi_2^*(s)$$

$$-\sum_{x+.04}^{\infty} G(s)g_0^{(2)}(s)\psi_2^*(s)\}. \tag{41}$$

Since $C_1(x)$, $G(x)$, $k(0)$, and $g_0^{(2)}(x)$ are known functions, it is clear that if $\psi_2^*(s)$ is known for all s greater than x, then the value of ψ_2^* at x can be obtained directly.

---

[6] E. Whittaker and G. Robinson, *The Calculus of Observations* (Blackie and Sons, London, 1947), p. 290.

When $x > 8.80$, the radial distribution function used here is equal to unity, and the differential equation has an asymptotic solution

$$\psi_2^*(x) \sim b/x^3. \tag{42}$$

If a value of b is chosen arbitrarily, a function $\psi_2^*(x, b)$ may be constructed by integrating analytically from infinity to $x = 8.80$ and then step by step to $x = 0$. This procedure gives a family of functions, each arising from a different value of b. If the correct b is selected, the resulting $\psi_2^*(x, b)$ is the solution of the integral equation. If the correct b is not used, the resulting $\psi_2^*(x, b)$ does not satisfy the boundary condition at $x = 0$. This condition may be converted to a normalization condition. The differential equation for ψ_2^* is integrated once,

$$x^2 g_0^{(2)}(x) \frac{d\psi_2^*(x)}{dx} = 6 \int_\infty^x g_0^{(2)}(s)\psi_2^*(s)ds + \int_\infty^x s^3 \frac{dg_0^{(2)}(s)}{ds} ds,$$

and the boundary condition is applied, so that,

$$-6 \int_0^\infty g_0^{(2)}(s)\psi_2^*(s)ds = \int_0^\infty s^3 \frac{dg_0^{(2)}(s)}{ds} ds,$$

or,

$$\int_0^\infty g_0^{(2)}(s)\psi_2^*(s)ds = \tfrac{1}{2}k(0). \tag{43}$$

Therefore, the correct value of b may be found by solving the equation

$$\int_0^\infty g_0^{(2)}(s)\psi_2^*(s, b)ds = \tfrac{1}{2}k(0). \tag{44}$$

Since $\psi_2^*(x, b)$ is linear in b, it is sufficient to evaluate this function for two values of b, solve a linear equation in b, and then interpolate to get the correct $\psi_2^*(x)$.

This procedure was carried out with the radial distribution function $g_L(x)$. When the trapezoidal rule was used to replace integrals by sums, the intervals were the same as in Appendix I. The functions $\psi_2^*(x, 0)$ and $\psi_2^*(x, -1)$ were calculated, and the correct value of b was found to be $b = 1.5209$. This was used to obtain the correct $\psi_2^*(x)$, and the integrals needed to calculate $I_2^*(c)$ were evaluated.

The Statistical Mechanical Theory of Transport Processes. VII. The Coefficient of Thermal Conductivity of Monatomic Liquids*

ROBERT W. ZWANZIG, JOHN G. KIRKWOOD, IRWIN OPPENHEIM† AND BERNI J. ALDER‡
Sterling Chemistry Laboratory, Yale University, New Haven, Connecticut

(Received November 30, 1953)

A molecular theory of the coefficient of thermal conductivity is developed from the general theory of transport processes presented in the first article of this series. The thermal conductivity of liquid argon at its normal boiling point is evaluated using the Lennard-Jones intermolecular potential and a theoretically determined radial distribution function. The theory leads to an explicit expression for the product of the thermal conductivity and the friction constant of the theory of Brownian motion. With a reasonable estimate of the friction constant, the results of the theory agree satisfactority with experiment.

I

Among the objectives of the statistical mechanical theory of transport processes outlined in the first article of this series[1](SMT I) are the investigation of the domain of validity of the empirical Fourier law of heat conduction and the determination of the coefficient of thermal conductivity of a fluid in terms of its molecular parameters. In the present article, the theory of thermal conductivity is developed for a one-component fluid whose molecules interact with central forces, and a numerical evaluation of the coefficient of thermal conductivity of liquid argon is performed.

Our discussion starts from the generalized Chandrasekhar equations[1] for the motion through phase space of the probability distributions of sets of one, two, and more molecules. An alternate approach is provided by the theory of Born and Green.[2] While their theory duplicates some of the general results of ours, it differs in the way in which dissipative effects are to be introduced into the equations satisfied by the distribution functions. They have not succeeded in constructing solutions for the distribution functions in sufficiently explicit form to yield useful results.

In the fourth article of this series[3] (SMT IV) an expression was derived for the heat current density in a fluid in terms of averages of molecular variables.

* This work was carried out with support from the U.S. Office of Naval Research, under contract with Yale University.

† Present address: National Bureau of Standards, Washington, D.C.

‡ Present address: Chemistry Department, University of California, Berkeley, California.

[1] J. G. Kirkwood, *J. Chem. Phys.* **14**, 180 (1946).

[2] M. Born and H. S. Green, *A General Kinetic Theory of Liquids* (Cambridge University Press, Cambridge, 1949).

[3] J. H. Irving and J. G. Kirkwood, *J. Chem. Phys.* **18**, 817 (1950).

The averages are performed with distribution functions in the phase space of a single molecule and with distribution functions in the configuration space of pairs of molecules. In order to relate the heat current density to the temperature gradient, it is necessary to determine the perturbing effect of a temperature gradient on these distribution functions. This is accomplished with the generalized Chandrasekhar equations. The derivation has been carried out in detail for the case of a one-component fluid whose molecules interact with the spherically symmetric potential energy

$$V_N = \sum_{\substack{i<j\\=1}}^{N-1} \sum^{N} V(R_{ij})$$

$$R_{ij} = |\mathbf{R}_i - \mathbf{R}_j|, \tag{1}$$

where $V(R)$ is the potential energy of a pair of molecules. The resulting expression for the coefficient of thermal conductivity κ, is

$$\mathbf{q} = -\kappa \nabla T, \tag{2}$$

$$\kappa = \kappa_K + \kappa_V, \tag{3}$$

$$\kappa_K = \frac{k^2 T}{2\zeta}\rho^{(1)} - \frac{k^2T^2}{6\zeta}\left(\frac{\partial \rho^{(1)}}{\partial T}\right)_P, \tag{4}$$

$$\kappa_V = \frac{\pi k T}{3\zeta}\rho^{(1)2}\int_0^\infty R^3\left(R\frac{dV}{dR} - V\right) g_0^{(2)}(R)\, \frac{d}{dR}\left[\frac{\partial}{\partial T}\log g_0^{(2)}(R)\right]_P dR$$

$$+ \frac{\pi k T}{\zeta}\rho^{(1)2}\left[\frac{\partial}{\partial T}\int_0^\infty (R^2 V - R^3 V')g_0^{(2)}(R)dR\right]_P, \tag{5}$$

where $\mathbf{q}$ is the heat current density, ∇T is the temperature gradient, κ_K is the momentum transport contribution to the thermal conductivity, and κ_V is the intermolecular force contribution. The other quantities in these equations are defined in this way: k is the Boltzmann constant, T is the absolute temperature, $\rho^{(1)}$ is the mean number of molecules per unit volume of the fluid, $g_0^{(2)}(R)$ is the equilibrium (unperturbed) radial distribution function of the fluid, and ζ is the friction constant. ζ is related to the coefficient of self-diffusion D of the fluid by

$$D = kT/\zeta. \tag{6}$$

The quantity $\zeta\kappa$ was evaluated for liquid argon at its normal boiling point, using experimentally determined equilibrium thermodynamic properties and a theoretically determined radial distribution function. The Lennard-Jones intermolecular potential was used. With an estimated value of the friction constant, $\zeta = 2.85 \times 10^{-10}$ g/sec, the final numerical result is $\kappa = 4.1 \times 10^{-4}$ cal/g sec °K. This may be compared with the experimental value $\kappa = 2.9 \times 10^{-4}$ cal/g sec °K.

II

In SMT IV, it was shown that the basic equations of hydrodynamics may be derived by performing the appropriate statistical mechanical averaging processes on microscopic variables. These equations are the equation of continuity,

$$(\partial\rho/\partial t) + \nabla_r \cdot \rho\mathbf{u} = 0, \tag{7}$$

where $\rho(\mathbf{r}; t)$ is the mass density and $\mathbf{u}(\mathbf{r}; t)$ is the bulk velocity of fluid; the equation of motion,

$$\frac{\partial\rho\mathbf{u}}{\partial t} + \nabla_r \cdot [\rho\mathbf{u}\mathbf{u}] = \mathbf{X} + \nabla_r \cdot \boldsymbol{\sigma}, \tag{8}$$

where $\mathbf{X}$ is the external force on the fluid and $\boldsymbol{\sigma}$ is the hydrodynamic stress tensor; and the equation of energy transport,

$$\frac{\partial E}{\partial t} + \nabla_r \cdot [E\mathbf{u} + \mathbf{q} - \mathbf{u} \cdot \boldsymbol{\sigma}] = 0, \tag{9}$$

where $E(\mathbf{r}; t)$ is the density (per unit mass) of internal energy, $\mathbf{q}$ is the heat current density, and $\mathbf{u} \cdot \boldsymbol{\sigma}$ represents the frictional work which is converted into heat. When the quantities ρ, E, $\mathbf{u}$, and $\boldsymbol{\sigma}$ are defined as averages of molecular variables, an expression for $\mathbf{q}$ in terms of averages of molecular variables may be obtained from the energy transport equation, Eq. (9). Before this expression is given, it will be necessary to define the distribution functions used in the averaging process.

The fundamental point of view of this theory is that macroscopic observables are determined by time averages of ensemble averages of molecular quantities. The averages are performed with probability densities $\bar{f}^{(n)}(\mathbf{p}, \mathbf{q}; t)$ that subsets of n molecules out of an N molecule system have momenta and coordinates $(\mathbf{p}, \mathbf{q})$,

$$\begin{aligned} \bar{f}^{(n)}(\mathbf{p}, \mathbf{q}; t) &= \frac{1}{\tau}\int_0^\tau f^{(n)}(\mathbf{p}, \mathbf{q}; t + s)ds \\ f^{(n)}(\mathbf{p}, \mathbf{q}; t) &= \int\int f^{(N)}(\mathbf{p}, \mathbf{q}, \mathbf{P}, \mathbf{Q}; t)d\mathbf{P}d\mathbf{Q}, \end{aligned} \tag{10}$$

where $(\mathbf{P}, \mathbf{Q})$ are the momenta and coordinates of the residual set of $N - n$ molecules, and $f^{(N)}(\mathbf{p}, \mathbf{q}, \mathbf{P}, \mathbf{Q}; t)$ is the probability density in the complete phase space of the N molecule system. (A more complete description of this theory of measurement, and the related distribution functions, is given in SMT I.) Another useful type of distribution function is the number density

$$\rho^{(n)}(\mathbf{q}; t) = \frac{N!}{(N - n)!}\int \bar{f}^{(n)}(\mathbf{p}, \mathbf{q}; t)d\mathbf{p}, \tag{11}$$

which is the density of systems in the $3n$-dimensional configuration space of the subset (n). In the configuration space of a single molecule, $\rho^{(1)}$ is the number density of molecules in the fluid. In the configuration space of pairs of molecules, the number density is

$$\rho^{(2)}(\mathbf{r}, \mathbf{r} + \mathbf{R}; t) = \rho^{(1)}(\mathbf{r}; t)\rho^{(1)}(\mathbf{r} + \mathbf{R}; t)g^{(2)}(\mathbf{r}, \mathbf{R}; t). \tag{12}$$

This defines the radial distribution function $g^{(2)}(\mathbf{r}, \mathbf{R}; t)$.

Some basic macroscopic variables are the mass density ρ of the fluid,

$$\rho(\mathbf{r}; t) = m\rho^{(1)}(\mathbf{r}; t), \tag{13}$$

where m is the mass of a single molecule, and the current density $\mathbf{j}^{(1)}$,

$$\mathbf{j}^{(1)}(\mathbf{r}; t) = \rho^{(1)}(\mathbf{r}; t)\mathbf{u}(\mathbf{r}; t) = N \int \frac{\mathbf{p}}{m} f^{(1)}(\mathbf{r}, \mathbf{p}; t) d\mathbf{p}. \tag{14}$$

Also,

$$\mathbf{j}_1{}^{(2)}(\mathbf{r}_1, \mathbf{r}_2; t) = N^2 \int\int \frac{\mathbf{p}_1}{m} \bar{f}^{(2)}(\mathbf{r}_1, \mathbf{r}_2, \mathbf{p}_1, \mathbf{p}_2; t) d\mathbf{p}_1 d\mathbf{p}_2 \tag{15}$$

is the projection on the space of molecule one of the current density in the pair space, or the current density at $\mathbf{r}_1$ when a molecule is fixed at $\mathbf{r}_2$, multiplied by the number density of molecules at $\mathbf{r}_2$.

It was shown in SMT IV that the heat current density $\mathbf{q}$ is given by

$$\mathbf{q} = \mathbf{q}_K + \mathbf{q}_V, \tag{16}$$

$$\mathbf{q}_K(\mathbf{r}; t) = \frac{Nm}{2} \int \left| \frac{\mathbf{p}}{m} - \mathbf{u} \right|^2 \left(\frac{\mathbf{p}}{m} - \mathbf{u} \right) f^{(1)}(\mathbf{r}, \mathbf{p}; t) d\mathbf{p}, \tag{17}$$

$$\mathbf{q}_V(\mathbf{r}; t) = \tfrac{1}{2} \int \left[V(R)\mathbf{1} + \frac{\mathbf{RR}}{R} \frac{dV(R)}{dR} \right] \cdot [\mathbf{j}_1{}^{(2)}(\mathbf{r}, \mathbf{r} + \mathbf{R}; t) - \mathbf{u}(\mathbf{r}; t)\rho^{(2)}(\mathbf{r}, \mathbf{r} + \mathbf{R}; t)] d\mathbf{R}, \tag{18}$$

where $\mathbf{1}$ is the unit dyad. A physical interpretation of this result is that $\mathbf{q}_K$ represents the average transport of kinetic energy relative to the bulk velocity of the fluid, and that in the expression for $\mathbf{q}_V$, the term containing $V(R)$ represents the transport of potential energy due to macroscopically imperceptible Brownian motion, while the term involving $V'(R)$ represents the work dissipated by this random motion. The Fourier heat law

$$\mathbf{q} = -\kappa \nabla T \tag{19}$$

defines the coefficient of thermal conductivity κ. It is therefore necessary to calculate the perturbation of $\bar{f}^{(1)}$ and $\bar{f}^{(2)}$ from equilibrium due to the temperature gradient ∇T.

The distribution functions $\bar{f}^{(1)}$ and $\bar{f}^{(2)}$ satisfy generalized Chandrasekhar equations [SMT I, Eqs. (59) and (60)]. The $\bar{f}^{(1)}$ equation is

$$\frac{\partial \bar{f}^{(1)}}{\partial t} + \frac{\mathbf{p}}{m} \cdot \nabla_r f^{(1)} + \nabla_p \cdot \mathbf{F}^{(1)} \bar{f}^{(1)} = \zeta \nabla_p \cdot \left[\left(\frac{\mathbf{p}}{m} - \mathbf{u} \right) \bar{f}^{(1)} + kT \nabla_p \bar{f}^{(1)} \right], \tag{20}$$

where

$$\mathbf{F}^{(1)} = {}^{(1)}\langle \mathbf{F} \rangle^0 + {}^{(1)}\mathbf{F}^\dagger. \tag{21}$$

The force ${}^{(1)}\langle \mathbf{F} \rangle^0$ is the average total intermolecular force on a molecule at $\mathbf{R}$ when the average is performed, in a canonical ensemble, over all the other molecules. The force ${}^{(1)}\mathbf{F}^\dagger$ is a perturbation arising from the departure of $\rho^{(2)}$

from its equilibrium value. The quantity ζ is the friction constant in the space of a single molecule. Its expression in terms of intermolecular forces is given in SMT I.

The differential equation for $\bar{f}^{(2)}$ is

$$\frac{d f^{(2)}}{\partial t}+\frac{\mathbf{p}_1}{m}\cdot\nabla_{R_1} f^{(2)}+\frac{\mathbf{p}_2}{m}\cdot\nabla_{R_2}\bar{f}^{(2)}+\nabla_{p_1}\cdot(\mathbf{F}_1{}^{(2)}f^{(2)})+\nabla_{p_2}\cdot(\mathbf{F}_2{}^{(2)}f^{(2)})$$

$$=\nabla_{p_1}\cdot\boldsymbol{\zeta}_1{}^{(2)}\cdot\left\{\left(\frac{\mathbf{p}_1}{m}-\mathbf{u}_1\right)f^{(2)}+kT\nabla_{p_1}f^{(2)}\right\}$$

$$+\nabla_{p_2}\cdot\boldsymbol{\zeta}_2{}^{(2)}\cdot\left\{\left(\frac{\mathbf{p}_2}{m}-\mathbf{u}_2\right)\bar{f}^{(2)}+kT\nabla_{p_2}\bar{f}^{(2)}\right\}; \tag{22}$$

$$\mathbf{F}_1{}^{(2)}={}^{(2)}\langle\mathbf{F}_1\rangle^0+{}^{(2)}\mathbf{F}_1\dagger \tag{23}$$

$$\mathbf{F}_2{}^{(2)}={}^{(2)}\langle\mathbf{F}_2\rangle^0+{}^{(2)}\mathbf{F}_2\dagger,$$

where ${}^{(2)}\langle\mathbf{F}_1\rangle^0$ is the average total intermolecular force on a molecule at $\mathbf{R}_1$, when a pair of molecules are fixed at $\mathbf{R}_1$ and $\mathbf{R}_2$ and the average is performed, in a canonical ensemble, over the rest of the molecules. ${}^{(2)}\mathbf{F}\dagger$ is a perturbing force arising from the departure of $\rho^{(3)}$ from its equilibrium value. The friction tensor $\boldsymbol{\zeta}^{(2)}$ is a second-rank tensor in the six-dimensional configuration space of a pair of molecules. Its relation to intermolecular forces is described in SMT I.

III

The momentum contribution $\mathbf{q}_K$ to the heat current density will be evaluated in this section. The general procedure is to multiply the differential equation for $\bar{f}^{(1)}$ by various functions of momentum and then integrate the resulting equations over momentum space.

When Eq. (20) is integrated directly over momentum space, the equation of continuity is obtained. When Eq. (20) is multiplied by $N\mathbf{p}/m$ and integrated over momentum space, one obtains

$$\frac{\partial\mathbf{j}^{(1)}}{\partial t}+N\nabla_r\cdot\int\frac{\mathbf{pp}}{m^2}\bar{f}^{(1)}(\mathbf{r},\mathbf{p};t)d\mathbf{p}=\frac{\mathbf{F}^{(1)}\rho^{(1)}}{m}. \tag{24}$$

(In these integrations, Green's theorem is used to eliminate terms of the form $\int\nabla_p\cdot\mathbf{G}d\mathbf{p}$ when the surface integral of the quantity $\mathbf{G}$ over the boundaries of momentum space vanishes, which will always be the case in this article.) To relate the second term in this equation to macroscopic quantities, a non-equilibrium temperature $T(\mathbf{r};t)$ is defined by

$$\frac{mN}{2}\int\left(\frac{\mathbf{p}}{m}-\mathbf{u}\right)\left(\frac{\mathbf{p}}{m}-\mathbf{u}\right)\bar{f}^{(1)}d\mathbf{p}=\frac{kT\rho^{(1)}}{2}\mathbf{1}. \tag{25}$$

The temperature at $\mathbf{r}$ is therefore proportional to the average kinetic energy, relative to the bulk velocity of the fluid of a molecule at $\mathbf{r}$. When this definition of temperature and the equation of continuity are used and nonlinear terms in the bulk velocity are neglected, one obtains

$$\mathbf{F}^{(1)} = \frac{1}{\rho^{(1)}} \nabla_r (kT\rho^{(1)}). \tag{26}$$

This implies that even in the case of constant density, a gradient in temperature produces an average force on a molecule.

Next, Eq. (20) is multiplied by $|\boldsymbol{\pi}|^2\boldsymbol{\pi}$, where $\boldsymbol{\pi} = (\mathbf{p}/m) - \mathbf{u}$, and integrated over momentum space. Green's theorem and the nonequilibrium definition of temperature are used, and nonlinear terms in $\mathbf{u}$, gradients of $\mathbf{u}$, and terms of order $1/\zeta^2$ are neglected. This leads to

$$\mathbf{q}_K = \frac{5kT}{6\zeta} \nabla_r(\rho^{(1)}kT) - \frac{Nm^2}{6\zeta} \nabla_r \cdot \int |\boldsymbol{\pi}|^2 \boldsymbol{\pi}\boldsymbol{\pi} f^{(1)} d\mathbf{p}. \tag{27}$$

It is still necessary to evaluate the last term. When Eq. (20) is multiplied by $|\boldsymbol{\pi}|^2\boldsymbol{\pi}\boldsymbol{\pi}$, integrated over momentum space, and nonlinear terms and terms of order $1/\zeta^2$ are neglected, one gets

$$\int |\boldsymbol{\pi}|^2 \boldsymbol{\pi}\boldsymbol{\pi} f^{(1)} d\mathbf{p} = \frac{4k^2T^2}{Nm^2} \rho^{(1)}\mathbf{1}. \tag{28}$$

Therefore,

$$\mathbf{q}_K = \frac{5kT}{6\zeta} \nabla_r(\rho^{(1)}kT) - \frac{2}{3\zeta} \nabla_r(\rho^{(1)}k^2T^2). \tag{29}$$

Since experimental observations of thermal conduction are performed at constant pressure, the indicated differentiations must be performed at constant pressure. The result is

$$\mathbf{q}_K = -\frac{k^2T}{2\zeta} \rho^{(1)} \nabla T + \frac{k^2T^2}{6\zeta} \left(\frac{\partial \rho^{(1)}}{\partial T}\right)_P \nabla T \tag{30}$$

or

$$\kappa_K = \frac{k^2T}{2\zeta} \rho^{(1)} - \frac{k^2T^2}{6\zeta} \left(\frac{\partial \rho^{(1)}}{\partial T}\right)_P. \tag{31}$$

IV

In this section, the intermolecular force contribution $\mathbf{q}_V$ to the heat current density will be evaluated. The object of the procedure to be described here is to obtain the expansion, in powers of the temperature gradient, of the quantity $(\mathbf{j}_1^{(2)} - \rho^{(2)}\mathbf{u}_1)$. To achieve this, the Chandrasekhar equation for $\bar{f}^{(2)}$ is multiplied by $\mathbf{p}_1$ and integrated over the six-dimensional space of $\mathbf{p}_1$ and $\mathbf{p}_2$. As in the evaluation of $\mathbf{q}_K$, some preliminary results must first be obtained.

When Eq. (22) is integrated directly over momentum pair space, the result is an equation of continuity in pair configuration space,

$$\frac{\partial \rho^{(2)}}{\partial t} + \nabla_{r_1} \cdot \mathbf{j}_1^{(2)} + \nabla_{r_2} \cdot \mathbf{j}_2^{(2)} = 0. \tag{32}$$

When Eq. (22) is multiplied by $\mathbf{p}_1\mathbf{p}_1$, integrated over $\mathbf{p}_1$ and $\mathbf{p}_2$, and terms of order $1/\zeta^2$ are neglected, an equation is obtained,

$$N^2 \int\int \frac{\mathbf{p}_1\mathbf{p}_1}{m} \bar{f}^{(2)} d\mathbf{p}_1 d\mathbf{p}_2 = kT\rho^{(2)}\mathbf{1} + m\mathbf{u}_1\mathbf{j}_1^{(2)}, \tag{33}$$

which is analogous to Eq. (25) in singlet space. When Eq. (22) is multiplied by $\mathbf{p}_1\mathbf{p}_2/m$ and integrated, one obtains

$$\boldsymbol{\zeta}_1{}^{(2)} \cdot \left\{ \int\int \frac{\mathbf{p}_2\mathbf{p}_1}{m} \bar{f}^{(2)} d\mathbf{p}_1 d\mathbf{p}_2 - \frac{\mathbf{u}_1\mathbf{j}_2{}^{(2)}}{N^2} \right\}$$

$$+ \boldsymbol{\zeta}_2{}^{(2)} \cdot \left\{ \int\int \frac{\mathbf{p}_1\mathbf{p}_2}{m} \bar{f}^{(2)} d\mathbf{p}_1 d\mathbf{p}_2 - \frac{\mathbf{u}_2\mathbf{j}_1{}^{(2)}}{N^2} \right\} = 0. \tag{34}$$

At this point, it is convenient to make an approximation on the form of the friction tensor in pair space,

$$\boldsymbol{\zeta}^{(2)} = \zeta \mathbf{1}_1 + \zeta \mathbf{1}_2, \tag{35}$$

where ζ is the scalar friction constant in singlet space and $\mathbf{1}_1$, $\mathbf{1}_2$ are unit dyads in $\mathbf{r}_1$, $\mathbf{r}_2$ space. This means that the dependence of the friction tensor on momenta and on the relative configuration of pairs of molecules is neglected. This approximation was also used in the theory of the viscosity coefficients (SMT III).

Now, Eq. (22) is multiplied by $\mathbf{p}_1$ and integrated over momenta. When the results of the preceding paragraphs are used, and second order terms in velocities and in $1/\zeta$ are neglected, one gets

$$\frac{m}{\zeta}\frac{\partial \mathbf{j}_1{}^{(2)}}{\partial t} + \frac{1}{\zeta} \nabla_{r_1}(kT\rho^{(2)}) - \frac{\mathbf{F}_1{}^{(2)}\rho^{(2)}}{\zeta} = -(\mathbf{j}_1{}^{(2)} - \rho^{(2)}\mathbf{u}_1). \tag{36}$$

A similar equation may be derived for the second molecule. Since the current density $\mathbf{j}^{(2)}$ is itself of order $1/\zeta$, the time derivative, which is of order $1/\zeta^2$, may be neglected. When the radial distribution function $g^{(2)}$ is introduced, and the perturbation force ${}^{(2)}\mathbf{F}\dagger$ is neglected, a simple rearrangement leads to

$$\mathbf{j}_1{}^{(2)} - \rho^{(2)}\mathbf{u}_1 = -\rho^{(1)}(\mathbf{r}_1)\rho^{(1)}(\mathbf{r}_2)\frac{kT}{\zeta}[\nabla_r g^{(2)} - g^{(2)}\nabla_{R_1}{}^{(T_1)} \log g_0{}^{(2)}]. \tag{37}$$

The following expression from the equilibrium theory of distribution functions has been used:

$${}^{(2)}\langle \mathbf{F}_1 \rangle^0 - {}^{(1)}\langle \mathbf{F}_1 \rangle^0 = kT\nabla_{R_1}{}^{(T_1)} \log g_0{}^{(2)}(R_{12}, T_1), \tag{38}$$

where $g_0{}^{(2)}$ is the equilibrium radial distribution function, and depends upon the relative separation R_{12} and on the temperature and pressure at $\mathbf{R}_1$. The notation $\nabla_R{}^{(T)}$ is used to indicate partial differentiation with respect to $\mathbf{R}$, keeping temperature T fixed. When the superscript is omitted, the differentiation is total, and may contain a term resulting from temperature gradients.

The perturbed $g^{(2)}(R)$ depends on a temperature gradient, but the equilibrium $g_0{}^{(2)}(R)$ depends only on a single temperature. In order to express $g^{(2)}(R)$ in terms of $g_0{}^{(2)}(R)$ and a perturbation, it is necessary to establish some convention about which temperature to use in $g_0{}^{(2)}(R)$. If $T(\mathbf{R})$ is the temperature at $\mathbf{R}$, the perturbation $g_1{}^{(2)}(R)$ will be defined by

$$g^{(2)}(\mathbf{R}_1, \mathbf{R}_{12}, T(\mathbf{R}_1), T(\mathbf{R}_2), P; t) = g_0{}^{(2)}(R_{12}, T(\mathbf{R}_1), P)$$

$$+ g_1{}^{(2)}(\mathbf{R}_1, \mathbf{R}_{12}, T(\mathbf{R}_1), T(\mathbf{R}_2), P; t). \tag{39}$$

The pressure P is indicated as an independent variable, rather than the density, since experimental studies of thermal conduction are performed at constant pressure. When this form of $g^{(2)}$ is substituted in Eq. (37) and the differentiations are performed, the relative pair current densities are

$$\begin{aligned}\mathbf{j}_1^{(2)} - \rho^{(2)}\mathbf{u}_1 &= -\rho^{(1)}(\mathbf{R}_1)\rho^{(1)}(\mathbf{R}_2)\frac{kT(\mathbf{R}_1)}{\zeta(\mathbf{R}_2)}\mathbf{A}_1 \\ \mathbf{j}_2^{(2)} - \rho^{(2)}\mathbf{u}_2 &= -\rho^{(1)}(\mathbf{R}_1)\rho^{(1)}(\mathbf{R}_2)\frac{kT(\mathbf{R}_2)}{\zeta(\mathbf{R}_2)}\mathbf{A}_2,\end{aligned} \tag{40}$$

where the friction constant ζ depends explicitly on temperature and hence implicitly on position, and

$$\mathbf{A}_1 = \nabla_{R_1} g_1^{(2)} - g_1^{(2)}\nabla_{R_1}^{(T_1)} \log g_0^{(2)}(R_{12}, T_1, P) + \frac{\partial g_0^{(2)}(R_{12}, T_1, P)}{\partial T_1}\nabla_{R_1} T_1, \tag{41}$$

$$\begin{aligned}\mathbf{A}_2 = &-\nabla_{R_1} g_1^{(2)} + g_1^{(2)}\nabla_{R_1}^{(T_1)} \log g_0^{(2)}(R_{12}, T_1, P) \\ &+ \left[g_0^{(2)}(R_{12}, T_1, P)\frac{\partial}{\partial T_1}\nabla_{R_1}^{(T_1)} \log g_0^{(2)}(R_{12}, T_1, P)\right] \\ &\times (\mathbf{R}_{12}\cdot\nabla_{R_1} T_1).\end{aligned} \tag{42}$$

In deriving these expressions, it was assumed that $g_1^{(2)}$ is of order ∇T, that higher-order terms in ∇T may be neglected, and that $\nabla_{R_1} g_1^{(2)} = -\nabla_{R_2} g_1^{(2)}$. It may be verified that $g_1^{(2)}$ actually has these properties. In the equation for $\mathbf{A}_2$, the expansion

$$\begin{aligned}\nabla_{R_2}^{(T_2)} &\log g_0^{(2)}(R_{12}, T_2, P) \\ &= -\nabla_{R_1}^{(T_1)} \log g_0^{(2)}(R_{12}, T_1, P) \\ &\quad - (\mathbf{R}_{12}\cdot\nabla_{R_1} T_1)\frac{\partial}{\partial T_1}\nabla_{R_1}^{(T_1)} \\ &\quad \times \log g_0^{(2)}(R_{12}, T_1, P) + O(\nabla T)^2,\end{aligned} \tag{43}$$

where

$$T(\mathbf{R}_2) - T(\mathbf{R}_1) = \mathbf{R}_{12}\cdot\nabla_{R_1} T_1 + O(\nabla T)^2, \tag{44}$$

was carried out.

A differential equation for $g_1^{(2)}$ will now be obtained. When the equations of continuity in pair space and in singlet space are combined, one obtains

$$\nabla_{R_1}\cdot(\mathbf{j}_1^{(2)} - \rho^{(2)}\mathbf{u}_1) + \nabla_{R_2}\cdot(\mathbf{j}_2^{(2)} - \rho^{(2)}\mathbf{u}_2) = -\rho^{(1)}(\mathbf{R}_1)\rho^{(1)}(\mathbf{R}_2)\frac{Dg^{(2)}}{Dt}, \tag{45}$$

where $Dg^{(2)}/Dt$ is a generalized Stokes derivative,

$$\frac{D}{Dt} = \frac{\partial}{\partial t} + \mathbf{u}_1 \cdot \nabla_{R_1} + \mathbf{u}_2 \cdot \nabla_{R_2}. \tag{46}$$

When the expressions for the relative pair current densities are substituted in Eq. (45) and terms of order $(\nabla T)^2$ are neglected, then

$$\frac{\zeta_1}{kT_1} \frac{Dg^{(2)}}{Dt} = \nabla_{R_1} \cdot \mathbf{A}_1 + \nabla_{R_2} \cdot \mathbf{A}_2. \tag{47}$$

When the values for $\mathbf{A}_1$ and $\mathbf{A}_2$ are substituted in this equation, a differential equation for $g_1{}^{(2)}$ is obtained,

$$\frac{\zeta_1}{kT_1} \frac{Dg_1{}^{(2)}}{Dt} = \nabla_{R_1} \cdot \Bigg\{ - 2\nabla_{R_1} g_1{}^{(2)} + 2g_1{}^{(2)} \times \nabla_{R_1}{}^{(T_1)} \log g_0{}^{(2)}(R_{12}, T_1, P) - \frac{\partial g_0{}^{(2)}(R_{12}, T_1, P)}{\partial T_1} \nabla_{R_1} T_1 + \left[g_0{}^{(2)}(R_{12}, T_1, P) \frac{\partial}{\partial T_1} \nabla_{R_1}{}^{(T_1)} \times \log g_0{}^{(2)}(R_{12}, T_1, P) \right] \mathbf{R}_{12} \cdot \nabla_{R_1} T_1 \Bigg\}. \tag{48}$$

A complete solution of this equation would lead to a molecular theory of the spectrum of relaxation times associated with heat flow due to temperature gradients. In order to get the steady-state thermal conductivity, it is sufficient to obtain the time-independent solution. It can be varied by substitution that

$$g_1{}^{(2)} = \frac{1}{2} \frac{\partial g_0{}^{(2)}(R_{12}, T_1, P)}{\partial T_1} \mathbf{R}_{12} \cdot \nabla_{R_1} T_1 \tag{49}$$

is a solution. This leads to the relative pair current density

$$\mathbf{j}_1{}^{(2)} - \rho^{(2)}\mathbf{u}_1 = [\rho^{(1)}]^2 \frac{kT_1}{2\zeta} g_0{}^{(2)} \nabla_{R_{12}}{}^{(T_1)} \frac{\partial \log g_0{}^{(2)}}{\partial T_1} \mathbf{R}_{12} \cdot \nabla T_1 - [\rho^{(1)}]^2 \frac{kT_1}{2\zeta} g_0{}^{(2)} \frac{\partial \log g_0{}^{(2)}}{\partial T_1} \nabla T_1. \tag{50}$$

The relative pair current density must satisfy certain conditions. It must have no current sources or sinks, and it must vanish when the two molecules are infinitely separated. These conditions are satisfied if the equilibrium radial distribution function has the physically reasonable properties of vanishing strongly at $R_{12} = 0$ and approaching unity at infinite separation.

This solution leads to the heat current density

$$\mathbf{q}_V = [\rho^{(1)}]^2 \frac{kT}{4\zeta} \int \left(V - R\frac{dV}{dR} \right) \frac{\mathbf{R}}{R} \frac{d}{dR} \frac{\partial \log g_0{}^{(2)}}{\partial T} (\mathbf{R} \cdot \nabla T) d\mathbf{R} - [\rho^{(1)}]^2 \frac{kT}{4\zeta} \int \left(V\mathbf{1} - \frac{\mathbf{RR}}{R^2} \frac{dV}{dR} \right) \cdot \nabla T \frac{\partial g_0{}^{(2)}}{\partial T} d\mathbf{R}. \tag{51}$$

When the integrations over angles are performed, the heat current density becomes

$$\mathbf{q}_V = [\rho^{(1)}]^2 \frac{\pi kT}{3\zeta} \nabla T \int_0^\infty R^3 \left(V - R \frac{dV}{dR} \right) g_0{}^{(2)}(R)$$
$$\times \frac{d}{dR} \left(\frac{\partial \log g_0{}^{(2)}}{\partial T} \right)_P dR - [\rho^{(1)}]^2 \frac{\pi kT}{\zeta} \nabla T$$
$$\times \int_0^\infty R^2 \left(V - \tfrac{1}{3} R \frac{dV}{dR} \right) \left(\frac{\partial g_0{}^{(2)}}{\partial T} \right)_P dR. \qquad (52)$$

Therefore, the potential energy contribution to the coefficient of thermal conductivity is

$$\kappa_V = [\rho^{(1)}]^2 \frac{\pi kT}{3\zeta} \int_0^\infty R^3 (RV' - V) g_0{}^{(2)}(R)$$
$$\times \frac{d}{dR} \left(\frac{\partial \log g_0{}^{(2)}}{\partial T} \right)_P dR + [\rho^{(1)}]^2 \frac{\pi kT}{\zeta}$$
$$\times \int_0^\infty R^2 (V - \tfrac{1}{3} RV') \left(\frac{\partial g_0{}^{(2)}}{\partial T} \right)_P dR. \qquad (53)$$

V

The theory which was developed in the preceding sections will now be applied to the calculation of the coefficient of thermal conductivity of liquid argon at its boiling point under a pressure of one atmosphere.

The intermolecular potential which will be used in this calculation is the Lennard-Jones potential,

$$V(R) = \epsilon \gamma(x),$$
$$x = R/a, \qquad (54)$$
$$\gamma(x) = 4 \left(\frac{1}{x^{12}} - \frac{1}{x^6} \right).$$

It is convenient to express distance in the reduced units $x = R/a$ and pressure, volume, and temperature in the reduced units

$$P^* = Pa^3/\epsilon,$$
$$T^* = Tk/\epsilon, \qquad (55)$$
$$v^* = v/Na^3.$$

Then, the quantity $\zeta\kappa$ may be expressed in reduced units,

$$(\zeta\kappa)_K = \frac{k\epsilon}{a^3} (\zeta\kappa)_K{}^*,$$
$$(56)$$
$$(\zeta\kappa)_V = \frac{k\epsilon}{a^3} (\zeta\kappa)_V{}^*,$$

where

$$(\zeta\kappa_K)^* = \frac{T^*}{2v^*}\left\{1 + \frac{T^*}{3v^*}\left(\frac{\partial v^*}{\partial T^*}\right)_{P^*}\right\} \tag{57}$$

and

$$(\zeta\kappa_V)^* = \frac{T^*}{2v^*}\left\{\frac{2\pi}{3v^*}\int_0^\infty x^3(x\gamma' - \gamma)g_0^{(2)}(x)\frac{d}{dx}\left(\frac{\partial \log g_0^{(2)}(x)}{\partial T^*}\right)_{P^*} dx - \frac{2\pi}{3v^*}\int_0^\infty x^2(x\gamma' - 3\gamma)\left(\frac{\partial g_0^{(2)}(x)}{\partial T^*}\right)_{P^*} dx\right\}. \tag{58}$$

The integrals may be evaluated if the radial distribution function $g_0^{(2)}(x)$ and its temperature derivative are known. Since the integrals depend rather sensitively on these quantities, it is advantageous to transform the integrals into another form in which a part may be obtained from experimentally available thermodynamic properties. The kinetic contribution $(\zeta\kappa_K)^*$ is already in such a form.

By partial integration and some simple rearrangements, $(\zeta\kappa_V)^*$ may be split into two parts,

$$(\zeta\kappa_V)^* = I_1 + I_2, \tag{59}$$

where

$$I_1 = \frac{\pi T^*}{3v^{*2}}\int_0^\infty (x^3\gamma - x^4\gamma')\frac{\partial g_0^{(2)}(x)}{\partial x}\left(\frac{\partial \log g_0^{(2)}(x)}{\partial T^*}\right)_{P^*} dx \tag{60}$$

and

$$I_2 = -\frac{\pi T^*}{3v^{*2}}\left[\frac{\partial}{\partial T^*}\int_0^\infty (4x^3\gamma' + x^4\gamma'' - 6x^2\gamma)g_0^{(2)}(x)dx\right]_{P_*}. \tag{61}$$

The pressure and internal energy of this fluid are given[4] by

$$\frac{P^*v^*}{T^*} = 1 - \frac{2\pi}{3v^*T^*}\int_0^\infty x^3\gamma'(x)g_0^{(2)}(x)dx \tag{62}$$

and

$$E^* = \tfrac{3}{2}T^* + \frac{2\pi}{v^*}\int_0^\infty x^2\gamma(x)g_0^{(2)}(x)dx, \tag{63}$$

where $E^* = E/N\epsilon$. Since $\gamma(x)$ has the Lennard-Jones form, so that

$$x^4\gamma'' = -19x^3\gamma' - 72x^2\gamma, \tag{64}$$

then the quantity I_2 is

$$I_2 = \frac{\pi T^*}{3v^{*2}}\left[\frac{\partial}{\partial T^*}\int_0^\infty (15x^3\gamma' + 78x^2\gamma)g_0^{(2)}(x)dx\right]_{P^*}. \tag{65}$$

It is possible to express I_2 in terms of thermodynamic variables. Making use of the expressions for P^*v^*/T^* and E^*, the result is

$$I_2 = \frac{T^*}{v^*}\left\{13C_P^* - 12 + \beta^*\left(13\Delta H^* + \frac{41}{2}T^* - 41P^*v^*\right)\right\}. \tag{66}$$

---

[4] Zwanzig, Kirkwood, Stripp, and Oppenheim, *J. Chem. Phys.* **21**, 1268 (1953).

where

$$C_P^* = \left(\frac{\partial H^*}{\partial T^*}\right)_{P^*}; \quad H^* = H/N\epsilon,$$

$$\Delta H^* = H^* - \frac{5}{2}T^*, \tag{67}$$

$$\beta^* = \frac{1}{v^*}\left(\frac{\partial v^*}{\partial T^*}\right)_{P^*}.$$

These are, in reduced units, the specific heat at constant pressure, the difference in enthalpy between the liquid and an ideal gas, and the coefficient of volume expansion.

The integral in I_1 cannot be expressed in terms of thermodynamic quantities in this way, and therefore must be calculated by direct integration. The radial distribution function which is used in this calculation was evaluated[4] for a fluid whose molecules interact with the Lennard-Jones potential, by solving the Born-Green integral equation in the superposition approximation. Since the $g_0^{(2)}(x)$ obtained in this way does not lead to a satisfactory pressure at the density and temperature of the normal boiling point, an empirical parameter c is introduced, and all integrals are evaluated with $g_0^{(2)}(cx)$ instead of $g_0^{(2)}(x)$. The value of c which leads to the correct pressure at the normal boiling point is[4] $c = 1.026$. The integral I_1 was evaluated as a function of c. The details of the calculation of $(\zeta\kappa_K)^*$, I_1, and I_2 are given in an appendix.

The Lennard-Jones parameters have been determined for argon by Michels, Wijker, and Wijker.[5] They are

$$\epsilon = 1.653 \times 10^{-14} \text{ erg},$$

$$a = 3.405 \times 10^{-8} \text{ cm}.$$

In cgs units, the conversion factor from $(\zeta\kappa)^*$ to $\zeta\kappa$ is $k\epsilon/a^3 = 5.779 \times 10^{-8}$. The conversion factor from ergs to calories is 4.1844×10^7 ergs per calorie. In reduced units the temperature and volume at the normal boiling point are $T^* = 0.7454$ and $v^* = 1.223$. The thermodynamic variables needed in the calculation of $(\zeta\kappa_K)^*$ and I_2, and the radial distribution function used to calculate I_1, were obtained for these values of the reduced temperature and volume.

The results of these calculations will now be given. The kinetic contribution to the thermal conductivity is

$$(\zeta\kappa_K)^* = 0.35.$$

The contribution I_2 to the thermal conductivity is

$$I_2 = 10.28.$$

The contribution $I_1(c)$ was calculated for several values of c. This function is only moderately sensitive to c. The most significant values of $I_1(c)$ are

$$I_1(1.000) = 50.89,$$

$$I_1(1.026) = 73.06.$$

[5] Michels, Wijker, and Wijker, *Physica* **15**, 627 (1949).

It is clear that the kinetic part of the thermal conductivity of this liquid is negligible, and that the thermodynamically evaluated part of the potential contribution is dominated by the part which must be calculated with an explicit knowledge of the radial distribution function. When the various contributions are added together, one obtains

$$(\zeta\kappa)^* = 61.5 \quad (c = 1.000),$$

$$(\zeta\kappa)^* = 84.7 \quad (c = 1.026).$$

The friction constant ζ was evaluated by the linear trajectory method, which will be described in a future article in this series. This calculation was performed for $c = 1$ and $c = 1.026$. The results are

$$\zeta(1) = 3.53 \times 10^{-10} \text{ g/sec},$$

$$\zeta(1.026) = 2.85 \times 10^{-10} \text{ g/sec}.$$

The thermal conductivity is therefore

$$\kappa(1) = 2.4 \times 10^{-4} \text{ cal/g sec °K},$$

$$\kappa(1.026) = 4.1 \times 10^{-4} \text{ cal/g sec °K}.$$

The thermal conductivity of argon at its normal boiling point was measured by Uhlir.[6] His result is

$$\kappa_{\text{expt}} = 2.9 \times 10^{-4} \text{ cal/g sec °K}.$$

The agreement is quite satisfactory. For $c = 1.026$, the difference between theory and experiment is forty percent. For $c = 1.000$, the difference is seventeen percent.

APPENDIX

For the calculation of $(\zeta\kappa_K)^*$ and I_2, various thermodynamic properties of argon are required. The values used were obtained from the *International Critical Tables*. Although they may be somewhat inaccurate, the contribution of $(\zeta\kappa_K)^*$ and I_2 to the total thermal conductivity is only about fifteen percent, so that any errors in these values will not lead to a significant error in the final result. The values which were used are

$$C_p = 10.1 \text{ cal/mole °K},$$

$$\Delta H = -1500 \text{ cal/mole},$$

$$\beta = \frac{1}{v}\left(\frac{\partial v}{\partial T}\right)_p = 0.00465 \text{ 1/°K},$$

$$T = 89\text{°K},$$

$$v = 29.0 \text{ cc/mole}.$$

In the calculation of $(\zeta\kappa_K)^*$ and I_2, the thermodynamic quantities were combined in their unreduced form, and then the results were reduced.

[6] A. Uhlir, Jr., *J. Chem. Phys.* **20**, 463 (1952).

In the calculation of I_1, the derivatives of $g_0^{(2)}(x)$ with respect to x and T^* are required. The method of calculation of $g_0^{(2)}(x)$ has been described.[4] The derivative $dg_0^{(2)}(x)/dx$ was evaluated using the differentiated form of Newton's interpolation formula, with the interval 0.01. The derivative $[\partial \log g_0^{(2)}(x)/\partial T^*]_p{}^*$ was converted to another form

$$\left(\frac{\partial \log g_0^{(2)}(x)}{\partial T^*}\right)_{P^*} = \left(\frac{\partial \log g_0^{(2)}(x)}{\partial T^*}\right)_{v^*} + \left(\frac{\partial \log g_0^{(2)}(x)}{\partial v^*}\right)_{T^*}\left(\frac{\partial v^*}{\partial T^*}\right)_{P^*}, \tag{68}$$

since $g_0^{(2)}(x)$ is available as a function of temperature and volume,

$$\log g_0^{(2)}(x) = \psi_0(x, v^*) + \frac{1}{T^*}\psi_1(x, v^*) + \frac{1}{T^{*2}}\psi_2(x, v^*). \tag{69}$$

The differentiation with respect to temperature was performed with this expression. The derivative of log $g_0^{(2)}(x)$ with respect to v^* was evaluated using the differentiated form of Lagrange's interpolation formula. The experimental value of $(\partial v^*/\partial T^*)_{P^*}$ was used. When this calculation was performed with the scale factor c, the equation

$$A(c) = \int_0^\infty (x^4\gamma' - x^3\gamma)\frac{\partial g_0^{(2)}(cx)}{\partial x} \times \left(\frac{\partial \log g_0^{(2)}(cx)}{\partial T^*}\right)_{P^*} dx = c^3A(1) - 52c^3(c^6 - 1) \times \int_0^\infty \frac{1}{y^9}\frac{dg_0^{(2)}(y)}{dy}\left(\frac{\partial \log g_0^{(2)}(y)}{\partial T^*}\right)_{P^*,c} dy + O\left(\frac{\partial c}{\partial T^*}\right) + O\left(\frac{\partial c}{\partial v^*}\right) \tag{70}$$

was used. The corrections arising from the dependence of c on T^* and v^* were estimated, using experimental data on the equation of state and the internal energy to evaluate $\partial c/\partial T^*$ and $\partial c/\partial v^*$. It was found that these corrections may be neglected. The integrals were evaluated numerically, using Simpson's rule with an 0.01 interval from $x = 0$ to $x = 1.12$, Simpson's rule with an 0.02 interval from $x = 1.12$ to $x = 1.28$, and the trapezoidal rule with an 0.04 interval for $x > 1.28$.

The Statistical Mechanical Theory of Transport Processes. VIII. Quantum Theory of Transport in Gases

JOHN ROSS* AND JOHN G. KIRKWOOD, *Sterling Chemistry Laboratory, Yale University, New Haven, Connecticut*

(Received February 22, 1954)

The quantum-mechanical analog of the Maxwell–Boltzmann equation of transport in gases of low density is derived from the quantum-mechanical equation for the motion in phase space of the Wigner function. The derivation is based upon the theory of phase-space transformation functions which is developed in this article. Although the present treatment resembles the derivation of Mori and Ono, it is simpler and more general. Particularly, the assumption of random *a priori* phases, an integral part of Mori and Ono's work, need not be applied explicitly. The Uhling and Uhlenbeck equation is verified in the Born collision approximation.

The fundamental equation of the kinetic theory of transport phenomena in dilute gases is the integro-differential Maxwell-Boltzmann equation. Kirkwood[1] obtained this equation from the principles of classical statistical mechanics in an analytic derivation which proceeded from the Liouville equation. The purpose of his analysis was: to establish a molecular theory of transport in gases based upon the statistical mechanical theory of transport processes presented in a previous paper[2]; to elucidate the usual physical arguments employed in deriving the Boltzmann equation; and to outline clearly the assumptions and approximations needed to arrive at this equation. Solutions of the Boltzmann equation, correct to various orders, have been obtained by Enskog, Chapman,[3] and Grad,[4] among others. These solutions have provided adequate theories of transport in dilute gases obeying classical mechanics by establishing relations between the macroscopic transport coefficients and molecular properties.

For quantum-mechanical systems composed of gases of low density the analog of the Maxwell-Boltzmann equation was formulated first by Nordheim[5] and Uhling and Uhlenbeck[6] in heuristic arguments proceeding from the classical equation. Essentially, these authors assumed the validity and sufficiency of the replacement of the classical collision cross section by its

---

* National Science Foundation Post-Doctoral Fellow, 1952–1953. Present address: Department of Chemistry, Brown University, Providence, Rhode Island.

[1] J. G. Kirkwood, *J. Chem. Phys.* **15**, 72 (1947).

[2] J. G. Kirkwood, *J. Chem. Phys.* **14**, 180 (1946).

[3] S. Chapman and T. G. Cowling, *Mathematical Theory of Non-Uniform Gases* (Cambridge University Press, Cambridge, 1939).

[4] H. Grad, *Comm. Pure Appl. Math.* **2**, 331 (1949).

[5] L. Nordheim, *Proc. Roy. Soc.* (London) **A119**, 689 (1928).

[6] E. A. Uhling and G. E. Uhlenbeck, *Phys. Rev.* **43**, 552 (1933).

quantum-mechanical counterpart. All theories and computations[7–10] of transport phenomena in quantum mechanical systems have been based upon this equation. Mori and Ono[11] obtained the Uhling and Uhlenbeck equation in a development which generalized Kirkwood's analysis to the quantum-mechanical problem. Their derivation proceeded from the quantum-mechanical Liouville equation in terms of the Wigner distribution function, the Wigner equation, as established by Wigner[12] and Irving and Zwanzig.[13] Their work, in relation to this article, is discussed below.

We shall present a derivation of the quantum-mechanical Boltzmann equation for reasons similar to those which motivated the derivation of the classical Boltzmann equation. Although our development, like Mori and Ono's, employs the Wigner equation as a starting point and bears some resemblance to their work, the present analysis is more general and is believed to be simpler.

In a previous paper of this series[13] the equation of motion of a quantum-mechanical N-particle system was written as

$$\frac{\partial f^{(N)}}{\partial t} + \sum_{k=1}^{N} \frac{\mathbf{p}_k}{m_k} \cdot \nabla_{\mathbf{R}_k} f^{(N)} + \boldsymbol{\theta} \cdot f^{(N)} = 0, \tag{1}$$

where $\mathbf{p}_k$ and $\mathbf{R}_k$ are the momenta and coordinates of the kth particle, and t is the time. The Wigner function,[12] $f^{(N)}$, can be considered as a quantum-mechanical phase space distribution function and it is defined as a Fourier transform of the density matrix:

$$f^{(N)}(\mathbf{R}, \mathbf{p}; t) = \left(\frac{1}{\pi\hbar}\right)^{3N} \int \cdots \int \exp\left(\frac{2i}{\hbar} \mathbf{p} \cdot \mathbf{Y}\right) \times \rho^{(N)}(\mathbf{R} - \mathbf{Y}, \mathbf{R} + \mathbf{Y}; t) d\mathbf{Y}, \tag{2}$$

where $\hbar$ is Planck's constant divided by 2π. The symbols $\mathbf{R}$, $\mathbf{Y}$, $\mathbf{p}$, etc. denote coordinates, etc., of the entire set of particles under consideration; integrations are understood to extend from $-\infty$ to $+\infty$ unless specified otherwise. The density matrix[14] is defined as

$$\rho^{(N)}(\mathbf{R} - \mathbf{Y}, \mathbf{R} + \mathbf{Y}; t) = \psi^*(\mathbf{R} + \mathbf{Y}; t)\psi(\mathbf{R} - \mathbf{Y}; t) \tag{3}$$

for a pure state, and as

$$\rho^{(N)}(\mathbf{R} - \mathbf{Y}, \mathbf{R} + \mathbf{Y}; t) = \sum_j w_j \psi_j^*(\mathbf{R} + \mathbf{Y}; t)\psi_j(\mathbf{R} - \mathbf{Y}; t) \tag{4}$$

for a mixed state (ensemble of systems), where $\boldsymbol{\Psi}_j$ is the wave function, and w_j

---

[7] E. A. Uhling, *Phys. Rev.* **46**, 917 (1934).
[8] E. J. Hellund and E. A. Uhling, *Phys. Rev.* **56**, 818 (1939).
[9] A. Isihara, *J. Phys. Soc.* (Japan) **5**, 213, 217 (1950).
[10] J. de Boer and R. B. Bird, University of Wisconsin Naval Research Laboratory Research Report CF 1509–13 (June, 1952).
[11] H. Mori and S. Ono, *Progr. Theoret. Phys.* (Japan) **8**, 327 (1952).
[12] E. P. Wigner, *Phys. Rev.* **40**, 749 (1932).
[13] J. M. Irving and R. W. Zwanzig, *J. Chem. Phys.* **19**, 1173 (1951).
[14] See J. von Neumann, *Mathematische Grundlage der Quantenmechanik* (Dover Publications, New York, 1943).

the statistical weight of the jth state of the ensemble. The operator $\boldsymbol{\theta}$ can be written in various forms; an integral representation is

$$\boldsymbol{\theta} \cdot f^{(N)} = \frac{i}{\hbar}\left(\frac{1}{\pi\hbar}\right)^{3N} \int \cdots \int [V(\mathbf{R} - \mathbf{x}) - V(\mathbf{R} + \mathbf{x})]$$

$$\times \exp\left[\frac{2i}{\hbar}(\mathbf{p} - \mathbf{p}') \cdot \mathbf{x}\right] f^{(N)}(\mathbf{R}, \mathbf{p}'; t) d\mathbf{p}' d\mathbf{x}, \tag{5}$$

where V is the potential derived from external and internal forces acting on the N-particle system. If the potential energy can be expanded in a Taylor series, then the $\boldsymbol{\theta}$ operator can also be written as a differential operator,

$$\boldsymbol{\theta} \cdot f^{(N)}(\mathbf{R}, \mathbf{p}; t) = -\frac{2}{\hbar} \sin\left[\frac{\hbar}{2} \nabla_{\mathbf{R}} \nabla_{\mathbf{p}}\right] V(\mathbf{R}) f^{(N)}(\mathbf{R}, \mathbf{p}; t), \tag{6}$$

where $\nabla_{\mathbf{R}}$ operates on the potential only. From the above definitions it is clear that the Wigner equation, Eq. (1), is a Fourier transform of Schrödinger's time dependent equation expressed in terms of the density matrix. The introduction of the Wigner function is justified by the advantage that the formation of phase space averages requires only direct integration of the product of the distribution function and the quantity to be averaged, whereas the density matrix formalism requires operator techniques.

As in the classical derivation it is necessary here to use distribution functions "coarse-grained" in time. These functions are defined as averages over an interval τ subsequent to the time t,

$$\bar{f}^{(N)}(\mathbf{R}, \mathbf{p}; t) = \frac{1}{\tau} \int_0^\tau f^{(N)}(\mathbf{R}, \mathbf{p}; t + s) ds. \tag{7}$$

It will be found that it is the time-smoothed distribution function $\bar{f}^{(1)}$ which will satisfy the quantum-mechanical Boltzmann equation.

Reduced distribution functions and reduced equations of motion are established in an analogous manner to the classical ones. Thus $f_N^{(n)}$, the distribution function of the subset $\{n\}$ taken from the set $\{N\}$ is formally

$$f_N^{(n)}(\mathbf{r}, \mathbf{p}; t) = \int \cdots \int f^{(N)}(\mathbf{r}, \mathbf{p}, \mathbf{R}, \mathbf{P}; t) d\mathbf{R} d\mathbf{P}, \tag{8}$$

where $\mathbf{r}$ and $\mathbf{p}$ refer to the set $\{n\}$, and $\mathbf{R}$ and $\mathbf{P}$ to the set $\{N - n\}$. The subscript N on the reduced distribution function serves as a reminder that generally these functions depend on the statistics obeyed by the N-particle system. The reduced equation of motion will be formulated with the aid of two hypotheses. First, it is assumed that the total potential can be written as a sum of pair potentials and external potentials,

$$V(\mathbf{R}) = \sum_{i=1}^{N} \phi_i(\mathbf{R}_i) + \tfrac{1}{2} \sum_{\substack{i=1 \\ i \neq j}}^{N} \sum_{j=1}^{N} U_{ij}(\mathbf{R}_i, \mathbf{R}_j). \tag{9}$$

The intermolecular potential U_{ij} is taken to be dependent upon the intermolecular distance $R_{ij} = |\mathbf{R}_j - \mathbf{R}_i|$ only, and thus is spherically symmetric; the range of the intermolecular potential is taken to be finite so that $U_{ij} = 0$ if $R_{ij} > \rho^0$. These two restrictions are not necessary requirements for the formulation of the reduced equation of motion but the present analysis is confined to such types of potentials. Secondly, it is postulated that the system is sufficiently dilute to permit the omission of interactions due to the indistinguishability of identical particles for all but a pair of particles at a time. This interaction, which is an apparent attraction between particles in the case of Bose-Einstein statistics but an apparent repulsion in the case of Fermi-Dirac statistics, becomes of importance when the average de Broglie wavelength of the particles of the system approaches the average distance between them. Later we shall be required to adopt the binary collision assumption which permits the reduction of the complex N body problem to the soluble pair equation of motion. This hypothesis roughly implies a state of dilution in the gas such that the average distance between molecules is large compared to the range of the intermolecular potential. Thus the interactions due to the statistics between the subset of two particles and the subset of the remaining $N - 2$ particles need to be considered only when the de Broglie wavelength is large compared to the range of the intermolecular potential; in helium for example, this situation arises at approximately 1°K. Furthermore, the approximate corrections for this density-dependent aspect of interactions due to quantum statistics introduce distribution functions, and thus density dependence, of a higher order than those remaining in the Boltzmann equation as a consequence of the binary collision assumption.

By means of the above two assumptions, Eq. (1) can be integrated over all coordinates and momenta, except those of the 1st particle, to yield, on construction of time averages,

$$\frac{\partial \bar{f}^{(1)}}{\partial t} + \frac{\mathbf{p}_1}{m_1} \cdot \nabla_{\mathbf{R}_1} \bar{f}^{(1)} + \boldsymbol{\theta}^{(e)} \cdot \bar{f}^{(1)} = -\frac{N_2}{\tau} \int \cdots \int_0^\tau$$

$$\times\ \boldsymbol{\theta}^{(2)} \cdot f^{(2)}(\mathbf{R}_1\mathbf{R}_2\mathbf{p}_1\mathbf{p}_2;\, t + s)\, d\mathbf{R}_2 d\mathbf{p}_2 ds, \qquad (10)$$

where $\boldsymbol{\theta}^{(e)}$, and $\boldsymbol{\theta}^{(2)}$ represent, respectively, the operators corresponding to external forces acting on the 1st particle and the intermolecular potential between the 1st and any other molecule of the remaining set of $(N - 1)$ identical molecules, denoted here by N_2.

The pair distribution function $f^{(2)}$ can be expressed in terms of singlet distribution functions

$$^{(2)}(\mathbf{R}_1\mathbf{R}_2\mathbf{p}_1\mathbf{p}_2;\, t + s) = [1 + \vartheta(\mathbf{R}_1\mathbf{R}_2\mathbf{p}_1\mathbf{p}_2;\, t + s)]$$

$$\times\ \{[\mathbf{O}_\pm] f^{(1)}(\mathbf{R}_1\mathbf{p}_1;\, t + s) f^{(1)}(\mathbf{R}_2\mathbf{p}_2;\, t + s)\}, \qquad (11)$$

where $[\mathbf{O}_\pm]$ is the symmetry operator for Wigner distribution functions describing systems of independent particles which obey Bose-Einstein, $[\mathbf{O}_+]$, or Fermi-Dirac statistics, $[\mathbf{O}_-]$. This symmetry operator, discussed in Appendix B, is obtained by symmetrizing the wave functions from which the Wigner distribution function is formulated. $[\mathbf{O}_\pm]$ is not a simple permutation operator but an integral operator. The correlation function $[1 + \vartheta(\mathbf{R}_1\mathbf{R}_2\mathbf{p}_1\mathbf{p}_2;\, t + s)]$ is defined by Eq. (11). The analysis will be restricted here to conditions for which the correlation integral

$$-N_2 \int \cdots \int_0^\tau \boldsymbol{\theta}^{(2)} \cdot [\vartheta(\mathbf{R}_1\mathbf{R}_2\mathbf{p}_1\mathbf{p}_2;\, t+s)]$$

$$\times \{[\mathbf{O}_\pm] f^{(1)}(\mathbf{R}_1\mathbf{p}_1;\, t+s) f^{(1)}(\mathbf{R}_2\mathbf{p}_2;\, t+s)\} d\mathbf{R}_2 d\mathbf{p}_2 ds$$

is bounded and of the order of a finite time interval τ_k; if this prevails, Eq. (10) reduces then to

$$\frac{\partial \bar{f}^{(1)}}{\partial t} + \frac{\mathbf{p}_1}{m_1} \cdot \nabla_{\mathbf{R}_1} \bar{f}^{(1)} + \boldsymbol{\theta}^{(e)} \cdot \bar{f}^{(1)}$$

$$= -\frac{N_2}{\tau} \int \cdots \int_0^\tau \boldsymbol{\theta}^{(2)} \cdot \{[\mathbf{O}_\pm] f^{(1)}(\mathbf{R}_1\mathbf{p}_1;\, t+s)$$

$$\times f^{(1)}(\mathbf{R}_2\mathbf{p}_2;\, t+s)\} d\mathbf{R}_2 d\mathbf{p}_2 ds + \mathrm{O}\left(\frac{\tau_k}{\tau}\right). \qquad (12)$$

The integral in Eq. (12) will be shown to be proportional to τ so that for sufficiently large values of τ the contributions of the deviation of the correlation function from unity to Eq. (12) can be made as small as desirable. This statement is similar to the assumption applied in the derivation of the classical Boltzmann equation, namely that the deviation of the correlation function from unity is a short-range function of the intermolecular forces and can be made negligibly small for sufficiently large values of τ. The requirement that the correlation integral be bounded is to be considered a part of the molecular chaos assumption, which is thus a necessary condition for this derivation.

At this point it is instructive to discuss the essential differences between the classical and quantum-mechanical derivation and the additional complications encountered in the latter case. The classical analysis proceeds from the equivalent of Eq. (10), where $\boldsymbol{\theta}^{(e)}$ and $\boldsymbol{\theta}^{(2)}$ in this case correspond to $-[\nabla_{\mathbf{R}_1}\phi(\mathbf{R}_1)] \cdot \nabla_{\mathbf{p}_1}$ and $-[\nabla_{\mathbf{R}_{12}} U(R_{12})] \cdot \nabla_{\mathbf{p}_1}$, by introducing phase-space transformation functions[15] which are found to satisfy the partial differential Liouville equation. The solutions of this equation are readily obtained and are Dirac δ functions which express the contact transformation of classical mechanics. They describe the path of motion of the system in phase space, a trajectory along which the distribution function remains invariant. Thus the time-smoothing process can be performed on the δ functions, which are the transformation functions of the distribution function, rather than on the distribution function itself. Subsequent integration over relative configuration space leads to the Maxwell-Boltzmann equation.

The quantum-mechanical analysis is more complex and the additional difficulties have their origin in the more intricate equation of motion. The Liouville equation for $f^{(2)}$ is a first-order, partial differential equation which is linear and homogeneous. It follows that $f^{(2)}$ is constant along the characteristics, which are the classical trajectories in phase space. Thus the only

---

[15] In Kirkwood's derivation this was accomplished in effect in his equivalent of Eq. (10) by introducing the Dirac δ functions and integrating over the phase-space of the 1st particle in the collision term.

physically interesting solution of the Liouville equation is the one exhibiting invariance along the path of motion. The Wigner equation, however, is an integro-differential equation, and the distribution function $f^{(2)}$, which provides a complete description in the two-body problem, is generally not invariant as the motion proceeds through phase space. The lack of invariance, which amounts to an apparent diffusion of the probability fluid in phase space, can be surmised from the formal analogy between the Schrödinger equation and the diffusion equation. It follows from this that the δ function is in general inadequate as a transformation function since it cannot account for the diffraction phenomena of quantum mechanical processes. Despite these additional difficulties, the theory of quantum-mechanical phase-space transformation seems a convenient as well as a very general formalism for the treatment of quantum dynamics.

In general, the temporal transformation function can be defined as the kernel of the following integral equation

$$f^{(N)}(\mathbf{R}, \mathbf{p}; t+s) = \int \cdots \int \times K^{(N)}(\mathbf{R}, \mathbf{p} | \mathbf{R}', \mathbf{p}'; s) f^{(N)}(\mathbf{R}', \mathbf{p}'; t) d\mathbf{R}' d\mathbf{p}', \tag{13}$$

yielding the distribution function at a given instant and position in phase space in terms of the known distribution at a previous time. Moyal[16] formulated a statistical theory of quantum mechanics in which he presented some of the properties of $K^{(N)}$.[17] The transformation function is a conditional probability formally analogous to such functions encountered in other stochastic processes as Brownian motion. It is a product of δ functions, $K^{(N)} = \delta(\mathbf{R} - \mathbf{R}')\delta(\mathbf{p} - \mathbf{p}')$, at $s = 0$ for all dynamical problems; this merely expresses the required initial condition. Furthermore, the transformation function is for all intervals a product of δ functions,

$$K^{(N)} = \delta[\mathbf{R} - \mathbf{R}(\mathbf{R}', \mathbf{p}'; s)]\delta[\mathbf{p} - \mathbf{p}(\mathbf{R}', \mathbf{p}'; s)],$$

expressing the contact transformation, for the deterministic problems of quantum mechanics: the free particle, the uniformly accelerated particle, and the harmonic oscillator. The dynamical properties of the quantum-mechanical system are contained implicitly in this function which thus expresses the probabilistic nature of the transitions characterizing the motion.

The formalism of the phase-space transformation function permits the reduction of the problem of the determination of the distribution function to the determination of the transformation function in terms of its parameters. Moyal obtained K as an infinite power series in s in which the coefficients are functions of the Hamiltonian of the system. This expansion is not convenient for an evaluation of K, not only because of possible convergence difficulties encountered at larger values of s, but also because the approximation of termination of the series does not seem to correspond to any useful perturbation treatment.

A more general method for the determination of the transformation function can be found by recourse to the theory of the analogous Markoffian

---

[16] J. E. Moyal, *Proc. Cambridge Phil. Soc.* **45**, 99 (1949).

[17] See also H. Jeffreys, *Phil. Mag.* **33**, 815 (1942).

transformation kernel which obeys the same differential equation as the distribution function itself. Substitution of Eq. (13) into Eq. (1) shows that $K^{(N)}$ is in fact the solution of the integro-differential equation

$$\frac{\partial K^{(N)}}{\partial s} + \sum_{k=1}^{N} \frac{\mathbf{p}_k}{m_k} \cdot \nabla_{\mathbf{R}_k} K^{(N)} + \boldsymbol{\theta} \cdot K^{(N)} = 0, \tag{14}$$

with initial condition

$$K^{(N)}(\mathbf{R}, \mathbf{p} | \mathbf{R}', \mathbf{p}'; 0) = \delta(\mathbf{R} - \mathbf{R}')\delta(\mathbf{p} - \mathbf{p}'), \tag{15}$$

at $s = 0$. Equation (14) reduces to the classical equation if the third and higher derivatives of the potential vanish. Under such conditions, $K^{(N)}$ reduces to a product of δ functions, as stated above.

Equation (14) must be considered a fundamental equation of quantum dynamics. The advantage of this equation over the corresponding one for the Wigner distribution function is established by the existence of known initial conditions which allow the construction of solutions. The importance of the transformation function, obtained as a solution of Eq. (14), for a rigorous treatment of scattering problems might be stressed here. The relations between the phase-space transformation function $K^{(N)}$, the wave transformation function, and the scattering cross section are given in Appendix A.

The analytic form of Eq. (14), as well as the initial condition, Eq. (15), for $K^{(N)}$ as defined by Eq. (13), is independent of the statistics obeyed by the particular system. It follows that this transformation function, which is completely determined by Eq. (14) and the given initial condition, does not depend on the statistics of the system. This fact facilitates greatly the solution of the equation for $K^{(N)}$.

The reduced transformation functions are formulated in a similar manner as the reduced distribution functions. In particular, the pair transformation function $K^{(2)}$ is given by

$$K^{(2)}(\mathbf{R}_1\mathbf{R}_2\mathbf{p}_1\mathbf{p}_2 | \mathbf{R}_1'\mathbf{R}_2'\mathbf{p}_1'\mathbf{p}_2'; s) = \int \cdots \int$$
$$\times K^{(N)}(\mathbf{R}_1 \cdots \mathbf{R}_N\mathbf{p}_1 \cdots \mathbf{p}_N | \mathbf{R}_1' \cdots \mathbf{R}_N'\mathbf{p}_1' \cdots \mathbf{p}_N'; s)$$
$$\times d\mathbf{R}_3 \cdots d\mathbf{R}_N d\mathbf{p}_3 \cdots d\mathbf{p}_N. \tag{16}$$

Integration of Eq. (13) over the unprimed coordinates and momenta of all particles except 1 and 2 yields

$$f^{(2)}(\mathbf{R}_1\mathbf{R}_2\mathbf{p}_1\mathbf{p}_2; t + s)$$
$$= \int \cdots \int K^{(2)}(\mathbf{R}_1\mathbf{R}_2\mathbf{p}_1\mathbf{p}_2 | \mathbf{R}_1'\mathbf{R}_2'\mathbf{p}_1'\mathbf{p}_2'; s) \tag{17}$$
$$\times f^{(N)}(\mathbf{R}_1' \cdots \mathbf{R}_N'\mathbf{p}_1 \cdots \mathbf{p}_N'; t) \times d\mathbf{R}_1' \cdots d\mathbf{R}_N' d\mathbf{p}_1' \cdots d\mathbf{p}_N',$$

$$f^{(2)}(\mathbf{R}_1\mathbf{R}_2\mathbf{p}_1\mathbf{p}_2; t + s)$$
$$= \int \cdots \int K^{(2)}(\mathbf{R}_1\mathbf{R}_2\mathbf{p}_1\mathbf{p}_2 | \mathbf{R}_1'\mathbf{R}_2'\mathbf{p}_1'\mathbf{p}_2'; s)$$
$$\times f^{(2)}(\mathbf{R}_1'\mathbf{R}_2'\mathbf{p}_1'\mathbf{p}_2'; t) d\mathbf{R}_1' d\mathbf{R}_2' d\mathbf{p}_1' d\mathbf{p}_2',$$

where the integrations of the distribution functions are performed with the aid of the hypothesis discussed above, that interactions due to quantum statistics between particles 1 or 2 and the set of the remaining $(N - 2)$ particles can be neglected.

The pair transformation function is determined as a solution of the integro-differential equation for $K^{(2)}$ obtained by integrating Eq. (14) over the coordinates and momenta of all particles except 1 and 2. If the density of the system under consideration is sufficiently small it becomes possible to apply the binary collision approximation, i.e., it is assumed that an adequate description of all encounters among the molecules of the system can be given in terms of collisions involving two molecules only. This implies that the probability of the simultaneous presence of three molecules in a volume of configuration space of approximate linear dimension L_τ is negligible compared to the probability of two molecules occupying this volume. (L_τ is the distance traversed by a *classical* particle with the same initial momentum as in the quantum-mechanical case in the time interval τ). Then the triplet transformation function plays no role and the pair transformation function $K^{(2)}$ is determined as a solution of the pair transformation function equation at zero density, which can be written in center-of-mass coordinates as

$$K^{(2)}(\mathbf{R}_1\mathbf{R}_2\mathbf{p}_1\mathbf{p}_2|\mathbf{R}_1'\mathbf{R}_2'\mathbf{p}_1'\mathbf{p}_2'; s) = \delta(\mathbf{R}_c - \mathbf{R}_c')\delta(\mathbf{p}_c - \mathbf{p}_c')K^{(2)}(\mathbf{R}, \mathbf{p}|\mathbf{R}', \mathbf{p}'; s) \tag{19}$$

$$\mathbf{R}_c = \tfrac{1}{2}(\mathbf{R}_2 + \mathbf{R}_1) \qquad \mathbf{R} = \mathbf{R}_2 - \mathbf{R}_1$$

$$\mathbf{p}_c = \mathbf{p}_2 + \mathbf{p}_1 \qquad \mathbf{p} = \tfrac{1}{2}(\mathbf{p}_2 - \mathbf{p}_1),$$

$$\frac{\partial K^{(2)}}{\partial s} + \frac{\mathbf{p}}{m}\cdot\nabla_{\mathbf{R}}K^{(2)} + \boldsymbol{\theta}\cdot K^{(2)}(\mathbf{R}, \mathbf{p}|\mathbf{R}', \mathbf{p}'; s) = 0 \tag{20}$$

$$\frac{1}{m} = \frac{1}{m_1} + \frac{1}{m_2},$$

$$\boldsymbol{\theta}\cdot K^{(2)}(\mathbf{R}, \mathbf{p}|\mathbf{R}', \mathbf{p}'; s) = \frac{i}{\hbar}\left(\frac{1}{\pi\hbar}\right)^3\int\cdots\int[U(\mathbf{R} - \mathbf{x}) - U(\mathbf{R} + \mathbf{x})] \times \exp\left[\frac{2i}{\hbar}(\mathbf{p} - \boldsymbol{\xi})\cdot\mathbf{x}\right]K^{(2)}(\mathbf{R}, \boldsymbol{\xi}|\mathbf{R}', \mathbf{p}'; s)d\mathbf{x}d\boldsymbol{\xi}, \tag{21}$$

with the initial condition

$$K^{(2)}(\mathbf{R}, \mathbf{p}|\mathbf{R}', \mathbf{p}'; 0) = \delta(\mathbf{R} - \mathbf{R}')\delta(\mathbf{p} - \mathbf{p}').$$

External forces are assumed to have sufficiently slowly-varying spatial dependence so as not to affect the collision between two particles.

An explicit solution of Eq. (20) can be effected by successive approximations based upon an expansion of the transformation function in which the potential of intermolecular force is treated as a perturbation, as in the Born collision theory. Thus, $K^{(2)}$ can be written as

$$K^{(2)} = K_0^{(2)} + K_1^{(2)} + K_2^{(2)}\cdots, \tag{22}$$

where the representation of the transformation function by the first two terms only corresponds to the well-known Born approximation in the solution of scattering problems. This expansion is analogous to the one usually employed for the wave transformation function, as shown in Appendix B. Substitution of this series into Eq. (20) yields, on equating terms of the same order of approximation, the set of equations

$$\frac{\partial K_0{}^{(2)}}{\partial s} + \frac{\mathbf{p}}{m} \cdot \nabla_R K_0{}^{(2)}(\mathbf{R}, \mathbf{p} | \mathbf{R}', \mathbf{p}'; s) = 0$$

$$\frac{\partial K_1{}^{(2)}}{\partial s} + \frac{\mathbf{p}}{m} \cdot \nabla_R K_1{}^{(2)} + \mathbf{\theta} \cdot K_0{}^{(2)} = 0 \tag{23}$$

$$\frac{\partial K_2{}^{(2)}}{\partial s} + \frac{\mathbf{p}}{m} \cdot \nabla_R K_2{}^{(2)} + \mathbf{\theta} \cdot K_1{}^{(2)} = 0$$

etc. with solutions

$$K_0{}^{(2)}(\mathbf{R}, \mathbf{p} | \mathbf{R}', \mathbf{p}'; s) = \delta(\mathbf{p} - \mathbf{p}')\delta(\mathbf{R} - \mathbf{R}' - \Delta \mathbf{R}) \quad \Delta \mathbf{R} = \mathbf{R} - \mathbf{R}' = \left(\frac{\mathbf{p}}{m}\right)s$$

$$K_1{}^{(2)}(\mathbf{R}, \mathbf{p} | \mathbf{R}', \mathbf{p}'; s) = -\int_0^s \exp\left[(s' - s)\frac{\mathbf{p}}{m} \cdot \nabla_R\right] \mathbf{\theta} \cdot K_0{}^{(2)} ds' \tag{24}$$

$$K_2{}^{(2)}(\mathbf{R}, \mathbf{p} | \mathbf{R}', \mathbf{p}'; s) = -\int_0^s \exp\left[(s' - s)\frac{\mathbf{p}}{m} \cdot \nabla_R\right] \mathbf{\theta} \cdot K_1{}^{(2)} ds'$$

etc. These Eqs. (24) represent the solution for $K^{(2)}$, when this function can be expanded as shown in Eq. (22).

The formal expression for the quantum-mechanical Boltzmann equation is obtained by the introduction of the transformation function into Eq. (12),

$$\frac{\partial \bar{f}^{(1)}}{\partial t} + \frac{\mathbf{p}_1}{m_1} \cdot \nabla_{R_1} \bar{f}^{(1)} + \mathbf{\theta}^{(e)} \cdot \bar{f}^{(1)}$$

$$= -\frac{N_2}{\tau} \int \cdots \int_0^\tau \mathbf{\theta}^{(2)} \cdot K^{(2)}(\mathbf{R}_1 \mathbf{R}_2 \mathbf{p}_1 \mathbf{p}_2 | \mathbf{R}_1' \mathbf{R}_2' \mathbf{p}_1' \mathbf{p}_2'; s)$$

$$\times \{[O_\pm] f^{(1)}(\mathbf{R}_1' \mathbf{p}_1'; t) f^{(1)}(\mathbf{R}_2' \mathbf{p}_2'; t)\}$$

$$\times d\mathbf{R}_1' d\mathbf{R}_2' d\mathbf{R}_2 d\mathbf{p}_1' d\mathbf{p}_2' d\mathbf{p}_2 ds + O\left(\frac{\tau k}{\tau}\right). \tag{25}$$

The pair transformation function $K^{(2)}$ is determined as indicated in the series of Eqs. (19)–(24), and Eq. (25) represents the quantum-mechanical Boltzmann equation of transport for dilute gases.

The particular case for which the series expansion of $K^{(2)}$ can be terminated after the second term will now be carried through explicitly. As stated this problem will be found equivalent to the Born approximation in the solution of scattering problems. Equation (25) can then be expressed by

$$\frac{\partial \bar{f}^{(1)}}{\partial t} + \frac{\mathbf{p}_1}{m_1} \cdot \nabla_{\mathbf{R}_1} \bar{f}^{(1)} + \boldsymbol{\theta}^{(e)} \cdot \bar{f}^{(1)}$$

$$= -\frac{N_2}{2\tau}\left(\frac{1}{2\pi h}\right)^3 \int \cdots \int_0^\tau \boldsymbol{\theta}^{(2)} \cdot [T_r]$$

$$\times \left\{ \exp\left[\frac{i}{\hbar}(\mathbf{p}'' - \mathbf{p}') \cdot \mathbf{R}'\right](K_0{}^{(2)} + K_1{}^{(2)})\right.$$

$$\times f^{(1)}\left[\left(\mathbf{R}_c - \frac{\mathbf{R}^0}{2}\right), \left(\frac{\mathbf{p}_c}{2} - \mathbf{p}^0\right); t\right]$$

$$\left.\times f^{(1)}\left[\left(\mathbf{R}_c + \frac{\mathbf{R}^0}{2}\right), \left(\frac{\mathbf{p}_c}{2} + \mathbf{p}^0\right); t\right]\right\}$$

$$\times\, d\mathbf{R}^0 d\mathbf{R}' d\mathbf{R}_2 d\mathbf{p}' d\mathbf{p}'' d\mathbf{p}_2 d\mathbf{p}^0 ds, \tag{26}$$

$$K_0{}^{(2)} = K_0{}^{(2)}\left[\mathbf{R}', \left(\frac{\mathbf{p}' + \mathbf{p}''}{2}\right) \middle| \mathbf{R}^0, \mathbf{p}^0; s\right]; \; [T_r] = [T_r(\mathbf{p}, \mathbf{p}', \mathbf{p}'', \mathbf{R})]$$

$$\mathbf{R} = \mathbf{R}_2 - \mathbf{R}_1 \qquad \mathbf{R}_c = \tfrac{1}{2}(\mathbf{R}_2 + \mathbf{R}_1)$$

$$\mathbf{p} = \tfrac{1}{2}(\mathbf{p}_2 - \mathbf{p}_1) \qquad \mathbf{p}_c = \mathbf{p}_2 + \mathbf{p}_1,$$

where the symmetrization operator is shown explicitly, and $[T_r]$ is given by Eq. (B10) of Appendix B. Quantities of the order of (τ_k/τ) have been omitted in Eq. (26). The terms containing $K_0{}^{(2)}$ can be shown to be zero with the aid of arguments analogous to those given below (see Appendix C).

The second term in the expansion of the transformation function, $K^{(2)}$, can be written from Eq. (24) as

$$K_1{}^{(2)}\left[\mathbf{R}', \left(\frac{\mathbf{p}' + \mathbf{p}''}{2}\right) \middle| \mathbf{R}^0, \mathbf{p}^0; s\right]$$

$$= -\frac{i}{\hbar}\left(\frac{1}{\pi\hbar}\right)^3 \int_0^s \exp\left[(s' - s)\left(\frac{\mathbf{p}' + \mathbf{p}''}{2m}\right) \cdot \nabla'_{\mathbf{R}}\right]$$

$$\times\, U(R'')\delta(\boldsymbol{\xi} - \mathbf{p}^0)\delta(\mathbf{R}' - \mathbf{R}^0 - \Delta\mathbf{R})$$

$$\times \left[\exp\left\{\frac{2i}{\hbar}\left[\left(\frac{\mathbf{p}' + \mathbf{p}''}{2}\right) - \boldsymbol{\xi}\right] \cdot (\mathbf{R}' - \mathbf{R}'')\right\}\right.$$

$$\left. - \exp\left\{-\frac{2i}{\hbar}\left[\left(\frac{\mathbf{p}' + \mathbf{p}''}{2}\right) - \boldsymbol{\xi}\right] \cdot (\mathbf{R}' - \mathbf{R}'')\right\}\right] \times d\mathbf{R}'' d\boldsymbol{\xi} ds' \tag{27}$$

on rearranging the $\boldsymbol{\theta}$ operator. Integration over $\boldsymbol{\xi}$ and s' is straightforward and the resultant expression for $K_1{}^{(2)}$ is introduced into Eq. (26). Integration over $\mathbf{R}^0$ is performed with the assumption that the distribution functions have only macroscopic space dependence that variations in these functions occur only over distances L_1, such that $L_1 \gg L_\tau$, where L_τ has been defined above. Then, to terms of the order of L_τ/L_1, $\delta(\mathbf{R}' - \mathbf{R}^0 - \Delta\mathbf{R})$ can be approximated by $\delta(\mathbf{R}' - \mathbf{R}^0)$. It should be noted that the range of integration over $\mathbf{R}^0$, and thus $\mathbf{R}'$, can be restricted to volumes in relative configuration space of linear extent L_τ, since the transformation function, i.e., the conditional probability of transition, is zero for R^0, $R' > L_\tau$. For this to hold true the range of the intermolecular forces, ρ^0, must be short such that $\rho^0 \ll L_\tau$. Thus, to these orders of approximation, the configurational arguments of the distribution functions, $(\mathbf{R}_c - \frac{1}{2}\mathbf{R}')$ and $(\mathbf{R}_c + \frac{1}{2}\mathbf{R}')$ can both be replaced by $\mathbf{R}_1$. It is this approximation which permits the integration of the remaining terms which depend upon $\mathbf{R}'$. Furthermore, it is this approximation which replaces the more restrictive assumption of random *a priori* phases which Mori and Ono found necessary to apply in their derivation.

With the aid of the preceding assumptions and the use of Eq. (27), Eq. (26) can be altered to read

$$\frac{\partial \bar{f}^{(1)}}{\partial t} + \frac{\mathbf{p}_1}{m_1} \cdot \nabla_{\mathbf{R}_1} \bar{f}^{(1)} + \boldsymbol{\theta}^{(e)} \cdot \bar{f}^{(1)}$$

$$= \frac{N_2}{2\tau} \frac{i}{\hbar} \left(\frac{1}{2\pi\hbar}\right)^3 \left(\frac{1}{\pi\hbar}\right)^6 \int \cdots \int_0^\tau \frac{U(R'') \exp\left[\frac{i}{\hbar}(\mathbf{p}'' - \mathbf{p}') \cdot \mathbf{R}'\right]}{2\left[\left(\frac{\mathbf{p}' + \mathbf{p}''}{2}\right) - \mathbf{p}^0\right] \cdot \left(\frac{\mathbf{p}' + \mathbf{p}''}{2m}\right)}$$

$$[\Lambda][B + B^*] f^{(1)}[\mathbf{R}_1, (\tfrac{1}{2}\mathbf{p}_c - \mathbf{p}^0); t]$$

$$\times f^{(1)}[\mathbf{R}_1, (\tfrac{1}{2}\mathbf{p}_c + \mathbf{p}^0); t] d\mathbf{R}' d\mathbf{R}'' d\mathbf{R}_2 d\mathbf{p}' d\mathbf{p}'' d\mathbf{p}^0 d\mathbf{p}_2 ds \qquad (28)$$

$$[\Lambda] = \Lambda_1 + \Lambda_2 + \Lambda_3 + \Lambda_4$$

$$\Lambda_1 = \exp\left[\frac{i}{\hbar}(\mathbf{p}' - \mathbf{p}'') \cdot \mathbf{R}\right](e^{\alpha_1} - e^{-\alpha_1});$$

$$\alpha_1 = \frac{i}{\hbar}[2\mathbf{p} - (\mathbf{p}' + \mathbf{p}'')] \cdot (\mathbf{R} - \mathbf{R}'')$$

$$\Lambda_2 = \exp\left[\frac{i}{\hbar}(-\mathbf{p}' + \mathbf{p}'') \cdot \mathbf{R}\right](e^{\alpha_2} - e^{-\alpha_2});$$

$$\alpha_2 = \frac{i}{\hbar}[2\mathbf{p} - (-\mathbf{p}' - \mathbf{p}'')] \cdot (\mathbf{R} - \mathbf{R}'')$$

$$\Lambda_3 = \pm \exp\left[\frac{i}{\hbar}(-\mathbf{p}' - \mathbf{p}'') \cdot \mathbf{R}\right](e^{\alpha_3} - e^{-\alpha_3});$$

$$\alpha_3 = \frac{i}{\hbar}[2\mathbf{p} - (-\mathbf{p}' + \mathbf{p}'')] \cdot (\mathbf{R} - \mathbf{R}'')$$

$$\Lambda_4 = \pm \exp\left[\frac{i}{\hbar}(\mathbf{p}' + \mathbf{p}'') \cdot \mathbf{R}\right](e^{\alpha_4} - e^{-\alpha_4});$$

$$\alpha_4 = \frac{i}{\hbar}[2\mathbf{p} - (\mathbf{p}' - \mathbf{p}'')] \cdot (\mathbf{R} - \mathbf{R}'')$$

$$B = \left[1 - \exp\left\{-\frac{2i}{\hbar}\left[\left(\frac{\mathbf{p}' + \mathbf{p}''}{2}\right) - \mathbf{p}^0\right] \cdot \left(\frac{\mathbf{p}' + \mathbf{p}''}{2m}\right)s\right\}\right]$$

$$\exp\left\{\frac{i}{\hbar}\left[\left(\frac{\mathbf{p}' + \mathbf{p}''}{2}\right) - \mathbf{p}^0\right] \cdot \mathbf{R}'\right\} I(\mathbf{p}' + \mathbf{p}'' - 2\mathbf{p}^0)$$

$$I(\mathbf{p}' + \mathbf{p}'' - 2\mathbf{p}^0) = \int \exp\left[-\frac{i}{\hbar}(\mathbf{p}' + \mathbf{p}'' - 2\mathbf{p}^0) \cdot \mathbf{R}\right] U(R)\, d\mathbf{R},$$

where B^* is the complex conjugate of B, and I^* the complex conjugate of I. Since the derivation is restricted to spherically symmetric intermolecular potentials, I^* equals I. The differential $d\mathbf{R}_2$ can be replaced by $d\mathbf{R}$, and the integrations over $\mathbf{R}'$ and $\mathbf{R}$ yield Dirac δ functions. These steps lead to the following equation after some tedious algebraic manipulations:

$$\frac{\partial \bar{f}^{(1)}}{\partial t} + \frac{\mathbf{p}_1}{m_1} \cdot \nabla_{\mathbf{R}_1} \bar{f}^{(1)} + \boldsymbol{\theta}^{(e)} \cdot \bar{f}^{(1)}$$

$$= \frac{N_2}{2\tau} \frac{i}{\hbar} \left(\frac{1}{2\pi h}\right)^3 \int \cdots \int_0^\tau [I(\mathbf{p} - \mathbf{p}') \pm I(-\mathbf{p} - \mathbf{p}')]^2$$

$$\left\{ \frac{\exp\left[-\frac{i}{\hbar}\left(\frac{p^2 - p'^2}{2m}\right)s\right] - \exp\left[\frac{i}{\hbar}\left(\frac{p^2 - p'^2}{2m}\right)s\right]}{\left(\frac{p^2 - p'^2}{2m}\right)} \right\}$$

$$\times \{f^{(1)}(\mathbf{R}_1\mathbf{p}_1'; t) f^{(1)}(\mathbf{R}_1\mathbf{p}_2'; t) - f^{(1)}(\mathbf{R}_1\mathbf{p}_1; t) f^{(1)}(\mathbf{R}_1\mathbf{p}_2; t)\} d\mathbf{p}' d\mathbf{p}_2 ds. \qquad (29)$$

The argument proceeds analogously to the solution of scattering problems by the method of variation of constants in the Schrödinger equation in the momentum representation. The remaining functions of s in Eq. (29) are easily reduced, and for sufficiently large values of τ this term

$$\frac{\sin^2\left[\left(\frac{p^2 - p'^2}{4m\hbar}\right)\tau\right]}{\left(\frac{p^2 - p'^2}{4m}\right)^2},$$

becomes a sharply-peaked function, similar to a δ function, at $p = p'$. This fact permits the evaluation of all other functions of $\mathbf{p}'$ at $p = p'$, which reduces the integration over $\mathbf{p}'$ to

$$\lim_{\tau \to \infty} \frac{1}{\tau} \int \frac{\sin^2\left[\left(\frac{p^2 - p'^2}{4m\hbar}\right)\tau\right]}{\left(\frac{p^2 - p'^2}{4m}\right)^2} p'^2 dp' d\Omega = \frac{2}{\hbar} m\pi p\, d\Omega.$$

Equation (29) now becomes

$$\frac{\partial \bar{f}^{(1)}}{\partial t} + \frac{\mathbf{p}_1}{m_1} \cdot \nabla_{\mathbf{R}_1} \bar{f}^{(1)} + \boldsymbol{\theta}^{(e)} \cdot \bar{f}^{(1)}$$

$$= N_2 \int \cdots \int \sigma(p, \Omega) \frac{p}{m} [f^{(1)}(\mathbf{R}_1\mathbf{p}_1'; t) f^{(1)}(\mathbf{R}_1\mathbf{p}_2'; t)$$

$$- f^{(1)}(\mathbf{R}_1\mathbf{p}_1; t) f^{(1)}(\mathbf{R}_1\mathbf{p}_2; t)] d\Omega d\mathbf{p}_2, \quad (30)$$

where $\sigma(p, \Omega)$ is the scattering cross section defined by

$$\sigma(p, \Omega) = \frac{1}{2}\left(\frac{m}{2\pi\hbar^2}\right)^2 [I(\mathbf{p} - \mathbf{p}') \pm I(-\mathbf{p} - \mathbf{p}')]^2 \quad (31)$$

and

$$|\mathbf{p} - \mathbf{p}'| = 2p \sin\left(\frac{\theta}{2}\right);$$

the polar axis is taken along $\mathbf{p}'$. Time averaging Eq. (30) over an interval τ, which leaves the left-hand side unaffected, yields

$$\frac{\partial \bar{f}^{(1)}}{\partial t} + \frac{\mathbf{p}_1}{m_1} \cdot \nabla_{\mathbf{R}_1} \bar{f}^{(1)} + \boldsymbol{\theta}^{(e)} \cdot \bar{f}^{(1)}$$

$$= N_2 \int \cdots \int \sigma(p, \Omega) \frac{p}{m} [\bar{f}^{(1)}(\mathbf{R}_1\mathbf{p}_1'; t) \bar{f}^{(1)}(\mathbf{R}_1\mathbf{p}_2'; t)$$

$$- \bar{f}^{(1)}(\mathbf{R}_1\mathbf{p}_1; t) \bar{f}^{(1)}(\mathbf{R}_1\mathbf{p}_2; t)] d\Omega d\mathbf{p}_2. \quad (32)$$

To obtain the above equation it is necessary to apply the additional condition

$$\overline{f^{(1)} f^{(1)}} = \bar{f}^{(1)} \bar{f}^{(1)}. \quad (33)$$

This is true to terms of first order for distributions close to equilibrium.

Equation (32) reduces to the Uhling and Uhlenbeck equation, (aside from the density dependent factors due to quantum statistics, which we ignored), if the external forces are assumed to be sufficiently slowly varying to warrant simplification of the term $\boldsymbol{\theta}^{(e)} \cdot \bar{f}^{(1)}$ to $- \nabla_{\mathbf{R}_1}\phi_1(\mathbf{R}_1) \cdot \nabla_{\mathbf{p}_1} \bar{f}^{(1)}$.

Although the question of the applicability of the Uhling and Uhlenbeck equation as an explicit formulation of the general quantum-mechanical Boltzmann equation remains unanswered, an opinion of the unlikelihood of its validity beyond the restrictions of the Born approximation seems warranted. This follows from the belief that the usual formulation of the quantum-mechanical scattering cross sections may be inadequate to describe the transition probabilities due to scattering as determined rigorously in terms of solutions of the integro-differential equation for the transformation function K. Proof of these assertions is under consideration.

Two derivations of the Boltzmann equation in quantum mechanics have been published previously. Mori and Ono's[11] analysis, like the present one, is based upon the Wigner equation. They apply time dependent perturbation methods to the density matrix and retain first order terms only. This is equivalent to the Born approximation in the solution of quantum-mechanical scattering problems; no formalism for a general solution is presented. To proceed, they find it necessary to simplify the density matrix by neglecting all non-diagonal terms of the matrix, which is equivalent to the hypothesis of random *a priori* phases and is an integral part of their treatment. It is this step which removes all configuration space dependence from the distribution functions and their derivation is limited to this extent. Use of the methods of second quantization yields the density dependent factors due to quantum statistics. Inclusion of these interactions seems superfluous since they become of importance under conditions where in general the Born approximation is inapplicable.

The other derivation, by H. S. Green,[18] also uses the Wigner equation as a starting point, but the concept of time-smoothed distribution functions is not introduced. The effect of quantum statistics is neglected entirely. Green attempts to obtain the Boltzmann equation by solving the Wigner equation for the pair distribution function directly, without any perturbation methods. Although he seems to effect such a solution, no final equation is given in a recognizable form of the Boltzmann equation. The quantum-mechanical cross section does not appear explicitly in his treatment, and no indications are apparent under what conditions his method leads to the Uhling and Uhlenbeck equation.

APPENDIX A

The wave transformation function $k(\mathbf{R}|\mathbf{R}'; s)$ is defined by the equation

$$\psi(\mathbf{R}; t + s) = \int k(\mathbf{R}|\mathbf{R}'; s)\psi(\mathbf{R}'; t)d\mathbf{R}', \tag{A1}$$

where ψ denotes the Schrödinger wave function, $\mathbf{R}$ the coordinates, t the time, and s a time interval. From the definitions of the Wigner distribution function, Eq. (2), and the phase-space transformation function, Eq. (13), the relation of the latter to the wave transformation function is seen to be

$$K^{(N)}(\mathbf{R}, \mathbf{p} \,|\, \mathbf{R}', \mathbf{p}'; s) = \left(\frac{2}{\pi\hbar}\right)^{3N} \int \cdots \int \times \exp\left[\frac{2i}{\hbar}(\mathbf{p}\cdot\mathbf{Y} - \mathbf{p}'\cdot\mathbf{Y}')\right] k^{*\,(N)}(\mathbf{R}+\mathbf{Y}\,|\,\mathbf{R}'+\mathbf{Y}'; s) \times k^{(N)}(\mathbf{R}-\mathbf{Y}|\mathbf{R}'-\mathbf{Y}'; s)d\mathbf{Y}d\mathbf{Y}', \tag{A2}$$

where N is the number of particles in the system.

The wave transformation function can be expanded in the form[19]

$$k = k_0 + k_1 + k_2 \cdots, \tag{A3}$$

where the potential of intermolecular force is treated as a perturbation. The physical significance of each term in this series is simply that the subscript of each term denotes the number of times the wave interacts with, or is scattered by, the potential field during the transition considered. The total conditional probability of transition of the wave function, $k^{(N)}(\mathbf{R}|\mathbf{R}'; s)$, consists then of

[18] H. S. Green, *Proc. Phys. Soc.* (London) **A66**, 325 (1953).
[19] R. P. Feynman, *Revs. Modern Phys.* **20**, 367 (1948).

the sum of ways in which the wave function can proceed from $\mathbf{R}'$ to $\mathbf{R}$ in the interval s. The individual terms of the expansion for the phase space transformation function, Eq. (22), are composed of corresponding terms of the expansion (A3) according to the relation (A2).

It is convenient sometimes to introduce the wave transformation function in the momentum representation, $k^{(N)}(\mathbf{p}|\mathbf{p}'; s)$. From the well-known Fourier transform relation between the wave functions in the coordinate and momentum representation, the equation for $k^{(N)}(\mathbf{p}|\mathbf{p}'; s)$, is

$$k^{(N)}(\mathbf{p}|\mathbf{p}'; s) = \left(\frac{1}{2\pi\hbar}\right)^{3N} \int \cdots \int \times \exp\left[-\frac{i}{\hbar}(\mathbf{p}\cdot\mathbf{R} - \mathbf{p}'\cdot\mathbf{R}')\right] k^{(N)}(\mathbf{R}|\mathbf{R}'; s)d\mathbf{R}d\mathbf{R}'. \tag{A4}$$

Integration of Eq. (A2) over $\mathbf{R}$ and $\mathbf{R}'$ yields, with the aid of Eq. (A4)

$$|k^{(N)}(\mathbf{p}|\mathbf{p}'; s)|^2 = \left(\frac{1}{2\pi\hbar}\right)^{3N} \int \cdots \int K^{(N)}(\mathbf{R}, \mathbf{p}|\mathbf{R}', \mathbf{p}'; s)d\mathbf{R}d\mathbf{R}'. \tag{A5}$$

For the determination of the relation between the phase-space transformation function and the scattering cross section, we shall define the term

$$B' \equiv \int \cdots \int [K(\mathbf{R}, \mathbf{p}|\mathbf{R}', \mathbf{p}'; s) - K_0(\mathbf{R}, \mathbf{p}|\mathbf{R}', \mathbf{p}'; s]d\mathbf{R}d\mathbf{R}', \tag{A6}$$

where K_0 is the first term in the expansion of K, Eq. (22). B' is seen to be the particular kind of conditional probability that the system will have momentum space coordinates $\mathbf{p}$ after an interval s, given the initial coordinates $\mathbf{p}'$. The subtraction of the K_0 term excludes transitions not induced by the potential field; these free-particle transitions are of no physical interest in the scattering problem. The probability of a transition from $\mathbf{p}'$ at $s = 0$ to the range of momenta $\mathbf{p}$, $\mathbf{p} + d\mathbf{p}$, after the interval s is $B'd\mathbf{p}$ or, in spherical coordinates, $B'p^2dpd\Omega$. Thus, the probability of a transition specified merely by the change of direction of the momentum vector, in the interval s, from the polar axis into the solid angle Ω, $\Omega + d\Omega$, is $[\int B'p^2dp]d\Omega$. But this probability per unit time, unit current, and unit solid angle is the definition of the scattering cross section, $\sigma(p, \Omega)$:

$$\sigma(p, \Omega) = \frac{\int B'p^2dp}{s\left(\frac{p}{m}\right)}. \tag{A7}$$

APPENDIX B[20]

Consider a system composed of two independent particles denoted by 1 and

[20] *Note added in proof.*—The treatment is restricted here to systems of two independent particles for which the unsymmetrized phase-space distribution function, i.e. the distribution function of a quantum-mechanical system obeying Boltzmann statistics, can be expressed at any one instant of time as a product of two singlet distribution functions, $f^{(2)}(R_1R_2p_1p_2; t) = f^{(1)}(R_1p_1; t)f^{(1)}(R_2p_2; t)$.

2. At first, let the particles be distinguishable, i.e., assume they obey Boltzmann statistics. In this case we choose the orthonormal set of plane wave functions

$$\phi_1(\mathbf{p}_1) = \left(\frac{1}{2\pi\hbar}\right)^{\frac{3}{2}} \exp\left(\frac{i}{\hbar}\mathbf{p}_1 \cdot \mathbf{R}_1\right), \tag{B1}$$

in terms of which the wave functions can be written as

$$\psi_1(\mathbf{R}_1; t) = \left(\frac{1}{2\pi\hbar}\right)^{\frac{3}{2}} \int a_1(\mathbf{p}_1; t) \exp\left(\frac{i}{\hbar}\mathbf{p}_1 \cdot \mathbf{R}_1\right) d\mathbf{p}_1, \tag{B2}$$

and similarly for particle 2. The Fourier transform of Eq. (B2) leads to an expression for $a_1(\mathbf{p}_1; t)$,

$$a_1(\mathbf{p}_1; t) = \left(\frac{1}{2\pi\hbar}\right)^{\frac{3}{2}} \int \psi_1(\mathbf{R}_1; t) \exp\left(-\frac{i}{\hbar}\mathbf{p}_1 \cdot \mathbf{R}_1\right) d\mathbf{R}_1. \tag{B3}$$

The Wigner function for the two-particle system is easily obtained from its definition Eq. (2). Since the density matrix of this system is

$$\psi_1^*(\mathbf{R}_1'; t)\psi_2^*(\mathbf{R}_2'; t)\psi_1(\mathbf{R}_1; t)\psi_2(\mathbf{R}_2; t),$$

it is seen that the pair Wigner function factors straightforwardly into the corresponding singlet Wigner functions,

$$f^{(2)}(\mathbf{R}_1\mathbf{R}_2\mathbf{p}_1\mathbf{p}_2; t) = f^{(1)}(\mathbf{R}_1\mathbf{p}_1; t) f^{(1)}(\mathbf{R}_2\mathbf{p}_2; t). \tag{B4}$$

For the case of indistinguishable particles, i.e., for systems obeying Bose-Einstein or Fermi-Dirac statistics, we choose the properly symmetrized plane wave function

$$\Phi(\mathbf{p}_1\mathbf{p}_2) = \frac{1}{\sqrt{2}}\left(\frac{1}{2\pi\hbar}\right)^3 \left\{\exp\left[\frac{i}{\hbar}(\mathbf{p}_1 \cdot \mathbf{R}_1 + \mathbf{p}_2 \cdot \mathbf{R}_2)\right]\right.$$
$$\left. \pm \exp\left[\frac{i}{\hbar}(\mathbf{p}_1 \cdot \mathbf{R}_2 + \mathbf{p}_2 \cdot \mathbf{R}_1)\right]\right\}, \tag{B5}$$

in terms of which the wave function for the two-particle system is written as

$$\psi(\mathbf{R}_1\mathbf{R}_2; t) = \int\int a_1(\mathbf{p}_1; t) a_2(\mathbf{p}_2; t) \Phi(\mathbf{p}_1\mathbf{p}_2) d\mathbf{p}_1 d\mathbf{p}_2. \tag{B6}$$

Wherever a choice of sign ($\pm$) occurs it is understood that the positive sign is applicable to Bose-Einstein systems whereas the negative sign is applicable to Fermi-Dirac statistics. It should be noted here that the symmetrization of wave functions, and of the density matrix, is adequately described by a permutation operation. This simplicity does not prevail in the symmetrization of Wigner functions.

The pair Wigner distribution function can be formulated with the aid of Eq. (B6) and becomes

$$f^{(2)}(\mathbf{R}_1\mathbf{R}_2\mathbf{p}_1\mathbf{p}_2;t) = \frac{1}{2}\left(\frac{1}{2\pi\hbar}\right)^6 \int\cdots\int$$

$$\times\, a_1^*(\mathbf{p}_1'';t)a_2^*(\mathbf{p}_2'';t)a_1(\mathbf{p}_1';t)a_2(\mathbf{p}_2';t)[T] \times d\mathbf{p}_1'd\mathbf{p}_2'd\mathbf{p}_1''d\mathbf{p}_2'', \qquad \text{(B7)}$$

$$[T] = \chi_1 + \chi_2 \pm \chi_3 \pm \chi_4$$

$$\chi_1 = \delta\left(\mathbf{p}_1 - \frac{\mathbf{p}_1' + \mathbf{p}_1''}{2}\right)\delta\left(\mathbf{p}_2 - \frac{\mathbf{p}_2' + \mathbf{p}_2''}{2}\right)$$

$$\times \exp\left\{\frac{i}{\hbar}[\mathbf{R}_1 \cdot (\mathbf{p}_1' - \mathbf{p}_1'') + \mathbf{R}_2 \cdot (\mathbf{p}_2' - \mathbf{p}_2'')]\right\},$$

$$\chi_2 = \delta\left(\mathbf{p}_1 - \frac{\mathbf{p}_2' + \mathbf{p}_2''}{2}\right)\delta\left(\mathbf{p}_2 - \frac{\mathbf{p}_1' + \mathbf{p}_1''}{2}\right)$$

$$\times \exp\left\{\frac{i}{\hbar}[\mathbf{R}_1 \cdot (\mathbf{p}_2' - \mathbf{p}_2'') + \mathbf{R}_2 \cdot (\mathbf{p}_1' - \mathbf{p}_1'')]\right\}, \qquad \text{(B8)}$$

$$\chi_3 = \delta\left(\mathbf{p}_1 - \frac{\mathbf{p}_2' + \mathbf{p}_1''}{2}\right)\delta\left(\mathbf{p}_2 - \frac{\mathbf{p}_1' + \mathbf{p}_2''}{2}\right)$$

$$\times \exp\left\{\frac{i}{\hbar}[\mathbf{R}_1 \cdot (\mathbf{p}_2' - \mathbf{p}_1'') + \mathbf{R}_2 \cdot (\mathbf{p}_1' - \mathbf{p}_2'')]\right\},$$

$$\chi_4 = \delta\left(\mathbf{p}_1 - \frac{\mathbf{p}_1' + \mathbf{p}_2''}{2}\right)\delta\left(\mathbf{p}_2 - \frac{\mathbf{p}_1'' + \mathbf{p}_2'}{2}\right)$$

$$\times \exp\left\{\frac{i}{\hbar}[\mathbf{R}_1 \cdot (\mathbf{p}_1' - \mathbf{p}_2'') + \mathbf{R}_2 \cdot (\mathbf{p}_2' - \mathbf{p}_1'')]\right\}.$$

Equation (B3) is now used to re-express the various a's in terms of wave functions. This procedure leads to the following equation

$$f^{(2)}(\mathbf{R}_1\mathbf{R}_2\mathbf{p}_1\mathbf{p}_2;t) = \frac{1}{2}\left(\frac{1}{2\pi\hbar}\right)^6 \int\cdots\int$$

$$\times \exp\left\{\frac{i}{\hbar}[\mathbf{R}_1' \cdot (\mathbf{p}_1'' - \mathbf{p}_1') + \mathbf{R}_2' \cdot (\mathbf{p}_2'' - \mathbf{p}_2')]\right\}[T]$$

$$\times f^{(1)}[\mathbf{R}_1', \tfrac{1}{2}(\mathbf{p}_1' + \mathbf{p}_1'');t] f^{(1)}[\mathbf{R}_2', \tfrac{1}{2}(\mathbf{p}_2' + \mathbf{p}_2'');t]$$

$$\times\, d\mathbf{R}_1'd\mathbf{R}_2'd\mathbf{p}_1'd\mathbf{p}_2'd\mathbf{p}_1''d\mathbf{p}_2''. \qquad \text{(B9)}$$

The equivalent of Eq. (B9) written in relative coordinates can be shown to be

$$f^{(2)}(\mathbf{R}_1\mathbf{R}_2\mathbf{p}_1\mathbf{p}_2;t) = \frac{1}{2}\left(\frac{1}{2\pi\hbar}\right)^3 \int\cdots\int \times \exp\left\{\frac{i}{\hbar}[\mathbf{R}'\cdot(\mathbf{p}''-\mathbf{p}')]\right\}[T_r]$$

$$\times f^{(1)}[(\mathbf{R}_c - \tfrac{1}{2}\mathbf{R}'), \tfrac{1}{2}(\mathbf{p}_c - \mathbf{p}' - \mathbf{p}''); t]$$

$$\times f^{(1)}[(\mathbf{R}_c + \tfrac{1}{2}\mathbf{R}'), \tfrac{1}{2}(\mathbf{p}_c + \mathbf{p}' + \mathbf{p}''); t]d\mathbf{R}'d\mathbf{p}'d\mathbf{p}''$$

$$[T_r] = \chi_1' + \chi_2' \pm \chi_3' \pm \chi_4'$$

$$\chi_1' = \delta[\mathbf{p} - \tfrac{1}{2}(\mathbf{p}' + \mathbf{p}'')]\exp\left[\frac{i}{\hbar}\mathbf{R}\cdot(\mathbf{p}' - \mathbf{p}'')\right] \tag{B10}$$

$$\chi_2' = \delta[\mathbf{p} - \tfrac{1}{2}(-\mathbf{p}' - \mathbf{p}'')]\exp\left[\frac{i}{\hbar}\mathbf{R}\cdot(-\mathbf{p}' + \mathbf{p}'')\right]$$

$$\chi_3' = \delta[\mathbf{p} - \tfrac{1}{2}(-\mathbf{p}' + \mathbf{p}'')]\exp\left[\frac{i}{\hbar}\mathbf{R}\cdot(-\mathbf{p}' - \mathbf{p}'')\right]$$

$$\chi_4' = \delta[\mathbf{p} - \tfrac{1}{2}(\mathbf{p}' - \mathbf{p}'')]\exp\left[\frac{i}{\hbar}\mathbf{R}\cdot(\mathbf{p}' + \mathbf{p}'')\right]$$

$$\mathbf{R}_c = \tfrac{1}{2}(\mathbf{R}_2 + \mathbf{R}_1); \qquad \mathbf{R} = \mathbf{R}_2 - \mathbf{R}_1;$$

$$\mathbf{p}_c = \mathbf{p}_2 + \mathbf{p}_1; \qquad \mathbf{p} = \tfrac{1}{2}(\mathbf{p}_2 - \mathbf{p}_1).$$

Equation (B9) or (B10) shows clearly that the symmetrization operation on the Wigner distribution functions cannot be represented by a permutation operator but is in fact represented by an integral operator. This integral operator, defined by Eq. (B9), can be written formally as

$$f^{(2)}(\mathbf{R}_1\mathbf{R}_2\mathbf{p}_1\mathbf{p}_2;t) = [\mathbf{O}_\pm]f^{(1)}(\mathbf{R}_1\mathbf{p}_1;t)f^{(1)}(\mathbf{R}_2\mathbf{p}_2;t). \tag{B11}$$

APPENDIX C

It is desired to show that the expression

$$A \equiv -\frac{N_2}{2\tau}\left(\frac{1}{2\pi\hbar}\right)^3 \int\cdots\int_0^\tau \boldsymbol{\theta}^{(2)}\cdot\left\{\exp\left[\frac{i}{\hbar}\mathbf{R}'\cdot(\mathbf{p}''-\mathbf{p}')\right][T_r]\right\}K_0^{(2)}$$

$$\times f^{(1)}[(\mathbf{R}_c - \tfrac{1}{2}\mathbf{R}^0)(\tfrac{1}{2}\mathbf{p}_c - \mathbf{p}^0);t]f^{(1)}[(\mathbf{R}_c + \tfrac{1}{2}\mathbf{R}^0)(\tfrac{1}{2}\mathbf{p}_c + \mathbf{p}^0);t]d\mathbf{R}'d\mathbf{R}^0d\mathbf{R}_2$$

$$d\mathbf{p}'d\mathbf{p}''d\mathbf{p}^0d\mathbf{p}_2ds \tag{C1}$$

$$K_0^{(2)}[\mathbf{R}', \tfrac{1}{2}(\mathbf{p}' + \mathbf{p}'')|\mathbf{R}^0, \mathbf{p}^0; s] = \delta[\mathbf{R}' - \mathbf{R}^0 - \Delta\mathbf{R}]\delta[\tfrac{1}{2}(\mathbf{p}' + \mathbf{p}'') - \mathbf{p}^0]$$

where $[T_r]$ is given by Eq. (B10) of Appendix B. The argument is analogous to the one presented above. It is assumed that the distribution functions have only macroscopic configuration space dependence such that variations of these functions occur only over distances L_1, where $L_1 \gg L_\tau$. L_τ is the distance traversed by a classical particle with the same initial momentum as in the quantum-mechanical problem in the time interval τ. Since the range of integration over $\mathbf{R}^0$ can be restricted to volumes of linear extent L_τ, it is seen that, to terms of the order of $L_\tau | L_1$ $\delta(\mathbf{R}' - \mathbf{R}^0 - \Delta\mathbf{R})$ can be approximated by $\delta(\mathbf{R}' - \mathbf{R}^0)$, and the distribution functions can be written as $f^{(1)}[\mathbf{R}_1, (\frac{1}{2}\mathbf{p}_c - \mathbf{p}^0); t]$ and $f^{(1)}[\mathbf{R}_1, (\frac{1}{2}\mathbf{p}_c + \mathbf{p}^0); t]$. The integrations over $\mathbf{R}^0$, $\mathbf{R}'$, and $\mathbf{R}$, where $d\mathbf{R}_2$ is replaced by $d\mathbf{R}$, can be carried out simply to yield

$$A = -\frac{i}{\hbar}\frac{N_2}{2\tau}\int \cdots \int_0^\tau f^{(1)}[\mathbf{R}_1, (\tfrac{1}{2}\mathbf{p}_c - \mathbf{p}'); t] f^{(1)}[\mathbf{R}_1, (\tfrac{1}{2}\mathbf{p}_c + \mathbf{p}'); t] [\Lambda'] U(R') d\mathbf{R}' d\mathbf{p}' d\mathbf{p}_2 ds$$

$$[\Lambda'] = \Lambda_1' + \Lambda_2' \pm \Lambda_3' \pm \Lambda_4'$$

$$\Lambda_1' = \delta(\mathbf{p} - \mathbf{p}')\left\{\exp\left[-\frac{2i}{\hbar}\mathbf{R}' \cdot (\mathbf{p} - \mathbf{p}')\right] - \exp\left[\frac{2i}{\hbar}\mathbf{R}' \cdot (\mathbf{p} - \mathbf{p}')\right]\right\}$$

$$\Lambda_2' = \delta(\mathbf{p} + \mathbf{p}')\left\{\exp\left[-\frac{2i}{\hbar}\mathbf{R}' \cdot (\mathbf{p} + \mathbf{p}')\right] - \exp\left[\frac{2i}{\hbar}\mathbf{R}' \cdot (\mathbf{p} + \mathbf{p}')\right]\right\} \tag{C2}$$

$$\Lambda_3' = \delta(\mathbf{p} - \mathbf{p}')\exp\left(-\frac{2i}{\hbar}\mathbf{p} \cdot \mathbf{R}'\right) - \delta(\mathbf{p} + \mathbf{p}')\exp\left(\frac{2i}{\hbar}\mathbf{p} \cdot \mathbf{R}'\right)$$

$$\Lambda_4' = \delta(\mathbf{p} + \mathbf{p}')\exp\left(-\frac{2i}{\hbar}\mathbf{p} \cdot \mathbf{R}'\right) - \delta(\mathbf{p} - \mathbf{p}')\exp\left(\frac{2i}{\hbar}\mathbf{p} \cdot \mathbf{R}'\right),$$

which, upon integration over $\mathbf{p}'$, reduces to zero.

The Statistical Mechanical Theory of Transport Processes. IX. Contribution to the Theory of Brownian Motion*

JOHN ROSS, *Metcalf Chemical Laboratories, Brown University, Providence, Rhode Island*

(Received May 6, 1955)

The equations of Brownian motion are derived from Liouville's equation in a treatment which parallels Kirkwood's statistical mechanical analysis but which is based upon the theory of phase space transformation functions. The transformation function obeys Liouville's equation and thus expresses the equations of motion; it is obtained as a solution of that equation by a consistent method of successive approximations which treats the forces as perturbations. Retention of first-order terms only in this solution leads to the Chandrasekhar equation and yields a tractable relation between the friction constant and the intermolecular forces. The restrictions imposed by the present derivation on the molecular interpretation of the equations of Brownian motion are discussed.

The phenomenological theory of Brownian motion is based upon the Langevin equation, which describes the motion of a Brownian particle, and the Fokker-Planck equation, which is a differential equation for the distribution function of a Brownian particle in velocity space. The Fokker-Planck equation has been generalized by Chandrasekhar[1] to an expression for the distribution function in phase space. In all these equations there appear an empirical parameter, the friction constant, which cannot be evaluated from the phenomenological theory. Kirkwood[2] has developed a statistical mechanical theory of transport processes based upon Liouville's equation and the hypothesis that macroscopic observables correspond to time averages of ensemble averages of molecular quantities.[3] With this hypothesis he derived from the fundamental equation of classical statistical mechanics the Maxwell-Boltzmann integro-differential equation for transport in gases of low density,[4] and the Langevin and Chandrasekhar equations describing Brownian motion. Furthermore, Kirkwood's analysis yielded an expression for the friction constant in terms of molecular forces. The dissipative mechanism of irreversible processes is embodied essentially in the existence of a plateau value of the friction constant. The evaluation of Kirkwood's formulation of this constant is very difficult and the existence of its plateau value has not been proven in general. The statistical mechanical theory of Brownian motion has been applied to the

---

* This article is one of a series on the statistical mechanical theory of transport processes by John G. Kirkwood and collaborators.

[1] S. Chandrasekhar, *Revs. Modern Phys.* **15**, 1 (1943).

[2] J. G. Kirkwood, *J. Chem. Phys.* **14**, 180 (1946).

[3] See M. Born and H. S. Green, *A General Kinetic Theory of Liquids* (Cambridge University Press, London, 1949) for an alternative approach to a statistical mechanical theory of transport processes.

[4] J. G. Kirkwood, *J. Chem. Phys.* **15**, 72 (1947).

calculation of transport coefficients in liquids from the potential of intermolecular force.[5-7]

This article offers a new statistical mechanical derivation of the equations of Brownian motion. The purpose of this analysis, illustrated with the development of the Chandrasekhar equation only, is to derive this equation from Liouville's equation and obtain an expression for the friction constant in terms of the intermolecular forces by the application of a consistent set of approximations, and to ascertain under what conditions a molecular interpretation of the equations of Brownian motion so derived might be valid. Although Kirkwood's method is followed closely, the present treatment differs in that use is made of the theory of phase space transformation functions[8] which affords some conceptual elucidations. The transformation function expresses the dynamics of the system and obeys Liouville's equation with readily obtained initial conditions. An exact solution for the transformation function can be effected for two particles interacting with a central field of force. This situation may occur in a gas of low density where the dynamics are described adequately by binary collisions, and use of this exact solution in Liouville's equation leads to the Maxwell-Boltzmann equation.[4] For all other cases it appears that the equation obeyed by the transformation function can be solved only by methods of successive approximations. In fact, it will be shown that the equations of Brownian motion can be obtained if the equation for the transformation function is solved by a consistent method of successive approximations in which the forces between particles are regarded as small perturbations on the motion. The consequences of the use of this type of solution are discussed below.

Consider a system of one component and N particles and let the subscripts 1, 2, 3 . . . denote specific particles. Liouville's equation for the normalized, specific distribution function in phase space of the entire set of N particles, $f^{(N)}(\mathbf{Rp}; t)$, is

$$\frac{\partial f^{(N)}}{\partial t} + \sum_{j=1}^{N} \left\{ \frac{\mathbf{p}_j}{m_j} \cdot \nabla_{\mathbf{R}_j} f^{(N)} + (\mathbf{F}_j + \mathbf{X}_j) \cdot \nabla_{\mathbf{p}_j} f^{(N)} \right\} = 0, \tag{1}$$

where $\mathbf{R}$ and $\mathbf{p}$ are the coordinates and momenta of all particles, m_j is the mass of the jth particle, t is the time, and $\mathbf{X}_j$ are the external forces and $\mathbf{F}_j$ the intermolecular forces exerted on the jth particle. For convenience it is assumed that the intermolecular force can be expressed as a sum of pair forces,

$$\mathbf{F}_j = \sum_{i=1 \neq j}^{N} \mathbf{F}_{ij}(R_{ij}); \quad R_{ij} = |\mathbf{R}_j - \mathbf{R}_i|. \tag{2}$$

The reduced distribution function for a subset of n particles can be obtained from $f^{(N)}$ by integration; thus $f^{(n)}$ can be written as

$$f^{(n)}(\mathbf{rp}; t) = \int \cdots \int f^{(N)}(\mathbf{rpQP}; t) d\mathbf{Q} d\mathbf{P}. \tag{3}$$

[5] Kirkwood, Buff, and Green, *J. Chem. Phys.* **17**, 988 (1949).
[6] Zwanzig, Kirkwood, Stripp, and Oppenheim, *J. Chem. Phys.* **21**, 2050 (1953).
[7] Zwanzig, Kirkwood, Oppenheim, and Alder, *J. Chem. Phys.* **22**, 783 (1954).
[8] J. Ross and J. G. Kirkwood, *J. Chem. Phys.* **22**, 1094 (1954).
[9] See reference 2, henceforth referred to as SMTI, for a discussion of these functions.

where **r** and **p** are the coordinates and momenta of the subset and **Q** and **P** the coordinates and momenta of the remaining set of $(N - n)$ particles. Distribution functions coarse-grained in time[9] are defined by the relation

$$\bar{f}^{(n)}(\mathbf{rp}; t) = \frac{1}{\tau}\int_0^\tau f^{(n)}(\mathbf{rp}; t + s)ds. \tag{4}$$

The equation obeyed by a reduced distribution function, coarse-grained in time, is obtained from Liouville's equation by integration over the appropriate coordinates and use of Eq. (4). The singlet distribution function, $\bar{f}^{(1)}(\mathbf{R}_1\mathbf{p}_1; t)$, for a specified particle with coordinates $\mathbf{R}_1$ and momenta $\mathbf{p}_1$ satisfies the equation

$$\frac{\partial f^{(1)}}{\partial t} + \frac{\mathbf{p}_1}{m_1} \cdot \nabla_{\mathbf{R}_1} f^{(1)} + \mathbf{X}_1 \cdot \nabla_{\mathbf{p}_1} f^{(1)} = \nabla_{\mathbf{p}_1} \cdot (N_2 \mathbf{\Omega}^{(1)}) \tag{5}$$

$$N_2 = N - 1 \tag{6}$$

$$\mathbf{\Omega}^{(1)} = -\frac{1}{\tau}\int_0^\tau \int \cdots \int \mathbf{F}_{12}(R_{12}) f^{(N)}(\mathbf{R}_1\mathbf{R}_2\mathbf{p}_1\mathbf{p}_2\mathbf{QP}; t + s) d\mathbf{Q}d\mathbf{P}d\mathbf{p}_2 d\mathbf{R}_2 ds. \tag{7}$$

Equations (5)–(7) are equivalent to Kirkwood's formulas (SMTI Eq. 49), but the present derivation proceeds with the application of the theory of phase space transformation functions.

The phase space transformation function $K^{(N)}(\mathbf{Rp}|\mathbf{R}_0\mathbf{p}_0; s)$ is the conditional probability density of finding the N-particle system with coordinates **R**, **p** in phase space after an interval s given that the original coordinates are $\mathbf{R}_0$, $\mathbf{p}_0$. Thus it can be defined by the integral equation

$$f^{(N)}(\mathbf{Rp}; t + s) = \int \cdots \int K^{(N)}(\mathbf{Rp}|\mathbf{R}_0\mathbf{p}_0; s) f^{(N)}(\mathbf{R}_0\mathbf{p}_0; t) d\mathbf{R}_0 d\mathbf{p}_0. \tag{8}$$

From Eqs. (1) and (8) it is seen that $K^{(N)}$ obeys Liouville's equation,

$$\frac{\partial K^{(N)}}{\partial s} + \sum_{j=1}^{N} \left\{ \frac{\mathbf{p}_j}{m_j} \cdot \nabla_{\mathbf{R}_j} K^{(N)} + (\mathbf{F}_j + \mathbf{X}_j) \cdot \nabla_{\mathbf{p}_j} K^{(N)} \right\} = 0, \tag{9}$$

with initial condition

$$K^{(N)}(\mathbf{Rp}|\mathbf{R}_0\mathbf{p}_0; 0) = \prod_{j=1}^{N} \delta(\mathbf{R}_j - \mathbf{R}_{j0})\delta(\mathbf{p}_j - \mathbf{p}_{j0}). \tag{10}$$

The determination of $K^{(N)}$ is therefore effected as a solution of Liouville's equation satisfying the condition Eq. (10). The transformation function constitutes a formulation of the equations of motion and one of its advantages resides in the fact that solutions of these equations can be obtained by well-defined approximation methods, the physical significance of which are readily apparent. The solution which leads to the Chandrasekhar equation upon introduction of the transformation function into Eq. (7) is obtained by a method of successive approximations which treats the forces between particles as small perturbations.[10] To this purpose let $(\mathbf{F}_j + \mathbf{X}_j)$ be replaced by $\lambda(\mathbf{F}_j + \mathbf{X}_j)$ in Eq. (9)

$$\frac{\partial K^{(N)}}{\partial s} + \sum_{j=1}^{N} \left\{ \frac{\mathbf{p}_j}{m_j} \cdot \nabla_{\mathbf{R}_j} K^{(N)} + \lambda(\mathbf{F}_j + \mathbf{X}_j) \cdot \nabla_{\mathbf{p}_j} K^{(N)} \right\} = 0, \qquad (11)$$

where λ is the expansion parameter, and let the transformation function be evolved in a power series in λ,

$$K^{(N)} = \sum_{n=0}^{\infty} \lambda^n K_n{}^{(N)}. \qquad (12)$$

Substitution of this series into Eq. (11), and the equating of like powers of λ, leads to the set of differential equations

$$\begin{aligned} &\frac{\partial K_0{}^{(N)}}{\partial s} + \sum_{j=1}^{N} \frac{\mathbf{p}_j}{m_j} \cdot \nabla_{\mathbf{R}_j} K_0{}^{(N)} = 0, \\ &\frac{\partial K_n{}^{(N)}}{\partial s} + \sum_{j=1}^{N} \left\{ \frac{\mathbf{p}_j}{m_j} \cdot \nabla_{\mathbf{R}_j} K_n{}^{(N)} + (\mathbf{F}_j + \mathbf{X}_j) \cdot \nabla_{\mathbf{p}_j} K_{n-1}{}^{(N)} \right\} = 0, \end{aligned} \qquad (13)$$

with solutions

$$\begin{aligned} &K_0{}^{(N)} = \prod_{j=1}^{N} \delta\left(\mathbf{R}_j - \mathbf{R}_{j0} - s\frac{\mathbf{p}_j}{m_j} \right) \delta(\mathbf{p}_j - \mathbf{p}_{j0}), \\ &K_m{}^{(N)} = -\int_0^s \exp\left[(s' - s) \sum_{j=1}^{N} \frac{\mathbf{p}_j}{m_j} \cdot \nabla_{\mathbf{R}_j} \right] \sum_{k=1}^{N} (\mathbf{F}_k + \mathbf{X}_k) \cdot \nabla_{\mathbf{p}_k} K_{n-1}{}^{(N)}(s') ds'. \end{aligned} \qquad (14)$$

The expression for $K_1{}^{(N)}$ can be reduced to

$$\begin{aligned} &K_1{}^{(N)} = -\sum_{j=1}^{N} \Delta\mathbf{p}_j{}^{(1)}(s) \cdot \nabla_{\mathbf{p}_j} \left\{ \prod_{k=1}^{N} \delta\left(\mathbf{R}_k - \mathbf{R}_{k0} - s\frac{\mathbf{p}_k}{m_k} \right) \delta(\mathbf{p}_k - \mathbf{p}_{k0}) \right\}, \\ &\Delta\mathbf{p}_j{}^{(1)}(s) = \int_0^s \left[\mathbf{F}_j\left(\mathbf{R}_0 + s'\frac{\mathbf{p}}{m} \right) + \mathbf{X}_j\left(\mathbf{R}_{j0} + s'\frac{\mathbf{p}_j}{m_j} \right) \right] ds', \\ &\Delta\mathbf{R}_j{}^{(0)}(s) = s\mathbf{p}_j/m_j, \end{aligned} \qquad (15)$$

as is shown in Appendix A. $\Delta\mathbf{R}_j{}^{(0)}(s)$ is the distance traversed by a free particle in the interval s, $\mathbf{F}_j[\mathbf{R}_0 + (s\mathbf{p}/m)]$ is the force on the particle travelling along a linear trajectory, and $\Delta\mathbf{p}_j{}^{(1)}(s)$ is the change in momentum due to this particular force. It is seen that $\Delta\mathbf{R}_j{}^{(0)}$ and $\Delta\mathbf{p}_j{}^{(1)}$ are the first terms respectively in the development in powers of λ of $\Delta\mathbf{R}_j$ and $\Delta\mathbf{p}_j$, the change in coordinates and momenta obtained from an exact solution of the equations of motion. That is, if the equations of motion

$$d\mathbf{R}_j/ds = \mathbf{p}_j/m_j, \quad d\mathbf{p}_j/ds = \lambda[\mathbf{F}_j + \mathbf{X}_j]$$

---

[10] This perturbation method is analogous to the Born approximations in the solution of scattering problems in quantum mechanics.

are solved by the above perturbation procedure one obtains

$$\begin{aligned} \Delta\mathbf{R}_j(s) &= \Delta\mathbf{R}_j^{(0)} + \lambda\Delta\mathbf{R}_j^{(1)} + \cdots \\ \Delta\mathbf{p}_j(s) &= \lambda\Delta\mathbf{p}_j^{(1)} + \lambda^2\Delta\mathbf{p}_j^{(2)} + \cdots. \end{aligned} \tag{16}$$

The transformation function can be written therefore to terms of the order of λ^2 as

$$K^{(N)}(\mathbf{Rp}|\mathbf{R}_0\mathbf{p}_0; s) = [1 - \lambda \sum_{j=1}^{N} \Delta\mathbf{p}_j^{(1)}(s) \cdot \nabla_{\mathbf{p}_j}] \prod_{k=1}^{N} \delta(\mathbf{R}_k - \mathbf{R}_{k0} - \Delta\mathbf{R}_k^{(0)})$$

$$\delta(\mathbf{p}_k - \mathbf{p}_{k0}) + O[\lambda^2], \tag{17}$$

where the terms in the expansion of the transformation function are of the same order of λ as of $\Delta\mathbf{p}^{(1)}$.

The above results may be compared with those derived from the formal representation of the transformation function by

$$K^{(N)}(\mathbf{Rp}|\mathbf{R}_0\mathbf{p}_0; s) = \prod_{j=1}^{N} \delta(\mathbf{R}_j - \mathbf{R}_{j0} - \Delta\mathbf{R}_j)\delta(\mathbf{p}_j - \mathbf{p}_{j0} - \Delta\mathbf{p}_j),$$

$$\Delta\mathbf{R}_j(s) = \int_0^s \frac{\mathbf{p}_j(s')}{m_j} ds', \tag{18}$$

$$\Delta\mathbf{p}_j(s) = \int_0^s \{\mathbf{F}_j[\mathbf{R}_0 + \Delta\mathbf{R}(s')] + \mathbf{X}_j[\mathbf{R}_{j0} + \Delta\mathbf{R}_j(s')]\} ds',$$

and subsequent Taylor series expansion of the δ functions in powers of $\Delta\mathbf{p}$. Essentially this is the method used in Kirkwood's analysis. The transformation function becomes, to terms of the order of $(\Delta\mathbf{p})^2$,

$$K^{(N)}(\mathbf{Rp}|\mathbf{R}_0\mathbf{p}_0; s) = [1 - \sum_{=1}^{N} \Delta\mathbf{p}_j(s) \cdot \Delta_{\mathbf{p}_j}] \prod_{k=1}^{N} \delta(\mathbf{R}_k - \mathbf{R}_{k0} - \Delta\mathbf{R}_k)\delta(\mathbf{p}_k - \mathbf{p}_{k0})$$

$$+ O[(\Delta\mathbf{p})^2]. \tag{19}$$

All higher terms in this expansion are omitted in his treatment on the supposition that for sufficiently large values of the time interval τ their contribution becomes vanishingly small, provided that the friction constant, derived from the retained terms of the order of $(\Delta\mathbf{p})$ approaches a plateau value independent of τ. In comparison with the present derivation, it should be noted that $\Delta\mathbf{p}_j$ appearing in Eqs. (18) and (19) is defined in terms of forces which are to be evaluated along the trajectory determined by the exact solution of the equation of motion. The appearance of $\Delta\mathbf{p}_j^{(1)}$ rather than $\Delta\mathbf{p}_j$ in the retained terms of $K^{(N)}(\mathbf{Rp}|\mathbf{R}_0\mathbf{p}_0; s)$, Eq. (17), is a consequence of the consistent application of perturbation theory to the evaluation of the transformation function, and leads to a different expression for the friction constant in terms of the intermolecular forces than that obtained by Kirkwood.

The derivation of the Chandrasekhar equation proceeds with the introduction of the transformation function into Eq. (7) which yields

$$\boldsymbol{\Omega}^{(1)} = -\frac{1}{\tau}\int_0^{\tau}\cdots\int \mathbf{F}_{12}(R_{12})K^{(N)}(\mathbf{R}_1\mathbf{R}_2\mathbf{p}_1\mathbf{p}_2\mathbf{P}\mathbf{Q}|\mathbf{R}_{10}\mathbf{R}_{20}\mathbf{p}_{10}\mathbf{p}_{20}\mathbf{P}_0\mathbf{Q}_0; s) \tag{20}$$
$$\times f^{(N)}(\mathbf{R}_{10}\mathbf{R}_{20}\mathbf{p}_{10}\mathbf{p}_{20}\mathbf{P}_0\mathbf{Q}_0; t)d\mathbf{P}d\mathbf{Q}d\mathbf{R}_2d\mathbf{p}_2dsd\mathbf{R}_{10}d\mathbf{R}_{20}d\mathbf{p}_{10}d\mathbf{p}_{20}d\mathbf{P}_0d\mathbf{Q}_0.$$

If $K^{(N)}$ is represented adequately by Eq. (17) then, to terms of the order of λ^2, or equivalently $(\Delta\mathbf{p}^{(1)})^2$, $\boldsymbol{\Omega}^{(1)}$ becomes

$$\boldsymbol{\Omega}^{(1)} = -\frac{1}{\tau}\int_0^{\tau}\int\cdots\int \mathbf{F}_{12}(R_{12})\{[1-\sum_{j=1}^{N}\Delta\mathbf{p}_j^{(1)}(s)\cdot\nabla_{\mathbf{p}_j}]\prod_{k=1}^{N}\delta(\mathbf{R}_k-\mathbf{R}_{k0})$$
$$\delta(\mathbf{p}_k-\mathbf{p}_{k0})\}\times f^{(N)}(\mathbf{R}_{10}\mathbf{R}_{20}\mathbf{p}_{10}\mathbf{p}_{20}\mathbf{P}_0\mathbf{Q}_0;t)$$
$$d\mathbf{P}d\mathbf{Q}d\mathbf{R}_2d\mathbf{p}_2dsd\mathbf{R}_{10}d\mathbf{R}_{20}d\mathbf{p}_{10}d\mathbf{p}_{20}d\mathbf{P}_0d\mathbf{Q}_0. \tag{21}$$

The conditions for which this approximation of the transformation function might be valid are discussed below. The function $\delta(\mathbf{R}_k-\mathbf{R}_{k0}-\Delta\mathbf{R}_k^{(0)})$ has been replaced by $\delta(\mathbf{R}_k-\mathbf{R}_{k0})$ on the assumption that the distribution functions have only macroscopic dependence on the configuration space coordinates.

The distribution function $f^{(N)}(\mathbf{R}_{10}\mathbf{R}_{20}\mathbf{p}_{10}\mathbf{p}_{20}\mathbf{P}_0\mathbf{Q}_0; t)$ in Eq. (21) needs to be transformed once more and can be written as

$$f^{(N)}(\mathbf{R}_{10}\mathbf{R}_{20}\mathbf{p}_{10}\mathbf{p}_{20}\mathbf{P}_0\mathbf{Q}_0; t)$$
$$= \int\cdots\int K^{(N)}(\mathbf{R}_{10}\mathbf{R}_{20}\mathbf{p}_{10}\mathbf{p}_{20}\mathbf{P}_0\mathbf{Q}_0|\mathbf{R}_1'\mathbf{R}_2'\,\mathbf{p}_1'\mathbf{p}_2'\mathbf{P}'\mathbf{Q}'; -s)$$
$$\times f^{(N)}(\mathbf{R}_1'\mathbf{R}_2'\mathbf{p}_1'\mathbf{p}_2'\mathbf{P}'\mathbf{Q}'; t+s)d\mathbf{R}_1'd\mathbf{R}_2'd\mathbf{p}_1'd\mathbf{p}_2'd\mathbf{P}'d\mathbf{Q}'. \tag{22}$$

The transformation function now becomes, to the same order of approximation as used previously,

$$K^{(N)}(\mathbf{R}_0\mathbf{p}_0|\,\mathbf{R}'\mathbf{p}'; -s) = [1+\lambda\sum_{j=1}^{N}\Delta\mathbf{p}_j^{(1)}(s)\cdot\nabla_{\mathbf{p}_j0}]\prod_{k=1}^{N}\delta(\mathbf{R}_k'-\mathbf{R}_{k0})\delta(\mathbf{p}_k'-\mathbf{p}_{k0}) \tag{23}$$
$$\Delta\mathbf{p}_j^{(1)}(s) = \int_0^s\left[\mathbf{F}_j\left(\mathbf{R}_0+s'\frac{\mathbf{p}_0}{m}\right)+\mathbf{X}_j\left(\mathbf{R}_{j0}+s'\frac{\mathbf{p}_{j0}}{m_j}\right)\right]ds',$$

and substitution of Eq. (23) into Eq. (22) leads to

$$f^{(N)}(\mathbf{R}_{10}\mathbf{R}_{20}\mathbf{p}_{10}\mathbf{p}_{20}\mathbf{P}_0\mathbf{Q}_0; t)$$
$$= [1+\sum_{j=l}^{N}\Delta\mathbf{p}_j^{(1)}(s)\cdot\nabla_{\mathbf{p}_j0}]f^{(N)}(\mathbf{R}_{10}\mathbf{R}_{20}\mathbf{p}_{10}\mathbf{p}_{20}\mathbf{P}_0\mathbf{Q}_0; t+s). \tag{24}$$

The distribution function $f^{(N)}$ can be related to the singlet distribution function by the formulas

$$f^{(N)}(\mathbf{R}_{10}\mathbf{R}_{20}\mathbf{p}_{10}\mathbf{p}_{20}\mathbf{P}_0\mathbf{Q}_0; t+s)$$
$$= f^{(2)}(\mathbf{R}_{10}\mathbf{R}_{20}\mathbf{p}_{10}\mathbf{p}_{20}; t+s) f^{(2,N-2)}(\mathbf{R}_{10}\mathbf{R}_{20}\mathbf{p}_{10}\mathbf{p}_{20}|\mathbf{P}_0\mathbf{Q}_0; t+s)$$
$$f^{(2)}(\mathbf{R}_{10}\mathbf{R}_{20}\mathbf{p}_{10}\mathbf{p}_{20}; t+s) \tag{25}$$
$$= \varphi^{(2)}(\mathbf{R}_{10}\mathbf{R}_{20}\mathbf{p}_{10}\mathbf{p}_{20}; t+s) f^{(1)}(\mathbf{R}_{10}\mathbf{p}_{10}; t+s) f^{(1)}(\mathbf{R}_{20}\mathbf{p}_{20}; t+s),$$

where $f^{(2,N-2)}$ is the relative probability density in the subspace P_0Q_0, given that particles 1 and 2 have specified coordinates, and $\varphi^{(2)}$ is the pair correlation function. A number of simplifications are now postulated. First, it is assumed that the environment of particles 1 and 2 is in statistical equilibrium and consequently $f^{(2,N-2)}$ can be replaced by its equilibrium value ${}^0f^{(2,N-2)}$. The contribution to $\mathbf{\Omega}^{(1)}$ resulting from the departure of $f^{(2,N-2)}$ from ${}^0f^{(2,N-2)}$ will be denoted by $\Delta\mathbf{\Omega}^{(1)}$, so that $\mathbf{\Omega}^{(1)} = {}^0\mathbf{\Omega}^{(1)} + \Delta\mathbf{\Omega}^{(1)}$. Secondly, it is assumed that the pair correlation function can be represented by its equilibrium value $\exp[-\beta W^{(2)}(R_{10}, R_{20})]$, where $W^{(2)}(R_{10}, R_{20})$ is the equilibrium potential of the average force exerted on the pair of particles 1 and 2. Thirdly, in the operation of differentiation with respect to $\mathbf{p}_{10}$ and $\mathbf{p}_{20}$, the dependence of ${}^0f^{(2,N-2)}$ on these variables is neglected, and deviations of the singlet distribution functions from their equilibrium values are disregarded. Thus the differentiations with respect to $\mathbf{p}_{10}$ and $\mathbf{p}_{20}$ yield

$$
\begin{gathered}
{}^0f^{(1)}(\mathbf{R}_{10}\mathbf{p}_{10}) - \left(\frac{\beta}{2\pi m_1}\right)^{\frac{3}{2}} \frac{1}{v} \exp\left\{-\beta\left[\frac{p_{10}{}^2}{2m_1} + W^{(1)}(\mathbf{R}_{10})\right]\right\} \\
\nabla_{\mathbf{p}_{10}}{}^0f^{(1)}(\mathbf{R}_{10}\mathbf{p}_{10}) = -\beta\frac{\mathbf{p}_{10}}{m_1}{}^0f^{(1)}(\mathbf{R}_{10}\mathbf{p}_{10}).
\end{gathered}
\tag{26}
$$

Substitution of Eqs. (22)–(26) into Eq. (21) and use of the above approximations alters that equation to read

$$\mathbf{\Omega}^{(1)} = {}^0\mathbf{\Omega}^{(1)} + \Delta\mathbf{\Omega}^{(1)},$$

$$
\begin{aligned}
{}^0\mathbf{\Omega}^{(1)} = -\frac{1}{\tau}\int_0^\tau \int \cdots \int \mathbf{F}_{12}(R_{12}) &\left[1 - \sum_{k=1}^{N} \Delta\mathbf{p}_k{}^{(1)} \cdot \nabla_{\mathbf{p}_k}\right] \\
&\left[1 - \beta\frac{\mathbf{p}_1}{m_1}\cdot\Delta\mathbf{p}_1{}^{(1)}(s) - \beta\frac{\mathbf{p}_2}{m_2}\cdot\Delta\mathbf{p}_2{}^{(1)}(s)\right] \\
\times \exp[-\beta W^{(2)}(R_{12})] f^{(1)}(\mathbf{R}_1\mathbf{p}_1; t+) f^{(1)}(\mathbf{R}_2\mathbf{p}_2; t+)& \\
{}^0f^{(2,N-2)}(\mathbf{R}_1\mathbf{R}_2\mathbf{p}_1\mathbf{p}_2|\mathbf{P}\mathbf{Q})\,d\mathbf{p}_2\,d\mathbf{R}_2\,d\mathbf{P}\,d\mathbf{Q}\,ds.&
\end{aligned}
\tag{27}
$$

Since all terms in the remaining sum vanish except $k = 1$, Eq. (27) can be rewritten as

$$
{}^{0}\boldsymbol{\Omega}^{(1)} = -\frac{1}{\tau}\int_0^\tau \int \cdots \int \mathbf{F}_{12}(R_{12})[1 - \Delta\mathbf{p}_1{}^{(1)}(s) \cdot \nabla_{\mathbf{p}_1}]
$$

$$
\left[1 - \beta\frac{\mathbf{p}_1}{m_1} \cdot \Delta\mathbf{p}_1{}^{(1)}(s) - \beta\frac{\mathbf{p}_2}{m_2} \cdot \Delta\mathbf{p}_2{}^{(1)}(s)\right]
$$

$$
\times \exp\,[-\beta W^{(2)}(R_{12})] f^{(1)}(\mathbf{R}_1\mathbf{p}_1;\, t+) f^{(1)}(\mathbf{R}_2\mathbf{p}_2;\, t+)
$$

$$
{}^{0}f^{(2,N-2)}(\mathbf{R}_1\mathbf{R}_2\mathbf{p}_1\mathbf{p}_2 | \mathbf{PQ})\, d\mathbf{P}\, d\mathbf{Q}\, d\mathbf{R}_2\, d\mathbf{p}_2\, ds. \tag{28}
$$

Except for the appearance of $\Delta\mathbf{p}_1{}^{(1)}$ and $\Delta\mathbf{p}_2{}^{(1)}$ rather than $\Delta\mathbf{p}_1$ and $\Delta\mathbf{p}_2$ in Eq. (28), this result agrees with that obtained by Kirkwood [SMTI Eqs. (54) and (55)] and the derivation, identical with his from here on, leads to the Fokker-Planck equation in phase space

$$
\frac{\partial \bar{f}^{(1)}}{\partial t} + \frac{\mathbf{p}_1}{m_1} \cdot \nabla_{\mathbf{R}_1} \bar{f}^{(1)} + \nabla_{\mathbf{p}_1} \cdot (\mathbf{F}_1{}^* + \mathbf{X}_1) \bar{f}^{(1)}
$$

$$
= \nabla_{\mathbf{p}_1} \cdot \zeta_1 \left\{ \frac{\mathbf{p}_1}{m_1} \bar{f}^{(1)} + kT \nabla_{\mathbf{p}_1} \bar{f}^{(1)} \right\},
$$

$$
\zeta_1 = \frac{N_2}{3kT\tau} \int_0^\tau \int_{-s}^0 \int \cdots \int \mathbf{F}_{12}(R_{12})\, \mathbf{F}_1 \left[\mathbf{R} + (s + s')\frac{\mathbf{p}}{m} \right] \tag{29}
$$

$$
{}^{0}f^{(1,N-1)}(\mathbf{R}_1\mathbf{p}_1 | \mathbf{PQ})\, d\mathbf{P}\, d\mathbf{Q}\, ds\, ds',
$$

where ζ_1 is the friction constant and the remainder of the symbols correspond to those in SMTI.

The present statistical mechanical derivation of the equations of Brownian motion shows that a molecular interpretation of these equations may be possible under certain limited conditions now to be discussed. The transformation function $K^{(N)}$, which expresses the solution to the equations of motion of the entire system, is obtained as an infinite series by a consistent method of successive approximations which treats the forces on the particles as perturbations. It is shown that the approximation of this function by the first two terms of the series, i.e., approximation to terms of the order of λ^2 or equivalently $(\Delta\mathbf{p}^{(1)})^2$, leads to the Chandrasekhar equation. That is, the equation here derived is valid for systems in which the particle under consideration suffers a small change in momentum in the time interval during which the friction constant has reached its plateau value. Physical situations fulfilling this requirement are a set of weakly interacting particles for which the kinetic energy is much greater than the potential energy at all times, and the motion of a heavy particle amidst much lighter particles.

The derivation leads to a friction constant which must be determined "along a linear trajectory," i.e., the force appearing in the integrand of the definition of the friction constant must be determined along a linear trajectory. Kirkwood[11] has shown that the evaluation of this constant so defined

[11] J. G. Kirkwood, private communication.

presents no difficulty and has proven that its plateau value exists for a system of infinite extent. This additional fact allows the conclusion that a theory of transport based upon the Chandrasekhar equation and the friction constant as here derived will predict the required dissipative mechanism of irreversible processes in systems of arbitrary density and infinite extent, subject to the limitations given in the foregoing.

The author wishes to express his gratitude to Professor John G. Kirkwood for his interest and for many helpful discussions of most aspects of this problem.

APPENDIX A

The second term in the expansion of the transformation function, Eq. (12), can be written

$$K_1{}^{(N)} = -\int_0^s \exp\left[(s'-s)\sum_{j=1}^{N}\frac{\mathbf{p}_j}{m_j}\cdot\nabla_{\mathbf{R}_j}\right]\sum_{k=1}^{N}(\mathbf{F}_k+\mathbf{X}_k)\cdot\nabla_{\mathbf{p}_k}$$

$$\left\{\prod_{n=1}^{N}\delta\left(\mathbf{R}_n-\mathbf{R}_{n0}-s'\frac{\mathbf{p}_n}{m_n}\right)\delta(\mathbf{p}_n-\mathbf{p}_{n0})\right\}ds' \tag{A1}$$

$$\mathbf{F}_k = \mathbf{F}_k(\mathbf{R}) = \mathbf{F}_k(\mathbf{R}_1\cdots\mathbf{R}_N)$$

$$\mathbf{X}_k = \mathbf{X}_k(\mathbf{R}_k),$$

as can be seen from the solution for the general term, Eq. (15). The exponential operator adds $(s'-s)\mathbf{p}_j/m_j$ to each $\mathbf{R}_j$ appearing in the operand, so that $K_1{}^{(N)}$ becomes

$$K_1{}^{(N)} = -\int_0^s \sum_{k=1}^{N}\left\{\mathbf{F}_k\left[\mathbf{R}+(s'-s)\frac{\mathbf{p}}{m}\right]\right.$$

$$\left.+\mathbf{X}_k\left[\mathbf{R}_k+(s'-s)\frac{\mathbf{p}_k}{m}\right]\right\}\cdot\nabla_{\mathbf{p}_k}\left\{\prod_{n=1}^{N}\delta\left(\mathbf{R}_n-\mathbf{R}_{n0}-s\frac{\mathbf{p}_n}{m_n}\right)\right.$$

$$\left.\delta(\mathbf{p}_n-\mathbf{p}_{n0})\right\}ds'. \tag{A2}$$

Because of the presence of the δ function, $[R_n - s(\mathbf{p}_n/m_n)]$ can be replaced by $\mathbf{R}_{n0}$ in $\mathbf{F}_k$ and $\mathbf{X}_k$; this yields the desired result

$$K_1{}^{(N)} = -\sum_{j=1}^{N}\Delta\mathbf{p}_j{}^{(1)}(s)\cdot\nabla_{\mathbf{p}_j}\left\{\prod_{k=1}^{N}\delta\left(\mathbf{R}_k-\mathbf{R}_{k0}-s\frac{\mathbf{p}_k}{m_k}\right)\delta(\mathbf{p}_k-\mathbf{p}_{k0})\right\}$$

$$\Delta\mathbf{p}_j{}^{(1)} = \int_0^s\left[\mathbf{F}_j\left(\mathbf{R}_0+s'\frac{\mathbf{p}}{m}\right)+\mathbf{X}_j\left(\mathbf{R}_{j0}+s'\frac{\mathbf{p}_j}{m_j}\right)\right]ds'. \tag{A3}$$

The Statistical Mechanical Theory of Transport Processes. X. The Heat of Transport in Binary Liquid Solutions*

Richard J. Bearman,† John G. Kirkwood, and Marshall Fixman,‡

Sterling Chemistry Laboratory, Yale University

I. INTRODUCTION

Denbigh,[1] Drickamer and collaborators,[2,3,4] Wirtz,[5] Wirtz and Hiby,[6] and Prigogine and co-workers[7] have written numerous papers containing molecular interpretations of the heat of transport and the related Soret coefficient in liquids. These have proceeded on the basis of special assumptions concerning the molecular structure of the liquid and the mechanism of the diffusion process, and have assumed the validity of the equilibrium statistical-mechanical distribution in the non-equilibrium case. In the present paper we remove the special assumptions and show from general statistical mechanics that the heat of transport consists not only of an equilibrium term but also a term which arises from the non-equilibrium perturbation to the distribution function. In the special case of a regular solution, the expression for the equilibrium contribution reduces to a thermodynamic equation that is similar to expressions obtained previously.

In this article we shall not utilize the generalized Fokker-Planck equations[8] which have been successfully used to calculate coefficients of viscosity and thermal conductivity.[9,10] Rather, we shall find it more convenient to proceed directly from the Liouville equation. To obtain an expression for the contribution of the intermolecular forces to the heat flux, we shall postulate a plausible generalization of the usual phenomenological equations of the thermodynamics of irreversible processes to the space of molecular pairs. Although we shall not prove it here, it may be shown that the same results can also be obtained (with greater labor) from the Fokker-Planck equations.

* This work was supported in part by the Office of Naval Research under contract Nonr-410(00) with Yale University.

† National Science Foundation Postdoctoral Fellow 1955–56. Present address: Department of Chemistry, University of Kansas, Lawrence, Kansas.

‡ Frank B. Jewett Fellow 1953–54. Present address: Department of Chemistry, Harvard University, Cambridge, Massachusetts.

[1] Denbigh, K. G., *Trans. Faraday Soc.* **48**, 1 (1952).

[2] Dougherty, E. L., Jr., and Drickamer, H. G., *J. Chem. Phys.* **23**, 295 (1955).

[3] Rutherford, W. M., and Drickamer, H. G., *J. Chem. Phys.* **22**, 1157 (1954).

[4] Tichacek, L. J., Kmak, W. S., and Drickamer, H. G., *J. Phys. Chem.* **60**, 660 (1956).

[5] Wirtz, K., *Ann. Physik* **36**, 295 (1939).

[6] Wirtz, K., and Hiby, J. W., *Physik. Z.* **44**, 369 (1943).

[7] Prigogine, I., Brouckère, L. de, and Armand, R., *Physica* **16**, 577 (1950).

[8] Kirkwood, J. G., *J. Chem. Phys.* **14**, 180 (1946).

[9] Zwanzig, R. W., Kirkwood, J. G., Stripp, K. F., and Oppenheim, I., *J. Chem. Phys.* **21**, 2050 (1953).

[10] Zwanzig, R. W., Kirkwood, J. G., Oppenheim, I., and Alder, B. J., *J. Chem. Phys.* **22**, 783, (1954).

II. PHENOMENOLOGICAL THEORY

The mass flux $\mathbf{j}_1$ of component 1 and heat flux $\mathbf{q}$ in a system of two components at uniform pressure are related to the gradient of the mole fraction of component 1 and the gradient of temperature by the phenomenological relations

$$-\mathbf{j}_1 = \frac{\Omega_{11}}{x_2} \frac{\partial \mu_1}{\partial x_1} \nabla x_1 + \Omega_{10} \nabla \ln T \tag{II.1}$$

$$-\mathbf{q} = \frac{\Omega_{01}}{x_2} \frac{\partial \mu_1}{\partial x_1} \nabla x_1 + \Omega_{00} \nabla \ln T \tag{II.2}$$

where x_α is the mole fraction of component α, μ_1 is the chemical potential of component 1, T is the absolute temperature, and Ω_{11}, Ω_{10}, Ω_{01} and Ω_{00} are the phenomenological coefficients.[11] The mass flux $\mathbf{j}_1$ is expressed as molecules per unit area per unit time relative to the local center of mass.

The heat of transport Q_1^* is defined by the equation

$$\mathbf{j}_1 Q_1^* = \mathbf{q} \tag{II.3}$$

when $\nabla T = 0$.

From Eqs. (II.1), (II.2) and (II.3) it follows that

$$Q_1^* = \frac{\Omega_{01}}{\Omega_{11}}$$

If the Onsager reciprocal relation $\Omega_{01} = \Omega_{10}$ is valid, then the heat of transport is related to the stationary state of the Soret effect, as may be seen readily by setting $\mathbf{j}_1 = 0$ in Eq. (II.1). Our calculation of the heat of transport will be based on Eq. (II.3) and the statistical-mechanical expression for $\mathbf{q}$, and so we shall nowhere require the reciprocal relation.

The value of Q_1^* (which depends only upon the local state), must be independent of the velocity of the center of mass, and in our equations below we have set this velocity equal to zero in order to facilitate the calculation.

III. STATISTICAL-MECHANICAL EXPRESSIONS FOR THE DENSITIES AND FLUXES

The single phase, two-component fluid system under consideration contains N molecules of which N_1 are of species 1 and N_2 are of species 2. The molecules of each species are labeled separately, so that the molecules of species α are numbered 1, 2, . . . N_α. For simplicity, we suppose that each molecule contains three degrees of translational freedom and no other degrees of freedom. The positions of the molecules of species α are denoted by the sequence of three vectors $\mathbf{R}_{\alpha_1}, \mathbf{R}_{\alpha_2}, \ldots \mathbf{R}_{\alpha N_\alpha}$, and their momenta by $\mathbf{P}_{\alpha_1}, \mathbf{P}_{\alpha_2}, \ldots \mathbf{P}_{\alpha_{N_\alpha}}$.

We denote the time-smoothed probability distribution function at a time t in a statistical ensemble of identical systems containing the N molecules by $\bar{f}(R_{1_2} \ldots R_{2_{N_2}}, \mathbf{P}_{1_1} \ldots \mathbf{P}_{2_{N_2}}; t)$. It obeys the Liouville equation

$$\frac{\partial \bar{f}}{\partial t} + \sum_{\gamma=1}^{2} \sum_{i=1}^{N_\gamma} \frac{\mathbf{P}_{\gamma i}}{m_\gamma} \cdot \nabla_{R\gamma_i} \bar{f} + \sum_{\gamma=1}^{2} \sum_{i=1}^{N_\gamma} \mathbf{F}_{\gamma_i} \cdot \nabla_{P\gamma_i} \bar{f} = 0 \tag{III.1}$$

[11] Groot, S. R. de, *Thermodynamics of Irreversible Processes*, Interscience, New York—London, 1951, Chap. VII.

where $\mathbf{F}_{\gamma_i}$ is the force on molecule i of species γ, and m_γ is the mass of a molecule of species γ.

The expectation value at a time t of any dynamical variable a is

$$<a;\bar{f}> = \int a(\mathbf{R}_{1_1} \ldots \mathbf{R}_{2N_2}, \mathbf{P}_{1_1} \ldots \mathbf{P}_{2N_2})\bar{f} d\mathbf{R}_{1_1} \ldots d\mathbf{R}_{2N_2} d\mathbf{P}_{1_1} \ldots d\mathbf{P}_{2N_2}$$

Using this notation, the concentration $c_\alpha(\mathbf{r}_1)$ of molecules α at time t at a point $\mathbf{r}_1$ in the system is

$$c_\alpha(\mathbf{r}_1) = \int \varphi_\alpha{}^{(1)}(\mathbf{r}_1, \mathbf{p}_1) d^3\mathbf{p}_1$$

where

$$\varphi_\alpha{}^{(1)} = <\nu_\alpha{}^{(1)}; \bar{f}>$$

$$\nu_\alpha{}^{(1)} = \sum_{i=1}^{N\alpha} \delta(\mathbf{R}_{\alpha_i} - \mathbf{r}_1)\delta(\mathbf{P}_{\alpha_i} - \mathbf{p}_1)$$

and $\delta(\mathbf{R}_{\alpha_i} - \mathbf{r}_1)$ and $\delta(\mathbf{P}_{\alpha_i} - \mathbf{p}_1)$ are Dirac delta functions.

The particle current density $\mathbf{j}_\alpha(\mathbf{r}_1)$ of species α at point $\mathbf{r}_1$ is

$$\mathbf{j}_\alpha(\mathbf{r}_1) = c_\alpha(\mathbf{r}_1)\mathbf{u}_\alpha(\mathbf{r}_1) = \int \frac{\mathbf{p}_1}{m_\alpha} \varphi_\alpha{}^{(1)}(\mathbf{r}_1, \mathbf{p}_1) d^3\mathbf{p}_1$$

where $\mathbf{u}_\alpha(\mathbf{r}_1)$ is the local velocity of species α.

In the space of ordered pairs of molecules of species α at a point $\mathbf{r}_1$ and species β at $\mathbf{r}_2$, the average number density $c_{\alpha\beta}{}^{(2)}(\mathbf{r}_1, \mathbf{r}_2)$ may be expressed as

$$c_{\alpha\beta}{}^{(2)}(\mathbf{r}_1, \mathbf{r}_2) = \int \varphi_{\alpha\beta}{}^{(2)}(\mathbf{r}_1, \mathbf{r}_2, \mathbf{p}_1, \mathbf{p}_2) d^3\mathbf{p}_1 d^3\mathbf{p}_2$$

where

$$\varphi_{\alpha\beta}{}^{(2)} = <\nu_{\alpha\beta}{}^{(2)}; \bar{f}>$$

and*

$$\nu_{\alpha\beta}{}^{(2)} = \sum_{j=1}^{N\beta} \sum_{\substack{i=1 \\ a_i \neq \beta_j}}^{N\alpha} \delta(\mathbf{R}_{\alpha_i} - \mathbf{r}_1)\delta(\mathbf{R}_{\beta_i} - \mathbf{r}_2)\delta(\mathbf{P}_{\alpha_i} - \mathbf{p}_1)\delta(\mathbf{P}_{\beta_j} - \mathbf{p}_2)$$

The particle current density in pair space $\mathbf{j}_{\alpha\beta}{}^{(2)}(\mathbf{r}_1, \mathbf{r}_2)$ is given by the six-component vector

$$\mathbf{j}_{\alpha\beta}{}^{(2)}(\mathbf{r}_1, \mathbf{r}_2) = c_{\alpha\beta}{}^{(2)}(\mathbf{r}_1, \mathbf{r}_2)\mathbf{u}_{\alpha\beta}{}^{(2)}(\mathbf{r}_1, \mathbf{r}_2)$$

$$= \int \left(\frac{\mathbf{p}_1}{m_\alpha} \oplus \frac{\mathbf{p}_2}{m_\beta}\right) \varphi_{\alpha\beta}{}^{(2)} d^3\mathbf{p}_1 d^3\mathbf{p}_2 \qquad \text{(III.2)}$$

where $\mathbf{u}_{\alpha\beta}{}^{(2)}(\mathbf{r}_1, \mathbf{r}_2)$ is the mean local velocity in pair space and the vector $\mathbf{p}_1/m_\alpha \oplus \mathbf{p}_2/m_\beta$ in six space in the direct sum of $\mathbf{p}_1/m_\alpha$ which lies in the three-dimensional momentum subspace of one molecule located at $\mathbf{r}_1$ and $\mathbf{p}_2/m_\beta$ which lies in the momentum subspace of the other molecule located at $\mathbf{r}_2$. The symbol $\oplus$ is used to generate vectors in six space from vectors in three space. The symbol $+$ will be used to denote sums of six-component vectors as well as three-component vectors.

* The symbolic notation $\alpha_i \neq \beta_j$ indicates that there is no term corresponding to $i = j$ when $\alpha = \beta$.

$\mathbf{j}_{\alpha\beta}^{(2)}$ may be written as the sum (in the six-dimensional configuration space of a molecular pair) of its projections onto the spaces of its first argument, $\mathbf{r}_1$, and its second argument, $\mathbf{r}_2$. Thus

$$\mathbf{j}_{\alpha\beta}^{(2)}(\mathbf{r}_1, \mathbf{r}_2) = \mathbf{j}_{\alpha\beta,1}^{(2)}(\mathbf{r}_1, \mathbf{r}_2) \oplus \mathbf{j}_{\alpha\beta,2}^{(2)}(\mathbf{r}_1, \mathbf{r}_2)$$

$$\mathbf{j}_{\alpha\beta,1}^{(2)} = \int \frac{\mathbf{p}_1}{m_\alpha} \varphi_{\alpha\beta}^{(2)} d^3\mathbf{p}_1 d^3\mathbf{p}_2$$

$$\mathbf{j}_{\alpha\beta,2}^{(2)} = \int \frac{\mathbf{p}_2}{m_\beta} \varphi_{\alpha\beta}^{(2)} d^3\mathbf{p}_1 d^3\mathbf{p}_2 \tag{III.3}$$

We now assume that the molecules interact with central forces only, the intermolecular potential V is the sum of pair potentials, and that external fields of force are absent. Therefore

$$V = \tfrac{1}{2} \sum_{\beta=1}^{2} \sum_{\alpha=1}^{2} \sum_{\substack{j=1 \\ \alpha_i \neq \beta_j}}^{N\beta} \sum_{i=1}^{N\alpha} V_{\alpha\beta}(R_{\alpha_i\beta_j})$$

where

$$R_{\alpha_i\beta_j} = |\mathbf{R}_{\beta_j} - \mathbf{R}_{\alpha_i}|$$

The force exerted on molecule i of species α by molecule j of species β is

$$\mathbf{F}_{\beta_j\alpha_i} = -\nabla_{R\alpha_i} V_{\alpha\beta}$$

and the total force, $\mathbf{F}_{\alpha_i}$, on molecule i of species α, is then

$$\mathbf{F}_{\alpha_i} = \sum_{\beta=1}^{2} \sum_{\substack{j=1 \\ \alpha_i \neq \beta_j}}^{N_\beta} \mathbf{F}_{\beta_j\alpha_i}$$

Under the above assumptions, the expression found by Irving and Kirkwood[12] for the heat flux $\mathbf{q}$ in a one-component system may be generalized readily to the two-component case, leading to the relations

$$\mathbf{q} = \mathbf{q}_k + \mathbf{q}_v - \sum_{\alpha=1}^{2} \mathbf{j}_\alpha \bar{H}_\alpha \tag{III.4}$$

$$\mathbf{q}_k(\mathbf{r}_1) = \sum_{\alpha=1}^{2} \int \frac{m_\alpha}{2} \left| \frac{\mathbf{p}_1}{m_\alpha} - \mathbf{u} \right|^2 \left(\frac{\mathbf{p}_1}{m_\alpha} - \mathbf{u} \right) \varphi_\alpha^{(1)} d^3\mathbf{p}_1 \tag{III.5}$$

$$\mathbf{q}_v(\mathbf{r}_1) = \tfrac{1}{2} \sum_{\beta=1}^{2} \sum_{\alpha=1}^{2} \int \left[V_{\alpha\beta}(r)\,\mathbf{1} - V'_{\alpha\beta}(r) \frac{\mathbf{r}\mathbf{r}}{r} \right]$$

$$\cdot\, [\mathbf{j}_{\alpha\beta,1}(\mathbf{r}_1, \mathbf{r}_1 + \mathbf{r}) - \mathbf{u}(\mathbf{r}_1) c_{\alpha\beta}^{(2)}(\mathbf{r}_1, \mathbf{r}_1 + \mathbf{r})] d^3\mathbf{r} \tag{III.6}$$

---

[12] Irving, J. H., and Kirkwood, J. G., *J. Chem. Phys.* **18**, 817 (1950).

where $\bar{H}_\alpha$ is the partial molecular enthalpy, $\mathbf{u}$ is the mean velocity of the local center of mass (zero in the present calculations), $\mathbf{r} = \mathbf{r}_2 - \mathbf{r}_1$, and $\mathbf{1}$ is the unit tensor of second rank. The term $\sum_{\alpha=1}^{2} \mathbf{j}_\alpha \bar{H}_\alpha$ which is zero in the one-component system arises in the macroscopic equations of transport for multi-component systems.[13*]

IV. THE GENERAL EXPRESSION FOR THE HEAT OF TRANSPORT

To evaluate $\mathbf{q}_k$, we shall employ the zero-order approximation to $\varphi_\alpha^{(1)}$, with Maxwellian distribution around the mean particle velocities $\mathbf{u}_\alpha$, and linearized with respect to $\mathbf{u}_a$,

$$\varphi_\alpha^{(1)}(\mathbf{r}_1, \mathbf{p}_1) = \frac{c_\alpha}{(2\pi m_\alpha kT)^{3/2}} e^{-p_1^2/2m_\alpha kT} \left(1 + \frac{\mathbf{u}_\alpha \cdot \mathbf{p}_1}{kT}\right) \tag{IV.1}$$

where k is Boltzmann's constant. Substituting Eq. (IV.1) into Eq. (III.5) and carrying out the integration yields

$$\mathbf{q}_k = \frac{5}{2} kT \sum_{\alpha=1}^{2} c_\alpha \mathbf{u}_\alpha \tag{IV.2}$$

The use of Eq. (IV.1) in Eq. (III.5) neglects quantities (negligible in liquids) of the order of the non-equilibrium terms in the kinetic contribution to the stress tensor.[9] More exact calculations using the generalized Fokker-Planck equations show that the neglected terms are actually equal to zero.

To evaluate $\mathbf{q}_\alpha$ we must express $\mathbf{j}_{\alpha\beta,1}^{(2)}$ as a function of the local velocities. In order to do this we shall postulate the validity in pair space of quasi-phenomenological relations strictly analogous to the phenomenological relations of the thermodynamics of irreversible processes. We find it convenient first to obtain expressions for the mean forces in the singlet and pair spaces.

The mean force $\bar{\mathbf{F}}_\alpha^{(1)}(\mathbf{r}_1)$ on a molecule of type α located at $\mathbf{r}_1$ is

$$c_\alpha(\mathbf{r}_1)\bar{\mathbf{F}}_\alpha^{(1)}(\mathbf{r}_1) = \left\langle \sum_{i=1}^{N_\alpha} \mathbf{F}_{\alpha_i} \delta(\mathbf{R}_{\alpha_i} - \mathbf{r}_1); f \right\rangle \tag{IV.3}$$

Similarly, the mean force $\mathbf{F}_{\alpha\beta}^{(2)}(\mathbf{r}_1, \mathbf{r}_2)$ in pair space, when a molecule of type α is at $\mathbf{r}_1$ and a molecule of type β is at $\mathbf{r}_2$, is

$$c_{\alpha\beta}^{(2)}(\mathbf{r}_1, \mathbf{r}_2)\bar{\mathbf{F}}_{\alpha\beta}^{(2)}(\mathbf{r}_1, \mathbf{r}_2)$$

$$= \left\langle \sum_{\substack{j=1 \\ \alpha_i \neq \beta_j}}^{N_\beta} \sum_{i=1}^{N_\alpha} (\mathbf{F}_{\alpha_i} \oplus \mathbf{F}_{\beta_j}) \delta(\mathbf{R}_{\alpha_i} - \mathbf{r}_1) \delta(\mathbf{R}_{\beta_j} - \mathbf{r}_2); f \right\rangle \tag{IV.4}$$

Multiplying Eq. (III.1) by $\mathbf{P}_{\alpha_j}\delta(\mathbf{R}_{\alpha_j} - \mathbf{r}_1)$ and integrating over all coordinates and momenta yields, upon neglecting inertial terms and terms of the order of the non-equilibrium terms in the kinetic contribution to the stress tensor,

$$kT\nabla_{r_1} c_\alpha(\mathbf{r}_1) - c_\alpha(\mathbf{r}_1)\bar{\mathbf{F}}_\alpha^{(1)}(\mathbf{r}_1) = 0 \tag{IV.5}$$

---

[13] Kirkwood, J. G., and Crawford, B. L., Jr., *J. Phys. Chem.* **56**, 1048 (1952).
* It should be noted that our $\mathbf{q}$ is denoted by $\mathbf{q}'$ in the Kirkwood and Crawford paper.

The non-equilibrium temperature is defined in terms of the kinetic energy per molecule averaged over all species, and this has been supposed equal to the kinetic energy per molecule averaged over a single species. Similarly, multiplying Eq. (III.1) by

$$(\mathbf{P}_{\alpha_j} \oplus \mathbf{P}_{\beta_k})\delta(\mathbf{R}_{\alpha_j} - \mathbf{r}_1)\delta(\mathbf{R}_{\beta_k} - \mathbf{r}_2)$$

and integrating gives

$$kT\nabla c_{\alpha\beta}{}^{(2)}(\mathbf{r}_1, \mathbf{r}_2) - c_{\alpha\beta}{}^{(2)}(\mathbf{r}_1, \mathbf{r}_2)\overline{\mathbf{F}}_{\alpha\beta}{}^{(2)}(\mathbf{r}_1, \mathbf{r}_2) = 0 \tag{IV.6}$$

where $\nabla = \nabla_{\mathbf{r}_1} \oplus \nabla_{\mathbf{r}_2}$, and $\oplus$ denotes a direct sum in the six-dimensional configuration space of a molecular pair.* To derive Eq. (IV.6), we have assumed that the mean kinetic energy of a species averaged in pair space is the same as the average in singlet space.† From the thermodynamics of isothermal systems in external fields of force. we know that if the gradient of chemical potential at a point is equal to the external force, the system is at equilibrium. By imposing suitable external fields we may obtain an equilibrium state of our system in which the concentration distribution (in singlet space but not in pair space) is the same as in the diffusing system. From Eq. (III.1) we find the following equations analogous to Eqs. (IV.5) and (IV.6) and valid in the system at equilibrium under these conditions

$$kT\nabla_{r_1}c_\alpha(\mathbf{r}_1) - c_\alpha(\mathbf{r}_1)\overline{\mathbf{F}}_\alpha{}^{(1,0)}(\mathbf{r}_1) = c_\alpha(\mathbf{r}_1)\nabla_{r_1}\mu_\alpha(\mathbf{r}_1) \tag{IV.7}$$

$$kT\nabla c_{\alpha\beta}{}^{(2,0)}(\mathbf{r}_1, \mathbf{r}_2) - c_{\alpha\beta}{}^{(2,0)}(\mathbf{r}_1, \mathbf{r}_2)\overline{\mathbf{F}}_{\alpha\beta}{}^{(2,0)}(\mathbf{r}_1, \mathbf{r}_2)$$
$$= c_{\alpha\beta}{}^{(2,0)}(\mathbf{r}_1, \mathbf{r}_2)[\nabla_{r_1}\mu_\alpha(\mathbf{r}_1) \oplus \nabla_{r_2}\mu_\beta(\mathbf{r}_2)] \tag{IV.8}$$

$\overline{\mathbf{F}}_\alpha{}^{(1,0)}$ and $\overline{\mathbf{F}}_{\alpha\beta}{}^{(2,0)}$ are the mean intermolecular forces in singlet space and pair space in this equilibrium state. Equations (IV.7) and (IV.8) are exact since the averages are performed in a canonical ensemble.

Subtracting Eq. (IV.5) from Eq. IV.7) we find that

$$\overline{\mathbf{F}}_\alpha{}^{(1)}(\mathbf{r}_1) - \overline{\mathbf{F}}_\alpha{}^{(1,0)}(\mathbf{r}_1) = \nabla_{r_1}\mu_\alpha(\mathbf{r}_1)$$

The phenomenological relations may be inverted to express the gradients of chemical potential as linear functions of the velocities, and therefore

$$\overline{\mathbf{F}}_\alpha{}^{(1)}(\mathbf{r}_1) - \overline{\mathbf{F}}_\alpha{}^{(1,0)}(\mathbf{r}_1) = \sum_\gamma N_\gamma\zeta_{\alpha\gamma}(\mathbf{r}_1)[\mathbf{u}_\gamma(\mathbf{r}_1) - \mathbf{u}_\alpha(\mathbf{r}_1)] \tag{IV.9}$$

The friction coefficients $\zeta_{\alpha\gamma}$ defined by this equation may be expressed as functions of the phenomenological coefficients.‡

* This use of the symbol ∇ is not to be confused with that in the phenomenological theory.

† Calculations using the Fokker–Planck equations show that this assumption is not exact to terms of order $\mathbf{u}_\alpha$. However, the additional terms do not contribute appreciably to the heat of transport.

‡ The coefficient ζ_{11} (or ζ_{22}) is defined by applying Eq. (IV.9) to a three-component system in which the third component is tracer component 1 (or 2) present in vanishingly small quantity.

We now postulate that the following equation in pair space, analogous to Eq. (IV.9) in singlet space, is valid:

$$\bar{\mathbf{F}}_{\alpha\beta}^{(2)}(\mathbf{r}_1, \mathbf{r}_2) - \bar{\mathbf{F}}_{\alpha\beta}^{(2,0)}(\mathbf{r}_1, \mathbf{r}_2) = \sum_{\gamma=1}^{2} \sum_{\sigma=1}^{2} \tfrac{1}{2}\zeta_{\alpha\beta;\gamma\sigma} \cdot \{(\mathbf{u}_\gamma(\mathbf{r}_1) \oplus \mathbf{u}_\sigma(\mathbf{r}_2)) - \mathbf{u}_{\alpha\beta}^{(2)}(\mathbf{r}_1, \mathbf{r}_2)\} \qquad \text{(IV.10)}$$

A heuristic justification for Eq. (IV.10) is that it reduces to the sum of two equations of the form of Eq. (IV.9) at large distances between $\mathbf{r}_1$ and $\mathbf{r}_2$ when the force and velocity in pair space approach the sums of the forces and velocities, respectively, in singlet space. Equation (IV.10) is not the only conceivable equation with this correct limiting property. Further justification is to be found in the fact that it is derivable from the generalized Fokker-Planck equations.

By comparing Eq. (IV.10) with Eq. (IV.9) at large distances, we see that an asymptotic value of the tensor $\zeta_{\alpha\beta;\gamma\sigma}$ is $N_\gamma\zeta_{\alpha\gamma}(\mathbf{r}_1)\mathbf{1}_1 \oplus N_\sigma\zeta_{\beta\sigma}(\mathbf{r}_2)\mathbf{1}_2$ where $\mathbf{1}_1$ is the unit tensor at $\mathbf{r}_1$ and $\mathbf{1}_2$ is the unit tensor at $\mathbf{r}_2$. In the remainder of this paper we shall make the approximation that

$$\zeta_{\alpha\beta;\gamma\sigma} = N_\gamma\zeta_{\alpha\gamma}\,\mathbf{1}_1 \oplus N_\sigma\zeta_{\beta\sigma}\,\mathbf{1}_2 \qquad \text{(IV.11)}$$

for all distances between $\mathbf{r}_1$ and $\mathbf{r}_2$.

Subtracting Eq. (IV.8) from the sum in six-dimensional space of Eq. (IV.7) for species α and species β, we have

$$\bar{\mathbf{F}}_{\alpha\beta}^{(2,0)}(\mathbf{r}_1, \mathbf{r}_2) - (\bar{\mathbf{F}}_\alpha^{(1,0)}(\mathbf{r}_1) \oplus \bar{\mathbf{F}}_\beta^{(1,0)}(\mathbf{r}_2)) = kT\nabla \ln g_{\alpha\beta}^{(2,0)}(\mathbf{r}_1, \mathbf{r}_2) \qquad \text{(IV.12)}$$

where the radial distribution function $g_{\alpha\beta}^{(2,0)}(\mathbf{r}_1, \mathbf{r}_2)$ is defined by

$$g_{\alpha\beta}^{(2,0)}(\mathbf{r}_1, \mathbf{r}_2) = \frac{c_{\alpha\beta}^{(2,0)}(\mathbf{r}_1, \mathbf{r}_2)}{c_\alpha(\mathbf{r}_1)c_\beta(\mathbf{r}_2)}$$

Substituting Eqs. (IV.5), (IV.6), (IV.9), (IV.11), and (IV.12) into Eq. (IV.10) yields upon neglecting terms of order u_α^2

$$\mathbf{j}_{\alpha\beta,1}^{(2)}(\mathbf{r}_1, \mathbf{r}_2) = c_{\alpha\beta}^{(2,0)}(\mathbf{r}_1, \mathbf{r}_2)\mathbf{u}_\alpha(\mathbf{r}_1) - c_{\alpha\beta}^{(2,0)}(\mathbf{r}_1, \mathbf{r}_2)D_\alpha(\mathbf{r}_1)\nabla_{r_1}\frac{g_{\alpha\beta}^{(2,1)}(\mathbf{r}_1, \mathbf{r}_2)}{g_{\alpha\beta}^{(2,0)}(\mathbf{r}_1, \mathbf{r}_2)}$$

or

$$\mathbf{j}_{\alpha\beta,1}^{(2)} = c_\alpha c_\beta g_{\alpha\beta}^{(2,0)}\mathbf{u}_\alpha - c_\alpha c_\beta D_\alpha[\nabla_{r_1} g_{\alpha\beta}^{(2,1)} - g_{\alpha\beta}^{(2,1)}\nabla_{r_1}\ln g_{\alpha\beta}^{(2,0)}] \qquad \text{(IV.13)}$$

where

$$g_{\alpha\beta}^{(2,1)} = g_{\alpha\beta}^{(2)} - g_{\alpha\beta}^{(2,0)}$$

and

$$g_{\alpha\beta}^{(2)} = \frac{c_{\alpha\beta}^{(2)}(\mathbf{r}_1, \mathbf{r}_2)}{c_\alpha(\mathbf{r}_1)c_\beta(\mathbf{r}_2)}$$

and the self-diffusion coefficient D_α of species α in the mixture is defined by

$$D_\alpha(\mathbf{r}_1) = \frac{kT}{\zeta_\alpha(\mathbf{r}_1)}$$

where

$$\zeta_\alpha(\mathbf{r}_1) = \sum_{\gamma=1}^{2} N_\gamma \zeta_{\alpha\gamma}(\mathbf{r}_1)$$

We shall now find an expression for $g_{\alpha\beta}^{(2,1)}/g_{\alpha\beta}^{(2,0)}$ for substitution into Eq. (IV.13). Multiplying Eq. (III.1) by $\delta(\mathbf{R}_{\alpha_j} - \mathbf{r}_1)\delta(\mathbf{R}_{\beta_k} - \mathbf{r}_2)$, integrating over coordinates and momenta, and neglecting inertial terms gives

$$\nabla_{r_1} \cdot \mathbf{j}_{\alpha\beta,1}{}^{(2)} + \nabla_{r_2} \cdot \mathbf{j}_{\alpha\beta,2}{}^{(2)} = 0$$

Substituting Eq. (IV.13) for $\mathbf{j}_{\alpha\beta,1}{}^{(2)}$ and a similar equation for $\mathbf{j}_{\alpha\beta,2}{}^{(2)}$ into this differential equation yields when terms of order $u_\alpha{}^2$ and ∇u_α are neglected

$$\frac{\mathbf{u}_\beta - \mathbf{u}_\alpha}{D_\alpha + D_\beta} \cdot \nabla_r g_{\alpha\beta}{}^{(2,0)} - \nabla_r \cdot \{\nabla_r g_{\alpha\beta}{}^{(2,1)} - g_{\alpha\beta}{}^{(2,1)} \nabla_r \ln g_{\alpha\beta}{}^{(2,0)}\} = 0 \qquad \text{(IV.14)}$$

Equation (IV.14) provides differential equations for the coefficients of the spherical harmonic expansion of $g_{\alpha\beta}{}^{(2,1)}/g_{\alpha\beta}{}^{(2,0)}$ when $\mathbf{u}_\beta - \mathbf{u}_\alpha$ is chosen as the polar axis in spherical coordinates. When the expansion is substituted into Eq. (IV.13) and thence into Eq. (IV.6) and an integration is carried out over all angles, only the term, A_1, involving the first Legendre polynomial, P_1, contributes to $\mathbf{q}_v$. This term may be written in the form

$$A_1 = \frac{1}{D_\alpha + D_\beta} \psi_{\alpha\beta}(r)\{\mathbf{e}_r \cdot (\mathbf{u}_\beta - \mathbf{u}_\alpha)\} \qquad \text{(IV.15)}$$

where $\mathbf{e}_r$ is the unit vector in the $\mathbf{r}$-direction and, by Eq. (IV.14), $\psi_{\alpha\beta}$ obeys the following differential equation:

$$g_{\alpha\beta}{}^{(2,0)} \frac{d^2\psi_{\alpha\beta}}{dr^2} + \left(\frac{dg_{\alpha\beta}{}^{(2,0)}}{dr} + \frac{2}{r} g_{\alpha\beta}{}^{(2,0)}\right)\frac{d\psi_{\alpha\beta}}{dr} - \frac{2g_{\alpha\beta}{}^{(2,0)}}{r^2}\psi_{\alpha\beta} = \frac{dg_{\alpha\beta}{}^{(2,0)}}{dr} \qquad \text{(IV.16)}$$

In the linear approximation to $g_{\alpha\beta}{}^{(2,1)}/g_{\alpha\beta}{}^{(2,0)}$, $g_{\alpha\beta}{}^{(2,0)}$ is equal to the radial distribution function in the equilibrium state achieved by the naturally diffusing system in the absence of an external field. It depends only on r. Because both the perturbed and equilibrium radial distribution functions approach unity as r approaches infinity, one boundary condition on $\psi_{\alpha\beta}$ is that it approaches zero as r approaches infinity. The other boundary condition arises because the relative pair current density $\mathbf{j}_{\alpha\beta,2}{}^{(2)} - \mathbf{j}_{\alpha\beta,1}{}^{(2)}$ must have no sources or sinks. If the potential is infinite for $r \leqq b$, this leads to the boundary condition

$$\lim_{r\to b^+} \frac{d\psi_{\alpha\beta}}{dr} = 1$$

Substituting Eqs. (IV.13) and (IV.15) into Eq. (III.6), integrating by parts, and using Eq. (IV.16) results in the following linearized expression for $\mathbf{q}_v$:

$$\mathbf{q}_v = (\mathbf{q}_v)_1 + (\mathbf{q}_v)_2$$

$$(\mathbf{q}_v)_1 = \tfrac{1}{2} \sum_{\alpha=1}^{2} \sum_{\beta=1}^{2} c_\alpha(\mathbf{r}_1) c_\beta(\mathbf{r}_1) \mathbf{u}_\alpha(\mathbf{r}_1) \cdot \int \left(V_{\alpha\beta}(r)\mathbf{1} - V'_{\alpha\beta}(r) \frac{\mathbf{rr}}{r} \right) g_{\alpha\beta}{}^{(2,0)}(r) d^3\mathbf{r}$$

$$(\mathbf{q}_v)_2$$

$$= \tfrac{1}{2} c_1 c_2 \frac{D_2 - D_1}{D_2 + D_1} [\mathbf{u}_1 - \mathbf{u}_2] \int \left[V_{21} - \frac{r}{3} V'_{21} - \frac{2}{3} r V'_{21} \left(\frac{d\psi_{21}}{dr} - 1 \right) \right] g_{21}{}^{(2,0)} d^3\mathbf{r} \tag{IV.17}$$

Eliminating u_2 in favor of u_1 and inserting Eqs. (III.4), (IV.2), and (IV.17) into Eq. (II.3) gives the following expression for $Q_1{}^*$:

$$Q_1{}^* = Q_{11}{}^* + Q_{12}{}^*$$

$$Q_{11}{}^* = (h_1 - \bar{H}_1) - (h_2 - \bar{H}_2) \frac{m_1}{m_2}$$

$$Q_{12}{}^* = \frac{1}{2} \frac{D_2 - D_1}{D_2 + D_1} \left(c_2 + c_1 \frac{m_1}{m_2} \right) \left\{ 2h_{21} - \frac{2}{3} \int r \left(\frac{d\psi_{21}}{dr} - 1 \right) V'_{21} g_{21}{}^{(2,0} d^3\mathbf{r} \right\} \tag{IV.18}$$

where

$$h_1 = c_1 h_{11} + c_2 h_{12} + \tfrac{5}{2} kT$$

$$h_2 = c_2 h_{22} + c_1 h_{21} + \tfrac{5}{2} kT$$

$$h_{\alpha\beta} = h_{\beta\alpha} = \tfrac{1}{2} \int \left(V_{\beta\alpha} - \frac{r}{3} V'_{\beta\alpha} \right) g_{\beta\alpha}{}^{(2,0)} d^3\mathbf{r}$$

h_1 and h_2 (which in general are *not* equal to $\bar{H}_1$ and $\bar{H}_2$ respectively) obey the following equation readily derivable from equilibrium statistical mechanics:

$$x_1 h_1 + x_2 h_2 = H \tag{IV.19}$$

where $\bar{H}$ is the mean molecular enthalpy.

Equation (IV.18) splits the heat of transport into two terms, the first of which is quasi-thermodynamic in that it involves only averages over equilibrium ensembles, and the second of which arises from the deviation of the distribution function in pair space from the equilibrium distribution function. $Q_{11}{}^*$ corresponds to the expressions for the heat of transport found by previous authors who have neglected the non-equilibrium perturbation to the distribution function.

V. AN APPROXIMATE FORMULA FOR THE HEAT OF TRANSPORT

By introducing an approximation into Eq. (IV.18), we can gain insight into the formula for the heat of transport. It suffices to use the assumption of regular solution theory that the radial distribution function is independent of composition.[14] Under this assumption we may differentiate Eq. (IV.19) (using the definition of partial molecular enthalpy) to obtain expressions for $h_{\alpha\beta}$ in terms of thermodynamic quantities. Substituting these into Eq. (IV.18) yields

$$Q_{11}^* = \frac{1}{2}\left(\frac{m_1 x_1}{m_2} + x_2\right)\frac{\bar{v}_1\bar{v}_2}{v}\left(\frac{\bar{L}_2}{\bar{v}_2} - \frac{\bar{L}_1}{\bar{v}_1}\right)$$

$$Q_{12}^* = \frac{1}{2v}\frac{D_2 - D_1}{D_2 + D_1}\left(\frac{m_1 x_1}{m_2} + x_2\right)\left\{\bar{v}_1\bar{v}_2\left(\frac{\bar{L}_1}{\bar{v}_1} + \frac{\bar{L}_2}{\bar{v}_2}\right)\right.$$

$$+ 2x_1(\bar{L}_1\bar{v}_1 - L_1 v_1) + 2x_2(\bar{L}_2\bar{v}_2 - L_2 v_2) \qquad \text{(V.1)}$$

$$\left. - \frac{2}{3}\int r\left(\frac{d\psi_{21}}{dr} - 1\right)V'_{21} g_{21}{}^{(2,0)} d^3\mathbf{r}\right\}$$

where v is the mean molecular volume, $\bar{v}_1$ and $\bar{v}_2$ are the partial molecular volumes of components 1 and 2, respectively, v_1 and v_2 are the molecular volumes of the pure components, $\bar{L}_1(=\bar{H}_1 - \frac{5}{2}kT)$ and $\bar{L}_2(=\bar{H}_2 - \frac{5}{2}kT)$ are the negatives of the latent heats of vaporization of components 1 and 2, respectively, from the solution to the ideal gas state, and L_1 and L_2 are the negatives of the latent heats of vaporization of the pure component to the ideal gas state. Although the derivation of Eq. (V.1) does not require the use of all of the postulates of regular solution theory, the equation may be further reduced by introduction of the regular solution theory chemical potential and the assumption of additivity of volumes.

[14] Hildebrand, J. H., and Scott, R. L., *The Solubility of Nonelectrolytes*, 3rd. ed., Reinhold, New York, 1950, Chap. VII.

The Statistical Mechanics of Transport Processes. XI. Equations of Transport in Multi-component Systems*

RICHARD J. BEARMAN† AND JOHN G. KIRKWOOD, *Sterling Chemistry Laboratory, Yale University, New Haven, Connecticut*

(Received August 30, 1957)

The equations of hydrodynamics including the equations of continuity, equations of motion of the individual components as well as the over-all equation of motion, and the energy transport equation are derived from statistical mechanics. Introduction of perturbations to the singlet and pair space distribution functions linearized in the temperature gradient, diffusion velocities, and the local rate of shear leads in the stationary case to the linear relations of irreversible thermodynamics between the gradients of temperature and chemical potential and the fluxes of heat and matter.

I. INTRODUCTION

The first objective of the statistical mechanical theory of transport processes is to derive the macroscopic equations of transport from the equations of molecular dynamics and to express such macroscopic quantities as the stress tensor and the fluxes of heat and matter as averages over molecular distribution functions. The second objective is the explicit determination of the perturbations in the distribution functions arising from departures from equilibrium and the calculation of transport parameters such as the coefficients of viscosity, heat conductivity and diffusion in terms of molecular variables. In the present article, we shall be concerned with the first objective for the case of multicomponent systems without chemical reactions.

We shall first generalize the results of Irving and Kirkwood[1] for a system of one component to multicomponent systems, deriving the equations of continuity, the equations of motion of the individual components as well as the over-all equation of motion, and the energy transport equation.[2] Comparison of these equations with their macroscopic counterparts leads to the desired expressions in terms of molecular variables for the fluxes of heat and matter, the total stress tensor, and the partial stress tensors and frictional mean forces entering into the equations of motion of the individual components.

Finally, we shall formulate expressions for the coefficients of viscosity and heat conductivity, the generalized diffusion coefficients, the heats of transport, and the thermal diffusion coefficients of the several components under the

* This work was supported by the Office of Naval Research. Contribution No. 1465 from the Sterling Chemistry Laboratory.

† Present address: Department of Chemistry, University of Kansas, Lawrence, Kansas.

[1] J. H. Irving and J. G. Kirkwood, *J. Chem. Phys.* **18**, 817 (1950).

[2] When supplemented by the postulate of local equilibrium, this set also determines the entropy transport equation. See J. G. Kirkwood and B. Crawford, Jr., *J. Phys. Chem.* **56**, 1048 (1952).

assumption that the non-equilibrium perturbations in the molecular pair distribution functions may be expressed as a linear function of the temperature gradient, the diffusion velocities, and the gradient of the local rate of shear. When these coefficients are introduced into the equations of motion of the individual components and into the expression for the heat flux, and the equations are specialized to the quasi-stationary case with the neglect of inertial terms, they become identical with the linear relations of irreversible thermodynamics between the gradients of temperature and chemical potential and the fluxes of heat and matter. Sufficient, but not necessary, conditions at the molecular level are presented for the validity of the Onsager reciprocal relations in the isothermal case.

The complete determination of the non-equilibrium perturbations to the distribution functions of condensed systems must await the development of a rigorous treatment of the second aspect of the statistical mechanical theory of irreversible processes, which is not treated in this paper. Approximate calculations may be based upon the generalized Fokker-Planck equations presented in earlier articles of this series.[3–6] For the dense gas of hard spheres, approximate calculations may also be carried out with the use of the modified Enskog equation recently derived from first principles.[7]

II. THE PHENOMENOLOGICAL THEORY

We consider an element of a fluid system containing ν components which are not chemically reacting, and we assume that the intensive thermodynamic functions of state at time t are determined through the equilibrium equations by the mean molecular energy E, the mean molecular volume v, and $\nu - 1$ composition variables $c_\alpha (c_\alpha = x_\alpha / v$, where x_α is the mole fraction of component α).[8] The flow pattern is determined by specifying the local velocity $\mathbf{u}_\alpha$ of each component α. However, more convenient independent variables are the velocity $\mathbf{u}$ of the local center of mass and $\nu - 1$ of the diffusion currents $\mathbf{j}_\alpha$. The velocity $\mathbf{u}$ is related to the velocities $\mathbf{u}_\alpha$, the densities ρ_α of the components and the density ρ of the element by the equations,

$$\rho \mathbf{u} = \sum_{\alpha=1}^{\nu} \rho_\alpha \mathbf{u}_\alpha,$$

$$\rho_\alpha = m_\alpha c_\alpha, \tag{2.1}$$

$$\rho = \sum_{\alpha=1}^{\nu} \rho_\alpha,$$

where m_α is the mass per molecule of component α, and the diffusion current $\mathbf{j}_\alpha$ is given by

$$\mathbf{j}_\alpha = c_\alpha (\mathbf{u}_\alpha - \mathbf{u}). \tag{2.2}$$

---

[3] J. G. Kirkwood, *J. Chem. Phys.* **14**, 180 (1946).
[4] Kirkwood, Buff, and Green, *J. Chem. Phys.* **17**, 988 (1949).
[5] Zwanzig, Kirkwood, Stripp, and Oppenheim, *J. Chem. Phys.* **21**, 2050 (1953).
[6] Zwanzig, Kirkwood, Oppenheim, and Alder, *J. Chem. Phys.* **22**, 783 (1954).
[7] Rice, Kirkwood, Ross, and Zwanzig (to be published).
[8] Some of our results will be independent of this hypothesis of local equilibrium.

Hydrodynamic Equations

The equation of continuity for each component is

$$(\partial \rho_\alpha / \partial t) + \nabla \cdot \rho_\alpha \mathbf{u}_\alpha = 0, \tag{2.3}$$

and summing over all of the components yields the equation of continuity of the element as a whole,

$$(\partial \rho / \partial t) + \nabla \cdot \rho \mathbf{u} = 0, \tag{2.4}$$

where the operator $\partial/\partial t$ is used to indicate that the time derivative is to be taken at a point fixed in space and not moving with the fluid.

The equation of motion may be written

$$\begin{aligned} \partial \rho \mathbf{u} / \partial t &= \nabla \cdot (\boldsymbol{\sigma} - \rho \mathbf{u}\mathbf{u}) + c\mathbf{X}, \\ c\mathbf{X} &= \sum_{\alpha=1}^{\nu} c_\alpha \mathbf{X}_\alpha, \\ c &= \sum_{\alpha=1}^{\nu} c_\alpha, \end{aligned} \tag{2.5}$$

where $\boldsymbol{\sigma}$ is the stress tensor, $c_\alpha \mathbf{X}_\alpha$ is the external force density acting upon component α, and $c\mathbf{X}$ is the total external force density acting upon the element. It may be asked if equations of motion for each component exist in the same sense that equations of continuity hold for the several components separately. We shall see below that such equations do exist, and are derived by using statistical mechanics.

The energy transport equation may be written in the form

$$\begin{aligned} &\frac{\partial \sum_{\alpha=1}^{\nu} c_\alpha (\bar{E}_\alpha + \frac{1}{2} m_\alpha u_\alpha^2)}{\partial t} \\ &= \sum_{\alpha=1}^{\nu} c_\alpha \mathbf{u}_\alpha \cdot \mathbf{X}_\alpha + \nabla \cdot \left[\mathbf{u} \cdot \boldsymbol{\sigma} - \mathbf{q} - \sum_{\alpha=1}^{\nu} \mathbf{j}_\alpha \left(\bar{H}_\alpha + \frac{m_\alpha u_\alpha^2}{2} \right) \right] \\ &\qquad - \nabla \cdot \sum_{\alpha=1}^{\nu} c_\alpha \left(\bar{E}_\alpha + \frac{m_\alpha u_\alpha^2}{2} \right) \mathbf{u}, \end{aligned} \tag{2.6}$$

where $\bar{E}_\alpha$ is the partial molecular energy of component α, $\bar{H}_\alpha$ is the partial molecular enthalpy of component α, and $\mathbf{q}$ is the heat flux.[9] If the external forces $\mathbf{X}_\alpha$ are the gradients of potentials, these are not included in E.

Phenomenological Relations

By experiment it has been found for many systems that the non-equilibrium components of the stress tensor are linear functions of the rate of strain $\dot{\boldsymbol{\epsilon}}$ and the divergence of the local velocity $\mathbf{u}$, and that the diffusion currents and heat flux are linear functions of the gradients of the chemical potentials μ_α of the

[9] This equation is identical with Eq. (18) of reference 2. However, our $\mathbf{q}$ differs by $\Sigma \mathbf{j}_\alpha p \bar{v}_\alpha$ (where $\bar{v}_\alpha$ is the partial molecular volume of α and p is the pressure) from the $\mathbf{q}$ used in the reference, and therefore the same $\mathbf{q}$ appears in our energy transport equation as in our phenomenological equation for the heat flux.

components and gradient of the temperature T. These relationships are often expressed by the following equations called phenomenological relations

$$\boldsymbol{\sigma} = -[p + (\tfrac{2}{3}\eta - \varphi)\nabla \cdot \mathbf{u}]\mathbf{1} + 2\eta\dot{\boldsymbol{\epsilon}},$$
$$\dot{\boldsymbol{\epsilon}} = \text{sym}\,\nabla\mathbf{u} \equiv \tfrac{1}{2}[(\nabla\mathbf{u}) + (\nabla\mathbf{u})^{\dagger}], \tag{2.7}$$

$$-\mathbf{j}_\alpha = \Omega_{\alpha 0}\nabla \ln T + \sum_{\beta=1}^{\nu} \Omega_{\alpha\beta}\nabla_T \mu_\beta',$$
$$-\mathbf{q} = \Omega_{00}\nabla \ln T + \sum_{\alpha=1}^{\nu} \Omega_{0\alpha}\nabla_T \mu_\alpha', \tag{2.8}$$
$$\nabla_T \mu_\alpha' = \nabla\mu_\alpha' + \bar{S}_\alpha \nabla T$$
$$= \nabla\mu_\alpha - \mathbf{X}_\alpha + \bar{S}_\alpha \nabla T.$$ [10]

Equation (2.7) is the usual Newtonian form of the stress tensor: η and φ are the coefficients of shear and bulk viscosity, respectively, p is the local equilibrium pressure, $\mathbf{1}$ is the unit dyad, and in Eq. (2.8), $\bar{S}_\alpha$ is the partial molecular entropy and Ω_{00}, $\Omega_{\alpha 0}$, $\Omega_{0\alpha}$, and $\Omega_{\alpha\beta}$ are called phenomenological coefficients. By virtue of microscopic considerations advanced by Onsager[11] it is assumed in discussions of the phenomenology that

$$\Omega_{0\alpha} = \Omega_{\alpha 0}, \tag{2.9}$$

$$\Omega_{\alpha\beta} = \Omega_{\beta\alpha}. \tag{2.10}$$

We shall see that Eq. (2.10) follows from the general statistical mechanical theory presented in this paper. However, more detailed molecular considerations are probably required for the derivation of Eq. (2.9).

Further restrictions on the phenomenological coefficients arise because not all of the diffusion fluxes $\mathbf{j}_\alpha$ are independent. Thus, by Eqs. (2.1) and (2.2), we find that

$$\sum_{\alpha=1}^{\nu} m_\alpha \mathbf{j}_\alpha = 0. \tag{2.11}$$

However, $\nabla \ln T$ and $\nabla_T \mu_\beta'$ are independent, and hence substituting Eq. (2.11) into Eq. (2.8) gives

$$\sum_{\alpha=1}^{\nu} m_\alpha \Omega_{\alpha 0} = 0,$$
$$\sum_{\alpha=1}^{\nu} m_\alpha \Omega_{\alpha\beta} = 0. \tag{2.12}$$

---

[10] The notation $\nabla_T \mu_\alpha'$ is used to indicate that by subtracting off the temperature dependence we are determining the gradient of μ_α' in an isothermal system with the same local state and concentration and pressure gradients as the system in question. This usage differs from that in the sections below on the statistical mechanical theory, where the subscript on the gradient operator denotes the independent variable with respect to which a function is differentiated.

[11] L. Onsager, *Phys. Rev.* **37**, 405 (1931); **38**, 2265 (1931).

These equations imply that the determinant of the matrix of the phenomenological coefficients vanishes, and therefore it is not possible to solve Eq. (2.8) for $\nabla \ln T$ and $\nabla_T \mu_\beta'$ as linear functions of the diffusion currents and heat flux. This difficulty may be avoided by using Eqs. (2.12), (2.9), and (2.10) to eliminate Ω_{01} and $\Omega_{\alpha 1}$ from Eq. (2.8),

$$
\begin{aligned}
-\mathbf{j}_\alpha &= \Omega_{\alpha 0} \nabla \ln T + \sum_{\beta=2}^{\nu} \Omega_{\alpha\beta} \nabla_T \left(\mu_\beta' - \frac{m_\beta}{m_1} \mu_1' \right), \\
-\mathbf{q} &= \Omega_{00} \nabla \ln T + \sum_{\beta=2}^{\nu} \Omega_{0\beta} \nabla_T \left(\mu_\beta' - \frac{m_\beta}{m_1} \mu_1' \right), \qquad (2.13) \\
\nabla_T \left(\mu_\beta' - \frac{m_\beta}{m_1} \mu_1' \right) &= \nabla_T \mu_\beta' - \frac{m_\beta}{m_1} \nabla_T \mu_1'.
\end{aligned}
$$

These equations may be inverted to give

$$
\begin{aligned}
-\nabla_T \left(\mu_\beta' - \frac{m_\beta}{m_1} \mu_1' \right) &= R_{\beta 0}' \mathbf{q} + \sum_{\alpha=2}^{\nu} R_{\beta\alpha}' \mathbf{j}_\alpha, \ \beta = 2 \cdots \nu, \\
-\nabla \ln T &= R_{00}' \mathbf{q} + \sum_{\alpha=2}^{\nu} R_{0\alpha}' \mathbf{j}_\alpha, \qquad (2.14) \\
R_{\alpha\beta}' &= \frac{|\Omega|_{\alpha\beta}}{|\Omega|}, \quad \alpha, \beta = 0, 2 \cdots \nu,
\end{aligned}
$$

where Ω is the determinant of the matrix of the phenomenological coefficients in Eq. (2.13) and $|\Omega|_{\alpha\beta}$ is the appropriate cofactor.

III. STATISTICAL MECHANICAL THEORY— THE DISTRIBUTION FUNCTION AND EXPRESSIONS FOR THE DENSITIES

We shall treat a ν-component system containing N molecules which are not chemically reacting, labeling each component by a number α which runs from 1 to ν. There are N_α molecules of species α, and the individual molecules of each species are labeled separately, so that molecules of species α are numbered 1, 2, $\cdots$, N_α. To simplify the analysis, we suppose that each molecule has three degrees of translational freedom and no others. We then may denote the position of molecule i of species α by the vector $\mathbf{R}_{\alpha i}$ and its momentum by $\mathbf{P}_{\alpha i}$.

The molecules are assumed to interact according to the laws of classical mechanics, and hence the time-smoothed probability distribution function

$$
f^{(N)}(\mathbf{R}_{11}, \mathbf{R}_{12}, \cdots \mathbf{R}_{\nu N_\nu}, \mathbf{P}_{11}, \mathbf{P}_{12}, \cdots \mathbf{P}_{\nu N_\nu}; t)
$$

at a time t in a statistical ensemble obeys the Liouville equation

$$
\frac{\partial \bar{f}^{(N)}}{\partial t} + \sum_{\gamma=1}^{\nu} \sum_{i=1}^{N_\gamma} \frac{\mathbf{P}_{\gamma i}}{m_\gamma} \cdot \nabla_{R_{\gamma i}} \bar{f}^{(N)} - \sum_{\gamma=1}^{\nu} \sum_{i=1}^{N_\gamma} \nabla_{R_{\gamma i}} U \cdot \nabla_{P_{\gamma i}} f^{(N)} = 0, \qquad (3.1)
$$

where U is the potential energy of the entire system.

The expectation value at a time t of any dynamical variable $\varphi(\mathbf{R}_{11} \cdots \mathbf{R}_{\nu N_\nu}, \mathbf{P}_{11} \cdots \mathbf{P}_{\nu N_\nu})$ may be written as $\langle \varphi ; f^{(N)} \rangle$, where, by definition,

$$\langle \varphi ; f^{(N)} \rangle = \int \varphi f^{(N)} d^3\mathbf{R}_{11} \cdots d^3\mathbf{R}_{\nu N_\nu} d^3\mathbf{P}_{11} \cdots d^3\mathbf{R}_{\nu N_\nu}. \tag{3.2}$$

If we define the microscopic particle densities in singlet phase space,

$$\nu_\alpha^{(1)} = \sum_{i=1}^{N\alpha} \delta(\mathbf{R}_{\alpha_i} - \mathbf{r}_1)\delta(\mathbf{P}_{\alpha_i} - \mathbf{p}_1), \tag{3.3}$$

where $\delta(\mathbf{R}_{\alpha_i} - \mathbf{r}_1)$ and $\delta(\mathbf{P}_{\alpha_i} - \mathbf{p}_1)$ are the appropriate Dirac delta functions, then the average densities in singlet space are given by

$$\omega_\alpha^{(1)} = \langle \nu_\alpha^{(1)} ; f^{(N)} \rangle. \tag{3.4}$$

Moreover, we may express the mean particle concentration c_α of molecules of type α at a point $\mathbf{r}_1$ by the relation

$$c_\alpha(\mathbf{r}_1) = \int \omega_\alpha^{(1)}(\mathbf{r}_1, \mathbf{p}_1) d^3\mathbf{p}_1. \tag{3.5}$$

Similarly, the mass current density $\rho_\alpha \mathbf{u}_\alpha$ of species α is

$$\rho_\alpha \mathbf{u}_\alpha = \int \mathbf{p}_1 \omega_\alpha^{(1)}(\mathbf{r}_1, \mathbf{p}_1) d^3\mathbf{p}_1, \tag{3.6}$$

where ρ_α is defined in Eq. (2.1).

In the configuration space of ordered pairs of molecules, the average number density $c_{\alpha\beta}^{(2)}$ of molecules of type α at $\mathbf{r}_1$ and type β at $\mathbf{r}_2$ is defined by the relation

$$c_{\alpha\beta}^{(2)}(\mathbf{r}_1, \mathbf{r}_2) = \int \omega_{\alpha\beta}^{(2)}(\mathbf{r}_1, \mathbf{r}_2, \mathbf{p}_1, \mathbf{p}_2) d^3\mathbf{p}_1 d^3\mathbf{p}_2, \tag{3.7}$$

where the average number density in pair phase space is

$$\omega_{\alpha\beta}^{(2)} = \langle \nu_{\alpha\beta}^{(2)} ; f^{(N)} \rangle \tag{3.8}$$

and $\nu_{\alpha\beta}^{(2)}$ is defined by the equation[12]

$$\nu_{\alpha\beta}^{(2)} = \sum_{i=1}^{N_\alpha} \sum_{\substack{j=1 \\ \alpha i \neq \beta j}}^{N_\beta} \delta(\mathbf{R}_{\alpha_i} - \mathbf{r}_1)\delta(\mathbf{R}_{\beta_j} - \mathbf{r}_2) \times \delta(\mathbf{P}_{\alpha_i} - \mathbf{p}_1)\delta(\mathbf{P}_{\beta_j} - \mathbf{p}_2). \tag{3.9}$$

The particle current density in pair space is the six-component vector

$$\begin{aligned} \mathbf{j}_{\alpha\beta}^{(2)} &= c_{\alpha\beta}^{(2)}(\mathbf{r}_1, \mathbf{r}_2)\mathbf{u}_{\alpha\beta}^{(2)}(\mathbf{r}_1, \mathbf{r}_2) \\ &= \int \left(\frac{\mathbf{p}_1}{m_\alpha} \oplus \frac{\mathbf{p}_2}{m_\beta} \right) \omega_{\alpha\beta}^{(2)} d^3\mathbf{p}_1 d^3\mathbf{p}_2,^{13} \end{aligned} \tag{3.10}$$

---

[12] The notation $\alpha i \neq \beta j$ is used to indicate that there is no term corresponding to $i = j$ when $\alpha = \beta$.

[13] The symbol $\oplus$ is here used to indicate that a six-space vector is being generated from two three-space vectors.

where $\mathbf{u}_{\alpha\beta}^{(2)}(\mathbf{r}_1, \mathbf{r}_2)$ is the mean local velocity in pair space and the vector

$$\mathbf{p}_1/m_\alpha \oplus \mathbf{p}_2/m_\beta$$

in six-space is the direct sum of $\mathbf{p}_1/m_\alpha$ which lies in the three-dimensional momentum subspace of a molecule of species α and $\mathbf{p}_2/m_\beta$ which lies in the momentum subspace of the other molecule of type β. The projections of $\mathbf{j}_{\alpha\beta}^{(2)}$ onto the spaces of its first argument $\mathbf{r}_1$ and its second argument $\mathbf{r}_2$ are

$$\begin{aligned} \mathbf{j}_{\alpha\beta,1}^{(2)} &= \int \frac{\mathbf{p}_1}{m_\alpha} \omega_{\alpha\beta}^{(2)} d^3\mathbf{p}_1 d^3\mathbf{p}_2, \\ \mathbf{j}_{\alpha\beta,2}^{(2)} &= \int \frac{\mathbf{p}_2}{m_\beta} \omega_{\alpha\beta}^{(2)} d^3\mathbf{p}_1 d^3\mathbf{p}_2, \end{aligned} \tag{3.11}$$

so that

$$\mathbf{j}_{\alpha\beta}^{(2)} = \mathbf{j}_{\alpha\beta,1}^{(2)} \oplus \mathbf{j}_{\alpha\beta,2}^{(2)}. \tag{3.12}$$

It is $\mathbf{j}_{\alpha\beta,1}^{(2)}$ which arises in the expression for the heat current density.

We now assume that the potential energy U of the system is of the form

$$U = \sum_{\alpha=1}^{\nu} \sum_{k=1}^{N\alpha} W_\alpha(\mathbf{R}_{\alpha k}) + \tfrac{1}{2} \sum_{\beta=1}^{\nu} \sum_{\substack{\alpha=1 \\ \alpha j \neq \beta k}}^{\nu} \sum_{k=1}^{N\beta} \sum_{j=1}^{N\alpha} V_{\alpha\beta}(R_{\alpha j \beta k}). \tag{3.13}$$

W_α is the potential energy of a molecule of species α arising from conservative external fields, and $V_{\alpha\beta}(R_{\alpha j\beta k})$, the mutual potential energy of a pair of molecules of species α and β, is a function only of the length $R_{\alpha j\beta k}$ of the vector

$$\mathbf{R}_{\alpha j\beta k} = \mathbf{R}_{\beta k} - \mathbf{R}_{\alpha j} \tag{3.14}$$

joining the centers of mass of the two molecules.

With this assumption, the formulas of Irving and Kirkwood for the total energy density

$$\sum_{\alpha=1}^{\nu} c_\alpha(\bar{E}_\alpha + \tfrac{1}{2} m_\alpha u_\alpha^2),$$

the sum of the kinetic energy density cE_k and the potential energy densities cE_v and cE_w, where

$$c = \sum_{\alpha=1}^{\nu} c_\alpha, \tag{3.15}$$

may be readily extended to multicomponent systems,

$$\begin{aligned} \sum_{\alpha=1}^{\nu} c_\alpha(\bar{E}_\alpha + \tfrac{1}{2} m_\alpha u_\alpha^2) &= cE_k + cE_v + cE_w, \\ cE_k &= \sum_{\alpha=1}^{\nu} \sum_{k=1}^{N\alpha} \left\langle \frac{P_{\alpha k}^2}{2m_\alpha} \delta(\mathbf{R}_{\alpha k} - \mathbf{r}_1); f^{(N)} \right\rangle, \\ cE_v &= \tfrac{1}{2} \sum_{\beta=1}^{\nu} \sum_{\substack{\alpha=1 \\ \alpha j \neq \beta k}}^{\nu} \sum_{k=1}^{N_\beta} \sum_{j=1}^{N_\alpha} \langle V_{\alpha\beta}(R_{\alpha j\beta k}) \delta(\mathbf{R}_{\beta k} - \mathbf{r}_1); f^{(N)} \rangle, \\ cE_w &= \sum_{\alpha=1}^{\nu} \sum_{k=1}^{N\alpha} W_\alpha(\mathbf{r}_1) \langle \delta(\mathbf{R}_{\alpha k} - \mathbf{r}_1); f^{(N)} \rangle. \end{aligned} \tag{3.16}$$

The quantity

$$\frac{1}{2} \sum_{\alpha=1}^{\nu} m_\alpha c_\alpha u_\alpha^2$$

is clearly the kinetic energy density of an element of fluid, and subtracting it from cE_k gives the contribution of the macroscopically imperceptible kinetic energy of the molecules to the total energy density. Irving and Kirkwood[1] did not choose to split up the total energy density into an internal energy density (cE) and an energy density of bulk motion. The usage in this paper is more in agreement with that in the usual phenomenological treatments and is consistent with the assumption of local equilibrium.[14]

IV. EQUATIONS OF TRANSPORT

Irving and Kirkwood[1] derived from Liouville's equation a general theorem which may be used directly to deduce each of the transport equations. In our notation their theorem is

$$\frac{\partial}{\partial t}\langle \varphi ; f^{(N)} \rangle$$

$$= \sum_{\gamma=1}^{\nu} \sum_{k=1}^{N_\gamma} \left\langle \frac{\mathbf{P}_{\gamma k}}{m_\gamma} \cdot \nabla_{R_{\gamma k}} \varphi - \nabla_{R_{\gamma k}} U \cdot \nabla_{P_{\gamma k}} \varphi ; f^{(N)} \right\rangle, \tag{4.1}$$

where φ is any scalar function (not explicitly dependent on time) of the dynamical variables. By consideration of each of the components of any vector $\boldsymbol{\varphi}$ separately, we see that φ may be replaced by $\boldsymbol{\varphi}$ in Eq. (4.1), provided that it is understood that the gradient of a vector is a dyad.

The derivations of the equations of continuity and energy transport from Eq. (4.1) follow the steps set forth by Irving and Kirkwood[1] in great detail, and hence we shall here only outline the derivations. On the other hand, the equations of motion will receive fuller discussion because the derivations are more complicated for several components than for a single component.

Equations of Continuity

The equation of continuity for each component is obtained from Eq. (4.1) by letting

$$\varphi = \sum_{j=1}^{N_\alpha} m_\alpha \delta(\mathbf{R}_{\alpha_j} - \mathbf{r}_1). \tag{4.2}$$

This gives

$$\frac{\partial}{\partial t}\langle \sum_{j=1}^{N_\alpha} m_\alpha \delta(\mathbf{R}_{\alpha_j} - \mathbf{r}_1); f^{(N)} \rangle = \langle \sum_{j=1}^{N_\alpha} \mathbf{P}_{\alpha_j} \cdot \nabla_{R_{\alpha_j}} \delta(\mathbf{R}_{\alpha_j} - \mathbf{r}_1); f^{(N)} \rangle. \tag{4.3}$$

By virtue of Eqs. (3.3), (3.4), (3.5), and (3.6), this equation reduces to the equation of continuity

$$(\partial \rho_\alpha / \partial t) + \nabla_{r_1} \cdot \rho_\alpha \mathbf{u}_\alpha = 0. \tag{2.3}$$

From these equations we may obtain the total equation of continuity, Eq. (2.4), by summing over all components.

---

[14] It should also be noted that the unit of E in the paper by Irving and Kirkwood is energy per unit volume, whereas in the present paper the unit is energy per molecule.

Hydrodynamical Equations of Motion

In this section we first consider the equations of motion of each component taken separately, and then derive the equation of motion of the fluid element as a whole by summing over all components.

To obtain the equation of motion of component α, we let

$$\boldsymbol{\varphi} = \sum_{j=1}^{N_\alpha} \mathbf{P}_{\alpha_j} \delta(\mathbf{R}_{\alpha_j} - \mathbf{r}_1) \tag{4.4}$$

in Eq. (4.1). We then have

$$\frac{\partial}{\partial t} \rho_\alpha \mathbf{u}_\alpha = - \nabla_{r_1} \cdot \left\langle \sum_{j=1}^{N_\alpha} \frac{\mathbf{P}_{\alpha_j} \mathbf{P}_{\alpha_j}}{m_\alpha} \delta(\mathbf{R}_{\alpha_j} - \mathbf{r}_1); f^{(N)} \right\rangle$$

$$- \nabla_{r_1} W_\alpha(\mathbf{r}_1) \langle \sum_{j=1}^{N_\alpha} \delta)\mathbf{R}_{\alpha_j} - \mathbf{r}_1); f^{(N)} \rangle + c_\alpha(\mathbf{r}_1) \overline{\mathbf{F}}_\alpha{}^{(1)}(\mathbf{r}_1), \tag{4.5}$$

where

$$c_\alpha(\mathbf{r}_1) \overline{\mathbf{F}}_\alpha{}^{(1)}(\mathbf{r}_1) = c_\alpha(\mathbf{r}_1) \sum_{\gamma=1}^{\nu} \overline{\mathbf{F}}_{\gamma\alpha}{}^{(1)}(\mathbf{r}_1),$$

$$c_\alpha(\mathbf{r}_1) \overline{\mathbf{F}}_{\gamma\alpha}{}^{(1)}(\mathbf{r}_1)$$

$$= - \sum_{\substack{k=1 \\ \alpha j \neq \gamma k}}^{N_\gamma} \sum_{j=1}^{N_\alpha} \langle \nabla_{R_{\alpha j}} V_{\gamma\alpha}(\mathbf{R}_{\gamma k \alpha j}) \delta(\mathbf{R}_{\alpha j} - \mathbf{r}_1); f^{(N)} \rangle. \tag{4.6}$$

$\overline{\mathbf{F}}_{\gamma\alpha}{}^{(1)}(\mathbf{r}_1)$ is the mean force exerted by all molecules of species γ on a molecule of species α at $\mathbf{r}_1$ and $\overline{\mathbf{F}}_\alpha{}^{(1)}(r_1)$ is the mean force exerted by all the molecules on a molecule of species α.

Adding and subtracting $\mathbf{u}$ in the first term on the right-hand side of Eq. (4.5), we find that

$$-\nabla_{r_1} \cdot \left\langle \sum_{j=1}^{N_\alpha} \frac{\mathbf{P}_{\alpha_j} \mathbf{P}_{\alpha_j}}{m_\alpha} \delta\,(\mathbf{R}_{\alpha_j} - \mathbf{r}_1); f^{(N)} \right\rangle = \nabla_{r_1} \cdot \rho_\alpha (\mathbf{uu} - \mathbf{uu}_\alpha - \mathbf{u}_\alpha \mathbf{u})$$

$$- \nabla_{r_1} \cdot \left\langle \sum_{j=1}^{N_\alpha} m_\alpha \left(\frac{\mathbf{P}_{\alpha_j}}{m_\alpha} - \mathbf{u} \right) \left(\frac{\mathbf{P}_{\alpha_j}}{m_\alpha} - \mathbf{u} \right) \delta(\mathbf{R}_{\alpha_j} - \mathbf{r}_1); f^{(N)} \right\rangle, \tag{4.7}$$

where we have used Eqs. (3.3), (3.4), and (3.6). The kinetic contribution to the partial stress tensor presently to be defined arises from the second term on the right-hand side of Eq. (4.7).

With the use of Eqs. (3.5) and (3.4), the second term on the right-hand side of Eq. (4.5) may be simplified readily,

$$-\nabla_{r_1} W_\alpha(\mathbf{r}_1) \langle \sum_{j=1}^{N\alpha} \delta(\mathbf{R}_{\alpha_j} - \mathbf{r}_1); f^{(N)} \rangle = - c_\alpha \nabla_{r_1} W_\alpha(\mathbf{r}_1). \tag{4.8}$$

Reduction of the third term on the right-hand side of Eq. (4.5) is more complicated when treating a multi-component system than when treating a single component system. By Eqs. (4.6), (3.7), (3.8), and (3.9)

$$c_\alpha \overline{\mathbf{F}}_{\gamma\alpha}{}^{(1)}(\mathbf{r}_1) = - \int \nabla_{r_1} V_{\gamma\alpha}(|\mathbf{r}_2 - \mathbf{r}_1|) c_{\alpha\gamma}{}^{(2)}(\mathbf{r}_1, \mathbf{r}_2) d^3\mathbf{r}_2. \tag{4.9}$$

Changing the independent variables from $\mathbf{r}_1$ and $\mathbf{r}_2$ to $\mathbf{r}_1$ and $\mathbf{r}$, where

$$\mathbf{r}_1 + \mathbf{r} = \mathbf{r}_2, \tag{4.10}$$

we have

$$-\int \nabla_{r_1} V_{\gamma\alpha}(|\mathbf{r}_2 - \mathbf{r}_1|) c_{\alpha\gamma}{}^{(2)}(\mathbf{r}_1, \mathbf{r}_2) d^3\mathbf{r}_2 = \int \frac{\mathbf{r}}{r} \frac{dV_{\gamma\alpha}}{dr} c_{\alpha\gamma}{}^{(2)}(\mathbf{r}_1, \mathbf{r}) d^3\mathbf{r}. \tag{4.11}$$

It is a consequence of the definition of the number density in pair space, Eq. (3.7), that

$$c_{\alpha\gamma}{}^{(2)}(\mathbf{r}_1, \mathbf{r}_2) = c_{\gamma\alpha}{}^{(2)}(\mathbf{r}_2, \mathbf{r}_1). \tag{4.12}$$

With the position of the molecule of the species represented by the first subscript of $c^{(2)}$ as the first argument and the relative position of the other molecule as the second argument, we may rewrite Eq. (4.12)

$$c_{\alpha\gamma}{}^{(2)}(\mathbf{r}_1, \mathbf{r}) = c_{\gamma\alpha}{}^{(2)}(\mathbf{r}_1 + \mathbf{r}, -\mathbf{r}). \tag{4.13}$$

We now assume that $c_{\gamma\alpha}{}^{(2)}(\mathbf{r}_1, \mathbf{r})$ varies so slowly with its first argument that, with negligible error, we may retain only the first two terms in a Taylor's series expansion about the point $\mathbf{r}_1$ (at equilibrium there is no dependence on $\mathbf{r}_1$). Thus

$$c_{\alpha\gamma}{}^{(2)}(\mathbf{r}_1, \mathbf{r}) = c_{\gamma\alpha}{}^{(2)}(\mathbf{r}_1, -\mathbf{r}) + \mathbf{r} \cdot \nabla_{r_1} c_{\gamma\alpha}{}^{(2)}(\mathbf{r}_1, -\mathbf{r}). \tag{4.14}$$

Substituting Eq. (4.14) into the right-hand side of Eq. (4.11) and using Eqs. (4.6) and (4.9) leads to the result

$$c_\alpha \overline{\mathbf{F}}_\alpha{}^{(1)} = \tfrac{1}{2} \sum_{\gamma=1}^{\nu} \int \frac{\mathbf{r}}{r} \frac{dV_{\gamma\alpha}}{dr} \{c_{\alpha\gamma}{}^{(2)}(\mathbf{r}_1, \mathbf{r}) - c_{\gamma\alpha}{}^{(2)}(\mathbf{r}_1, \mathbf{r})\} d^3\mathbf{r}$$
$$+ \nabla_{r_1} \cdot \tfrac{1}{2} \sum_{\gamma=1}^{\nu} \int \frac{\mathbf{rr}}{r} \frac{dV_{\gamma\alpha}}{dr} c_{\gamma\alpha}{}^{(2)}(\mathbf{r}_1, \mathbf{r}) d^3\mathbf{r}. \tag{4.15}$$

It is now convenient to introduce the pair correlation function $g_{\alpha\gamma}{}^{(2)}(\mathbf{r}_1. \mathbf{r})$ defined by the equation

$$c_{\alpha\gamma}{}^{(2)}(\mathbf{r}_1, \mathbf{r}) = c_\alpha(\mathbf{r}_1) c_\gamma(\mathbf{r}_1 + \mathbf{r}) g_{\alpha\gamma}{}^{(2)}(\mathbf{r}_1, \mathbf{r}). \tag{4.16}$$

In each of the integrals in Eq. (4.15), the integrands vanish when $\mathbf{r}$ exceeds the range of intermolecular force. Under ordinary circumstances c_γ is sensibly constant over distances of this magnitude, and therefore

$$c_{\alpha\gamma}{}^{(2)}(\mathbf{r}_1, \mathbf{r}) = c_\alpha(\mathbf{r}_1) c_\gamma(\mathbf{r}_1) g_{\alpha\gamma}{}^{(2)}(\mathbf{r}_1, \mathbf{r}). \tag{4.17}$$

Substituting Eq. (4.17) into Eq. (4.15) yields

$$c_\alpha \overline{\mathbf{F}}_\alpha{}^{(1)} = c_\alpha \overline{\mathbf{F}}_\alpha{}^{(1)*} + \nabla_{r_1} \cdot \tfrac{1}{2} \sum_{\gamma=1}^{\nu} c_\alpha c_\gamma \int \frac{\mathbf{rr}}{r} \frac{dV_{\gamma\alpha}}{dr} g_{\gamma\alpha}{}^{(2)}(\mathbf{r}_1, \mathbf{r}) d^3\mathbf{r}, \tag{4.18}$$

where we have introduced the nomenclature

$$c_\alpha \overline{\mathbf{F}}_\alpha{}^{(1)*} = \tfrac{1}{2} \sum_{\gamma=1}^{\nu} c_\alpha c_\gamma \int \frac{\mathbf{r}}{r} \frac{dV_{\gamma\alpha}}{dr} \{g_{\alpha\gamma}{}^{(2)}(\mathbf{r}_1, \mathbf{r}) - g_{\gamma\alpha}{}^{(2)}(\mathbf{r}_1, \mathbf{r})\} d^3\mathbf{r}. \tag{4.19}$$

Substituting Eqs. (4.7), (4.8), and (4.18) into Eq. (4.5), we write the partial equation of motion in a final form analogous to the total equation of motion of a fluid element,

$$\frac{\partial \rho_\alpha \mathbf{u}_\alpha}{\partial t} = \nabla_{r_1} \cdot [\boldsymbol{\sigma}_\alpha - \rho_\alpha(\mathbf{u}_\alpha \mathbf{u} + \mathbf{u}\mathbf{u}_\alpha - \mathbf{u}\mathbf{u})] + c_\alpha \overline{\mathbf{F}}_\alpha{}^{(1)*} + c_\alpha \mathbf{X}_\alpha. \qquad (4.20)$$

In Eq. (4.20), the partial stress tensor $\boldsymbol{\sigma}_\alpha$, consisting of the sum of a kinetic contribution $(\boldsymbol{\sigma}_\alpha)_k$ and an intermolecular force contribution $(\boldsymbol{\sigma}_\alpha)_v$, is defined by

$$\boldsymbol{\sigma}_\alpha = (\boldsymbol{\sigma}_\alpha)_k + (\boldsymbol{\sigma}_\alpha)_v,$$

$$(\boldsymbol{\sigma}_\alpha)_k = -\left\langle \sum_{j=1}^{N\alpha} m_\alpha \left(\frac{\mathbf{P}_{\alpha j}}{m_\alpha} - \mathbf{u}\right)\left(\frac{\mathbf{P}_{\alpha j}}{m_\alpha} - \mathbf{u}\right)\delta(\mathbf{R}_{\alpha j} - \mathbf{r}_1); f^{(N)}\right\rangle,$$

$$(4.21)$$

$$(\boldsymbol{\sigma}_\alpha)_v = \sum_{\gamma=1}^{\nu} (\boldsymbol{\sigma}_{\alpha\gamma})_v,$$

$$(\boldsymbol{\sigma}_{\alpha\gamma})_v = \tfrac{1}{2} c_\alpha c_\gamma \int \frac{\mathbf{r}\mathbf{r}}{r} \frac{dV_{\gamma\alpha}}{dr} g_{\gamma\alpha}{}^{(2)}(\mathbf{r}_1, \mathbf{r}) d^3\mathbf{r}.$$

We have also used the relation

$$c_\alpha \mathbf{X}_\alpha = -\, c_\alpha \nabla_{r_1} W_\alpha. \qquad (4.22)$$

From the definition of $c_\alpha \overline{\mathbf{F}}_\alpha{}^{(1)*}$,

$$\sum_{\alpha=1}^{\nu} c_\alpha \overline{\mathbf{F}}_\alpha{}^{(1)*} = 0, \qquad (4.23)$$

and therefore summing Eq. (4.20) over all components gives the macroscopic equation of motion of the element

$$\frac{\partial}{\partial t}\rho \mathbf{u} = \nabla_{r_1} \cdot (\boldsymbol{\sigma} - \rho \mathbf{u}\mathbf{u}) + c\mathbf{X}, \qquad (2.5)$$

where

$$\boldsymbol{\sigma} = \boldsymbol{\sigma}_k + \boldsymbol{\sigma}_i,$$

$$\boldsymbol{\sigma}_k = \sum_{\alpha=1}^{\nu} (\boldsymbol{\sigma}_\alpha)_k = -\sum_{\alpha=1}^{\nu} \sum_{j=1}^{N_\alpha} \left\langle m_\alpha \left(\frac{\mathbf{P}_{\alpha j}}{m_\alpha} - \mathbf{u}\right) \times \left(\frac{\mathbf{P}_{\alpha j}}{m_\alpha} - \mathbf{u}\right)\delta(\mathbf{R}_{\alpha j} - \mathbf{r}_1); f^{(N)}\right\rangle, \qquad (4.24)$$

$$\boldsymbol{\sigma}_v = \sum_{\alpha=1}^{\nu} (\boldsymbol{\sigma}_\alpha)_v = \tfrac{1}{2}\sum_{\gamma=1}^{\nu} \sum_{\alpha=1}^{\nu} c_\alpha c_\gamma \int \frac{\mathbf{r}\mathbf{r}}{r}\frac{dV_{\gamma\alpha}}{dr} g_{\gamma\alpha}{}^{(2)}(\mathbf{r}_1, \mathbf{r}) d^3\mathbf{r}.$$

Energy Transport Equation

With the use of Eq. (3.16) to evaluate

$$\sum_{\alpha=1}^{\nu} c_\alpha \left(\bar{E}_\alpha + \frac{m_\alpha u_\alpha{}^2}{2}\right)\mathbf{u},$$

Eq. (4.24) to evaluate $\mathbf{u} \cdot \boldsymbol{\sigma}$, and Eq. (4.1) to evaluate

$$\frac{\partial}{\partial t} \sum_{\alpha=1}^{\nu} \left(c_\alpha \bar{E}_\alpha + \frac{m_\alpha u_\alpha^2}{2} \right)$$

the energy transport equation, Eq. (2.6), may be obtained by following the lengthy derivation given in detail by Irving and Kirkwood. The molecular interpretation of $\mathbf{q}$ is given by the following equations:

$$\mathbf{q} = \mathbf{J}_k + \mathbf{J}_v - \sum_{\alpha=1}^{\nu} \mathbf{j}_\alpha \left(\bar{H}_\alpha + \frac{m_\alpha u_\alpha^2}{2} \right),$$

$$\mathbf{J}_k = \sum_{\alpha=1}^{\nu} \sum_{j=1}^{N_\alpha} \left\langle \frac{m_\alpha}{2} \left(\frac{\mathbf{P}_{\alpha j}}{m_\alpha} - \mathbf{u} \right)^2 \left(\frac{\mathbf{P}_{\alpha j}}{m_\alpha} - \mathbf{u} \right) \delta(\mathbf{R}_{\alpha j} - \mathbf{r}_1); f^{(N)}, \right\rangle \tag{4.25}$$

$$\mathbf{J}_v = \sum_{\alpha=1}^{\nu} \sum_{\gamma=1}^{\nu} \tfrac{1}{2} \int \left[V_{\alpha\gamma}(r)\mathbf{1} - \frac{\mathbf{rr}}{r} \frac{dV_{\alpha\gamma}(r)}{dr} \right] \cdot [\mathbf{j}_{\alpha\gamma,1}{}^{(2)}(\mathbf{r}_1, \mathbf{r}) - c_{\gamma\alpha}{}^{(2)}(\mathbf{r}_1, \mathbf{r})\mathbf{u}] d^3\mathbf{r}.$$

When linearized in the diffusion fluxes $\mathbf{j}_\alpha$, the term

$$\sum_{\alpha=1}^{\nu} \mathbf{j}_\alpha \left(\bar{H}_\alpha + \frac{m_\alpha u_\alpha^2}{2} \right)$$

reduces to

$$\sum_{\alpha=1}^{\nu} \mathbf{j}_\alpha \bar{H}_\alpha.$$

$\mathbf{J}_k$ is the kinetic contribution and $\mathbf{J}_v$ is the intermolecular force contribution to the total energy flux, $\mathbf{J}_k + \mathbf{J}_v$, relative to the local center of mass. The term

$$\sum_{\alpha=1}^{\nu} \mathbf{j}_\alpha \left(\bar{H}_\alpha + \frac{m_\alpha u_\alpha^2}{2} \right)$$

arises because in the definition of the heat flux we wish to distinguish between that part of the flux which is associated with the macroscopically observable enthalpy transport and that part which is associated with the unobservable microscopic motion of the molecules. The division of the energy flux into the two terms $\mathbf{q}$ and

$$\sum_{\alpha=1}^{\nu} \mathbf{j}_\alpha \left(\bar{H}_\alpha + \frac{m_\alpha u_\alpha^2}{2} \right)$$

is arbitrary from the statistical mechanical standpoint. Another possible division, for example, is the one made by Kirkwood and Crawford who define the heat flux as

$$\mathbf{J}_k + \mathbf{J}_v - \sum_{\alpha=1}^{\nu} \mathbf{j}_\alpha \left(\bar{E}_\alpha + \frac{m_\alpha u_\alpha^2}{2} \right).$$

However, their entropy transport equation assumes simpler form with the definition of heat flux of Eq. (4.25).

V. FURTHER DEVELOPMENT OF THE EQUATIONS OF MOTION AND HEAT TRANSPORT

In this section we shall transform the equations of motion of the several components with the use of the concept of local equilibrium, which involves the separation of the molecular distribution functions into equilibrium terms and perturbation terms. When the perturbation terms in the distribution functions are represented as linear functions of the diffusion velocities, the temperature gradient, and the rate of shear, quasi-stationary equations of motion are obtained, in which the average force acting on each component is separated into a thermodynamic term involving the local gradients of chemical potential, a thermal term proportional to the temperature gradient, a frictional term proportional to the diffusion velocities relative to the local center of mass, and a viscous term involving the rate of shear. In the stationary case or when inertial terms and viscous terms are negligible, these special equations reduce to linear relations between forces and fluxes of the phenomenological theory of irreversible thermodynamics.

We remark that at constant temperature there exists a state of equilibrium, corresponding to arbitrary gradients of composition and pressure, when a set of auxiliary forces, $\mathbf{X}_\alpha' = \nabla\mu_\alpha - \mathbf{X}_\alpha$, are imposed upon the several components, and μ_α is the chemical potential of component α appropriate to the local temperature, pressure, and composition, excluding contributions from external forces $\mathbf{X}_\alpha$ which act on the system. The existence of such a state is assured by the equilibrium theories of thermodynamics and statistical mechanics. Thus, the Gibbs criteria of equilibrium in an isothermal system subject to external forces are

$$\begin{aligned} \nabla\mu_\alpha - \mathbf{X}_\alpha' - \mathbf{X}_\alpha &= 0, \\ \nabla p &= -\sum_{\alpha=1}^{\nu} c_\alpha(\mathbf{X}_\alpha + \mathbf{X}_\alpha'). \end{aligned} \tag{5.1}$$

This equilibrium state will be selected as the zero-order state from which the perturbations in the molecular distribution functions are measured. We now write the pair correlation functions $g_{\alpha\beta}^{(2)}$ and the singlet densities $\omega_\alpha^{(1)}$ in the μ-phase space of component α in the form

$$\begin{aligned} g_{\alpha\beta}^{(2)} &= g_{\alpha\beta}^{(2,0)} + g_{\alpha\beta}^{(2,1)}, \\ \omega_\alpha^{(1)} &= \omega_\alpha^{(1,0)} + \omega_\alpha^{(1,1)}, \\ \omega_\alpha^{(1,0)}(\mathbf{p}_1, \mathbf{r}_1) &= (2\pi m_\alpha kT)^{-\frac{3}{2}} c_\alpha(\mathbf{r}_1) \exp\left[-(\mathbf{p}_1 - m_\alpha\mathbf{u})^2/2m_\alpha kT\right], \end{aligned} \tag{5.2}$$

where $g_{\alpha\beta}^{(2,0)}$ is the pair correlation function in the isothermal equilibrium ensemble under the action of the auxiliary external forces, $\mathbf{X}_\alpha' = \nabla_T\mu_\alpha - \mathbf{X}_\alpha$, corresponding to the local temperature, pressure, concentrations c_α, gradients of concentration, and gradient of pressure, and $\omega_\alpha^{(1,0)}$ is the corresponding phase space density in an ensemble of systems under uniform translation with the local particle velocity $\mathbf{u}$. Equations (5.2) thus define the perturbations $g_{\alpha\beta}^{(2,1)}$ and $\omega_\alpha^{(1,1)}$ and similar equations could be formulated for the definition of all other distribution function perturbations. The partial stress tensors $\boldsymbol{\sigma}_\alpha$, Eq. (4.21), and the forces $\overline{\mathbf{F}}_\alpha{}^{(1)*}$, Eq. (4.19), may now be separated into equilibrium and perturbation terms:

$$\boldsymbol{\sigma}_\alpha = -p_\alpha \mathbf{1} + \boldsymbol{\sigma}_\alpha{}^{(1)},$$

$$p_\alpha = c_\alpha kT - \tfrac{1}{6}\sum_{\gamma=1}^{\nu} c_\alpha c_\gamma \int r \frac{dV_{\alpha\gamma}}{dr} g_{\alpha\gamma}{}^{(2,0)} d^3\mathbf{r}, \tag{5.3}$$

where $\sigma_\alpha{}^{(1)}$ represents the contribution to the right-hand side of Eq. (4.21) arising from the perturbations in the distribution functions,

$$\overline{\mathbf{F}}_\alpha{}^{(1)*} = \overline{\mathbf{F}}_\alpha{}^{(1,0)*} + \overline{\mathbf{F}}_\alpha{}^{(1,1)*},$$

$$c_\alpha \overline{\mathbf{F}}_\alpha{}^{(1,1)*} = \tfrac{1}{2}\sum_{\gamma=1}^{\nu} c_\alpha c_\gamma \int \frac{\mathbf{r}}{r}\frac{dV_{\alpha\gamma}}{dr}[g_{\alpha\gamma}{}^{(2,1)}(\mathbf{r}_1, \mathbf{r}) - g_{\gamma\alpha}{}^{(2,1)}(\mathbf{r}_1, \mathbf{r})] d^3\mathbf{r}, \tag{5.4}$$

where $\overline{\mathbf{F}}_\alpha{}^{(1,0)*}$ represents the equilibrium contribution to the average intermolecular force acting on a molecule of type α located at point $\mathbf{r}_1$.[15]

We now specialize each of the equations of motion Eqs. (4.20), to the isothermal equilibrium case by imposing the auxiliary external forces $\mathbf{X}_\alpha' = \nabla_T \mu_\alpha - \mathbf{X}_\alpha$. Under the action of the total forces $\mathbf{X}_\alpha + \mathbf{X}_\alpha'$, the partial accelerations vanish as also do the perturbations in $\boldsymbol{\sigma}_\alpha$ and in the forces $\overline{\mathbf{F}}_\alpha{}^{(1)*}$, and we obtain (writing ∇ for ∇_{r1})

$$-\nabla_T p_\alpha + c_\alpha \overline{\mathbf{F}}_\alpha{}^{(1,0)*} + c_\alpha \nabla_T \mu_\alpha = 0, \quad \alpha = 1 \cdots \nu,$$

$$\nabla = \nabla_T + (\nabla \ln T)\left(\frac{\partial}{\partial \ln T}\right)_{P, c_\gamma}. \tag{5.5}$$

We next substitute Eqs. (5.3) and (5.4) into the equations of motion, Eqs. (4.20) and eliminate all terms, $\nabla_T p_\alpha$, from the resulting equations by mean of Eqs. (5.5) to obtain

$$\frac{\partial \rho_\alpha \mathbf{u}_\alpha}{\partial t} = \nabla \cdot [\boldsymbol{\sigma}_\alpha{}^{(1)} - \rho_\alpha(\mathbf{u}_\alpha \mathbf{u} + \mathbf{u}\mathbf{u}_\alpha - \mathbf{u}\mathbf{u})] - c_\alpha \nabla_T \mu_\alpha + c_\alpha \mathbf{F}_\alpha{}^* + c_\alpha \mathbf{X}_\alpha,$$

$$\mathbf{F}_\alpha{}^* = \overline{\mathbf{F}}_\alpha{}^{(1,1)*} - \frac{1}{c_\alpha}\left(\frac{\partial p_\alpha}{\partial \ln T}\right)_{P, c_\gamma} \nabla \ln T. \tag{5.6}$$

We shall now attempt to formulate explicit expressions for the frictional and thermal forces $\mathbf{F}_\alpha{}^*$ and the stress tensor perturbations $\boldsymbol{\sigma}_\alpha{}^{(1)}$ appearing in the equations of motion, Eqs. (5.6), as well as for the heat flux $\mathbf{q}$, given in general form by Eq. (4.25). In order to accomplish this objective, we shall

[15] The sum of the pressures p_α is equal to the total pressure p. It can be readily shown that since the conservative auxiliary forces are derivable from a slowly varying potential on the molecular scale of distance, that the p_α and p have values sensibly identical with those in the absence of these forces.

employ the following stationary representations of the distribution function perturbations, linear in the perturbation parameters,

$$\frac{\omega_\alpha{}^{(1,1)}}{\omega_\alpha{}^{(1,0)}} = -\mathbf{b}_\alpha(\mathbf{p}_1) : \dot{\boldsymbol{\epsilon}}^* + \frac{\mathbf{p}_1 \cdot (\mathbf{u}_\alpha - \mathbf{u})}{kT}$$

$$+ \sum_{\gamma=1}^{\nu} \mathbf{d}_{\alpha\gamma}(\mathbf{p}_1) \cdot (\mathbf{u}_\gamma - \mathbf{u}) + \mathbf{a}_\alpha(\mathbf{p}_1) \cdot \nabla \ln T,$$

$$\frac{g_{\alpha\beta}{}^{(2,1)}}{g_{\alpha\beta}{}^{(2,0)}} = \psi_{\alpha\beta}{}^{(1)}(r)\frac{\mathbf{r}}{r} \cdot (\mathbf{u}_\beta - \mathbf{u}_\alpha) + \chi_{\alpha\beta}(r)\frac{\mathbf{r}}{r} \cdot \nabla \ln T$$

$$+ \psi_{\alpha\beta}{}^{(0)}(r)\nabla \cdot \mathbf{u} + \psi_{\alpha\beta}{}^{(2)}(r)\frac{\mathbf{r} \cdot \dot{\boldsymbol{\epsilon}}^* \cdot \mathbf{r}}{r^2}$$

+ spherical harmonics of higher order,

$$\mathbf{j}_{\alpha\beta,1}{}^{(2)} = c_\alpha c_\beta \mathbf{u}_{\alpha\beta,1}{}^{(2)} g_{\alpha\beta}{}^{(2,0)},$$

$$\mathbf{u}_{\alpha\beta,1}{}^{(2)} = \mathbf{u}_\alpha + \Delta\mathbf{u}_{\alpha\beta,1}{}^{(2)},$$

$$\Delta\mathbf{u}_{\alpha\beta,1}{}^{(2)} = \boldsymbol{\lambda}_{\alpha\beta} \cdot (\mathbf{u}_\beta - \mathbf{u}_\alpha) + \boldsymbol{\xi}_{\alpha\beta} \cdot \nabla \ln T, \tag{5.7}$$

$$\dot{\boldsymbol{\epsilon}}^* = \dot{\boldsymbol{\epsilon}} - \tfrac{1}{3}\nabla \cdot \mathbf{u}\,\mathbf{1},$$

where the scalar functions of the relative coordinates of molecular pairs, $\psi_{\alpha\beta}{}^{(0)}$, $\psi_{\alpha\beta}{}^{(1)}$, $\psi_{\alpha\beta}{}^{(2)}$, $\chi_{\alpha\beta}$, the vector functions $\mathbf{d}_{\alpha\beta}$, $\mathbf{a}_\alpha$, and the tensor functions $\mathbf{b}_\alpha$, $\boldsymbol{\lambda}_{\alpha\beta}$, $\boldsymbol{\xi}_{\alpha\beta}$, remain to be determined by an explicit non-equilibrium theory of molecular distribution functions, which is not the subject of this article. The functions are further subject to conditions imposed by the requirement of isotropy in fluid phases and by the macroscopic definition of the heat flux. Since by orthogonality, only spherical harmonics of order zero and two in the polar and azimuthal angles defining the direction of the intermolecular vector $\mathbf{r}$, contribute to the partial stress tensor $\boldsymbol{\sigma}_\alpha{}^{(1)}$ and only spherical harmonics of order unity contribute to $\bar{\mathbf{F}}_\alpha{}^{(1,1)*}$, it is unnecessary for our purposes to specify explicitly spherical harmonics of higher order in the second of Eqs. (5.7). In conformity with the customary phenomenological theory of classical fluids, nonlinear terms in the diffusion velocities and the temperature gradient as well as all spatial derivatives of the diffusion velocities and spatial derivatives of temperature higher than the first are assumed to make negligible contributions to the distribution function perturbations of Eqs. (5.7). Moreover, for the sake of simplicity, the most general linear functions of the diffusion velocities have not been employed in the representation of the $g_{\alpha\beta}{}^{(2,1)}$. As we shall presently observe, the assumed form of $g_{\alpha\beta}{}^{(2,1)}$ implies the validity of the reciprocal relations in isothermal diffusion.

When Eqs. (5.7) are introduced into Eqs. (4.19), (4.21), (4.25), and (5.3), the following expressions for the forces $\bar{\mathbf{F}}_\alpha{}^{(1,1)*}$, the heat flux $\mathbf{q}$ and the partial stress tensors $\boldsymbol{\sigma}_\alpha^{(1)}$ are obtained,

$$\bar{\mathbf{F}}_\alpha^{(1,1)*} = -\sum_{\beta=1}^{\nu} \zeta_{\alpha\beta} c_\beta (\mathbf{u}_\alpha - \mathbf{u}_\beta) - \gamma_{\alpha 0}^{(1)} \nabla \ln T,$$

$$\mathbf{q} = \kappa T \nabla \ln T + \sum_{\beta=1}^{\nu} Q_\beta^* \mathbf{j}_\beta, \tag{5.8}$$

$$\boldsymbol{\sigma}_\alpha^{(1)} = (\varphi_\alpha - \tfrac{2}{3}\eta_\alpha)\mathbf{1}\nabla \cdot \mathbf{u} + 2\eta_\alpha \dot{\boldsymbol{\epsilon}},$$

where the coefficients $\zeta_{\alpha\beta}$ and $\gamma_{\alpha 0}^{(1)}$ are given by the relations,

$$\zeta_{\alpha\beta} = \tfrac{1}{6} \int \frac{dV_{\alpha\beta}}{dr} [\psi_{\alpha\beta}^{(1)} + \psi_{\beta\alpha}^{(1)}] g_{\alpha\beta}^{(2,0)} d^3\mathbf{r},$$

$$\gamma_{\alpha 0}^{(1)} = \tfrac{1}{6} \sum_{\beta=1}^{\nu} c_\beta \int \frac{dV_{\alpha\beta}}{dr} [\chi_{\beta\alpha} - \chi_{\alpha\beta}] g_{\alpha\beta}^{(2,0)} d^3\mathbf{r}. \tag{5.9}$$

In the second of Eqs. (5.8), the thermal conductivity κ and the heats of transport Q_α^* are determined by the relations,

$$\kappa\mathbf{1} = \kappa_k\mathbf{1} + \tfrac{1}{2}\sum_{\beta=1}^{\nu}\sum_{\alpha=1}^{\nu} c_\alpha c_\beta \int \left[V_{\alpha\beta}\mathbf{1} - \frac{\mathbf{rr}}{r}\frac{dV_{\alpha\beta}}{dr} \right] \cdot \boldsymbol{\xi}_{\alpha\beta} g_{\alpha\beta}^{(2,0)} d^3\mathbf{r},$$

$$\kappa_k\mathbf{1} = \sum_{\alpha=1} \int \frac{p_1^2}{2m_\alpha}\frac{\mathbf{p}_1}{m_\alpha} \mathbf{a}_\alpha \omega_\alpha^{(1,0)} d^3\mathbf{p}_1,$$

$$Q_\alpha^* = h_\alpha^{(0)} + h_\alpha^{(1)} - \bar{H}_\alpha, \tag{5.10}$$

$$h_\alpha^{(0)} = \tfrac{5}{2}kT + \tfrac{1}{2}\sum_{\beta=1}^{\nu} c_\beta \int \left[V_{\alpha\beta} - \frac{r}{3}\frac{dV_{\alpha\beta}}{dr} \right] g_{\alpha\beta}^{(2,0)} d^3\mathbf{r},$$

$$h_\alpha^{(1)}\mathbf{1} = \sum_{\beta=1}^{\nu} \int \frac{p_1^2}{2m_\alpha}\frac{\mathbf{p}_1}{m_\alpha} \mathbf{d}_{\alpha\beta}\omega_\alpha^{(1,0)} d^3\mathbf{p}_1 + \tfrac{1}{2}\sum_{\substack{\gamma=1 \\ \gamma\neq\alpha}}^{\nu} c_\gamma \int \left[V_{\alpha\gamma} - \frac{r}{3}\frac{dV_{\alpha\gamma}}{dr} \right] \times [\boldsymbol{\lambda}_{\gamma\alpha} - \boldsymbol{\lambda}_{\alpha\gamma}] g_{\alpha\gamma}^{(2,0)} d^3\mathbf{r}.$$

In the last of Eqs. (5.8) determining the partial stress tensors $\boldsymbol{\sigma}_\alpha^{(1)}$, the partial coefficients of shear viscosity, η_α and bulk viscosity φ_α are given by the expressions,

$$\eta_\alpha = (\eta_\alpha)_k + \frac{1}{30}\sum_{\beta=1}^{\nu} c_\alpha c_\beta \int r \frac{dV_{\alpha\beta}}{dr} \psi_{\alpha\beta}^{(2)} g_{\alpha\beta}^{(2,0)} d^3\mathbf{r},$$

$$(\eta_\alpha)_k = \tfrac{1}{2} \int \mathbf{b}_\alpha : \frac{\mathbf{p}_1\mathbf{p}_1}{m_\alpha} \omega_\alpha^{(1,0)} d^3\mathbf{p}_1, \tag{5.11}$$

$$\varphi_\alpha = \tfrac{1}{6}\sum_{\beta=1}^{\nu} c_\alpha c_\beta \int r \frac{dV_{\alpha\beta}}{dr} \psi_{\alpha\beta}^{(0)} g_{\alpha\beta}^{(2,0)} d^3\mathbf{r}.$$

By virtue of Eqs. (5.8) and the second of Eqs. (5.6), we obtain the following expressions for the total frictional force $\mathbf{F}_\alpha{}^*$ and for $\nabla \ln T$,

$$\mathbf{F}_\alpha{}^* = - \sum_{\beta=1}^{\nu} R_{\alpha\beta}\mathbf{j}_\beta - R_{\alpha 0}\mathbf{q}, \quad \alpha = 1 \cdots \nu,$$

$$\nabla \ln T = - \sum_{\beta=1}^{\nu} \mathbf{R}_{0\beta}\mathbf{j}_\beta - R_{00}\mathbf{q}, \tag{5.12}$$

where

$$R_{\alpha\alpha} = \sum_{\substack{\gamma\neq\alpha \\ =1}}^{\nu} \frac{c_\gamma}{c_\alpha} \zeta_{\alpha\gamma} + (\gamma_{\alpha 0} Q_\alpha{}^*/\kappa T),$$

$$R_{\alpha\beta} = - \zeta_{\alpha\beta} + (\gamma_{\alpha 0} Q_\beta{}^*/\kappa T), \quad \alpha \neq \beta,$$

$$R_{\alpha 0} = - \gamma_{\alpha 0}/\kappa T,$$

$$R_{0\beta} = - Q_\beta{}^*/\kappa T,$$

$$R_{00} = 1/\kappa T,$$

$$\gamma_{\alpha 0} = \frac{1}{c_\alpha}\left(\frac{\partial p_\alpha}{\partial \ln T}\right)_{P,\, c\gamma} + \gamma_{\alpha 0}{}^{(1)}.$$

The introduction of Eqs. (5.8) and (5.12) into Eqs. (5.6) leads to a final set of quasi-stationary equations of motion for the several components, linearized with respect to the diffusion and heat fluxes and products of these quantities and the hydrodynamic particle velocity $\mathbf{u}$, but not with respect to $\mathbf{u}$ itself

$$\frac{\partial \rho_\alpha \mathbf{u}_\alpha}{\partial t} + \nabla \cdot (\rho_\alpha \mathbf{u}\mathbf{u}) = \eta_\alpha \nabla^2 \mathbf{u} + (\varphi_\alpha + \eta_\alpha/3)\nabla\nabla \cdot \mathbf{u} - c_\alpha \nabla_T \mu_\alpha$$

$$- \sum_{\beta=1}^{\nu} c_\alpha R_{\alpha\beta}\mathbf{j}_\beta - c_\alpha R_{\alpha 0}\mathbf{q} + c_\alpha \mathbf{X}_\alpha, \quad \alpha = 1 \cdots \nu, \tag{5.13}$$

$$\mathbf{q} = - \kappa T \nabla \ln T + \sum_{\beta=1}^{\nu} Q_\beta{}^* \mathbf{j}_\beta.$$

Equations (5.13) are quasi-stationary in the sense that the use of Eqs. (5.7) involves the neglect of explicit dependence of the distribution function perturbations on the time. When the equations of motion, Eqs. (5.13), are summed over all components, the Navier-Stokes equation is obtained,

$$\rho(d\mathbf{u}/dt) = - \nabla p + \eta \nabla^2 \mathbf{u} + (\varphi + \eta/3)\nabla\nabla \cdot \mathbf{u} + c\mathbf{X},$$

$$\eta = \sum_{\alpha=1}^{\nu} \eta_\alpha, \quad \varphi = \sum_{\alpha=1}^{\nu} \varphi_\alpha,$$

$$\sum_{\alpha=1}^{\nu} c_\alpha \mathbf{F}_\alpha{}^* = 0, \tag{5.14}$$

$$\sum_{\alpha=1}^{\nu} c_\alpha \nabla_T \mu_\alpha = \nabla p,$$

$$d/dt = (\partial/\partial t) + \mathbf{u} \cdot \nabla.$$

When the inertial terms and viscous stresses vanish or may be considered negligible, Eqs. (5.13) reduce to the phenomenological linear relations between forces and fluxes of irreversible thermodynamics,

$$\nabla_T \mu_\alpha' = -\sum_{\beta=1}^{\nu} R_{\alpha\beta}\mathbf{j}_\beta - R_{\alpha 0}\mathbf{q}, \quad \alpha = 1 \cdots \nu,$$
$$\nabla \ln T = -\sum_{\beta=1}^{\nu} R_{0\beta}\mathbf{j}_\beta - R_{00}\mathbf{q}. \tag{5.15}$$

Because the matrix $R_{\alpha\beta}$ is singular, Eqs. (5.15) must be transformed into the following form in which one of the mass fluxes, say $\mathbf{j}_1$, is eliminated with the use of the linear dependence of the $\mathbf{j}_\beta$, before inversion

$$\nabla_T\left(\mu_\alpha' - \frac{m_\alpha}{m_1}\mu_1'\right) = -\sum_{\beta=2}^{\nu} R_{\alpha\beta}'\mathbf{j}_\beta - R_{\alpha 0}'\mathbf{q},$$
$$\nabla \ln T = -\sum_{\beta=2}^{\nu} R_{0\beta}'\mathbf{j}_\beta - R_{00}'\mathbf{q},$$
$$R_{\alpha\beta}' = R_{\alpha\beta} - \frac{m_\alpha}{m_1}R_{1\beta} - \frac{m_\beta}{m_1}R_{\alpha 1} + \frac{m_\alpha m_\beta}{m_1^2}R_{11}, \tag{5.16}$$
$$R_{\alpha 0}' = R_{\alpha 0} - \frac{m_\alpha}{m_1}R_{10}, \quad R_{0\beta}' = R_{0\beta} - \frac{m_\beta}{m_1}R_{01},$$
$$R_{00}' = R_{00}.$$

When Eqs. (5.16) are inverted and symmetrized with the use of the linear dependence between the $\mathbf{j}_\alpha$, we obtain

$$-\mathbf{j}_\alpha = \Omega_{\alpha 0}\nabla \ln T + \sum_{\beta=1}^{\nu}\Omega_{\alpha\beta}\nabla_T\mu_\beta', \quad \alpha = 1 \cdots \nu,$$
$$-\mathbf{q} = \Omega_{00}\nabla \ln T + \sum_{\beta=1}^{\nu}\Omega_{0\beta}\nabla_T\mu_\beta',$$
$$\Omega_{1\beta} = -\sum_{\alpha=2}^{\nu}\frac{m_\alpha}{m_1}\Omega_{\alpha\beta}, \quad \beta = 0 \cdots \nu \tag{5.17}$$
$$\Omega_{\alpha\beta} = \frac{|R'|_{\alpha\beta}}{|R'|}, \quad \Omega_{\alpha 1} = -\sum_{\beta=2}^{\nu}\frac{m_\beta}{m_1}\Omega_{\alpha\beta}, \quad \alpha = 0, 2 \cdots \nu,$$

where $|R'|$ is the determinant of the matrix $R_{\alpha\beta}'$ and $|R'|_{\alpha\beta}$ is the appropriate minor. The detailed proof of the Onsager reciprocal relations, $\Omega_{\beta\alpha} = \Omega_{\alpha\beta}$, on the molecular level must be based upon an explicit non-equilibrium theory of the molecular distribution function. By virtue of the fact that the matrix of the frictional coefficients $\zeta_{\alpha\beta}$ of Eq. (5.9) is symmetric, we observe that the present theory implies the validity of the reciprocal relations in the isothermal case and is consistent with heat-matter reciprocal relations if the following relations are valid

$$\left(\frac{\partial p_\alpha}{\partial T}\right)_{P,c_\gamma} + \frac{c_\alpha \gamma_{\alpha 0}^{(1)}}{T} = \frac{c_\alpha Q_\alpha^*}{T}, \quad \alpha = 1 \cdots \nu. \tag{5.18}$$

Equation (5.18) is analogous in form to the Clapeyron equation of equilibrium thermodynamics. Although the present theory is consistent with the reciprocal relations, it is formulated on too general a level to permit a positive statement concerning their validity. A detailed proof of the reciprocal relations on the molecular level would have to rest on an explicit non-equilibrium theory of the distribution functions.

Finally we remark that the equations of motion for the several components, and the heat flux equation, Eqs. (5.12), when combined with the equations of continuity and the equation of energy transport, under the postulate of local equilibrium, yield a determinate set of partial differential equations, which, supplemented by appropriate initial and boundary conditions, allow the determination of the temperature, the concentrations c_α of the several components, the diffusion fluxes $\mathbf{j}_\alpha$ and the hydrodynamic particle velocity as functions of position and time in the interior of a multicomponent fluid system.

The Statistical Mechanical Theory of Transport Processes. XII. Dense Rigid Sphere Fluids

STUART A. RICE,* JOHN G. KIRKWOOD, JOHN ROSS,† AND ROBERT W. ZWANZIG‡
Department of Chemistry, Yale University, New Haven, Connecticut

(Received March 13, 1959)

The theory of transport in a dense fluid of rigid spheres is developed from classical statistical mechanics by the use of phase space transformation functions. A modified Maxwell-Boltzmann integro-differential equation for the distribution function in μ space is derived, and the difference between this equation and the Enskog equation is discussed. To obtain a formulation of the stress tensor and heat flux solely in terms of binary collisions, it is necessary to allow the time of coarse graining to be very short. The implications of this are discussed with relation to the general principles of the statistical mechanics of transport. The viscosity and thermal conductivity of the dense rigid sphere fluid are calculated. The viscosity is the same as that first computed by Enskog, but the thermal conductivity differs from his calculations.

I. INTRODUCTION

The kinetic theory of gases based on the Maxwell-Boltzmann equation of transport is limited to the region of low densities[1-6] wherein the dynamics of the system is described by binary collisions, the contributions due to deviations of the pair correlation function from unity are made negligible, and the computation of the flux vectors takes account only of molecular transfer. The reduction of the dynamical behavior of the low-density gas to the discussion of two body encounters is possible because the molecules execute free motion which is interrupted by isolated binary collisions: the transport of the collisional invariants (mass, momentum, energy) occurs, therefore, primarily by the bodily movement of the molecules.

In dense gases none of these simple circumstances prevails. The evolution of the system in time is determined by binary, successive binary, triple, etc.,

---

* Department of Chemistry and Institute for the Study of Metals, University of Chicago, Chicago, Illinois.

† Department of Chemistry, Brown University, Providence, Rhode Island.

‡ National Bureau of Standards, Washington, D.C.

[1] J. G. Kirkwood, *J. Chem. Phys.* **15**, 72 (1947).

[2] J. G. Kirkwood and J. Ross, *Proceedings of the Conference on the Statistical Mechanics of Transport* (Interscience Publishers, Inc., New York, 1958).

[3] J. Yvon, *Actualités Scientifique et Industrielles* (Hermann et Cie, Paris, 1935), No. 203.

[4] M. Born and H. S. Green, *A General Kinetic Theory of Liquids* (Cambridge University Press, London, 1949).

[5] N. Bogolubov, *J. Phys.* (U.S.S.R.) **10**, 265 (1946).

[6] H. L. Frisch, *J. Chem. Phys.* **22**, 1713 (1954).

collisions for some of which analytical solutions for the trajectories are not known. The pair correlation function in dense fluids differs considerably from unity in equilibrium systems and no doubt in non-equilibrium systems as well. Finally, the proximity of the molecules requires the inclusion of collisional transfer in the evaluation of the flux vectors; in fact, in dense fluids the direct contribution of the intermolecular forces to the fluxes may be dominant over that due to molecular transfer.[7]

There have been a number of attempts to surmount some of these difficulties.[8–11] In 1922 Enskog[11] modified the Maxwell-Boltzmann equation of transport for the particular molecular model of hard spheres in a derivation based on plausible physical arguments. He introduced what is now known as the equilibrium pair correlation function, evaluated the collisional transfer, but maintained all other dilute gas approximations. Collins and Raffel,[12] and Longuet-Higgins and Pople[13] have also discussed the theory of transport in a dense fluid of hard spheres. The first of these investigations follows closely the original calculations of Enskog with the modification that the concentration of the centers of the nearest neighbors around a given collision sphere is assumed to be given by the reciprocal of the molecular volume. The second investigation proceeds by physical arguments from the two assumptions that (a) the spatial pair distribution function depends only on the temperature and density and not on the temperature gradient or rate of strain, and (b) that the velocity distribution function of a single particle is Maxwellian with a mean equal to the local hydrodynamic velocity, and a spread determined by the local temperature. The method used avoids the systematic study of the behavior of the singlet space distribution function and therefore leads to an approximation of lower order than that of the Enskog theory. Lastly, Curtiss and Snider[8] have advanced an approach to moderately dense gases in which all the simplifying features of the Maxwell-Boltzmann equation are retained but there are included terms derived from the spatial variation of the singlet distribution function and the collisional transfer is evaluated. This addition provides in the limit of equilibrium, for the contribution of the second virial coefficient in the equation of state. Their work is referred to again in the final discussion.

The purpose of this communication is the establishment of sufficient conditions necessary for an analytic derivation of the equation of transport from Liouville's equation as well as the transport coefficients for a gas of hard spheres at moderate densities. The relation of the method and results obtained to the work of Enskog and Curtiss and Snider is discussed.

II. DERIVATION OF TRANSPORT EQUATION

Consider a one-component system containing N structureless particles with the positions and momenta specified by the $2N$ vectors $\mathbf{R}_1 \cdots \mathbf{R}_N, \mathbf{p}_1 \cdots \mathbf{p}_N$.

---

[7] H. S. Green, *Molecular Theory of Fluids* (North-Holland Publishing Company, Amsterdam, 1952).

[8] R. F. Snider and C. F. Curtiss, *J. Phys. Fluids* **1**, 122 (1958).

[9] For a discussion of time smoothing, see J. G. Kirkwood, *J. Chem. Phys.* **14**, 180 (1946).

[10] J. H. Irving and J. G. Kirkwood, *J. Chem. Phys.* **18**, 817 (1950).

[11] See, for example, S. Chapman and T. G. Cowling, *The Mathematical Theory of Non-Uniform Gases* (Cambridge University Press, London, 1939), Chap. 16.

[12] F. C. Collins and H. Raffel, *J. Chem. Phys.* **22**, 1728 (1954).

[13] H. C. Longuet-Higgins and J. Pople, *J. Chem. Phys.* **25**, 884 (1956).

The normalized specific distribution function in the $6N$-dimensional phase space satisfies Liouville's equation

$$\frac{\partial f^{(N)}}{\partial t} + \sum_{j=1}^{N} \left\{ \frac{\mathbf{p}_j}{m_j} \cdot \nabla_{R_j} f^{(N)} + \mathbf{F}_j \cdot \nabla_{p_j} f^{(N)} \right\} = 0, \tag{1}$$

where the subscripts denote specific molecules (i.e., $\mathbf{p}_j$ and m_j are the momentum and mass of particle j), $\mathbf{F}_j$ is the intermolecular force exerted on the jth molecule by the other $(N-1)$ molecules, and t is the time. It is convenient to define a set of reduced distribution functions, $f^{(n)}$, by the relation

$$f^{(n)}(\mathbf{rp}; t) = \int \cdots \int f^{(N)}(\mathbf{rpQP}; t) d\mathbf{P} d\mathbf{Q}, \tag{2}$$

where $\mathbf{r}$ and $\mathbf{p}$ are the coordinates and momenta of the subset of n particles, and $\mathbf{Q}$ and $\mathbf{P}$ the coordinates and momenta of the remaining set of $(N-n)$ particles. If it is assumed that the intermolecular force, $\mathbf{F}_j$, can be expressed as the sum of pair forces

$$\mathbf{F}_j = \sum_{i \neq j} \mathbf{F}_{ij}(|\mathbf{R}_j - \mathbf{R}_i|), \tag{3}$$

and, if distribution functions coarse grained in time are defined by the relation

$$\bar{f}^{(n)}(\mathbf{rp}; t) = \frac{1}{\tau} \int_0^{\tau} f^{(N)}(\mathbf{rp}; t+s) ds, \tag{4}$$

the integration of Eq. (1) over the coordinates and momenta of $(N-1)$ particles followed by coarse graining in time, leads to the relation

$$\frac{\partial \bar{f}^{(1)}}{\partial t} + \frac{\mathbf{p}_1}{m_1} \cdot \nabla_{R_1} \bar{f}^{(1)} = -\frac{(N-1)}{\tau} \int_0^{\tau} \int \cdots \int \mathbf{F}_{12} \cdot \nabla_{p_1} f^{(2)}(\mathbf{R}_1 \mathbf{R}_2 \mathbf{p}_1 \mathbf{p}_2; t+s) \times d\mathbf{R}_2 d\mathbf{p}_2 ds. \tag{5}$$

Let $\{\mathbf{Rp}\}$ be the phase space coordinates at time $(t+s)$ of the phase point which was at $\{\mathbf{R'p'}\}$ at time t; the conservation of density in phase space may be expressed as

$$f^{(N)}(\mathbf{Rp}; t+s) = f^{(N)}(\mathbf{R'p'}; t). \tag{6}$$

Such relations do not hold for reduced distribution functions since these functions do not obey Liouville's equation. The density of points at $\{\mathbf{Rp}\}$ in the $6N$-dimensional phase space may also be written as

$$f^{(N)}(\mathbf{Rp}; t+s) = \int \cdots \int K^{(N)}(\mathbf{Rp}/\mathbf{R'p'}; s) f^{(N)}(\mathbf{R'p'}; t) d\mathbf{R'} d\mathbf{p'}, \tag{7}$$

which defines the transformation function $K^{(N)}$ as the conditional probability density of finding the N particle system at $\{\mathbf{Rp}\}$ in phase space at time $(t+s)$ if the system was at $\{\mathbf{R'p'}\}$ at time t. Substitution of Eq. (7) into Eq. (1) leads to

$$\frac{\partial K^{(N)}}{\partial s} + \sum_{j=1}^{N} \left\{ \frac{\mathbf{p}_j}{m_j} \cdot \nabla_{R_j} K^{(N)} + \mathbf{F}_j \cdot \nabla_{p_j} K^{(N)} \right\} = 0, \tag{8}$$

$$K^{(N)}(\mathbf{Rp}/\mathbf{R'p'}; 0) = \prod_{j=1}^{N} \delta(\mathbf{p}_j - \mathbf{p}_j') \delta(\mathbf{R}_j - \mathbf{R}_j'), \tag{9}$$

which shows that the transformation function $K^{(N)}$ obeys Liouville's equation.[14]

The general procedure in classical mechanics for the solution of a mechanical problem consists of a search for a canonical transformation from the coordinates and momenta at time $(t + s)$ to a new set of coordinates, say the values of **R** and **p** at time t. If such a transformation can be found, the transformation equations which relate the coordinates and momenta at time $(t + s)$ to those at time t give the solution to the problem since, by definition, they express the coordinates and momenta at time $(t + s)$ directly in terms of the coordinates and momenta at time t. Thus, the functions $K^{(N)}$ are the formal representation of the canonical transformation and therefore the solution to the equation of motion of the N body system. $K^{(N)}$ as a solution of the N-body problem must also describe a trajectory in phase space along which the distribution function is constant, and it is for this reason that $K^{(N)}$ satisfies Liouville's equation.

Since the equations of classical mechanics are deterministic, the general solution of Eq. (8) can be written as

$$K^{(N)}(\mathbf{Rp}/\mathbf{R}'\mathbf{p}'; \tau) = \prod_{j=1}^{N} \delta(\mathbf{R}_j - \mathbf{R}_j' - \Delta\mathbf{R}_j(\tau))\delta(\mathbf{p}_j - \mathbf{p}_j' - \Delta\mathbf{p}_j(\tau)), \quad (10)$$

where $\Delta\mathbf{R}_j(\tau)$ and $\Delta\mathbf{p}_j(\tau)$ are the increments in position and momentum vectors for particle j in the time interval τ determined from the solution of the equations of motion of the N body system.

In addition to the integral relation (2), the probability density $f^{(N)}$ may be related to the reduced distribution functions $f^{(N)}$ by

$$f^{(N)}(\mathbf{rpQP}; t) = f^{(n)}(\mathbf{rp}; t) f^{(n/N-n)}(\mathbf{rp}/\mathbf{QP}; t), \quad (11)$$

where the relative probability density $f^{(n/N-n)}$ is defined by Eq. (11). By substitution of Eq. (11) into Eq. (7), and using Eq. (2),

$$f^{(n)}(\mathbf{rp}; t + s) = \int \cdots \int K^{(n)}(\mathbf{rp}/\mathbf{r}'\mathbf{p}'; s) f^{(n)}(\mathbf{r}'\mathbf{p}'; t) d\mathbf{r}' d\mathbf{p}', \quad (12)$$

where

$$K^{(n)}(\mathbf{rp}/\mathbf{r}'\mathbf{p}'; s) = \int \cdots \int K^{(N)}(\mathbf{rpQP}/\mathbf{r}'\mathbf{p}'\mathbf{Q}'\mathbf{P}'; s) \\ f^{(n/N-n)}(\mathbf{r}'\mathbf{p}'/\mathbf{Q}'\mathbf{P}'; t) d\mathbf{P} d\mathbf{Q} d\mathbf{P}' d\mathbf{Q}'. \quad (13)$$

The substitution of Eq. (12) into Eq. (5) then leads to

$$\frac{\partial f^{(1)}}{\partial t} + \frac{\mathbf{p}_1}{m} \cdot \nabla_{R_1} f^{(1)} = -\frac{(N-1)}{\tau} \int_0^{\tau} \int \cdots \int \mathbf{F}_{12} \\ \cdot \nabla_{p_1} K^{(2)}(s) f^{(2)}(\mathbf{R}_1'\mathbf{R}_2'\mathbf{p}_1'\mathbf{p}_2'; t)\, d\mathbf{R}_2 d\mathbf{p}_2 ds d\mathbf{R}_1' d\mathbf{R}_2' d\mathbf{p}_1' d\mathbf{p}_2'. \quad (14)$$

The multiplication of Eq. (8) by

$$f^{(2/N-2)}(\mathbf{R}_1'\mathbf{R}_2'\mathbf{p}_1'\mathbf{p}_2'/\mathbf{Q}'\mathbf{P}'; t)$$

[14] Further discussion of these phase space distribution functions will be found in J. Ross and J. G. Kirkwood, *J. Chem. Phys.* **22**, 1094 (1954); J. Ross, *ibid.* **24**, 375 (1956).

and integration over $d\mathbf{P}$, $d\mathbf{Q}$, $d\mathbf{P}'$, and $d\mathbf{Q}'$ gives

$$\frac{\partial K^{(2)}}{\partial s} + \frac{\mathbf{p}_1}{m} \cdot \nabla_{R_1} K^{(2)} + \frac{\mathbf{p}_2}{m} \cdot \nabla_{R_2} K^{(2)} + \mathbf{F}_{12} \cdot \nabla_{p_1} K^{(2)} + \mathbf{F}_{21} \cdot \nabla_{p_2} K^{(2)}$$

$$= \sum_{j=3}^{N} \int \cdots \int \{\mathbf{F}_{1_j} \cdot \nabla_{p_1} + \mathbf{F}_{2_j} \cdot \nabla_{p_2}\} K^{(N)}(s)$$

$$f^{(2/N-2)}\,(\mathbf{R}_1{}'\mathbf{R}_2{}'\mathbf{p}_1{}'\mathbf{p}_2{}'/\mathbf{Q}'\mathbf{p};\,'t)\,d\mathbf{P}\,d\mathbf{Q}\,d\mathbf{P}'\,d\mathbf{Q}'. \quad (15)$$

Finally, with the definition of the pair correlation function $g^{(2)}(\mathbf{R}\mathbf{p};\, t)$,

$$f^{(2)}(\mathbf{R}_1\mathbf{R}_2\mathbf{p}_1\mathbf{p}_2;\, t) = g^{(2)}(\mathbf{R}_1\mathbf{R}_2\mathbf{p}_1\mathbf{p}_2;\, t) f^{(1)}(\mathbf{R}_1\mathbf{p}_1;\, t) f^{(1)}(\mathbf{R}_2\mathbf{p}_2;\, t), \quad (16)$$

we conclude our general considerations and turn to the study of dense fluids.

III. THE DENSE HARD SPHERE FLUID

In this section we shall utilize, in a physical manner, some unique features of the hard sphere potential. Mathematical justification for the physical arguments used will be presented at a later date. As first noted by Enskog, by the definition of a hard sphere, the frequency of simultaneous triple collisions can be neglected relative to the frequency of binary collisions. If the trajectory of a given molecule is followed in time, for a hard sphere fluid this may be described as a sequence of successive binary collisions. If attention is restricted to very short time intervals, it is physically plausible that, in the limit as $\tau \to +0$, single binary collisions are isolated. For longer time intervals, successive binary collisions must be considered.

Consider now that the time scale is so chosen that $\tau \to +0$ and only isolated binary collisions occur. Then the only nonzero forces are between molecules 1 and 2, say. Thus $\mathbf{F}_{1j} = \mathbf{F}_{2j} = 0$, $j \neq 1, 2$, and Eq. (15) leads to the limiting equation

$$\lim_{\tau \to +0} \frac{\partial K^{(2)}}{\partial s} + \frac{\mathbf{p}_1}{m} \cdot \nabla_{R_1} K^{(2)} + \frac{\mathbf{p}_2}{m} \cdot \nabla_{R_2} K^{(2)} + \mathbf{F}_{12} \cdot \nabla_{p_1} K^{(2)}$$

$$+ \mathbf{F}_{21} \cdot \nabla_{p_2} K^{(2)} = 0. \quad (17)$$

The notation, $\tau \to +0$ or $s \to +0$ is taken to mean that τ and s approach an arbitrarily small but positive quantity. Equation (17) is a Liouville equation in pair space for the transformation function $K^{(2)}$. Corresponding to the formal solution (10), $K^{(2)}$ becomes

$$K^{(2)}(\mathbf{R}_1\mathbf{R}_2\mathbf{p}_1\mathbf{p}_2/\mathbf{R}_1{}'\mathbf{R}_2{}'\mathbf{p}_1{}'\mathbf{p}_2{}';\, s)$$

$$= \prod_{i=1}^{2} \delta(\mathbf{R}_i - \mathbf{R}_i{}' - \Delta\mathbf{R}_i(s))\delta(\mathbf{p}_i - \mathbf{p}_i{}' - \Delta\mathbf{p}_i(s)), \quad (18)$$

where the increments in momenta and coordinates are defined as before. If Eq. (18) is solved for $\mathbf{F}_{12} \cdot \nabla_{p1} K^{(2)}$, the result substituted into Eq. (14), and that equation integrated with the aid of a representation for the delta function, there results the relation

$$\frac{\partial f^{(1)}}{\partial t} + \frac{\mathbf{p}_1}{m} \cdot \nabla_{R_1} f^{(1)} = \Omega,$$

$$\Omega = \frac{(N-1)}{\tau} \int_0^\tau \int \cdots \int \Big\{ \delta(\mathbf{R}_1 - \mathbf{R}_1' - \Delta\mathbf{R}_1)\delta(\mathbf{R}_2 - \mathbf{R}_2' - \Delta\mathbf{R}_2)$$

$$\frac{\partial}{\partial s}[\delta(\mathbf{p}_1 - \mathbf{p}_1' - \Delta\mathbf{p}_1)\delta(\mathbf{p}_2 - \mathbf{p}_2' - \Delta\mathbf{p}_2)]\Big\} g^{(2)}(\mathbf{R}_1'\mathbf{R}_2'\mathbf{p}_1'\mathbf{p}_2'; t)$$

$$\times f^{(1)}(\mathbf{R}_1'\mathbf{p}_1'; t) f^{(1)}(\mathbf{R}_2'\mathbf{p}_2'; t) d\mathbf{R}_2 d\mathbf{p}_2 ds d\mathbf{R}_1' d\mathbf{R}_2' d\mathbf{p}_1' d\mathbf{p}_2'. \quad (19)$$

To proceed further, the pair correlation function $g^{(2)}$ must be evaluated. In general $g^{(2)}$ depends upon the coordinates and momenta of the pair of particles as well as the time. Explicit calculation of $g^{(2)}$ requires the consideration of three body distribution functions, etc. In the spirit of this analysis, wherein $\tau \to +0$, it is without gross inconsistency to attempt to approximate $g^{(2)}$ by the local equilibrium pair correlation function, $g_0^{(2)}$. This must be viewed as an approximation, the validity of which must be estimated by a separate analysis in which there is a detailed treatment of the relationship between the potentials of mean force in equilibrium and non-equilibrium systems. The approximation is introduced here as a postulate which enables the explicit evaluation of $g^{(2)}(R)$ in terms of thermodynamic variables. Integration of Eq. (17) over $\mathbf{p}_1'$, $\mathbf{p}_2'$, $\mathbf{R}_1'$, $\mathbf{R}_2'$ leads to

$$\Omega = \frac{(N-1)}{\tau} \int_0^\tau \int \int \frac{\partial}{\partial s} g_0^{(2)}(\mathbf{R}_1 - \Delta\mathbf{R}_1, \mathbf{R}_2 - \Delta\mathbf{R}_2) f^{(1)}(\mathbf{R}_1 - \Delta\mathbf{R}_1,$$

$$\mathbf{p}_1 - \Delta\mathbf{P}_1; t) f^{(1)}(\mathbf{R}_2 - \Delta\mathbf{R}_2, \mathbf{p}_2 - \Delta\mathbf{p}_2; t) d\mathbf{R}_2 d\mathbf{p}_2 ds, \quad (20)$$

which can be integrated readily to give

$$\Omega = \frac{(N-1)}{\tau} \int \int \{ g_0^{(2)}(\mathbf{R}_1 - \Delta\mathbf{R}_1, \mathbf{R}_2 - \Delta\mathbf{R}_2) f^{(1)}(\mathbf{R}_1 - \Delta\mathbf{R}_1, \mathbf{p}_1 - \Delta\mathbf{P}_1; t)$$

$$f^{(1)}(\mathbf{R}_2 - \Delta\mathbf{R}_2, \mathbf{p}_2 - \Delta\mathbf{p}_2; t) - g_0^{(2)}(\mathbf{R}_1\mathbf{R}_2) f^{(1)}(\mathbf{R}_1\mathbf{p}_1; t)$$

$$\times f^{(1)}(\mathbf{R}_2\mathbf{p}_2; t)\} d\mathbf{R}_2 d\mathbf{p}_2. \quad (21)$$

Equations (19)–(21) are valid, of course, only in the limit as $\tau \to +0$. In the limit of an infinitesimally small time interval, the increments in coordinates $\Delta\mathbf{R}_1$ and $\Delta\mathbf{R}_2$ approach zero. This is, of course, not so for the increments in momenta since they are altered by the collision which must occur in the interval τ if the integrand is not to vanish. Furthermore, it is clear that as $\tau \to +0$, the positions of molecules 1 and 2 must differ by just one hard sphere diameter, σ. By centering a cylinderical coordinate system on molecule 1 with Z axis antiparallel to the relative momentum of the pair of molecules and coarse graining with respect to time again, it is found that

$$\mathfrak{L}^{(1)}\bar{f}^{(1)} = (N-1)g_0{}^{(2)}(\mathbf{R}_1, \sigma)\int \frac{\mathbf{p}_{12}}{\mu}[\bar{f}^{(1)}(\mathbf{R}_1, \mathbf{p}_1 - \Delta\mathbf{p}_1; t)$$

$$\times f^{(1)}(\mathbf{R}_2, \mathbf{p}_2 - \Delta\mathbf{p}_2; t) - \bar{f}^{(1)}(\mathbf{R}_1\mathbf{p}_1; t)\bar{f}^{(1)}(\mathbf{R}_2\mathbf{p}_2; t)]d\mathbf{p}_2 b\,db\,d\epsilon, \quad (22)$$

where b is the collision parameter, $\mathbf{p}_{12}/\mu$ the relative velocity of particles one and two, μ the reduced mass, and the integration is over all collisions specified by b and the azimuthal angle ϵ, and where $\mathfrak{L}^{(1)}$ is the operator

$$\mathfrak{L}^{(1)} = \frac{\partial}{\partial t} + \frac{\mathbf{p}_1}{m}\cdot\nabla_{R_1}. \quad (23)$$

The distribution functions dependent on $\mathbf{R}_2$ may be expanded in a Taylor series around $\mathbf{R}_1$ and only first-order terms retained. With this approximation, Eq. (22) becomes

$$\mathfrak{L}^{(1)}\bar{f}^{(1)} = J_1 + J_2$$

$$J_1 = (N-1)g_0{}^{(2)}(\mathbf{R}_1, \sigma)\iint\{\bar{f}^{(1)}(\mathbf{R}_1, \mathbf{p}_1 - \Delta\mathbf{p}_1; t)\bar{f}^{(1)}(\mathbf{R}_1, \mathbf{p}_2 - \Delta\mathbf{p}_2; t)$$

$$- \bar{f}^{(1)}(\mathbf{R}_1, \mathbf{p}_1; t)\bar{f}^{(1)}(\mathbf{R}_1, \mathbf{p}_2; t)\}\frac{\mathbf{p}_{12}}{\mu}b\,db\,d\epsilon\,d\mathbf{p}_{12}$$

$$(24)$$

$$J_2 = (N-1)g_0{}^{(2)}(\mathbf{R}_1, \sigma)\iint\{\bar{f}^{(1)}(\mathbf{R}_1, \mathbf{p}_1 - \Delta\mathbf{p}_1; t)\,\sigma\mathbf{k}\cdot\nabla_{R_1}$$

$$\bar{f}^{(1)}(\mathbf{R}_1, \mathbf{p}_2 - \Delta\mathbf{p}_2; t) - \bar{f}^{(1)}(\mathbf{R}_1, \mathbf{p}_1; t)\sigma\mathbf{k}\cdot\nabla_{R_1}\bar{f}^{(1)}(\mathbf{R}_1\mathbf{p}_2; t)\}\frac{\mathbf{p}_{12}}{\mu}b\,db\,d\epsilon\,d\mathbf{p}_{12},$$

where $\mathbf{k}$ is a unit vector in the direction of the line of centers of the colliding hard spheres on contact, and the local equilibrium pair correlation function is obtained from the equation of state,

$$\frac{pv}{kT} = 1 + \frac{2\pi}{3vkT}\int_0^\infty V'(R_{12})g_0{}^{(2)}(R_{12})R_{12}{}^3dR_{12} \quad (25)$$

or

$$\frac{pv}{kT} = 1 + \frac{2\pi\sigma^3}{3v}g_0{}^{(2)}(\sigma). \quad (26)$$

To conclude this section, it will be recalled that the principal assumptions made are the following.

1. The evolution in time of a two-body subset is given by the pair Liouville equation for the transformation or distribution function; i.e., the dynamics of the system is determined by binary collisions only, with the exclusion of correlated successive binary, triple, etc., collisions. This hypothesis, essential for dilute gas theory, may be expected to hold at finite densities for the particular model of hard spheres in the limit as the time interval τ appearing in the transformation function approaches an arbitrarily small but positive value.

It is clear that the hypothesis does not hold for any molecular model at finite density and finite τ for then the dynamics would be influenced by higher order collisions. The conjecture that triple collisions, etc., need not be taken into account for hard spheres requires analytical verification which has not been presented so far.

2. The pair correlation function is taken to be independent of momenta and is approximated by the equilibrium pair correlation function.

3. With the time scale chosen, the time interval is so short that two molecules exchange momentum at constant intermolecular separation. A complete collision does not require appreciable motion of the centers of mass of the molecules.

IV. COEFFICIENTS OF VISCOSITY AND HEAT CONDUCTION OF A DENSE FLUID OF RIGID SPHERES

In the formulation of a statistical mechanical theory of transport processes Kirkwood[9] proposed that an observable quantity be identified with the ensemble average of the corresponding microscopic variables coarse-grained in time. With this postulate Irving and Kirkwood[10] derived the following expressions for the stress tensor $\boldsymbol{\sigma}$ and heat flux $\mathbf{q}$:

$$\boldsymbol{\sigma}_K(\mathbf{R}_1;t) = -\sum_{k=1}^{N}\int\cdots\int\frac{1}{\tau}\int_0^{\tau}\left(\frac{\mathbf{p}_k}{m}-\mathbf{u}\right)\left(\frac{\mathbf{p}_k}{m}-\mathbf{u}\right)\delta(\mathbf{R}_k-\mathbf{R}_1)f^{(N)}ds\,d\mathbf{R}\,d\mathbf{p} \tag{27}$$

$$\boldsymbol{\sigma}_V(\mathbf{R}_1;t) = \tfrac{1}{2}\sum_{j}^{N}\sum_{k}^{N}\int\cdots\int\frac{1}{\tau}\int_0^{\tau}\mathbf{R}_{jk}\nabla V(R_{jk})\delta(\mathbf{R}_j-\mathbf{R}_2)\delta(\mathbf{R}_k-\mathbf{R}_1)\, f^{(N)}ds\,d\mathbf{R}\,d\mathbf{p}\,d\mathbf{R}_{12} \tag{28}$$

$$\mathbf{q}_K(\mathbf{R}_1;t) = \frac{m}{2}\sum_{k=1}^{N}\int\cdots\int\frac{1}{\tau}\int_0^{\tau}\left|\frac{\mathbf{p}_k}{m}-\mathbf{u}\right|^2\left(\frac{\mathbf{p}_k}{m}-\mathbf{u}\right)\delta(\mathbf{R}_k-\mathbf{R}_1)f^{(N)}ds\,d\mathbf{R}\,d\mathbf{p} \tag{29}$$

$$\mathbf{q}_V(\mathbf{R}_1;t) = \sum_{j}^{N}\sum_{k}^{N}\frac{1}{2\tau}\int_0^{\tau}\Big\{[V(R_{jk})\mathbf{1}-\mathbf{R}_{jk}\nabla V(R_{jk})]\cdot \Big[\Big\langle\frac{\mathbf{p}_k}{m}\delta(\mathbf{R}_k-\mathbf{R}_1)\delta(\mathbf{R}_j-\mathbf{R}_2);f^{(N)}\Big\rangle - \mathbf{u}(\mathbf{R}_1,t)\langle\delta(\mathbf{R}_k-\mathbf{R}_1)\delta(\mathbf{R}_j-\mathbf{R}_2);f^{(N)}\rangle\Big]\Big\}ds\,d\mathbf{R}_{12}, \tag{30}$$

where the convenient definition

$$\langle\alpha;f^{(N)}\rangle = \int\cdots\int\alpha(\mathbf{R},\mathbf{p})f^{(N)}d\mathbf{R}\,d\mathbf{p} \tag{31}$$

has been used. As usual, $\boldsymbol{\sigma}_K$ and $\boldsymbol{\sigma}_V$ are the kinetic and intermolecular force parts of the stress tensor, and $\mathbf{q}_K$ and $\mathbf{q}_V$ are the kinetic and intermolecular force parts of the heat flux. Integration permits reduction of these equations to the point where only pair distribution functions appear. The pair distribution functions will be related to singlet distribution functions by Eq. (16).

The evaluation of the flux densities requires the solution of the transport equation, Eq. (24), for the singlet distribution function. Since J_1 is simply the collision term of the Maxwell-Boltzmann equation multiplied by the pair correlation function $g_0^{(2)}(\sigma)$, the procedure follows the Chapman-Enskog solution. Let the singlet distribution function be written as

$$f^{(1)} = f_0^{(1)}(1 + \Phi^{(1)}), \tag{32}$$

where $f_0^{(1)}$ is the zero-order local equilibrium singlet distribution function,

$$f_0^{(1)}(1) = \frac{(2\pi mkT)^{-\frac{3}{2}}}{v} \exp\left[-(\mathbf{p}_1 - m\mathbf{u})^2/2mkT\right], \tag{33}$$

and $\Phi^{(1)}$ is the perturbation. From Eq. (16) it is observed that

$$\Phi^{(2)} = \Phi_1^{(1)} + \Phi_2^{(1)} \tag{34}$$

neglecting terms of second order. When the radial distribution function is isotropic (as is assumed herein), Eq. (34) is exact to terms of the form $\nabla \ln T$ and $\nabla \mathbf{u}$. Thus, the neglect of terms of the form $\Phi_1^{(1)}\Phi_2^{(1)}$ is equivalent to the neglect of terms of order $(\nabla \ln T)^2$ etc., and any possible coupling between the perturbations to the singlet distribution functions is an effect of higher order than those considered. The perturbation to the distribution function in pair space is then the sum of the perturbations to the component singlet space distribution functions (to the first order in $\Phi^{(1)}$).

The perturbation functions, $\Phi^{(1)}$, may be shown to have the form

$$\Phi^{(1)} = -\mathbf{A} \cdot \nabla_{R_1} \ln T - \mathbf{B} : \nabla_{R_1} \mathbf{u}, \tag{35}$$

where the vector **A** and the tensor **B** are evaluated by the same methods as used in the study of dilute gases. It will be sufficient for our purposes to expand **A** and **B** in a power series in Sonine polynomials and to terminate this series after the first term in the expansion. The details of the calculations will be presented in another paper and we here quote the results ($g_0^{(2)}(\sigma) = g(\sigma)$):

$$\mathbf{A}_1 = -\left(\frac{2kT}{m}\right)^{\frac{1}{2}} \frac{\{[15v/4Ng(\sigma)] + (6\pi\sigma^3/4)\}[\frac{5}{2} - W_1^2]}{4\Omega^{(2,2)}} \mathbf{W}_1, \tag{36}$$

$$\mathbf{B}_1 = \frac{5v\{[1/Ng(\sigma)] + (4\pi\sigma^3/15v)\}}{4\Omega^{(2,2)}} [\mathbf{W}_1\mathbf{W}_1 - \tfrac{1}{3}W_1^2\mathbf{1}], \tag{37}$$

where the reduced velocity $\mathbf{W}_1$ is defined by

$$\mathbf{W} = (m/2kT)^{\frac{1}{2}}([\mathbf{p}_1/m) - \mathbf{u}], \tag{38}$$

and where the reduced cross section $\Omega^{(2,2)}$ is obtained from the relation

$$\Omega^{(l,s)} = \left(\frac{4\pi kT}{m}\right) \int\int \gamma^{2s+3}(1 - \cos{}^l\chi) \exp(-\gamma^2) b\,db\,d\gamma, \tag{39}$$

$$\gamma = (m/4kT)^{\frac{1}{2}} \mathbf{p}_{12}/\mu, \tag{40}$$

with χ the angle of deflection in a binary collision. Reduction of Eqs. (27) and (29) to the form,

$$\lim_{\tau\to+0} \boldsymbol{\sigma}_K = -\int \bar{f}^{(1)}\left(\frac{\mathbf{p}}{m}-\mathbf{u}\right)\left(\frac{\mathbf{p}}{m}-\mathbf{u}\right)d\mathbf{p}, \tag{41}$$

$$\lim_{\tau\to+0} \mathbf{q}_K = \frac{m}{2}\int \bar{f}^{(1)}\left|\frac{\mathbf{p}}{m}-\mathbf{u}\right|^2\left(\frac{\mathbf{p}}{m}-\mathbf{u}\right)d\mathbf{p}, \tag{42}$$

followed by substitution of Eqs. (35)–(37) and comparison with the phenomenological defining equations of the transport coefficient, leads to the results:

$$\eta_K = \frac{5kT}{8\Omega^{(2,2)}}\left[\frac{1}{Ng(\sigma)}+\frac{4\pi\sigma^3}{15v}\right], \tag{43}$$

$$\kappa_K = \frac{75k^2T}{32m\Omega^{(2,2)}}\left[\frac{1}{Ng(\sigma)}+\frac{2\pi\sigma^3}{5v}\right], \tag{44}$$

$$\Omega^{(2,2)} = \left(\frac{4\pi kT}{m}\right)^{\frac{1}{2}}\sigma^2, \tag{45}$$

where η_K is the kinetic contribution to the viscosity and κ_K is the kinetic contribution to the heat conductivity. The expressions for the viscosity and thermal conductivity agree with the kinetic contribution found by Enskog. The first term of both η_K and κ_K are seen to be simply $[Ng(\sigma)]^{-1}$ times the viscosity and thermal conductivity of a dilute gas of hard spheres. The second term arises from the accounted difference in position of the centers of mass of molecules i and j.

The evaluation of the intermolecular force contribution to the flux densities requires somewhat more detailed consideration. Consider first the stress tensor. The applicability of the binary collision approximation for the description of the dynamics requires the interval of time over which the distribution function is coarse grained be short enough that no successive binary collisions occur. This condition on the interval τ, i.e., in the limit of very small τ permits the calculation of the flux densities. Choose a cylindrical coordinate system with origin on molecule one and with Z axis antiparallel to the direction of the relative momentum of the colliding pair. Unless the Z coordinate lies between

$$\sigma\cos\frac{\chi}{2} \leq Z \leq \frac{p_{12}}{\mu}\tau + \sigma\cos\frac{\chi}{2}, \tag{46}$$

the pair does not collide and the change in momentum is zero. The angle χ is related to the collision parameter b and the relative momentum by the well-known formula

$$\frac{\chi}{2} = \int_\sigma^\infty \frac{bp_{il}{}^0 dR/R^2}{[(1-b^2/R^2)p_{il}{}^2 - 2\mu V(R)]^{\frac{1}{2}}}. \tag{47}$$

On approach to the limit $\tau \to +0$, and recognition that $\nabla_{R_{12}}V(R_{12})$ is simply equal to the rate of change of momentum in the collision, there results

$$\lim_{\tau\to+0} \partial_V(\mathbf{R}_1; t)$$

$$= \frac{N(N-1)}{2} \int \cdots \int \sigma \mathbf{k} \Delta \mathbf{p}_{12} f^{(2)} \frac{p_{12}}{\mu} b db d\epsilon d\mathbf{p}_1 d\mathbf{p}_2 \quad \Delta \mathbf{p}_{12} = 2\mathbf{p}_{12} \cos\chi/2, \tag{48}$$

where, as before, $\mathbf{k}$ is a unit vector pointing in the direction of the line of centers when the rigid spheres are in contact. To transform Eq. (48) use is made of the dynamics of the binary collision to obtain

$$\Delta \mathbf{p}_{12} = -2(\mathbf{p}_{12} \cdot \mathbf{k})\mathbf{k} \tag{49}$$

so that

$$\partial_V(\mathbf{R}_1; t) = \frac{2N(N-1)\sigma g(\sigma)}{m} \int \cdots \int \mathbf{kk}(\mathbf{p}_{12} \cdot \mathbf{k}) f^{(1)}(1) f^{(1)}(2) p_{12} d\mathbf{p}_1 d\mathbf{p}_2 b db d\epsilon. \tag{50}$$

Once again, the substitution of Eqs. (33), (34), and (35) followed by integration leads to the relation

$$\eta_V = \frac{5kT}{8\Omega^{(2,2)}} \left[\frac{4\pi\sigma^3}{15v} + \left(\frac{4\pi\sigma^3}{15v}\right)^2 Ng(\sigma) \right], \tag{51}$$

which is identical with the result obtained by Enskog. The total coefficient of shear viscosity thus becomes

$$\eta = \eta_K + \eta_V = \frac{5kT}{8\Omega^{(2,2)}} \left[\frac{1}{Ng(\sigma)} + \frac{8\pi\sigma^3}{15v} + \left(\frac{4\pi\sigma^3}{15v}\right)^2 Ng(\sigma) \right]. \tag{52}$$

The intramolecular force contribution to the heat conductivity may be computed in a similar manner. First, however, it is seen that the quantity $V(R)\mathbf{1}$ is zero when the spheres are not in contact and the product $V\mathbf{1}$ and the pair distribution function is zero when the intermolecular separation is less than or equal to the hard sphere diameter. Thus for hard spheres, the term $V(R)\mathbf{1}$ does not contribute to the heat flux.

Secondly, the quantity

$$\sum_{\substack{j \\ j\neq k}}^{N} \sum_{k}^{N} [\langle (\mathbf{p}_k/m)\delta(\mathbf{R}_k - \mathbf{R}_1)\delta(\mathbf{R}_j - \mathbf{R}_2); f^{(N)}\rangle$$
$$- \mathbf{u}(\mathbf{R}_1; t) \langle \delta(\mathbf{R}_k - \mathbf{R}_1)\, \delta(\mathbf{R}_j - \mathbf{R}_2); f^{(N)}\rangle] \tag{53}$$

is seen to be the projection onto the space of $\mathbf{R}_1$ of the particle current density at $(\mathbf{R}_1, \mathbf{R}_2)$ in pair space minus the pair density at $(\mathbf{R}_1, \mathbf{R}_2)$ times the velocity $\mathbf{u}$, and therefore is the peculiar velocity of the center of mass,

$$\frac{1}{2}\left[\left(\frac{\mathbf{p}_1}{m} - \mathbf{u}\right) + \left(\frac{\mathbf{p}_2}{m} - \mathbf{u}\right)\right], \tag{54}$$

in the space of $\mathbf{R}_1$. With the relation

$$\Delta \mathbf{p}_{12} = -\int_0^\tau \nabla V(R_{12}(s)) ds \tag{55}$$

and integration by parts, the following expression is found:

$$-\int_0^\tau \frac{1}{2}\left[\left(\frac{\mathbf{p}_1}{m}-\mathbf{u}\right)+\left(\frac{\mathbf{p}_2}{m}-\mathbf{u}\right)\right]\nabla V(R_{12}(s))ds$$
$$=\frac{1}{2}\left[\left(\frac{\mathbf{p}_1}{m}-\mathbf{u}\right)+\left(\frac{\mathbf{p}_2}{m}-\mathbf{u}\right)\right]\cdot\Delta\mathbf{p}_{12}, \quad (56)$$

since the other terms vanish by the conservation of energy. Application of the dynamics of the binary collision, Eq. (49) verifies that the flux density reduces to

$$\mathbf{q}_V = -\frac{N(N-1)\sigma g(\sigma)}{m^2}\int\cdots\int \mathbf{k}(\mathbf{k}\cdot\mathbf{p}_{12})\mathbf{k}$$
$$\cdot(\mathbf{p}_1 - m\mathbf{u} + \mathbf{p}_2 - m\mathbf{u})p_{12}\bar{f}^{(1)}(1)\bar{f}^{(1)}(2)bdbd\epsilon d\mathbf{p}_1 d\mathbf{p}_2. \quad (57)$$

The use of Eqs. (53), (54), and (55) followed by integration leads to the relation

$$\kappa_V = \frac{75k^2T}{32m\Omega^{(2,2)}}\left[\frac{8\pi\sigma^3}{15v}+\frac{16}{75}\left(\frac{\pi\sigma^3}{v}\right)^2 Ng(\sigma)\right], \quad (58)$$

and this result differs from that of Enskog. Addition of Eqs. (44) and (58) shows that the total thermal conductivity is

$$\kappa = \kappa_K + \kappa_V$$
$$= \frac{75k^2T}{32m\Omega^{(2,2)}}\left[\frac{1}{Ng(\sigma)}+\frac{14\pi\sigma^3}{15v}+\frac{16}{75}\left(\frac{\pi\sigma^3}{v}\right)^2 Ng(\sigma)\right]. \quad (59)$$

Thus, in the total thermal conductivity, both the v^{-1} and v^{-2} terms differ from those computed by Enskog.

V. DISCUSSION

The purpose of this communication has been to establish a postulatory basis from which the Enskog theory of a dense hard sphere fluid could be rigorously derived. The results can be compared with the work of Enskog and Curtiss and Snider. Enskog modified the Maxwell-Boltzmann equation with the aid of physical arguments and arrived at the following equation presumed to be valid for a gas of hard spheres at arbitrary density§[16]

$$\mathfrak{L}^{(1)}f^{(1)} = \iiint [Y(\mathbf{R}_1 + \tfrac{1}{2}\sigma\mathbf{k})f^{(1)}(\mathbf{R}_1, \mathbf{p}_1'; t)f^{(1)}(\mathbf{R}_1 + \sigma\mathbf{k}, \mathbf{p}_2'; t)$$
$$- Y(\mathbf{R}_1 - \tfrac{1}{2}\sigma\mathbf{k})f^{(1)}(\mathbf{R}_1, \mathbf{p}_1; t)f^{(1)}(\mathbf{R}_1 - \sigma\mathbf{k}, \mathbf{p}_2; t)]\frac{p_{12}}{\mu}bdbd\epsilon d\mathbf{p}_2. \quad (60)$$

§ Enskog used the symbol Y for the function which represented the shielding effect on the colliding pair of molecules of all molecules, other than the pair. He proposed that this function be determined from the equation of state and the identification with the equilibrium pair correlation function may be made. At equilibrium the pair correlation function is independent of position in space in the absence of external forces and neglect of surface effects and depends only on the relative configuration of two molecules. Thus, in terms of the equation of state,

$$(pv/kT) = 1 + (2\pi\sigma^3/3v)Y$$

completing the identification of $g(\sigma)$ and Y.

[15] M. S. Green, *J. Chem. Phys.* **25**, 836 (1956).

[16] Hirschfelder, Curtiss, and Bird, *The Molecular Theory of Gases and Liquids* (John Wiley & Sons, Inc., New York, 1954).

The Enskog theory of dense gases is based on a perturbation solution of Eq. (60) identical in principle with the one used in the theory of dilute gases.[8] The expansion of Eq. (60) in a Taylor series about $\mathbf{R}_1$ yields,

$$\mathfrak{L}^{(1)}f^{(1)} = J_1' + J_2' + J_3'$$

$$J_1' = Y\int\cdots\int [f^{(1)}(\mathbf{R}_1, \mathbf{p}_1'; t)f^{(1)}(\mathbf{R}_1, \mathbf{p}_2'; t) - f^{(1)}(\mathbf{R}_1\mathbf{p}_1; t) \times f^{(1)}(\mathbf{R}_1\mathbf{p}_2; t)]d\Sigma$$

$$J_2' = Y\int\cdots\int [\mathbf{k}\cdot(f^{(1)}(\mathbf{R}_1\mathbf{p}_1'; t)\nabla_{R_1}f^{(1)}(\mathbf{R}_1\mathbf{p}_2'; t) + f^{(1)}(\mathbf{R}_1\mathbf{p}_1; t) \times \nabla_{R_1}f^{(1)}(\mathbf{R}_1\mathbf{p}_2; t)]\sigma d\Sigma$$

$$J_3' = \tfrac{1}{2}\nabla_{R_1}Y\cdot\int\cdots\int [f^{(1)}(\mathbf{R}_1\mathbf{p}_1'; t)f^{(1)}(\mathbf{R}_1\mathbf{p}_2'; t) + f^{(1)}(\mathbf{R}_1\mathbf{p}_1; t) \times f^{(1)}(\mathbf{R}_1\mathbf{p}_2; t)]\mathbf{k}\sigma d\Sigma \quad (61)$$

$$d = \frac{p_{12}}{\mu}bdbd\epsilon d\mathbf{p}_2.$$

Comparison with Eq. (24) shows disagreement in the spatial dependence of the correlation and distribution functions. The origin of the disparity is evident. In Enskog's verbal derivation use is made of the phrases "before the collision" and "after the collision" in reference to the independent variables of these functions; in the case of configuration coordinates they are assigned the above values. The present analysis, however, clearly exhibits the fact that in the limit of small time intervals τ the times referred to in the phrases "before the collision" and "after the collision" become identical and therefore the differences between the respective configuration coordinates vanish.

An objection to this argument could be made by claiming that Enskog's transport equation does not depend on the specification of a time interval τ nor on its duration. The claim is not valid: Enskog's transport equation includes only parameters sufficient for the description of binary collisions so that the time evolution of the distribution function as proscribed by his equation is determined solely by a binary collision mechanism. It was seen, however, that the validity of this approximation for the evaluation of the dynamics of the system is appropriate, at finite density, only as the time interval τ approaches zero regardless of the particular analytical model chosen for the interaction between molecules. The limitation on the interval τ, infinitesimally small, is necessary because thus, although there are included for consideration successive uncorrelated collisions, correlated binary collisions, triple collisions, etc., are excluded.[9,17] At moderate densities this may suffice but becomes untenable at high densities.

The transport equation used by Curtiss and Snider was derived by Bogolubov and Born and Green:

$$\mathfrak{L}^{(1)}f^{(1)} = \int\cdots\int f_0^{(1)}f_0^{(1)}[\Phi_{10} + \Phi_{20} - \Phi_1 - \Phi_2]d\Sigma + J_1'' + J_2'',$$

$$J_i'' = \frac{2}{m^2}\int\int \nabla_R V\cdot\nabla_{p_{12}/\mu}(\Delta_i)d\mathbf{R}d\mathbf{p}_2,$$

[17] A different type of coarse graining has been used by M. S. Green, *J. Chem. Phys.* **20**, 1281 (1952); T. Koga, *ibid.* **23**, 2275 (1955); R. Brout, *Physica* **22**, 509 (1956).

$$\Delta_1 = \tfrac{1}{2}\mathbf{R}' \cdot [f_0^{(1)}(1)\nabla_{R_1} f_0^{(1)}(2) - f_0^{(1)}(2)\nabla_{R_1} f_0^{(1)}(1)],$$

$$\Delta_2 = \tfrac{1}{2}\mathbf{R} \cdot \nabla_{R_1} f_0^{(1)}(1) f_0^{(1)}(2).$$

The pair correlation function is assumed to be unity and all density dependent terms are thought to be included which lead, in the equilibrium limit, to the equation of state up to and including the second virial coefficient. Since derivatives with respect to momentum appear in the first density correction, this transport equation differs from the present one as well as from Enskog's equation.

A comparison of the results obtained for the transport coefficients is given in Table I.

TABLE I.

$$\kappa^{cs} = \kappa_0 \left[1 + \frac{29}{90}\frac{\pi\sigma^3}{v} + \left(\frac{128}{675\pi} + \frac{1}{45}\right)\left(\frac{\pi\sigma^3}{v}\right)^2\right]$$

$$\kappa^{RKRZ} = \kappa_0 \left[\frac{1}{g(\sigma)} + \frac{14}{15}\frac{\pi\sigma^3}{v} + \frac{16}{75}\left(\frac{\pi\sigma^3}{v}\right)^2 g(\sigma)\right]$$

$$= \kappa_0 \left[1 + \frac{31}{60}\frac{\pi\sigma^3}{v} + 0.0859\left(\frac{\pi\sigma^3}{v}\right)^2\right]$$

$$\left\{\text{after putting } g(\sigma) = 1 + \frac{5}{12}\frac{\pi\sigma^3}{v} + 0.1274\left(\frac{\pi\sigma^3}{v}\right)^2\right\}$$

$$\kappa_0 = \frac{75k}{64\sigma^2}\left(\frac{kT}{m\pi}\right)^{\frac{1}{2}}$$

$$\eta^{cs} = \eta_0 \left[1 + \frac{7}{30}\frac{\pi\sigma^3}{v} + \frac{32}{75\pi}\left(\frac{\pi\sigma^3}{v}\right)^2\right]$$

$$\eta^{RKRZ} = \eta_0 \left[\frac{1}{g(\sigma)} + \frac{8}{15}\frac{\pi\sigma^3}{v} + \frac{16}{225}\left(\frac{\pi\sigma^3}{v}\right)^2 g(\sigma)\right]$$

$$= \eta_0 \left[1 + \frac{7}{60}\frac{\pi\sigma^3}{v} - 0.0563\left(\frac{\pi\sigma^3}{v}\right)^2\right]$$

$$\left\{\text{after putting } g(\sigma) = 1 + \frac{5}{12}\frac{\pi\sigma^3}{v} + 0.1274\left(\frac{\pi\sigma^3}{v}\right)^2\right\}$$

$$\eta_0 = \frac{5}{16\sigma^2}\left(\frac{mkT}{\pi}\right)^{\frac{1}{2}}$$

The expression obtained by Curtiss and Snider should agree with the others shown in Table I if (σg) is set equal to unity. However, no agreement is obtained, even when $g(\sigma)$ is expanded in powers of the density.

VI. ACKNOWLEDGMENT

We wish to thank Professor R. J. Bearman for several helpful discussions.

Correction: The Statistical-Mechanical Theory of Transport

(a) The symbol μ, referred to as a reduced mass, is not the usual reduced mass, and is defined by

$$\frac{\mathbf{p}_{12}}{\mu} = (\mathbf{p}_2/m) - (\mathbf{p}_1/m)$$

All calculations were performed using this relation.

(b) In Eqs. (51) and (52), the coefficient of $Ng(\sigma)$ should read:

$$\left(\frac{4}{25} + \frac{48}{25\pi}\right)\left(\frac{2\pi\sigma^3}{3v}\right)^2$$

(c) In Eqs. (58) and (59), the coefficient of $Ng(\sigma)$ should read:

$$\left(\frac{36}{75} + \frac{192}{150\pi}\right)\left(\frac{2\pi\sigma^3}{3v}\right)^2$$

(d) In Table I, the coefficients of $(\pi\sigma^3/v)^2$ in the density expansions for κ^{RKRZ} and η^{RKRZ} should read 0.4402 and 0.3842, respectively. The lines immediately preceding the density expansions should be modified in accordance with items (b) and (c) above.

The Statistical Mechanics of Transport Processes. XIV. Linear Relations in Multi-component Systems*

JOHN G. KIRKWOOD,** *Sterling Chemistry Laboratory,† Yale University, New Haven, Connecticut*

AND

DONALD D. FITTS, *Department of Chemistry, University of Pennsylvania, Philadelphia 4, Pennsylvania*

(Received May 11, 1960)

A classical treatment of the time dependence of a phase-space distribution function for a system near equilibrium is presented. The non-equilibrium distribution function is expressed as a stationary zero-order function plus a perturbation term and is used to obtain the diffusion and heat fluxes by averaging the appropriate dynamical variables. When only terms linear in the gradients of the local temperature, the chemical potentials, and the velocity of the local centers of mass are retained, the usual linear relations result and explicit expressions for the phenomenological coefficients are obtained. These expressions agree with the results of Mori and of Green and are shown to obey the Onsager reciprocal relations.

With the use of the statistical-mechanical theory of transport processes as developed by Kirkwood,[1] Irving and Kirkwood[2] have derived the macroscopic equations of transport for one-component systems from the equations of molecular dynamics. Their results have been generalized to multi-component systems by Bearman and Kirkwood.[3] Thus, macroscopic quantities such as the stress tensor and fluxes of matter and heat are expressed as averages over non-equilibrium molecular distribution functions.

The next objective of the statistical-mechanical theory of transport processes is the determination of the time dependence of a deviation of the phase space distribution function from its equilibrium form. Since the decay of this deviation gives rise to transport phenomena, an evaluation of its time dependence determines the various transport coefficients in terms of molecular variables. These transport coefficients may then be calculated for particular systems. We attempt here to fulfill part of this objective.

---

* The work presented in this article was started when both authors were at Yale University. A preliminary report was given by Professor Kirkwood at the International School of Physics of the Italian Physical Society in June, 1959 and published in *Nuovo cimento Supplemento* [**16**, (1960)]. This article was prepared by D.D.F. after the death of Professor Kirkwood.

**"Kirkwood—Deceased."

† Contribution No. 1611.

[1] J. G. Kirkwood, *J. Chem. Phys.* **14**, 180 (1946).

[2] J. H. Irving and J. G. Kirkwood, *J. Chem. Phys.* **18**, 817 (1950).

[3] R. J. Bearman and J. G. Kirkwood, *J. Chem. Phys.* **28**, 136 (1958).

In this article we develop a method for treating the time dependence of a distribution function for a system near equilibrium. We restrict our discussion to classical systems, although the same treatment could be developed quantum mechanically by replacing the probability density in phase space with the Wigner distribution function.[4,5] The temporal development of the non-equilibrium distribution function is governed by Liouville's equation. We express this distribution function as a zero-order function plus a perturbation term. Upon introducing a specific zero-order function and neglecting all terms except those linear in the macroscopic parameters which determine the deviations from equilibrium,[6] we obtain explicit expressions for the phenomenological coefficients which appear in the linear relations for the heat flux and for the diffusion current densities of the various components in the system. These expressions involve time integrals of temporal correlation functions of dynamical variables and are independent of our choice for the zero-order distribution function. The phenomenological coefficients are shown to obey the Onsager reciprocal relations.[7] We do not attempt here to calculate numerical values of these coefficients for specific systems.

In Sec. I we consider the general first-order perturbation theory for the non-equilibrium distribution function. In Sec. II, we introduce a specific zero-order local-equilibrium distribution function and linearize it. Section III treats the linear relations for the diffusion fluxes, while Sec. IV deals with the heat flux. In Sec. V we prove the Onsager reciprocal relations for the phenomenological coefficients that appear in the linear relations obtained in Secs. III and IV. Section VI is devoted to a brief discussion of our results and to a comparison of our treatment with those of Mori[8] and of Green.[9]

I

We consider a ν component non-equilibrium system containing N molecules which are not chemically reacting. Each component is labeled by the index α, which runs from 1 to ν. There are N_α molecules of species α; the individual molecules of each component α are numbered $1, 2, \cdots, N_\alpha$. Each molecule is assumed for simplicity to have only three degrees of translational freedom and no others. The position and momentum of molecule i of component α may, therefore, be denoted by the vectors $\mathbf{R}_{\alpha i}$ and $\mathbf{p}_{\alpha i}$, respectively. We may occasionally let $\mathbf{R}$ denote the set of N vectors $\mathbf{R}_{11}, \mathbf{R}_{12}, \cdots, \mathbf{R}_{\nu N_\nu}$ and $\mathbf{p}$ the set $\mathbf{p}_{11}, \mathbf{p}_{12}, \cdots, \mathbf{p}_{\nu N_\nu}$.

We shall be concerned with a time-smoothed probability distribution function $\bar{f}^{(N)}(\mathbf{R}, \mathbf{p}, t)$ for the non-equilibrium N-particle system. For a temporal coarse graining,[1] we may consider a uniformly weighted average over an interval τ,

$$\bar{f}^{(N)}(\mathbf{R}, \mathbf{p}, t) = \tau^{-1} \int_0^\tau f^{(N)}(\mathbf{R}, \mathbf{p}, t + s)ds, \tag{1.1}$$

[4] E. Wigner, *Phys. Rev.* **40**, 749 (1932).
[5] J. H. Irving and R. W. Zwanzig, *J. Chem. Phys.* **19**, 1173 (1951).
[6] In this regard, our treatment is similar to the Chapman-Enskog treatment of the Boltzmann equation.
[7] L. Onsager, *Phys. Rev.* **37**, 405; **38**, 2265 (1931).
[8] H. Mori, *Phys. Rev.* **112**, 1829 (1958).
[9] M. S. Green, *J. Chem. Phys.* **22**, 398 (1954).

where $f^{(N)}(\mathbf{R}, \mathbf{p}, t)$ is the probability density in phase space at time t of an appropriate statistical ensemble. The interval τ is determined by the time resolution of the instruments employed in the measurement of the macroscopic observable. We discuss the interval τ further in Sec. VI.

This temporal averaging of the distribution function does not need to be uniformly weighted in time; another possible temporal coarse graining is

$$\bar{f}^{(N)}(\mathbf{R}, \mathbf{p}, t) = \tau^{-1} \int_0^\infty \exp(-s/\tau) f^{(N)}(\mathbf{R}, \mathbf{p}, t + s) ds. \tag{1.2}$$

In general, this coarse graining in time may be expressed as

$$\bar{f}^{(N)}(\mathbf{R}, \mathbf{p}, t) = \int_{-\infty}^{\infty} w(s) f^{(N)}(\mathbf{R}, \mathbf{p}, t + s) ds, \tag{1.3}$$

where $w(s)$ is a normalized weighting function. In an experimental measurement, the observed result should be independent of $w(s)$ if the characteristic width τ of $w(s)$ is short relative to the relaxation times τ_r for the transport processes occurring in the system. Therefore, we shall adopt here the simple Kirkwood form (1.1).

The molecules in the system are assumed to obey the laws of classical mechanics. Consequently,[1] the time-smoothed probability distribution function $\bar{f}^{(N)}(\mathbf{R}, \mathbf{p}, t)$ for the non-equilibrium system at a time t obeys the Liouville equation

$$L\bar{f}^{(N)} + i(\partial \bar{f}^{(N)}/\partial t) = 0, \tag{1.4}$$

where i is the imaginary unit and L is the self-adjoint Liouville operator,

$$L = i \sum_{\alpha=1}^{\nu} \sum_{l=1}^{N_\alpha} [(\mathbf{p}_{\alpha l}/m_\alpha) \cdot \nabla_{\mathbf{R}_{\alpha l}} + (\mathbf{X}_{\alpha l} + \mathbf{F}_{\alpha l}) \cdot \nabla_{\mathbf{p}_{\alpha l}}]. \tag{1.5}$$

In Eq. (1.5) m_α is the molecular mass of component α, $\mathbf{X}_{\alpha l}$ is the external force acting on molecule l of species α, and $\mathbf{F}_{\alpha l}$ is the intermolecular force exerted on this molecule by the other $(N - 1)$ molecules.

We assume that the intermolecular force $\mathbf{F}_{\alpha l}$ has a pairwise additive form,

$$\mathbf{F}_{\alpha l} = \sum_{\beta=1}^{\nu} \sum_{\substack{j=1 \\ \alpha l \neq \beta j}}^{N_\beta} \mathbf{F}_{\beta j \alpha l}, \tag{1.6}$$

where $\mathbf{F}_{\beta j \alpha l}$ is the force acting on molecule l of species α due to molecule j of species β. The notation of $\alpha l \neq \beta j$ indicates that there is no term corresponding to $l = j$ when $\alpha = \beta$. The force $\mathbf{F}_{\beta j \alpha l}$ may be expressed in terms of the mutual potential energy $V_{\alpha\beta}$ of a pair of molecules of species α and β,

$$\mathbf{F}_{\beta j \alpha l} = - \nabla_{\mathbf{R}_{\alpha l}} V_{\alpha\beta}(R_{\beta j \alpha l}), \tag{1.7}$$

where $V_{\alpha\beta}$ is a function only of the magnitude of the vector distance

$$\mathbf{R}_{\beta j \alpha l} = \mathbf{R}_{\alpha l} - \mathbf{R}_{\beta j} \tag{1.8}$$

between the centers of masses of the two molecules.

The non-equilibrium system under consideration has gradients of temperature T, of the velocity $\mathbf{u}$ of the local centers of mass, and of the chemical potentials μ_α of the ν chemical components.[10] The deviation from equilibrium is measured by r such parameters, which we write as γ_k where k runs from 1 to r. As each of the parameters γ_k approaches zero, the system approaches equilibrium.

We assume that the non-equilibrium system is sufficiently close to equilibrium that we may discard terms in the distribution function $\bar{f}^{(N)}$ higher than those linear in γ_k. Under this assumption we write $\bar{f}^{(N)}$ as the sum of a zero-order distribution function $\bar{f}_0^{(N)}$ and a perturbation term $\bar{f}_1^{(N)}$,

$$\bar{f}^{(N)} = \bar{f}_0^{(N)}(\gamma_1, \cdots, \gamma_r) + \bar{f}_1^{(N)} \tag{1.9}$$

with

$$\bar{f}_1^{(N)} = \sum_{k=1}^{r} \gamma_k \bar{f}_{1k}^{(N)}. \tag{1.10}$$

The zero-order distribution function $\bar{f}_0^{(N)}$ may be taken from a wide variety of possible choices. It must, of course, reduce to the equilibrium distribution function $f_{\text{eq}}^{(N)}$ when each of the parameters γ_k vanishes. Otherwise convenience is the only criterion in the selection of $\bar{f}_0^{(N)}$. However, we choose $\bar{f}_0^{(N)}$ to be stationary, i.e., $\bar{f}_0^{(N)}$ is not an explicit function of time.

The quantities $\bar{f}_{1k}^{(N)}$ are not functions of the parameters γ_k. Therefore, the perturbation term $\bar{f}_1^{(N)}$ contains all those terms, linear in the γ_k, which are not included in $\bar{f}_0^{(N)}$. In principle, it is possible for $\bar{f}_0^{(N)}$ to contain all the linear terms and for $\bar{f}_1^{(N)}$ to vanish. However, if we select $\bar{f}_0^{(N)}$ to be stationary, then $\bar{f}_1^{(N)}$ may not be zero at all times.

Since we wish to retain in $\bar{f}^{(N)}$ only terms which are linear in the γ_k, we expand $\bar{f}_0^{(N)}$ in a Taylor series about equilibrium and discard quadratic and higher terms in γ_k. As a result, $\bar{f}_0^{(N)}$ has the form

$$\bar{f}_0^{(N)} = f_{\text{eq}}^{(N)} + \sum_{k=1}^{r} \gamma_k (\partial \bar{f}_0^{(N)}/\partial \gamma_k)_{\text{eq}} \tag{1.11}$$

and Eq. (1.9) becomes

$$\bar{f}^{(N)} = f_{\text{eq}}^{(N)} + \sum_{k=1}^{r} \gamma_k (\partial \bar{f}_0^{(N)}/\partial \gamma_k)_{\text{eq}} + \bar{f}_1^{(N)}. \tag{1.12}$$

When Eq. (1.9) is substituted into the Liouville equation (1.4), we obtain

$$L\bar{f}_0^{(N)} + L\bar{f}_1^{(N)} + i(\partial \bar{f}_1^{(N)}/\partial t) = 0. \tag{1.13}$$

[10] When these gradients are sufficiently small, it is reasonable to regard the system as possessing local equilibrium character. Arbitrary initial gradients of the temperature and of the chemical potentials of the various components would imply a gradient in the hydrodynamic pressure, as may be seen from the Gibbs-Duhem equation. Consequently, acoustic waves would propagate across the system as time progresses. The Gibbs-Duhem equation may be employed, on the other hand, to provide a restriction on the initial gradients to suppress acoustic waves. In the general situation, however, the diffusion and heat currents defined in Secs. III and IV refer to flows *relative* to the local acoustic motion of the fluid medium.

The term $\partial \bar{f}_0^{(N)}/\partial t$ vanishes because $\bar{f}_0^{(N)}$ is stationary. Now the quantity $L\bar{f}_0^{(N)}$ may be expressed in the form

$$L\bar{f}_0^{(N)} = -i\sum_{k=1}^{r} \gamma_k B_k \bar{f}_0^{(N)} = -iB\bar{f}_0^{(N)}, \tag{1.14}$$

where B is defined by

$$B(\mathbf{R}, \mathbf{p}) = \sum_{k=1}^{r} \gamma_k B_k(\mathbf{R}, \mathbf{p}). \tag{1.15}$$

The actual form of the coefficients B_k depends on the choice of the zero-order distribution function $\bar{f}_0^{(N)}$. Substitution of Eq. (1.14) into Eq. (1.13) yields a differential equation for the perturbation term $\bar{f}_1^{(N)}$ in the non-equilibrium distribution function,

$$(\partial \bar{f}_1^{(N)}/\partial t) - iL\bar{f}_1^{(N)} - B\bar{f}_0^{(N)} = 0. \tag{1.16}$$

We take as the origin of time ($t = 0$) that instant when the perturbation $\bar{f}_1^{(N)}$ to the distribution function $\bar{f}^{(N)}$ is turned on. Prior to the time $t = 0$, we assume that the system is maintained in a steady state with a distribution function $\bar{f}_0^{(N)}$ by the application of appropriate external forces and heat reservoirs. These fictitious external forces are not to be confused with the real external forces $\mathbf{X}_{\alpha l}$ acting on the system. The maintenance of such a steady state by this method has been discussed in detail by McLennan[11] and therefore will not be elaborated on here. At the time $t = 0$, we remove these fictitious external forces and heat reservoirs and allow the system to approach equilibrium; i.e., we allow the parameters γ_k to decay to zero. During this decay process, the distribution function $\bar{f}^{(N)}$ for the system is represented by Eq. (1.9), which defines $\bar{f}_1^{(N)}$ when $\bar{f}_0^{(N)}$ is given. Since $\bar{f}_0^{(N)}$ is stationary, in time $\bar{f}_1^{(N)}$ decays to its equilibrium value $(f_{\text{eq}}^{(N)} - \bar{f}_0^{(N)})$ with a relaxation time τ_r.

With the boundary condition that $\bar{f}_1^{(N)}$ vanishes for negative values of time t, the solution of the differential equation (1.16) is

$$\bar{f}_1^{(N)}(t) = \int_0^t \exp\,[-i(s' - t)L]B(\mathbf{R}_{s'}, \mathbf{p}_{s'})f_{\text{eq}}^{(N)}ds', \tag{1.17}$$

where $\bar{f}_0^{(N)}$ has been replaced by $f_{\text{eq}}^{(N)}$ in order to avoid quadratic and higher terms in γ_k. We have also introduced the convention that $\mathbf{R}_t$, $\mathbf{p}_t$ are the values of $\mathbf{R}$, $\mathbf{p}$ at time t if $\mathbf{R}_0$, $\mathbf{p}_0$ are their values at time $t = 0$, i.e., $\mathbf{R}_t = \mathbf{R}(\mathbf{R}_0, \mathbf{p}_0, t)$ and $\mathbf{p}_t = \mathbf{p}(\mathbf{R}_0, \mathbf{p}_0, t)$. The homogeneous solutions of Eq. (1.16) vanish upon application of the boundary condition. If we introduce the variable of integration $s = 2s' - t$ into Eq. (1.17), we obtain

$$\bar{f}_1^{(N)}(t) = \tfrac{1}{2}\int_{-t}^{t} \exp[-i(s - t)L/2]B(\mathbf{R}_{(s+t)/2}, \mathbf{p}_{(s+t)/2})f_{\text{eq}}^{(N)}ds. \tag{1.18}$$

[11] J. A. McLennan, Jr., *Phys. Rev.* **115**, 1405 (1959).

If ϕ is any function of $\mathbf{R}(t)$ and $\mathbf{p}(t)$, but is not an explicit function of time (i.e., $\partial\phi/\partial t = 0$), then the total time derivative of $\phi(\mathbf{R}_t, \mathbf{p}_t)$ is

$$d\phi/dt = \sum_{\alpha=1}^{\nu} \sum_{l=1}^{N_\alpha} [(d\mathbf{R}_{\alpha l}/dt) \cdot \nabla_{\mathbf{R}_{\alpha l}}\phi + (d\mathbf{p}_{\alpha l}/dt) \cdot \nabla_{\mathbf{p}_{\alpha l}}\phi] = - iL\phi, \tag{1.19}$$

where the Liouville operator is given by Eq. (1.5) and does not contain the fictitious external forces or the effects of the heat reservoirs discussed previously. Integration of Eq. (1.19) from a time t to a time $t + s$ yields

$$\phi(\mathbf{R}_{t+s}, \mathbf{p}_{t+s}) = \exp(-isL)\phi(\mathbf{R}_t, \mathbf{p}_t), \tag{1.20}$$

where the operator $\exp(-isL)$ is defined by the relation

$$\exp(-isL) = \sum_{n=0}^{\infty} \frac{(-is)^n}{n!} L^n. \tag{1.21}$$

On applying Eq. (1.20) to Eq. (1.18), we obtain

$$f_1^{(N)}(t) = \tfrac{1}{2} \int_{-t}^{t} B(\mathbf{R}_s, \mathbf{p}_s) f_{\mathrm{eq}}^{(N)} ds. \tag{1.22}$$

We may integrate over negative values of t in Eq. (1.22) if we acknowledge that $\mathbf{R}$ and $\mathbf{p}$ are extrapolated backward in time by Eq. (1.20) to values which they would have had in the absence of the fictitious external forces and heat reservoirs, since these effects are not contained in the operator L. Since the equilibrium distribution function by definition does not change with time (neither explicitly nor implicitly), it is not affected by the various time transformations which were made.

The expectation value G_{obs} of any dynamical variable $G(\mathbf{R}, \mathbf{p})$ at the time t may be expressed as $\langle G; \bar{f}^{(N)} \rangle$, where, by definition,

$$\langle G; \bar{f}^{(N)} \rangle = \iint G(\mathbf{R}, \mathbf{p}) \bar{f}^{(N)}(\mathbf{R}, \mathbf{p}, t) d\mathbf{R} d\mathbf{p}. \tag{1.23}$$

In Eq. (1.23) the product $G\bar{f}^{(N)}$ is integrated over all of phase space. The distribution function $\bar{f}^{(N)}$, correct to first-order terms in the γ_k, is given in Eq. (1.12), so that in this linear approximation G_{obs} is:

$$\begin{aligned} G_{\mathrm{obs}} &= G^{(0)} + G_{\mathrm{I}}^{(1)} + G_{\mathrm{II}}^{(1)}, \\ G^{(0)} &= \langle G; f_{\mathrm{eq}}^{(N)} \rangle, \\ G_{\mathrm{I}}^{(1)} &= \sum_{k=1}^{r} \gamma_k \langle G; (\partial \bar{f}_0^{(N)}/\partial \gamma_k)_{\mathrm{eq}} \rangle, \\ G_{\mathrm{II}}^{(1)} &= \langle G; f_1^{(N)} \rangle. \end{aligned} \tag{1.24}$$

In view of Eq. (1.22), $G_{\mathrm{II}}^{(1)}$ becomes

$$G_{\mathrm{II}}^{(1)} = \tfrac{1}{2} \int_{-t}^{t} \langle G(\mathbf{R}_t, \mathbf{p}_t) B(\mathbf{R}_s, \mathbf{p}_s) ; f_{\mathrm{eq}}^{(N)} \rangle ds. \tag{1.25}$$

For any given dynamical variable $G(\mathbf{R}, \mathbf{p})$, the values of $G^{(0)}$, $G_{\mathrm{I}}^{(1)}$, $G_{\mathrm{II}}^{(1)}$ depend upon the choice of the zero-order distribution function $f_0^{(N)}$; some of these quantities may vanish.

II

We now introduce a pseudocanonical zero-order distribution function $f_0^{(N)}$ for the non-equilibrium system under consideration,

$$f_0^{(N)} = A \exp\left[- \sum_{\beta=1}^{\nu} \sum_{j=1}^{N_\beta} \frac{(\mathbf{p}_{\beta j} - m_\beta \mathbf{u}_{\beta j})^2}{2 m_\beta k T_{\beta j}} - \sum_{\alpha=1}^{\nu} \sum_{\beta=1}^{\nu} \sum_{\substack{i=1 \\ \alpha i \neq \beta j}}^{N_\alpha} \sum_{j=1}^{N_\beta} \frac{V_{\alpha\beta}(R_{\beta j \alpha i})}{k(T_{\alpha i} + T_{\beta j})} - \sum_{\beta=1}^{\nu} \sum_{j=1}^{N_\beta} \frac{\phi_{\beta j}}{k T_{\beta j}} \right], \tag{2.1}$$

where k is the Boltzmann constant and A is a normalizing factor. This form of $f_0^{(N)}$, analogous to the equilibrium canonical distribution, is consistent with our assumption of small gradients of T, $\mathbf{u}$, and μ_α and hence, of local equilibrium.

The first term in the exponential of Eq. (2.1) represents a velocity distribution which is Gaussian about the local hydrodynamic velocity. The local temperature and the local hydrodynamic velocity at the position in ordinary three-dimensional space of molecule j of species β are $T_{\beta j}$ and $\mathbf{u}_{\beta j}$, respectively. Thus, $T_{\beta j}$ and $\mathbf{u}_{\beta j}$ are abbreviations for $T(\mathbf{R}_{\beta j})$ and $\mathbf{u}(\mathbf{R}_{\beta j})$. The temperature $T_{\alpha l}$ is related to $T_{\beta j}$ by

$$T_{\alpha l} = T_{\beta j} + \mathbf{R}_{\beta j \alpha l} \cdot \nabla T, \tag{2.2}$$

where $\mathbf{R}_{\beta j \alpha l}$ is the vector defined in Eq. (1.8) and ∇T is the gradient of $T(\mathbf{r}, t)$ with respect to the position vector $\mathbf{r}$ in ordinary three-dimensional space. Similarly, $\mathbf{u}_{\alpha l}$ is related to $\mathbf{u}_{\beta j}$ by

$$\mathbf{u}_{\alpha l} = \mathbf{u}_{\beta j} + \mathbf{R}_{\beta j \alpha l} \cdot \nabla \mathbf{u}. \tag{2.3}$$

In the third term, $\phi_{\beta j}$ is the potential of a fictitious external force acting on molecule j of species β. As we mentioned in Sec. I, it is these fictitious forces and heat reservoirs which keep the system in a steady state before the time $t = 0$. In order to prevent diffusive flow in this stationary state, the potential $\phi_{\beta j}$ of the pseudoforce on molecule j of component β must be the negative of the chemical potential of species β at the position $\mathbf{R}_{\beta j}$. Therefore, the desired form for $f_0^{(N)}$ is

$$f_0^{(N)} = A \exp\left[- \sum_{\beta=1}^{\nu} \sum_{j=1}^{N_\beta} \frac{(\mathbf{p}_{\beta j} - m_\beta \mathbf{u}_{\beta j})^2}{2 m_\beta k T_{\beta j}} - \sum_{\alpha=1}^{\nu} \sum_{\beta=1}^{\nu} \sum_{\substack{i=1 \\ \alpha i \neq \beta j}}^{N_\alpha} \sum_{j=1}^{N_\beta} \frac{V_{\alpha\beta}(R_{\beta j \alpha i})}{k(T_{\alpha i} + T_{\beta j})} + \sum_{\beta=1}^{\nu} \sum_{j=1}^{N_\beta} \frac{\mu_{\beta j}}{k T_{\beta j}} \right], \tag{2.4}$$

where $\mu_{\beta j}$ is an abbreviation for $\mu_\beta(\mathbf{R}_{\beta j})$.

In order to determine the coefficients B_k in Eq. (1.14), we operate on $\bar{f}_0^{(N)}$ given in Eq. (2.4) with the Liouville operator L and then discard all terms which are of higher order than linear in $\nabla\mathbf{u}$, $\nabla \ln T$, and $\nabla\mu_\alpha$. When Eqs. (2.2) and (2.3) are substituted into the expression for $L\bar{f}_0^{(N)}$, Eqs. (1.6) and (1.7) are used to cancel two terms, and only linear terms are retained, we obtain:

$$B = (kT)^{-1}\{\mathbf{S}\colon \nabla\mathbf{u} - \mathbf{Q}\cdot\nabla \ln T - \sum_{\alpha=1}^{\nu}\sum_{l=1}^{N_\alpha}(\mathbf{p}_{\alpha l}'/m_\alpha)\cdot[T\nabla(\mu_\alpha/T) - \mathbf{X}_\alpha]\delta(\mathbf{R}_{\alpha l} - \mathbf{r})\}, \tag{2.5}$$

where

$$\mathbf{S} = -\sum_{\alpha=1}^{\nu}\sum_{l=1}^{N_\alpha}(\mathbf{p}_{\alpha l}'\mathbf{p}_{\alpha l}'/m_\alpha)\delta(\mathbf{R}_{\alpha l} - \mathbf{r}) + \tfrac{1}{2}\sum_{\alpha=1}^{\nu}\sum_{\beta=1}^{\nu}\sum_{\substack{l=1 \\ \alpha l\neq\beta j}}^{N_\alpha}\sum_{j=1}^{N_\beta}\mathbf{R}_{\beta j\alpha l}\nabla_{\mathbf{R}_{\alpha l}}V_{\alpha\beta}(R_{\beta j\alpha l})\delta(\mathbf{R}_{\alpha l} - \mathbf{r}),$$

$$\mathbf{Q} = \sum_{\alpha=1}^{\nu}\sum_{l=1}^{N_\alpha}(\mathbf{p}_{\alpha l}'/m_\alpha)\cdot[(p_{\alpha l}'^2/2m_\alpha)\,\mathbf{1} + \tfrac{1}{2}\mathbf{\Lambda}_{\alpha l}]\delta(\mathbf{R}_{\alpha l} - \mathbf{r}), \tag{2.6}$$

$$\mathbf{\Lambda}_{\alpha l} = \sum_{\substack{\beta=1 \\ \alpha l\neq\beta j}}^{\nu}\sum_{j=1}^{N_\beta}[V_{\alpha\beta}(R_{\beta j\alpha l})\,\mathbf{1} - \mathbf{R}_{\beta j\alpha l}\nabla_{\mathbf{R}_{\alpha l}}V_{\alpha\beta}(R_{\beta j\alpha l})].$$

In Eqs. (2.5) and (2.6), $\delta(\mathbf{R}_{\alpha l} - \mathbf{r})$ in the Dirac delta function, $\mathbf{1}$ is the unit dyadic, and $\mathbf{p}_{\alpha l}'$ represents the momentum of the molecule relative to the hydrodynamical motion of the local center of mass; thus

$$\mathbf{p}_{\alpha l}' = \mathbf{p}_{\alpha l} - m_\alpha\mathbf{u}. \tag{2.7}$$

III

Now that we have an expression for B for our choice of the zero-order distribution function $\bar{f}_0^{(N)}$, we may determine some of the transport properties for the non-equilibrium system through the use of Eqs. (1.24) and (1.25). We shall use the conclusions of Bearman and Kirkwood[3] to determine the diffusion current density of species α and the heat current density for our non-equilibrium system. In this section we consider the diffusion fluxes. Section IV deals with the heat flux.

The flow pattern of the system is determined by specifying the local mean velocity $\mathbf{u}_\alpha$ of each component α. The velocity $\mathbf{u}$ of the local center of mass is given by

$$\rho\mathbf{u} = \sum_{\alpha=1}^{\nu}\rho_\alpha\mathbf{u}_\alpha, \tag{3.1}$$

where ρ_α is the partial mass density of species α and ρ is the total mass density,

$$\rho = \sum_{\alpha=1}^{\nu}\rho_\alpha. \tag{3.2}$$

The diffusion current density of component α is defined by the relation

$$\mathbf{j}_\alpha = (\rho_\alpha / m_\alpha)\,(\mathbf{u}_\alpha - \mathbf{u}). \tag{3.3}$$

The diffusion fluxes $\mathbf{j}_\alpha$ are not all independent, for

$$\sum_{\alpha=1}^{\nu} m_\alpha \mathbf{j}_\alpha = 0, \tag{3.4}$$

from Eqs. (3.1) and (3.3).

According to Bearman and Kirkwood,[3] the diffusion flux $\mathbf{j}_\alpha$ is given in terms of microscopic variables by

$$\mathbf{j}_\alpha(\mathbf{r}) = \left\langle \sum_{i=1}^{N_\alpha} (\mathbf{p}_{\alpha i}'/m_\alpha)\delta(\mathbf{R}_{\alpha i} - \mathbf{r});\, f^{(N)} \right\rangle. \tag{3.5}$$

Therefore, the dynamical variable G to be used in calculating $\mathbf{j}_\alpha$ from Eqs. (1.24) is

$$G(\mathbf{R}_t, \mathbf{p}_t) = \sum_{i=1}^{N_\alpha} (\mathbf{p}_{\alpha it}'/m_\alpha)\delta(\mathbf{R}_{\alpha it} - \mathbf{r}). \tag{3.6}$$

The term $G^{(0)}$ immediately integrates to zero, since G in Eq. (3.6) is odd in $\mathbf{p}_{\alpha i}$ and $f_{\text{eq}}^{(N)}$ is even in $\mathbf{p}_{\alpha i}$. For similar reasons, the term $G_{\text{I}}^{(1)}$ also vanishes. The term $G_{\text{II}}^{(1)}$, however, does not vanish. Substituting Eq. (3.6) into Eq. (1.25) and using Eq. (2.5) for the quantity B, we obtain:

$$\mathbf{j}_\alpha(\mathbf{r}) = -\,\boldsymbol{\Omega}_{\alpha 0} \cdot \nabla \ln T - \sum_{\beta=1}^{\nu} \boldsymbol{\Omega}_{\alpha\beta} \cdot [T\nabla(\mu_\beta/T) - \mathbf{X}_\beta], \tag{3.7}$$

where

$$\boldsymbol{\Omega}_{\alpha 0} = (2kT)^{-1} \int_{-t}^{t} \langle \sum_{i=1}^{N_\alpha} (\mathbf{p}_{\alpha it}'/m_\alpha)\mathbf{Q}_s \delta(\mathbf{R}_{\alpha it} - \mathbf{r});\, f_{\text{eq}}^{(N)} \rangle ds,$$

$$\begin{aligned}\boldsymbol{\Omega}_{\alpha\beta} = (2kT)^{-1} \int_{-t}^{t} \langle \sum_{i=1}^{N_\alpha} \sum_{j=1}^{N_\beta} &(\mathbf{p}_{\alpha it}'/m_\alpha)(\mathbf{p}_{\beta js}'/m_\beta) \\ &\times \delta(\mathbf{R}_{\alpha it} - \mathbf{r})\delta(\mathbf{R}_{\beta js} - \mathbf{r});\, f_{\text{eq}}^{(N)} \rangle ds.\end{aligned} \tag{3.8}$$

The quantity $\mathbf{Q}_s$ is an abbreviation for $\mathbf{Q}(\mathbf{R}_s, \mathbf{p}_s)$. The coefficient of the force $\nabla\mathbf{u}$ vanishes because the integrand of the phase integral is an odd function of $\mathbf{p}_{\alpha i}$. This result is to be expected from Curie's theorem[12] that tensor forces do not cause vector fluxes.

The phenomenological coefficients in Eqs. (3.8) may be somewhat simplified by carrying out the indicated summations:

$$\boldsymbol{\Omega}_{\alpha 0} = \frac{N_\alpha}{2m_\alpha kT} \int_{-t}^{t} \langle \mathbf{p}_{\alpha 1t}' \mathbf{Q}_s \delta(\mathbf{R}_{\alpha 1t} - \mathbf{r});\, f_{\text{eq}}^{(N)} \rangle ds, \tag{3.9}$$

---

[12] P. Curie, *J. phys.* **3**, 393 (1894); *Oeuvres de Pierre Curie* (Gauthier-Villars, Paris, 1908), p. 118–141.

$$\mathbf{\Omega}_{\alpha\beta} = \frac{N_\alpha N_\beta}{2m_\alpha m_\beta kT} \int_{-t}^{t} \langle \mathbf{p}_{\alpha 1t}' \mathbf{p}_{\beta 1s}' \delta(\mathbf{R}_{\alpha 1t} - \mathbf{r}) \delta(\mathbf{R}_{\beta 1s} - \mathbf{r}); \times f_{\text{eq}}^{(N)} \rangle ds \quad (\alpha \neq \beta), \tag{3.10}$$

$$\mathbf{\Omega}_{\alpha\alpha} = \frac{N_\alpha (N_\alpha - 1)}{2m_\alpha^2 kT} \int_{-t}^{t} \langle \mathbf{p}_{\alpha 1t}' \mathbf{p}_{\alpha 2s}' \delta(\mathbf{R}_{\alpha 1t} - \mathbf{r}) \delta(\mathbf{R}_{\alpha 2s} - \mathbf{r}); \times f_{\text{eq}}^{(N)} \rangle ds + \frac{N_\alpha}{2m_\alpha^2 kT} \int_{-t}^{t} \langle \mathbf{p}_{\alpha 1t}' \mathbf{p}_{\alpha 1s}' \delta(\mathbf{R}_{\alpha 1t} - \mathbf{r}) \times \delta(\mathbf{R}_{\alpha 1s} - \mathbf{r}); f_{\text{eq}}^{(N)} \rangle ds. \tag{3.11}$$

Since the forces $\nabla \ln T$, $[T\nabla(\mu_\beta/T) - \mathbf{X}_\beta]$ are independent of one another, substitution of Eq. (3.7) into Eq. (3.4) gives

$$\sum_{\alpha=1}^{\nu} m_\alpha \mathbf{\Omega}_{\alpha 0} = 0, \qquad \sum_{\alpha=1}^{\nu} m_\alpha \mathbf{\Omega}_{\alpha\beta} = 0. \tag{3.12}$$

These relations also follow from Eqs. (3.9)–(3.11), since the linear momentum of the system is conserved.

IV

We now determine the heat current density for the non-equilibrium system. Since there exists some arbitrariness in the definition of the heat flux,[13] a number of heat fluxes may be defined; they differ from one another by functions of position $\mathbf{r}$ only. The heat flux $\mathbf{q}$ to be considered here must satisfy the relationship[7,14]

$$\Phi = - \sum_{\alpha=1}^{\nu} \mathbf{j}_\alpha \cdot [T\nabla(\mu_\alpha/T) - \mathbf{X}_\alpha] - \mathbf{q} \cdot \nabla \ln T, \tag{4.1}$$

where Φ/T is the rate per unit volume of the internal entropy production in the non-equilibrium system. Only if $\mathbf{q}$ satisfies Eq. (4.1) may we expect the Onsager reciprocal relations to hold. The heat flux $\mathbf{q}$ as determined by Eq. (4.1) is identical with the conduction current density of the internal energy.[15]

According to Bearman and Kirkwood,[3] this heat flux $\mathbf{q}$ is given in terms of microscopic variables by

$$\mathbf{q}(\mathbf{r}) = \langle \mathbf{Q}; f^{(N)} \rangle, \tag{4.2}$$

where $\mathbf{Q}$ is defined in Eqs. (2.6). When the dynamical variable $\mathbf{Q}_t$ is substituted for $G(\mathbf{R}_t, \mathbf{p}_t)$ in Eqs. (1.24), $G^{(0)}$ and $G_{\text{I}}^{(1)}$ integrate to zero because their integrands are odd functions of $\mathbf{p}_{\alpha i}$. Substitution of $\mathbf{Q}_t$ and Eq. (2.5) into Eq. (1.25) yields

$$\mathbf{q} = - \mathbf{\Omega}_{00} \cdot \nabla \ln T - \sum_{\alpha=1}^{\nu} \mathbf{\Omega}_{0\alpha} \cdot [T\nabla(\mu_\alpha/T) - \mathbf{X}_\alpha], \tag{4.3}$$

---

[13] J. G. Kirkwood and B. Crawford, Jr., *J. Phys. Chem.* **56**, 1048 (1952).

[14] S. R. deGroot, *Thermodynamics of Irreversible Processes* (North-Holland Publishing Company, Amsterdam, 1952), pp. 6–7.

[15] Footnote reference 14, pp. 94–100.

where

$$\mathbf{\Omega}_{00} = \frac{1}{2kT}\int_{-t}^{t} \langle \mathbf{Q}_t \mathbf{Q}_s; f_{\text{eq}}^{(N)} \rangle ds, \tag{4.4}$$

$$\mathbf{\Omega}_{0\alpha} = \frac{N_\alpha}{2m_\alpha kT}\int_{-t}^{t} \langle \mathbf{Q}_t \mathbf{p}_{\alpha 1s}{}' \delta(\mathbf{R}_{\alpha 1s} - \mathbf{r}); f_{\text{eq}}^{(N)} \rangle ds. \tag{4.5}$$

In Eq. (4.3) the term linear in $\nabla\mathbf{u}$ integrates to zero in accord with Curie's theorem.

It should be noted that the phenomenological coefficients $\mathbf{\Omega}_{\alpha 0}$, $\mathbf{\Omega}_{\alpha\beta}$, $\mathbf{\Omega}_{00}$, $\mathbf{\Omega}_{0\alpha}$ in Eqs. (3.9)–(3.11), (4.4), and (4.5) are *not* functions of position $\mathbf{r}$, even though Dirac delta functions involving $\mathbf{r}$ occur in these expressions. Since the equilibrium distribution function is not dependent on position, these delta functions integrate to unity in the integration over phase space.

V

We now show that the phenomenological coefficients given in Eqs. (3.9), (3.10), and (4.5) obey the Onsager reciprocal relations,[7] i.e.,

$$\mathbf{\Omega}_{0\alpha} = \mathbf{\Omega}_{\alpha 0} \qquad (\alpha = 1, 2, \cdots, \nu), \tag{5.1}$$

$$\mathbf{\Omega}_{\alpha\beta} = \mathbf{\Omega}_{\beta\alpha} \qquad (\alpha, \beta = 1, 2, \cdots, \nu). \tag{5.2}$$

We consider first the coefficients $\mathbf{\Omega}_{\alpha 0}$ given in Eq. (3.9). The phase space integral which appears in $\mathbf{\Omega}_{\alpha 0}$ is

$$\langle \mathbf{p}_{\alpha 1t}{}' \delta(\mathbf{R}_{\alpha 1t} - \mathbf{r}) \mathbf{Q}_s; f_{\text{eq}}^{(N)} \rangle.$$

Since the microscopic variables taken at time s are related to the same variables taken at time t by

$$\phi(\mathbf{R}_s, \mathbf{p}_s) = \exp[-i(s-t)L]\phi(\mathbf{R}_t, \mathbf{p}_t), \tag{5.3}$$

this phase space integral becomes

$$\langle \mathbf{p}_{\alpha 1t}{}' \delta(\mathbf{R}_{\alpha 1t} - \mathbf{r}) \exp[-i(s-t)L] \mathbf{Q}_t; f_{\text{eq}}^{(N)} \rangle.$$

If the operator $\exp[-i(s-t)L]$ is expanded according to Eq. (1.21), the nth term in the summation is

$$n!^{-1}[-i(s-t)]^n \langle \mathbf{p}_{\alpha 1t}{}' \delta(\mathbf{R}_{\alpha 1t} - \mathbf{r}) L^n \mathbf{Q}_t; f_{\text{eq}}^{(N)} \rangle.$$

When n is odd, the integrand here is odd in the momentum of each molecule and therefore integrates to zero. When n is even, however, the phase space integral does not vanish. Consequently, the original phase space integral is an even function of $(s-t)$ and may be written as

$$\langle \mathbf{p}_{\alpha 1t}{}' \delta(\mathbf{R}_{\alpha 1t} - \mathbf{r}) \exp[-i(t-s)L] \mathbf{Q}_t; f_{\text{eq}}^{(N)} \rangle.$$

This phase space integral may be regarded as a function of the dynamical variables at time t, averaged over an equilibrium distribution at that time.

However, the equilibrium distribution is stationary by definition, so that it does not matter whether we take such an average at time t or at some other time, say s. Under this translation of the time scale, the phase space integral which appears in $\mathbf{\Omega}_{\alpha 0}$ becomes

$$\langle \mathbf{p}_{\alpha 1s}'\delta(\mathbf{R}_{\alpha 1s} - \mathbf{r})\mathbf{Q}_t; f_{\text{eq}}^{(N)}\rangle.$$

This phase space integral, however, is exactly that which appears in $\mathbf{\Omega}_{0\alpha}$ in Eq. (4.5). As a result, the Onsager relations (5.1) are proved.

To prove the Onsager reciprocal relations for $\mathbf{\Omega}_{\alpha\beta}$, which are given in Eq. (3.10), we repeat exactly the same procedure as before, except that we replace $\mathbf{Q}$ by $\mathbf{p}_{\beta 1}'\delta(\mathbf{R}_{\beta 1} - \mathbf{r})$. The relations (5.2) follow in a straightforward manner.

VI

By developing a perturbation theory for the non-equilibrium distribution function, we have obtained the linear relations for diffusion and heat flow in a multi-component system without chemical reactions. In order to obtain these linear relations, we have neglected terms in the distribution function which are of higher order than linear in the parameters γ_k, i.e., in $\nabla \ln T$, $\nabla\mathbf{u}$, and $\nabla\mu_\alpha$. The analysis presented here is valid whenever the parameters γ_k are sufficiently small that quadratic and higher terms in γ_k may be neglected. However, from this treatment we are not able to draw any conclusions regarding the situations under which this linear description is adequate.

The time integrals of the temporal correlation functions which appear in the phenomenological coefficients $\mathbf{\Omega}_{00}$, $\mathbf{\Omega}_{0\alpha}$, $\mathbf{\Omega}_{\alpha 0}$, $\mathbf{\Omega}_{\alpha\beta}$ may be expressed in a different, but equivalent form. By making the substitution $s = t + s''$ in Eq. (1.25), we obtain

$$G_{\text{II}}^{(1)} = -\tfrac{1}{2}\int_0^{-2t} \langle G(\mathbf{R}_t, \mathbf{p}_t) B(\mathbf{R}_{t+s''}, \mathbf{p}_{t+s''}); f_{\text{eq}}^{(N)}\rangle ds''. \tag{6.1}$$

Now the time correlation function

$$\langle G(\mathbf{R}_t, \mathbf{p}_t) B(\mathbf{R}_{t+s''}, \mathbf{p}_{t+s''}); f_{\text{eq}}^{(N)}\rangle$$

has a value which is not zero in the neighborhood of $s'' = 0$. However, when s'' has reached a certain value τ_c, this correlation function vanishes. Therefore, we may cut off the integral in Eq. (6.1) at τ_c and obtain

$$G_{\text{II}}^{(1)} = -\tfrac{1}{2}\int_0^{\tau_c} \langle G(\mathbf{R}_t, \mathbf{p}_t) B(\mathbf{R}_{t+s''}, \mathbf{p}_{t+s''}); f_{\text{eq}}^{(N)}\rangle ds''. \tag{6.2}$$

Equation (6.2) may be used in place of Eq. (1.25) to determine the phenomenological coefficients for diffusion and heat transport. In a theory of irreversible processes based on regression of fluctuations in an equilibrium system,[16] Fixman has also obtained expressions for transport coefficients involving time correlation functions similar to Eq. (6.2).

At the time $t = 0$, the fictitious external forces and heat reservoirs which maintain the system in a stationary state are removed. The system then rapidly attains local equilibrium character. By local equilibrium we mean that

[16] M. Fixman, *J. Chem. Phys.* **26**, 1421 (1957); **28**, 397 (1958).

equilibrium exists in regions whose linear extents are large compared with the mean free path of the molecules in the system, but are small compared with the linear extent of the entire system. The time interval required for the system to attain local equilibrium is τ_0. The relaxation time for the entire system to reach equilibrium is τ_r. Since τ_r increases with the size of the system, while τ_0 is independent of the size, we have $\tau_0 \ll \tau_r$ for a large system.

We now consider the time smoothing of the distribution function over an interval τ as stated by Eq. (1.1) and the time correlation over an interval τ_c as given by Eq. (6.2). As indicated in Eqs. (1.1) and (6.2), we choose a time t after the system has attained local equilibrium and before it has reached thermodynamic equilibrium. In the case of Eq. (1.1), we then average $f^{(N)}$ over an interval τ from the time t to the time $(t + \tau)$. For the time correlation function in Eq. (6.2), we average over an interval τ_c from time t to time $(t + \tau_c)$. In order that the temporal coarse graining of the distribution function $f^{(N)}$ be independent of the interval τ, it is necessary that

$$\tau_c \ll \tau \ll \tau_r. \tag{6.3}$$

As a consequence of these inequalities, the value of $G_{\text{II}}^{(1)}$ in Eq. (6.2) remains unchanged if we replace τ_c in the limit of integration by the coarse-graining time interval τ. Our notation for the four time intervals discussed here is the same as that of Mori,[8] who also discusses the relationships expressed in Eq. (6.3).

By a quantum-mechanical correlation function method which is similar to the classical procedure used here, Mori[8] has derived the linear relations for diffusion and heat transport and has obtained explicit expressions for the phenomenological coefficients in these linear relations. When we transform Mori's equations for diffusion and heat flow to our choice of diffusion fluxes $\mathbf{j}_\alpha$ and heat flux $\mathbf{q}$ and then take the classical limit of these equations, his expressions for the phenomenological coefficients are the same as our expressions for these coefficients obtained with the use of Eq. (6.2) instead of Eq. (1.25).

The method presented here differs from that of Mori in several respects. The averages in our classical treatment are formed with the canonical ensemble, whereas in Mori's quantum-mechanical theory, they are computed with the grand canonical ensemble. Moreover, we provide a physical basis for what Mori calls the coarse graining of the distribution function at the origin of time, i.e., for the boundary condition on $\bar{f}_1^{(N)}$.

In Mori's treatment, the temporal coarse graining of the distribution function is taken over an interval of time τ starting with the origin of time ($t = 0$). Thus, during at least part of the interval τ, the system has not yet attained local equilibrium. Consequently, Mori is forced to extend the interval τ so that $\tau \gg \tau_0$ in order to obtain results which are independent of τ. This procedure may lead to difficulties as, for example, in the case of a dense rigid sphere fluid.[17] For such a fluid in which only binary collisions are considered, the time interval τ must be taken as infinitesimally small, so that successive binary collisions are not included. During this short interval, the system would not yet have attained local equilibrium. Therefore, we prefer to wait until after the time interval τ_0 before carrying out the time smoothing of $f^{(N)}$.

---

[17] S. A. Rice, J. G. Kirkwood, J. Ross, and R. W. Zwanzig, *J. Chem. Phys.* **31**, 575 (1959).

In an approach which differs from both Mori's method and the treatment presented here, Green[9] has also derived the linear relations for diffusion and heat flow and has obtained expressions for the phenomenological coefficients which appear therein. In Green's classical treatment, averages are taken in the microcanonical ensemble with fixed momentum and energy. Although Mori has claimed that Green's expression for the thermal conductivity $\mathbf{\Omega}_{00}$ is not in accord with his theory, Green[18] has recently shown that his expression for $\mathbf{\Omega}_{00}$ differs from that of Mori only by quantities which are completely negligible for large systems. We may conclude, therefore, that our results are also in agreement with those of Green.

ACKNOWLEDGMENTS

One of us (D.D.F.) would like to thank Dr. Frank Stillinger for many stimulating and helpful discussions during the course of this work and for a critical reading of the manuscript. He would also like to thank Dr. Eugene Helfand for several suggestions for improving the presentation of this work.

---

[18] M. S. Green, *Phys. Rev.* **119**, 829 (1960).

The Statistical Mechanical Theory of Irreversible Processes in Solutions of Flexible Macromolecules.

VISCO-ELASTIC BEHAVIOR

JOHN G. KIRKWOOD, *Gates and Crellin Laboratories of Chemistry, California Institute of Technology, Pasadena, California*

(Received April 25, 1949)

I. INTRODUCTION

It is our aim in the present article to outline a general theory of irreversible processes in solutions of flexible macromolecules and to make an application of the theory to a study of the visco-elastic properties of such solutions. The theory is based on an analysis of Brownian motion in the space of the internal coordinates of a macromolecule, as was the theory of dielectric loss of polar polymers developed by Fuoss and Kirkwood.[1] However, hydrodynamic interaction of the chain elements is here taken into account in determining the components of the diffusion tensor and the methods of Riemannian geometry, employed by Kramers[2] in his treatment of viscosity, are employed to advantage in the formulation.

The treatment of visco-elastic behavior extends the theory of intrinsic viscosity developed by Kirkwood and Riseman[3] in a significant manner. It is found that the influence of Brownian motion has not been adequately taken into account in previous theories of the intrinsic viscosity of macromolecules, both rigid and flexible. When the hydrodynamic torques are equated not to zero, but to the rotatory diffusional torques, it is found that the statistical orientation of the macromolecule in the velocity field of the solvent, which is responsible for flow birefringence, contributes a linear as well as non-linear terms in the rate of shear to the stress, and thus to the Newtonian part of the intrinsic viscosity. This term, which has previously been neglected exhibits relaxation phase lags in the non-stationary case and imparts to the solution a rigidity modulus of the kind observed by Mason, Baker, and collaborators.[4]

II. GENERAL THEORY

We shall be concerned with the statistics of a linear polymer molecule $(CHX)_{2n+1}$ immersed in a solvent of low molecular weight. We shall ignore internal degrees of the side groups X and impose the restraints of fixed bond angle γ and fixed bond distance b_0 in the chain. The skeletal elements CHX are numbered from $-n$ to $+n$ and are connected by $2n$ bond vectors $\mathbf{b}_l$ of length $\mathbf{b}_0$ directed from bond $l-1$ to bond l, for $l \geqq 1$ and from bond l to

---

[1] R. M. Fuoss and J. G. Kirkwood, *J. Chem. Phys.* **9**, 329 (1941).
[2] H. A. Kramers, *J. Chem. Phys.* **14**, 415 (1946).
[3] J. G. Kirkwood and J. Riseman, *J. Chem. Phys.* **16**, 565 (1948).
[4] Mason, Baker, McSkemin and Heiss, *Phys. Rev.* **73**, 1074 (1948).

$l + 1$ for $l \leqq -1$. We shall denote by chain space, that subspace of $2n + 4$ dimensions of the $6n + 3$ dimensional configuration space of the $2n + 1$ chain elements onto which it is projected by the restraints of constant bond angle and constant bond distance. The generalized coordinates q^α of chain space are chosen as follows:

q^α is the angle between bond planes $(\mathbf{b}_{\alpha-1} \times \mathbf{b}_\alpha)$ and $(\mathbf{b}_{\alpha+1} \times \mathbf{b}_\alpha)$; $-n+1 \leqslant \alpha < -1$ and $1 < \alpha \leqslant n$.

q^{-1} is the angle between $(\mathbf{b}_2 \times \mathbf{b}_1)$ and $(\mathbf{e}_z \times \mathbf{b}_1)$.

q^0 is the angle between $(\mathbf{b}_{-1} \times \mathbf{b}_1)$ and $(\mathbf{e}_z \times \mathbf{b}_1)$.

q^{-1} is the angle between $(\mathbf{b}_{-2} \times \mathbf{b}_{-1})$ and $(\mathbf{b}_1 \times \mathbf{b}_{-1})$.

q^{-n} and q^n are respectively the polar and azimuthal angles ϑ and φ of bond $\mathbf{b}_n$ relative to an external system of coordinates $\mathbf{e}_x$, $\mathbf{e}_y$, $\mathbf{e}_z$.

q^{n+1}, q^{n+2}, q^{n+3} are the rectangular coordinates x_0, y_0, z_0 of the chain center of mass.

We denote by $\mathbf{R}$ the position of element l in the common 3-space of all elements spanned by the unit vectors $\mathbf{e}_x$, $\mathbf{e}_y$, $\mathbf{e}_z$ and by $\mathbf{R}^l$ the position of that element in its 3-dimensional subspace of the $6n + 3$-dimensional configuration space of the system of $2n + 1$ elements. The position of l as a subscript or superscript has no significance from the standpoint of tensor calculus in this connection. The configuration of the chain is specified by the $6n + 3$ dimensional vector $\mathbf{R}$.

$$\mathbf{R} = \sum_{l=-n}^{+n} \mathbf{R}_l \tag{1}$$

and the chain space is spanned by $2n + 4$ covariant vectors, $\mathbf{a}_\alpha$

$$\mathbf{a}_\alpha = \sum_{=-n}^{+n} \frac{\partial \mathbf{R}}{\partial q^\alpha} \tag{2}$$

where the derivative $\partial \mathbf{R}^l / \partial q^\alpha$ is taken at constant values of all other q^β and subject to the restraints of constant bond angle and constant bond distance. The metric tensor $g_{\alpha\beta}$ of chain space is given by

$$g^{\alpha\beta} = \sum \frac{\partial \mathbf{R}}{\partial q^\alpha} \cdot \frac{\partial \mathbf{R}^l}{\partial q^\beta} = \sum_{l=-n}^{+n} \frac{\partial \mathbf{R}_l}{\partial q^\alpha} \cdot \frac{\partial \mathbf{R}}{\partial q^\beta}$$

$$g = |g^{\alpha\beta}|$$

$$\mathbf{a}^\alpha = \sum_\beta g^{\alpha\beta} \mathbf{a}_\beta$$

$$g^{\alpha\beta} = \frac{|g|_{\alpha\beta}}{|g_{\alpha\beta}|} = \frac{|g|_{\alpha\beta}}{g} \tag{3}$$

where $\mathbf{a}^\alpha$ is the contravariant vector reciprocal to $\mathbf{a}_\alpha$. Methods of calculation of the $g_{\alpha\beta}$ are presented in a later article.

We denote by $f(q,t)$ the probability density in chain space of the ensemble from which a system is sampled in the act of making a macroscopic observation. In the canonical equilibrium ensemble,

$$f^0(q) = e^{\beta[A_0 - V_0(q)]}$$

$$\beta = 1/kT \tag{4}$$

where A_0 is the internal configurational free energy of a molecule and $V_0(q)$ is the potential of the mean internal hindering torques, including for example van der Waals interaction between non-neighboring chain elements which prevent overlapping configurations. The mean value of a function $\varphi(q)$ of the chain coordinates is given by the expression,

$$\bar{\varphi} = \int \ldots \int \sqrt{g}\varphi(q) f(q,t) \prod_\alpha dq^\alpha. \tag{5}$$

The probability density $f(q,t)$ is to be determined by the theory of Brownian motion in the manner which we will now describe. We suppose the macromolecule to be bathed in a fluid continuum of viscosity coefficient η_0. If the velocity $\mathbf{u}$ of chain element l differs from the velocity $\mathbf{v}_l$ the fluid would have if that element were absent from the chain, it is supposed to experience a frictional force, $\mathbf{F}_l$, of magnitude

$$\mathbf{F} = \zeta \mathbf{w}_l$$

$$\mathbf{w}_l = \mathbf{v}_l - \mathbf{u}_l \tag{6}$$

where ζ is the Brownian motion friction constant, common to all chain elements. From the three dimensional vectors $\mathbf{F}_l$, $\mathbf{u}_l$, and $\mathbf{v}_l$, we may construct $6n + 3$ dimensional vectors in the configuration space of chain elements,

$$\mathbf{F} = \sum_{l=-n}^{+n} \mathbf{F}^l$$

$$\mathbf{u} = \sum_{l=-n}^{+n} \mathbf{u}^l$$

$$\mathbf{v} = \sum_{l=-n}^{+n} \mathbf{v}^l \tag{7}$$

where $\mathbf{u}$ has no components outside of chain space, while $\mathbf{F}$ and $\mathbf{v}$ may have components outside. Thus

$$\mathbf{u} = \sum_\alpha \mathbf{a}_\alpha \dot{q}^\alpha. \tag{8}$$

If the fluid is in a state of motion with velocity field $\mathbf{v}^0(\mathbf{R})$ before introduction of the entire macromolecule, we may define a configuration vector,

$$\mathbf{v}^0 = \sum_{l=-n}^{+n} \mathbf{v}^{0l}$$

$$\mathbf{v}_l^0 = \mathbf{v}^0(\mathbf{R}_l) \tag{9}$$

which will in general differ from $\mathbf{v}$ due to the hydrodynamic perturbations produced by the other chain elements of the molecule at the point of location of any given element l. These perturbations are determined in the quasi-stationary case by the Oseen formula

$$\mathbf{v}_l = \mathbf{v}_l^0 - \sum_{\substack{s=-n \\ \neq l}}^{+n} \mathbf{T}_{ls} \cdot \mathbf{F}_s$$

$$\mathbf{T}_{ls} = \frac{1}{8\pi\eta_0 R_{ls}} \left[\mathbf{1} + \frac{\mathbf{R}_{ls}\mathbf{R}_{ls}}{R_{ls}^2} \right]. \tag{10}$$

Equation (10) may be generalized to configuration space in the form

$$\mathbf{v} = \mathbf{v}_0 - \mathbf{T} \cdot \mathbf{F}$$

$$\mathbf{T} = \sum_{\substack{l,s \\ =-n}}^{+n} \mathbf{T}^{ls} \tag{11}$$

$$\mathbf{T}^{ls} = \frac{1}{8\pi\eta_0 R_{ls}} \left[\mathbf{1}^{ls} + \frac{\mathbf{R}_{ls}^l \mathbf{R}_{ls}^s}{R_{ls}^2} \right]$$

$$\mathbf{R}^l \cdot \mathbf{1}^{ls} \cdot \mathbf{R}^s = \mathbf{R}_l \cdot \mathbf{R}_s$$

where $\mathbf{R}^{ls}$ means a vector in l-space with direction and magnitude equal to those of $\mathbf{R}_{ls}$ in the common 3-space of all chain elements. If we define a friction tensor $\zeta_{\alpha\beta}$ chain space by the relations,

$$F_\alpha = \sum \zeta_{\alpha\beta}(\nu^{0\beta} - \dot{q}^\beta) \tag{12}$$

we obtain from Eqs. (6), (7), (8), and (11) the system of equations,

$$\zeta_{\alpha\beta} = \zeta g_{\alpha\beta} - \zeta \sum_\nu T_\alpha^\nu \zeta_{\nu\beta}. \tag{13}$$

From Eq. (13), we obtain by the methods of tensor calculus,

$$(\zeta^{-1})^{\alpha\beta} = \frac{g^{\alpha\beta}}{\zeta} + T^{\alpha\beta}$$

$$D^{\alpha\beta} = kT(\zeta^{-1})^{\alpha\beta} = kT \left\{ \frac{g^{\alpha\beta}}{\zeta} + T^{\alpha\beta} \right\} \tag{14}$$

Eq. (14) thus determines the contravariant components of the generalized diffusion tensor in chain space. The first term $kTg^{\alpha\beta}/\zeta$ is the expression employed by Fuoss and the writer in their theory of dielectric loss. The second term $T^{\alpha\beta}$ takes account of the hydrodynamic interaction of the chain elements neglected in the earlier theory.

We are now prepared to formulate the generalized diffusion equation satisfied by the probability density $f(q,t)$. If inertial terms are neglected, the theory of Brownian motion gives the relations,

$$\left[F_\alpha + X_\alpha - \frac{\partial V_0}{\partial q^\alpha} \right] f - kT \frac{\partial f}{\partial q^\alpha} = 0 \tag{15}$$

$$F^\alpha f = \sum \zeta_{\alpha\beta}[\nu^{0\beta} f - j^\beta]$$

$$j^\beta = f\dot{q}^\beta$$

where X_α is a covariant component of the external force and j^β is a contravariant component of the probability current density in chain space. The current density satisfies the continuity equation,

$$\frac{1}{\sqrt{g}} \sum_\beta \frac{\partial(\sqrt{g} j^\beta)}{\partial q^\beta} + \frac{\partial f}{\partial t} = 0. \tag{16}$$

Elimination of j^β between Eqs. (15) and Eq. (16) yields the partial differential equation,

$$\sum_{\alpha,\beta} \frac{1}{\sqrt{g}} \frac{\partial \sqrt{g}}{\partial q^\beta} \left\{ D^{\alpha\beta} \frac{\partial f}{\partial q^\alpha} + \frac{D^{\alpha\beta}}{kT} \frac{\partial V_0}{\partial q^\alpha} f \right\} - \frac{\partial f}{\partial t}$$

$$= \sum_{\alpha,\beta} \frac{1}{\sqrt{g}} \frac{\partial \sqrt{g}}{\partial q^\beta} \left\{ \frac{D^{\alpha\beta}}{kT} X_\alpha f + g^{\alpha\beta} v_\alpha^0 f \right\} \tag{17}$$

with the boundary conditions that f be single-valued in the internal chain space coordinates, specifying the internal and external orientation of the macromolecule, supplemented by appropriate boundary conditions in the center of mass space determined by the experimental arrangements imposed by the observer. Except in the cases of translational diffusion and sedimentation, the center of gravity coordinates are in general redundant, since f can be considered to be independent of them.

The right hand side of Eq. (17) will in general be of order κ, where κ is a parameter, say the amplitude of an external electric field or the rate of strain in the unperturbed velocity field in the solvent. When κ vanishes, the distribution function f has its equilibrium form or decays to this form with the vanishing of transients. The linearization of Eq. (17) with respect to κ gives

$$L(e^{\beta V_0/2} f) - \frac{\partial (e^{\beta V_0/2} f)}{\partial t} = \kappa e^{\beta A_0} Q$$

$$L = \sum_{\alpha,\beta} \frac{1}{\sqrt{g}} \frac{\partial \sqrt{g}}{\partial q_\alpha} \left(D^{\alpha\beta} \frac{\partial}{\partial q^\beta} \right) + W$$

$$W = \frac{1}{2kT} \sum_{\alpha,\beta} \frac{1}{\sqrt{g}} \frac{\partial \sqrt{g}}{\partial q^\alpha} \left(D^{\alpha\beta} \frac{\partial V_0}{\partial q^\beta} \right) - \frac{1}{(2kT)^2} \sum_{\alpha,\beta} D^{\alpha\beta} \frac{\partial V_0}{\partial q^\alpha} \frac{\partial V_0}{\partial q^\beta} \tag{18}$$

$$\kappa Q = \frac{e^{\beta V_0/2}}{\sqrt{g}} \sum_{\alpha,\beta} \frac{\partial \sqrt{g}}{\partial q^\beta} \left\{ \left[\frac{D^{\alpha\beta}}{kT} X_\alpha + g^{\alpha\beta} v_\alpha^0 \right] e^{-\beta V_0} \right\}.$$

Expansion of the probability density f in powers of κ in the form,

$$f(q,t) = e^{\beta[A_0 - V_0/2]} \left\{ e^{-\beta V_0/2} + \kappa \int_{-\infty}^{+\infty} f_1(q, \omega) e^{i\omega t} d\omega \right\}$$

$$K(\omega, q) = \int_{-\infty}^{+\infty} Q(q,t) e^{-i\omega t} dt \tag{19}$$

leads to the equations,

$$Lf_1 - i\omega f_1 = K \tag{20}$$

the solution of which may be expanded in the eigen functions ψ_λ of the self-adjoint operator L

$$L\psi_\lambda + \lambda\psi_\lambda = 0$$

$$f_1 = -\sum_\lambda \frac{K_\lambda \psi_\lambda(q)}{\lambda + i\omega} \tag{21}$$

$$K_\lambda = \int \cdots \int \sqrt{g}\psi_\lambda{}^* K \prod_\alpha dq^\alpha$$

where K^λ is the expansion coefficient of K in the orthonormal set ψ.

Mean values of functions $\varphi(q)$ not explicitly dependent on time, given by Eq. (5), may be expressed with the aid of Eqs. (19) and (21) in the form,

$$\bar{\varphi} = \bar{\varphi}^0 + \kappa \int_{-\infty}^{+\infty} \Phi_1(\omega) e^{i\omega t} d\omega + O(\kappa^2)$$

$$\bar{\varphi}^0 = \int \cdots \int \sqrt{g}\, e^{\beta(A_0 - V_0)} \varphi(q) \prod_\alpha dq^\alpha$$

$$\Phi_1(\omega) = -\sum_\lambda \frac{K_\lambda \varphi_\lambda{}^*}{\lambda + i\omega}$$

$$\varphi_\lambda = \int \cdots \int \sqrt{g}\, e^{\beta(A_0 - V_0/2)} \varphi(q) \psi_\lambda(q) \prod_\alpha dq^\alpha . \tag{22}$$

The relaxation time spectrum of the polymer chain is composed of the reciprocals $1/\lambda$ of the eigen values of the operator $-L$ of Eq. (21). Thus an alternative manner of writing $\Phi_1(\omega)$ is the following,

$$\Phi_1(\omega) = -\sum_\tau \frac{\tau \varphi_\lambda{}^* K_\lambda}{1 + i\omega\tau}$$

$$\lambda = {}^1/_\tau \tag{23}$$

where the sum extends over all relaxation times of the spectrum. When the spectrum is closely spaced relative to $1/\omega$, the sum may be approximated by an integral over $0 \leqslant \tau \leqslant \infty$, with a weighting function determined by $\varphi_\lambda{}^* K_\lambda$.

The formal theory which has been presented relates the average values of functions of the configuration coordinates q in chain space to the relaxation time spectrum and the eigen-functions of the diffusion operator L, to terms linear in the perturbation parameter κ, in a manner which allows a general description of irreversible process in solutions of macromolecules, for example dielectric loss, viscous flow, streaming birefringence. Extension of the theory to include non-linear terms in κ is easily accomplished and is necessary in the analysis of non-Newtonian flow and in the determination of the extinction angle in flow birefringence.

III. APPLICATION TO VISCO-ELASTIC BEHAVIOR

We will undertake here only the application of the general theory presented in Section II to the linear visco-elastic behavior of high polymer solutions. In addition to yielding an exact formulation of the intrinsic viscosity, the theory provides an explanation for the rigidity modulus, observed by Baker and Mason, in the propagation of high frequency shear waves through high polymer solutions. This latter effect arises from terms which, to the writer's knowledge, have been consistently neglected in previous theories of intrinsic viscosity. It has been the custom to equate the hydrodynamic torques acting on a macromolecule to zero. Actually, with the neglect of inertial terms, these torques should be balanced by the rotatory diffusion torques, determined by the components of the gradient of the probability density $f(q)$. Thus departures of $f(q)$ from equilibrium in the velocity field of the solvent contribute not only non-Newtonian terms (used here in the sense of non-linear terms) to the stress, but also a linear term and therefore to the intrinsic viscosity. Since this term exhibits relaxation, its contribution to the viscosity is complex and the solution exhibits rigidity, vanishing for shears of zero frequency and approaching an asymptotic value at high frequency.

With the neglect of inertial terms in the Navier-Stokes equation, we may still employ Eq. (13) of Kirkwood and Riseman,[3]

$$
\begin{aligned}
[\eta] &= N\zeta G/100M\eta_0 \\
G &= \frac{1}{\zeta\dot{\epsilon}} \sum_{l=-n}^{+n} \langle (\mathbf{F}_l \cdot \mathbf{e}_x)(\mathbf{R}_{0l} \cdot \mathbf{e}_y) \rangle_{\mathrm{Av}} \\
\mathbf{v}_l^0 &= \dot{\epsilon}(\mathbf{R}_{0l} \cdot \mathbf{e}_y)\mathbf{e}_x \\
\dot{\epsilon} &= \dot{\epsilon}^0 e^{i\omega t}
\end{aligned}
\tag{24}
$$

for a simple shear in the direction $\mathbf{e}_x$, propagated in the direction $\mathbf{e}_y$, where M is the molecular weight of the polymer and the other symbols have their usual significance; Eq. (24) is based on the Oseen[5] formula for the perturbations in the velocity field produced by the point forces $-\mathbf{F}_l$ of hydrodynamic resistance which the chain elements exert on the fluid.

If the function G is complex, $[\eta]$ is also complex, and

$$
\begin{aligned}
[\eta] &= [\eta'] - i[\eta''] \\
G &= G' - iG'' \\
[\eta'] &= N\zeta G'/100M\eta_0 \\
[\eta''] &= N\zeta G''/100M\eta_0.
\end{aligned}
\tag{25}
$$

[5] See J. M. Burgers, Chap. III, Second Report on Viscosity and Plasticity, Amsterdam Academy of Sciences, Nordemann, 1938.

The intrinsic rigidity $[\mu]$ is phenomenologically related to $[\eta'']$ in the following manner

$$[\mu] = \lim_{c \to 0} \mu/c$$

$$[\mu] = \omega\eta_0[\eta''] = N\zeta\omega G''/100M. \tag{26}$$

We now proceed to the determination of G' and G''. Eq. (7) of Kirkwood and Riseman,

$$\mathbf{F}_l = -\zeta(\mathbf{v}_l^0 - \mathbf{u}_l) - \zeta \sum_{s=-n}^{+n} \mathbf{T}_{ls} \cdot \mathbf{F}_s \tag{27}$$

may still be used to determine the hydrodynamic forces $\mathbf{F}$, but a more exact determination of the velocities $\mathbf{u}_l$ of the chain elements is required for our present task. Returning to Eq. (15), we set the external torques X_α equal to zero, and for simplicity also the internal torques $-\partial V_0/\partial q^\alpha$, arising from interactions between the chain elements. The latter can be formally included without difficulty, if desired. We then obtain

$$\nu^{0\alpha} - u^\alpha = \sum_\beta D^{\alpha\beta} \frac{\partial \log f}{\partial q^\beta} \tag{28}$$

$$\mathbf{v}^0 - \mathbf{u} = \mathbf{v}^0 - \sum_\alpha \mathbf{a}_\alpha \left[\nu^{0\alpha} - \sum D^{\alpha\beta} \frac{\partial \log f}{\partial q^\beta}\right],$$

since $\mathbf{u}$ has no components outside of chain space. In previous theories of the intrinsic viscosity of macromolecules, it has been the practice to set the right hand side of the first of Eq. (28) equal to zero. Use of Eq. (28) after projection on the sub-spaces of the chain elements l in Eq. (27) yields,

$$\mathbf{F}_l + \zeta \sum_{\substack{s=-n \\ \neq l}}^{+n} \mathbf{T}_{ls} \cdot \mathbf{F}_s =$$

$$= -\zeta\dot{\epsilon}\left\{\mathbf{e}_x(\mathbf{R}_{0l} \cdot \mathbf{e}_y) - \sum_{s=-n}^{+n} \sum_{\alpha,\beta} g^{\alpha\beta} \frac{\partial \mathbf{R}_{0l}}{\partial q^\alpha} (\mathbf{e}_y \cdot \mathbf{R}_{0s}) \left(\mathbf{e}_x \cdot \frac{\partial \mathbf{R}_{0s}}{\partial q^\beta}\right)\right\}$$

$$-\zeta \sum_{\alpha,\beta} D^{\alpha\beta} \frac{\partial \log f}{\partial q^\beta} \frac{\partial \mathbf{R}_{0l}}{\partial q^\alpha}. \tag{29}$$

A series of routine mathematical transformations paralleling those of Kirkwood and Riseman lead, with the aid of solutions, Eq. (21), for the perturbation in the distribution function, to the following results

$$[\eta'] = [\eta']_\infty + \frac{N\zeta M}{3600 M_0^2 \eta_0} \sum_\tau \frac{\tau H_1(\tau)}{1 + \omega^2\tau^2}$$

$$[\eta']_\infty = \frac{N\zeta M}{3600 M_0^2 \eta_0} H_0 \tag{30}$$

$$[\mu] = \frac{N\zeta M}{3600 M_0^2} \sum_\tau \frac{\omega^2\tau^2 H_1(\tau)}{1 + \omega^2\tau^2}$$

where the quantities H_0 and $H_1(\tau)$ are to be determined as follows,

$$H_0 = \frac{1}{n} \sum_{l=-n}^{+n} \bar{\varphi}_{ll}^0$$

$$\varphi_{ll} = \mathbf{Tr}(\varphi_{ll})$$

$$\varphi_{l'l} = \mathbf{h}_{l'l} - \frac{\sigma}{n^{\frac{1}{2}}} \sum_{\substack{s=-n \\ \neq l}}^{+n} \mathbf{T}_{ls}^* : \varphi_{l's}$$

$$\sigma = \left(\frac{M}{M_0}\right)^{\frac{1}{2}} \zeta/(12\pi^3)^{\frac{1}{2}}\eta_0 \tag{31}$$

$$\mathbf{T}_{ls}^* = \left(\frac{\pi}{6}\right)^{\frac{1}{2}} \mathbf{T}_{ls}$$

$$\mathbf{h}_{l'l} = 3(\mathbf{R}_{0l'}\ \mathbf{R}_{0l})/n$$

$$-\frac{9}{n} \sum_{s=-n}^{+n} \sum_{\alpha,\beta} g^{\alpha\beta} \left(\mathbf{e}_{y'} \frac{\mathbf{R}_{0l}}{\partial q^{\beta}}\right) \left(\mathbf{e}_x \cdot \frac{\partial \mathbf{R}_{0s}}{\partial q_{\beta}}\right) (\mathbf{e}_y \cdot \mathbf{R}_{0s}) \mathbf{e}_x R_{0l}$$

where $\bar{\varphi}_{ll}^0$ is the unperturbed mean value, calculated with the equilibrium distribution function in chain space. If the mean value of $\mathbf{T}_{ls}^{*0} : \varphi_{l's}^0$ is approximated by $\bar{\mathbf{T}}_{ls}^{*0} : \bar{\varphi}_{l's}^0$, and the sums are replaced by integrals, $[\eta']_\infty$ may be determined from the integral equations of Kirkwood and Riseman, with the improvement that the inhomogeneous part $\mathbf{h}_{l'l}$ is more accurately determined than in their theory.

The relaxation function $H_1(\tau)$ is determined by the following relations,

$$H_1(\tau) = K_\lambda^{(1)*} K_\lambda^{(2)}$$

$$K_\lambda^{(1)} = \frac{1}{n} \sum_{l=-n}^{+n} \mathbf{Tr}(\mathbf{R}_{ll}^{(1)})_\lambda$$

$$K^{(2)} = \frac{1}{n} \sum_{l=-n}^{+n} (K_{ll}^{(2)})_\lambda$$

$$K_{ll}^{(2)} = 3 \sum_{\alpha,\beta} \frac{1}{\sqrt{g}} \frac{d\sqrt{g}}{\partial q^\alpha} \left\{ g^{\alpha\beta} (\mathbf{e}_y \cdot \mathbf{R}_{0l}) \left(\mathbf{e}_x \cdot \frac{\partial \mathbf{R}_{0l}}{\partial q_\beta}\right) \right\} \tag{32}$$

$$K_{l'l}^{(1)} = 3 \sum_{\alpha,\beta} \frac{1}{\sqrt{g}} \frac{\partial \sqrt{g}}{\partial q^\alpha} \left\{ D^{\alpha\beta} (\mathbf{e}_x \mathbf{R}_{0l'}) \left(\mathbf{e}_y \cdot \frac{\partial \mathbf{R}_{0l}}{\partial q^\beta}\right) \right\}$$

$$- \frac{\sigma}{n^{\frac{1}{2}}} \sum_{\substack{-n \\ \neq l}}^{+n} \mathbf{T}_{ls}^* : K_{l's}^{(1)}$$

where $(\mathbf{K})_{l'l}^{(1)}{}_\lambda$ and $(K_{ll}^{(2)})_\lambda$ are expansion coefficients of these functions in the orthonormal set of eigen functions ψ of the diffusion operator L, to be calculated by the last of Eqs. (22). The coefficients $(K_{l'l}^{(1)})_\lambda$ may be calculated by integral equations of the Kirkwood-Riseman type, if $(\mathbf{T}^*_{l's}):(\mathbf{K}^{(2)}_{l's})_\lambda$ is approximated by

$$(\mathbf{T}^*_{ls})_\lambda : (\mathbf{K}^{(2)}_{l's})_\lambda$$

In order to use our general theory for purposes of calculation, it will doubtless be necessary to employ certain fairly drastic simplifying approximations. We shall not undertake this task here. The conclusions to be drawn from the general theory appear to be of considerable interest. Hydrodynamic perturbation of the statistical density in chain space is found to contribute to the intrinsic viscosity as well as to produce such effects as flow birefringence in solutions of flexible macromolecules. For shearing strains of high frequency, relaxation delays in the response of the distribution function give rise to a rigidity modulus, vanishing at zero frequency. The contribution $[\eta]'_\infty$ to the real part of the intrinsic viscosity is probably significantly smaller than estimated by previous theories, which fail to allow for adjustment of the motion of the chain to the flow in the solvent through internal rotatory degrees of freedom. The present theory, through Eq. (31), at least indicates how such adjustment will manifest itself.

The Statistical Mechanics of Irreversible Processes in Polymer Solutions*

JEROME J. ERPENBECK AND JOHN G. KIRKWOOD, *Sterling Chemistry Laboratory, Yale University, New Haven, Connecticut*

(Received June 23, 1958)

The Kirkwood theory of irreversible processes in polymer solutions has been reformulated so as to include all contributions to the frictional forces exerted on the monomer units. The generalized diffusion equation for the nonequilibrium distribution function derived on this basis contains a new perturbation term, dependent upon the external field of force. The solution of this equation may be expressed by a perturbation expansion analogous to that given previously.

The general theory has been applied to the intrinsic viscosity problem. Although the general theory reverts to the previous one, new techniques have been applied which enable the intrinsic viscosity and rigidity to be expressed in terms of the eigenfunctions and eigenvalues of the Oseen interaction tensor and the generalized diffusion operator. Moreover, a second formulation of the viscosity has been devised in which the result appears in terms of appropriate time correlation functions.

I. INTRODUCTION

A general theory of irreversible processes in dilute polymer solution was previously formulated by one of the authors.[1,2] This theory was based upon a complete analysis of the rotational and translational Brownian motion of a single macromolecule, subject to the hydrodynamic interactions between solute and solvent.

A significant difference between that theory and previous treatments lay in the equating of the hydrodynamic torques acting on each polymer chain element, not to zero, but rather to the so-called rotatory diffusional torques, which are the forces due to the Brownian motion of the solute. The necessity of this procedure, which leads to an exact evaluation of the velocity of the chain elements, was first pointed out by Kuhn.[3]

In applying the theory of Brownian motion, the hydrodynamic interactions as given by the Oseen formula[4] were introduced in the computation of the diffusion tensor which is proportional to the inverse of the frictional tensor. The components of the frictional tensor, however, were taken as zero outside of chain space, the configuration space of internal rotational coordinates

* This work was supported by the Office of Naval Research.

[1] J. G. Kirkwood, *Rec. trav. chim.* **68**, 649 (1949).

[2] J. G. Kirkwood, *J. Polymer Sci.* **12**, 1 (1954).

[3] W. Kuhn and H. Kuhn, *Helv. Chim. Acta* **37**, 97 (1944).

[4] J. M. Burgers, *Second Report on Viscosity and Plasticity* (Amsterdam Academy of Sciences, Nordemann, 1938), Chap. III.

along which the polymer is constrained to move by the restrictions of constant bond length and bond angle. Thus, the contributions to the frictional force from the motion of the solvent along coordinates not in chain space were neglected. The present paper presents a reformulation of the theory with the inclusion of a complete frictional tensor. It will be shown that a new perturbation to the equilibrium distribution function arises, and this new term depends upon the external field acting upon the solution.

The general theory was applied to the viscoelastic behavior of polymer solutions in the earlier paper and the corrected general theory presented here does not affect the validity of these results since there is no external force field to be taken into account. Now, however, a new treatment of this problem is given which permits the expression of the intrinsic viscosity and rigidity in terms of the eigenvalues and eigenfunctions of the generalized diffusion operator and the Oseen interaction tensor. Although the formal solution involves a sum of expansion coefficients in the eigenfunctions of the diffusion operator, the problem of determining this sum may be completely avoided by a conversion to a time integration of time correlation functions. This formulation of the problem would seem, then, to lend itself more readily to a specific calculation of the viscoelasticity of coiling-type polymers.

II. GENERAL THEORY

The system consists of an unbranched chain of $2n + 1$ monomer units immersed in a low molecular weight solvent of viscosity coefficient η_0. Each monomer unit (chain element) is characterized by a molecular weight M_0 and a friction constant ζ, with respect to the solvent. The configuration space of the molecule (of $6n + 3$ dimensions) is projected onto chain space by the constraints of constant bond length and bond angle. Chain space is a $2n + 4$ dimensional space and the coordinates associated with it are denoted q^1, $q^2, \cdots, q^{2n+4}$. These include the $2n - 1$ angles of internal rotation, the 3 coordinates of the center of mass relative to an external coordinate system and the 2 orientation angles of the molecule in the external system. We denote the $4n - 1$ coordinates of configuration space complementary to chain space by $q^{2n+5}, q^{2n+6}, \cdots, q^{6n+3}$. These could be chosen in a large number of ways, e.g., the bond length and bond angle coordinates.

The geometry of configuration space is described by the covariant components of the metric tensor

$$g_{\alpha\beta} = \sum_{l} (\partial \mathbf{R}^l / \partial q^\alpha) \cdot (\partial \mathbf{R}^l / \partial q^\beta), \tag{1}$$

where $\mathbf{R}^l$ is the position vector of element l in the 3-dimensional space of element l. The components of $g_{\alpha\beta}$ within chain space are identical with those of the earlier theory. The components involving complementary space depend upon the choice of $q^{2n+5}, \cdots, q^{6n+3}$. We shall assume that these have been chosen orthogonal to chain space coordinates, so that the components of the metric tensor are zero between chain space and its complementary space.

The contravariant components of the metric tensor are given in the usual way:

$$g^{\alpha\beta} = |g|_{\alpha\beta}/g \tag{2}$$

where $|g|_{\alpha\beta}$ is the cofactor of $g_{\alpha\beta}$ in the determinant $|g_{\alpha\beta}| = g$. Since g consist of two blocks, one for chain space and one for orthogonal complementary space, we may write for g,

$$g = g_{(1)}g_{(2)},$$

where

$$g_{(1)} = |g_{\alpha\beta}|(\alpha, \beta \leq 2n + 4)$$

and

$$g_{(2)} = |g_{\alpha\beta}|(\alpha, \beta \geq 2n + 5).$$

Thus, the components of $g^{\alpha\beta}$ within chain space are identical with those used in the earlier paper. Likewise $g^{\alpha\beta}$ disappear between chain space and complementary space.

Configuration space is spanned by the covariant basis vectors

$$\mathbf{a}_\alpha = \sum_l (\partial \mathbf{R}^l/\partial q^\alpha). \tag{3}$$

The covariant components of any $6n + 3$ dimensional vector or tensor will be given by

$$F_\alpha = \mathbf{F} \cdot \mathbf{a}_\alpha,$$

$$T_{\alpha\beta} = \mathbf{a}_\alpha \cdot \mathbf{T} \cdot \mathbf{a}_\beta.$$

The contravariant or mixed components will involve contravariant components of the basis vectors. We shall generally be interested in components in chain space, e.g.,

$$F^\alpha = \sum_{\nu=1}^{2n+4} g^{\alpha\nu}\mathbf{a}_\nu \cdot \mathbf{F},$$

$$(\alpha, \beta \leq 2n + 4)$$

$$T^{\alpha\beta} = \sum_{\frac{1}{2},\, \nu=1}^{2n+4} g^{\alpha\mu}g^{\beta\nu}\mathbf{a}_\mu \cdot \mathbf{T} \cdot \mathbf{a}_\nu.$$

This prescription is identical with that given by Kirkwood[1,2] in considering chain space only, since the sums need only extend over chain space, the other terms being zero.

The following conventions will be followed in the notation: Greek subscripts and superscripts will be used for components along the basis vectors $\mathbf{a}_\alpha$ and $\mathbf{a}^\alpha$. Latin superscripts will be used for the projections of $6n + 3$ dimensional vectors and tensors onto the 3-dimensional Cartesian coordinate system of the indicated chain element. Latin subscripts will be used for these same projections when referred to the Cartesian system common to all chain elements.

The previous notation is retained: $\mathbf{v}_l^0$ is the velocity of fluid at the point $\mathbf{R}_l$ previous to the introduction of the polymer; $\mathbf{u}_l$ is the velocity of monomer unit l at $\mathbf{R}_l$; $\mathbf{v}_l$ is the perturbed velocity in the fluid at the point $\mathbf{R}_l$, due to the presence in solution of the $2n$ monomer units other than the lth. The frictional force acting upon monomer unit l is given by

$$\mathbf{F}_l = \zeta(\mathbf{v}_l - \mathbf{u}_l). \tag{4}$$

The 3-dimensional vectors may be generalized to $6n + 3$ dimensional configuration space vectors thus:

$$\mathbf{F} = \sum_l \mathbf{F}^l$$
$$\mathbf{v}^0 = \sum_l \mathbf{v}^{0l}$$
$$\mathbf{u} = \sum_l \mathbf{u}^l$$
$$\mathbf{v} = \sum_l \mathbf{v}^l. \tag{5}$$

In general, these vectors have components in chain space and complementary space. $\mathbf{u}$, however, has only chain space components because of the bond length and bond angle restraints.

The velocity perturbation vector is given by the generalized Oseen expression,

$$\mathbf{v} = \mathbf{v}^0 - \mathbf{T} \cdot \mathbf{F},$$
$$\mathbf{T} = \sum_{l,s} \mathbf{T}^{ls} = \sum_{l,s} (1/8\pi\eta_0 |R_{ls}|)[\mathbf{1}^{ls} + (\mathbf{R}_{ls}{}^l \mathbf{R}_{ls}{}^s / R_{ls}{}^2)], \tag{6}$$

where R_{ls} is the separation of elements l and s and $\mathbf{1}^{ls}$ is the unit tensor in the 3 space common to elements l and s.

The foregoing expressions represent no departure from the previous presentation. The frictional tensor, with components $\zeta_{\alpha\beta}$ is, however, defined in configuration space by the relation,

$$F_\alpha = \sum_{\beta=1}^{6n+3} \zeta_{\alpha\beta}(v^{0\beta} - u^\beta), \tag{7}$$

and the sum extends not only over chain space but also complementary space. The components of the frictional tensor do not disappear between chain space and complementary space, as we shall see presently, and therefore the velocity differences, $(v^{0\beta} - u^\beta)$ in complementary space (where $u^\beta = 0$) contribute to the components of the frictional force in chain space.

Solving Eq. (4) for the component F_α, using the Oseen expression (6) for the velocity perturbation and equating the result to Eq. (7), one finds

$$\zeta_{\alpha\beta} = \zeta g_{\alpha\beta} - \zeta \sum_{\nu=1}^{6n+3} T_\alpha{}^\nu \zeta_{\nu\beta}. \tag{8}$$

Although identical in form with the result of Kirkwood, the latter contained a sum only over chain space. However, Eq. (8) yields for the inverse frictional tensor,

$$(\zeta^{-1})^{\alpha\beta} = (g^{\alpha\beta}/\zeta) + T^{\alpha\beta} = (D^{\alpha\beta}/kT); \tag{9}$$

$D^{\alpha\beta}$ are the contravariant components of the diffusion tensor. The components $T^{\alpha\beta}$ are to be found from the relation

$$T^{\alpha\beta} = \sum_{\mu,\,\nu=1}^{2n+4} g^{\alpha\mu} g^{\beta\nu} T_{\mu\nu}. \tag{10}$$

Equations (9) and (10) are identical with the earlier results.

The generalized equation for Brownian motion is

$$[F_\alpha + X_\alpha - (\partial V_0/\partial q^\alpha)]f(\mathbf{q}, t) - kT(\partial f(\mathbf{q}, t)/\partial q^\alpha) = 0, \tag{11}$$

where $f(\mathbf{q}, t)$ is the probability density in chain space, X_α is a covariant component of the external force, and V_0 is the internal potential energy. $\mathbf{q}$ is used to denote the entire set of chain space coordinates, $q^1, q^2, \cdots, q^{2n+4}$. The probability current density j^β enters from the term

$$F_\alpha f = \sum_{\beta=1}^{6n+3} \zeta_{\alpha\beta}(v^{0\beta}f - j^\beta),$$

$$j^\beta = u^\beta f, \tag{12}$$

and satisfies the continuity equation,

$$\sum_{\beta=1}^{2n+4} \frac{1}{g^{\frac{1}{2}}} \frac{\partial[g^{\frac{1}{2}} j^\beta]}{\partial q^\beta} + \frac{\partial f}{\partial t} = 0. \tag{13}$$

Upon noting that the probability current density disappears outside of chain space, we eliminate j^β from Eqs. (11), (12), and (13) to obtain

$$\sum_{\alpha,\beta=1}^{2n+4} \frac{1}{g^{\frac{1}{2}}} \frac{\partial g^{\frac{1}{2}}}{\partial q^\beta} \frac{D^{\alpha\beta}}{kT} \left[kT \frac{\partial f}{\partial q^\alpha} + \frac{\partial V_0}{\partial q^\alpha} f \right] - \frac{\partial f}{\partial t}$$

$$= \sum_{\alpha,\beta=1}^{2n+4} \frac{1}{g^{\frac{1}{2}}} \frac{\partial g^{\frac{1}{2}}}{\partial q^\beta} \left[\frac{D^{\alpha\beta}}{kT} X_\alpha f + g^{\alpha\beta} v_\alpha^0 f \right]$$

$$+ \sum_{\beta=1}^{2n+4} \sum_{\alpha=2n+5}^{6n+3} \frac{1}{g^{\frac{1}{2}}} \frac{\partial g^{\frac{1}{2}}}{\partial q^\beta} \left[\frac{D^{\alpha\beta}}{kT} X_\alpha f \right]. \tag{14}$$

The last term on the right of Eq. (14) was not included before and it is seen to contribute to the perturbed distribution function in the presence of an external field. The components of the diffusion tensor between chain space and complementary space to be used in this new term are given by Eq. (9):

$$D^{\alpha\sigma} = kT \sum_{l,s} (\partial \mathbf{R}_l/\partial q^\alpha) \cdot \mathbf{T}_{ls} \cdot (\partial \mathbf{R}_s/\partial q^\sigma)$$

$$\alpha \leq 2n + 4, \ \sigma \geq 2n + 5.$$

If we define

$$L = \sum_{\alpha,\beta=1}^{2n+4} \frac{1}{g^{\frac{1}{2}}} \frac{\partial g^{\frac{1}{2}}}{\partial q^\alpha} \left[D^{\alpha\beta} \frac{\partial}{\partial q^\beta} \right] + W,$$

$$W = \frac{1}{2kT} \sum_{\alpha,\beta=1}^{2n+4} \frac{1}{g^{\frac{1}{2}}} \frac{\partial g^{\frac{1}{2}}}{\partial q^\alpha} \left[D^{\alpha\beta} \frac{\partial V_0}{\partial q^\beta} \right] - \left(\frac{1}{2kT} \right)^2 \sum_{\alpha,\beta=1}^{2n+4} D^{\alpha\beta} \frac{\partial V_0}{\partial q^\alpha} \frac{\partial V_0}{\partial q^\beta},$$

$$Q = -f_0^{-\frac{1}{2}} \sum_{\alpha,\beta=1}^{2n+4} \frac{1}{g^{\frac{1}{2}}} \frac{\partial g^{\frac{1}{2}}}{\partial q^\alpha} \left[\frac{D^{\alpha\beta}}{kT} X_\alpha + g^{\alpha\beta} v_\beta^0 \right] f_0^{\frac{1}{2}} (\ )$$

$$- f_0^{\frac{1}{2}} \sum_{\alpha=1}^{2n+4} \sum_{\beta=2n+5}^{6n+3} \frac{1}{g^{\frac{1}{2}}} \frac{\partial g^{\frac{1}{2}}}{\partial q^\alpha} \left[\frac{D^{\alpha\beta}}{kT} X_\beta f_0^{\frac{1}{2}} (\ ) \right], \tag{15}$$

then Eq. (14) becomes

$$L(f_0^{-\frac{1}{2}}f) - [\partial(f_0^{-\frac{1}{2}}f)/\partial t] = -\,Q(f_0^{-\frac{1}{2}}f), \tag{16}$$

where f_0 is the unperturbed, equilibrium distribution function,

$$f_0(\mathbf{q}) = \exp\,(A_0 - V_0)/kT.$$

The perturbation series solution of Eq. (16) in terms of the orthonormal eigenfunctions of the self-adjoint operator L,

$$L\psi_\lambda(\mathbf{q}) = -\,\lambda\psi_\lambda(\mathbf{q}) \tag{17}$$

is identical to the solution given by Kirkwood, *viz.*

$$f(\mathbf{q}, t) = f_0^{\frac{1}{2}}[f_0^{\frac{1}{2}} + \sum_{s=1}^{\infty} \rho^{(s)}(\mathbf{q}, t)\kappa^s], \tag{18}$$

$$Q = \sum_{s=1}^{\infty} Q^{(s)}\kappa^s,$$

where κ is the perturbation parameter (e.g., the magnitude of the rate of shear) and where

$$\rho^{(s)}(\mathbf{q}, t) = \int_{-\infty}^{+\infty} e^{i\omega t}G^{(s)}(\mathbf{q}, \omega)d\omega,$$

$$G^{(1)}(\mathbf{q}, \omega) = \sum_{\lambda} \frac{B_\lambda{}^{(1)}(\omega)}{\lambda + i\omega}\psi_\lambda(\mathbf{q}),$$

$$B_\lambda{}^{(1)} = \frac{1}{2\pi}\int_{-\infty}^{+\infty} e^{-i\omega t}(f_0^{-\frac{1}{2}}Q^{(1)}f_0^{\frac{1}{2}})_\lambda dt. \tag{19}$$

The subscript λ is used to denote the λth expansion coefficient, *viz.*

$$(h)_\lambda = \int g^{\frac{1}{2}}h(\mathbf{q})f_0^{\frac{1}{2}}(\mathbf{q})\psi_\lambda{}^*(\mathbf{q})d\mathbf{q}$$

where $d\mathbf{q} = dq^1dq^2 \cdots dq^{2n+4}$. Expressions for higher order corrections to the distribution function may also be computed.[2]

In view of Eq. (19), the ensemble average of a function $\chi(\mathbf{q})$ may be written

$$\bar{\chi}(t) = \sum_{s=0}^{\infty} \bar{\chi}^{(s)}(t)\kappa^s,$$

$$\bar{\chi}^{(s)}(t) = \int (g)^{\frac{1}{2}}\chi(\mathbf{q})f_0^{\frac{1}{2}}(\mathbf{q})\rho^{(s)}(\mathbf{q}, t)d\mathbf{q}. \tag{20}$$

III. INTRINSIC VISCOSITY

The viscoelastic properties of polymer solutions are determined by the hydrodynamic forces, $-\mathbf{F}_l$, exerted by the chain elements on the solvent. For time-dependent rates of strain, these forces not only increase the viscosity coefficient but also impart a rigidity to the solution. Kirkwood and Riseman[5] have shown that the complex viscosity is given by

$$[\eta] = N\zeta G/100M\eta_0,$$

$$G = (1/\zeta\dot{\epsilon}) \sum_l \langle(\mathbf{F}_l \cdot \mathbf{e}_x)(\mathbf{R}_{0l} \cdot \mathbf{e}_y)\rangle,$$

$$\mathbf{v}_l{}^0 = \dot{\epsilon}(\mathbf{R}_{0l} \cdot \mathbf{e}_y)\mathbf{e}_x,$$

$$\dot{\epsilon} = \dot{\epsilon}_0 e^{i\omega t} \tag{21}$$

for a simple alternating shear of frequency $\omega/2\pi$ in the $\mathbf{e}_x$ direction, propagated in the direction $\mathbf{e}_y$. N is Avogadro's number, M is the molecular weight of the molecule, and $\mathbf{R}_{0l}$ is the position vector of element l relative to the center of mass of the molecule. The forces $\mathbf{F}_l$ satisfy the set of equations,

$$\mathbf{F}_l + \zeta \sum_{s\neq l} \mathbf{T}_{ls} \cdot \mathbf{F}_s = \zeta(\mathbf{v}_l{}^0 - \mathbf{u}_l). \tag{22}$$

These may be generalized to a single equation in configuration space in the usual way:

$$(\mathbf{1} + \zeta\mathbf{T}) \cdot \mathbf{F} = \zeta(\mathbf{v}^0 - \mathbf{u}). \tag{23}$$

We may expand $\mathbf{F}$ as a linear combination of the eigenvectors of the tensor $\boldsymbol{\tau} = \mathbf{1} + \zeta\mathbf{T}$. The eigenvectors $\boldsymbol{\varphi}_j$(j, of course, has no significance with regard to the space of $\boldsymbol{\varphi}_j$) and eigenvalues σ_j obey the relations

$$\boldsymbol{\tau} \cdot \boldsymbol{\varphi}_j = \sigma_j \boldsymbol{\varphi}_j \qquad (j = 1, 2, \cdots, 6n + 3). \tag{24}$$

We may write, then,

$$\mathbf{F} = \zeta \sum_j \frac{(\mathbf{v}^0 - \mathbf{u}) \cdot \boldsymbol{\varphi}_j}{\sigma_j} \boldsymbol{\varphi}_j. \tag{25}$$

The $\boldsymbol{\varphi}_j$ are $6n + 3$ dimensional vectors and may be expressed as

$$\boldsymbol{\varphi}_j = \sum_k \boldsymbol{\varphi}_j{}^k,$$

where the 3-dimensional vector $\boldsymbol{\varphi}_j{}^k$, is the projection of $\boldsymbol{\varphi}_j$, onto the subspace of element k. Equation (25) may then be written

$$\mathbf{F}_l = \zeta \sum_j \sum_k \frac{(\mathbf{v}_k{}^0 - \mathbf{u}_k) \cdot \boldsymbol{\varphi}_{jk}}{\sigma_j} \boldsymbol{\varphi}_{jl}. \tag{26}$$

The $\boldsymbol{\varphi}_{jk}$ are determined by Eq. (24) to satisfy the set of equations,

$$\boldsymbol{\varphi}_{jk} = [\zeta/(\sigma_j - 1)] \sum_{l\neq k} \mathbf{T}_{kl} \cdot \boldsymbol{\varphi}_{jl}. \tag{27}$$

These eigenvectors depend upon configuration variables and hence an explicit determination will not be possible unless the $\boldsymbol{\varphi}_{jk}$ are replaced by

---

[5] J. G. Kirkwood and J. Riseman, *J. Chem. Phys.* **16**, 565 (1948).

average values. With such an approximation, Eq. (27) may be reduced to a homogeneous integral equation of the Kirkwood-Riseman type. A useful method for the solution of such equations has been developed by Auer and Gardner.[6]

In order to obtain the hydrodynamic forces $\mathbf{F}_l$ through Eq. (26), we require the velocities $\mathbf{u}_l$ of chain element l. These were determined in the previous theory by balancing the components of the diffusional forces of Brownian motion by the hydrodynamic forces in chain space yielding

$$\mathbf{u}_l = \sum_{\alpha=1}^{2n+4} v^{0\alpha}(\partial \mathbf{R}_{0l}/\partial q^\alpha) - \sum_{\alpha,\beta=1}^{2n+4} D^{\alpha\beta}(\partial \log f/\partial q^\beta)(\partial \mathbf{R}_{0l}/\partial q^\alpha), \tag{28}$$

when the external and internal forces are set to zero. Combining Eqs. (26) and (28), we obtain

$$\begin{aligned}(1/\zeta\dot{\epsilon})(\mathbf{F}_l \cdot \mathbf{e}_x)(\mathbf{R}_{0l} \cdot \mathbf{e}_y) &= \sum_j \Bigg\{ \sum_k \frac{\alpha_{jk}\alpha_{jl}}{\sigma_j} (\mathbf{R}_{0l} \cdot \mathbf{e}_y)(\mathbf{R}_{0k} \cdot \mathbf{e}_y) \\ &- \sum_{k,s} \sum_{\alpha,\beta=1}^{2n+4} \frac{\alpha_{jl}}{\sigma_j} g^{\alpha\beta} \left(\frac{\partial \mathbf{R}_{0k}}{\partial q^\alpha} \cdot \boldsymbol{\varphi}_{jk}\right)\left(\frac{\partial \mathbf{R}_{0s}}{\partial q^\beta} \cdot \mathbf{e}_x\right)(\mathbf{R}_{0l} \cdot \mathbf{e}_y)(\mathbf{R}_{0s} \cdot \mathbf{e}_y) \\ &+ (1/\dot{\epsilon}) \sum_k \sum_{\alpha,\beta=1}^{2n+4} \frac{\alpha_{jl}}{\sigma_j} D^{\alpha\beta} \frac{\partial \log f}{\partial q^\beta}\left(\frac{\partial \mathbf{R}_{0k}}{\partial q^\alpha} \cdot \boldsymbol{\varphi}_{jk}\right)(\mathbf{R}_{0l} \cdot \mathbf{e}_y), \end{aligned} \tag{29}$$

in which we have let $\alpha_{jk} = \boldsymbol{\varphi}_{jk} \cdot \mathbf{e}_x$. The Newtonian part of the viscosity (the terms linear in $\dot{\epsilon}_0$) is given, in view of Eq. (20), by the average of Eq. (29) over the equilibrium distribution function f_0. Therefore, we have for G,

$$G = \sum_j (H_j^{(0)} - H_j^{(1)} + H_j^{(2)}), \tag{30}$$

where

$$\begin{aligned} H_j^{(0)} &= \sum_{l,k} \left\langle \frac{\alpha_{jk}\alpha_{jl}}{\sigma_j} (\mathbf{R}_{0k} \cdot \mathbf{e}_y)(\mathbf{R}_{0l} \cdot \mathbf{e}_y) \right\rangle_0, \\ H_j^{(1)} &= \sum_{l,k,s} \Bigg\langle \sum_{\alpha,\beta=1}^{2n+4} \frac{\alpha_{jl}}{\sigma_j} g^{\alpha\beta} \left(\frac{\partial \mathbf{R}_{0k}}{\partial q^\alpha} \cdot \boldsymbol{\varphi}_{jk}\right)\left(\frac{\partial \mathbf{R}_{0s}}{\partial q^\beta} \cdot \mathbf{e}_x\right) \\ &\qquad \times (\mathbf{R}_{0s} \cdot \mathbf{e}_y)(\mathbf{R}_{0l} \cdot \mathbf{e}_y) \Bigg\rangle_0. \end{aligned} \tag{31}$$

$H_j^{(2)}$ arises from the average of the third term in Eq. (29) and is a result of the equating of the hydrodynamic torques to the rotatory diffusion torques. To first order in $\dot{\epsilon}_0$, the perturbation parameter, the diffusional torques are given by Eq. (18) to be

$$\frac{\partial \log f}{\partial q^\beta} = f_0^{-1} \left[\frac{\partial f_0}{\partial q^\beta} + \dot{\epsilon}_0 \frac{\partial (f_0^{\frac{1}{2}} \rho^{(1)})}{\partial q^\beta} - \dot{\epsilon}_0 f_0^{\frac{1}{2}} \rho^{(1)} \frac{\partial f_0}{\partial q^\beta}\right] e^{i\omega t}. \tag{32}$$

---

[6] P. L. Auer and C. S. Gardner, *J. Chem. Phys.* **23**, 1545 (1955).

Combining Eq. (32) with the third term of Eq. (29) and averaging over f_0, we obtain

$$H_j^{(2)} = \sum_{k,l}\sum_{\lambda} \frac{B_\lambda (K_j^{(l,k)})_\lambda^*}{\lambda + i\omega} = \sum_{\lambda} \frac{B_\lambda (K_j)_\lambda^*}{\lambda + i\omega}, \tag{33}$$

where

$$K_j^{(l,k)} = f_0^{-1} \sum_{\alpha,\beta=1}^{2n+4} \frac{1}{g^{\frac{1}{2}}} \frac{\partial g^{\frac{1}{2}}}{\partial q^\alpha} \left[\frac{\alpha_{jl}}{\sigma_j} D^{\alpha\beta} \left(\frac{\partial \mathbf{R}_{0k}}{\partial q^\beta} \cdot \boldsymbol{\varphi}_{jk} \right) (\mathbf{R}_{0l} \cdot \mathbf{e}_y) f_0 \right],$$

$$B = -\frac{f_0^{-\frac{1}{2}} Q f_0^{\frac{1}{2}}}{\dot{\epsilon}} = f_0^{-1} \sum_{l} \sum_{\alpha,\beta=1}^{2n+4} \frac{1}{g^{\frac{1}{2}}} \frac{\partial g^{\frac{1}{2}}}{\partial q^\alpha} \left[g^{\alpha\beta} (\mathbf{R}_{0l} \cdot \mathbf{e}_y) \left(\frac{\partial \mathbf{R}_{0l}}{\partial q^\beta} \cdot \mathbf{e}_x \right) f_0 \right].$$

Setting $[\eta] = [\eta'] - i[\mu]/\omega\eta_0$, we may solve for the intrinsic viscosity

$$[\eta'] = \frac{N\zeta}{100M\eta_0} \sum_j \left\{ H_j^{(0)} - H_j^{(1)} + \sum_\lambda \frac{\lambda B_\lambda (K_j)_\lambda^*}{\lambda^2 + \omega^2} \right\} \tag{34}$$

and the intrinsic rigidity

$$[\mu] = \frac{N\zeta}{100M} \sum_j \sum_\lambda \frac{\omega^2 B_\lambda (K_j)_\lambda^*}{\lambda^2 + \omega^2}. \tag{35}$$

These results may also be expressed in a somewhat different form which does not require explicit knowledge of the eigenvalues and eigenfunctions of the operator L. The sum over the eigenvalue spectrum in Eq. (33) may be written

$$H_j^{(2)} = \int (g)^{\frac{1}{2}} (g')^{\frac{1}{2}} B(\mathbf{q}') K_j(\mathbf{q}) f_0^{\frac{1}{2}}(\mathbf{q}) f_0^{\frac{1}{2}}(\mathbf{q}') M(\mathbf{q}, \mathbf{q}') d\mathbf{q} d\mathbf{q}', \tag{36}$$

where

$$M(\mathbf{q}, \mathbf{q}') = \sum_\lambda \frac{\psi_\lambda^*(\mathbf{q}') \psi_\lambda(\mathbf{q})}{\lambda + i\omega}.$$

$M(\mathbf{q}, \mathbf{q}')$ may also be written

$$M(\mathbf{q}, \mathbf{q}) = \int_0^\infty e^{-i\omega s} \sum_\lambda \psi_\lambda^*(\mathbf{q}') e^{sL} \psi_\lambda(\mathbf{q}) ds$$

Now e^{sL} is a transformation which transforms a function of the coordinates at time t to a later time $t + s$, i.e.,

$$e^{sL} G(\mathbf{q}_t) = G(\mathbf{q}_{t+s}).$$

$\mathbf{q}_{t+s}$ is the phase point onto which the phase point $\mathbf{q}_t$ at time t moves in a time interval s. Thus

$$M(\mathbf{q}, \mathbf{q}') = \int_0^\infty e^{-i\omega s} \delta(\mathbf{q}_t - \mathbf{q}_{t+s}) ds,$$

where $\delta(\mathbf{q})$ is the $2n + 4$ dimensional Dirac delta function. Thus, we obtain

$$H_j^{(2)} = \int_0^\infty \langle B(\mathbf{q}_{t+s}) K_j(\mathbf{q}_t) \rangle_0 e^{-i\omega s} ds \tag{37}$$

the zero subscript indicating an average over the equilibrium distribution function. This type of average quantity is known as a time correlation function. One would expect this latter expression for $H_j^{(2)}$ to be more easily approximated than Eq. (33) which requires the eigenfunctions and eigenvalues of the operator L explicitly. The time correlation function might be approximated by means of a suitable moment expansion of L in the equilibrium ensemble, whereby the first term of the expansion would reflect in a simple way the relaxation effects suitable for this diffusion process.

In order to apply these general results to a coiling-type polymer, many simplifying assumptions such as those employed in the theory of dielectric dispersion of Hammerle and Kirkwood[7] will no doubt be required. This problem is presently under investigation.

It should be noted that the general ideas used here are applicable, independently of the model. The recent calculation of Zimm[8] may be considered an application of this theory to the Rouse-Bueche model.[9] In this case the distribution function depends upon coordinates of the entire configuration space and the simplifying aspect of the reduction of the problem to one in chain space is lost. However, with the introduction of a Hooke's law potential of internal force, Zimm's calculation follows as an application of the present formulation.

---

[7] W. G. Hammerle and J. G. Kirkwood, *J. Chem. Phys.* **23**, 1743 (1955).
[8] B. H. Zimm, *J. Chem. Phys.* **24**, 269 (1956).
[9] P. E. Rouse, *J. Chem. Phys.* **21**, 1272 (1953); F. Bueche, *J. Chem. Phys.* **22**, 603 (1954).

Erratum: The Statistical Mechanics of Irreversible Processes in Polymer Solutions*

[*J. Chem. Phys.* **29**, 909 (1958)]

JEROME J. ERPENBECK† AND JOHN G. KIRKWOOD,‡ *Sterling Chemistry Laboratory, Yale University, New Haven, Connecticut*

The theory presented in the above paper has been found to contain an error, arising from our inadvertent use of Eq. (11)[1] for Brownian motion outside of chain space. Herein, we correct this error, whence the perturbation term in the diffusion equation is now made up of the original Kirkwood term[2] plus a term in the velocity field outside of chain space; the "correction" term in the external force field is no longer obtained, but a new prescription for the calculation of the diffusion tensor is required.

The development of our paper is retained up to Eq. (9), at which point it is necessary to define the diffusion tensor as the inverse of the projection of the frictional tensor onto chain space;[3]

$$\sum_{\beta=1}^{2n+4} (D^{\alpha\beta}/kT)\zeta_{\beta\gamma} = \delta_{\gamma}^{\alpha},\ \alpha, \gamma \leq 2n+4. \tag{C.1}$$

The generalized Eq. (11) of Brownian motion is found by equating the hydrodynamic torque to the diffusion torque. Outside of chain space, however, Eq. (11) is useful only in defining the constraints of bond lengths and bond angles in terms of an internal potential. We can proceed correctly to the diffusion Eq. (14), however, through the correct diffusion tensor, whence we obtain

$$\sum_{\alpha,\beta=1}^{2n+4} \frac{1}{g^{\frac{1}{2}}}\frac{\partial g^{\frac{1}{2}}}{\partial q^{\beta}}\frac{D^{\alpha\beta}}{kT}\left[kT\frac{\partial f}{\partial q^{\alpha}} + \frac{\partial V_0}{\partial q^{\alpha}} f\right] - \frac{\partial f}{\partial t} =$$

$$\sum_{\alpha,\beta=1}^{2n+4} \frac{1}{g^{\frac{1}{2}}}\frac{\partial g^{\frac{1}{2}}}{\partial q^{\beta}}\left[\frac{D^{\alpha\beta}}{kT}X_{\alpha}f + g^{\alpha\beta}v_{\alpha}^{0}f\right] + \sum_{\alpha,\beta=1}^{2n+4} \frac{1}{g^{\frac{1}{2}}}\frac{\partial g^{\frac{1}{2}}}{\partial q^{\beta}}\left[\frac{D^{\alpha\beta}}{kT}\sum_{\gamma=2n+5}^{6n+3}\zeta_{\alpha\gamma}v^{0\gamma}f\right]. \tag{C.2}$$

The first term on the right is the original Kirkwood term while the second is new, involving the frictional force associated with the structural constraints on the molecule. The perturbation operator of Eq. (15) becomes

$$Q = -f_0^{-\frac{1}{2}}\sum_{\alpha,\beta=1}^{2n+4} \frac{1}{g^{\frac{1}{2}}}\frac{\partial g^{\frac{1}{2}}}{\partial q^{\beta}}\left\{\frac{D^{\alpha\beta}}{kT}\left[X_{\alpha} + \sum_{\gamma=1}^{6n+3}\zeta_{\alpha\gamma}v^{0\gamma}\right]f_0^{\frac{1}{2}}(\quad)\right\}. \tag{C.3}$$

---

* This work was supported by the Office of Naval Research.

† Present address: Los Alamos Scientific Laboratory, Los Alamos, New Mexico.
‡ Deceased.

[1] Equation numbers, not containing the letter C, refer to equations in the original paper.
[2] J. G. Kirkwood, *Rec. tran. chim.* **68**, 649 (1949); *J. Polymer Sci.* **12**, 1 (1954).
[3] Yuichi Ikeda, *Bull. Koboyasi Institute of Physical Research* **6**, 44 (1956).

The perturbation solution to the diffusion equation remains correct, regardless of the precise nature of Q.

Errors have been introduced into the intrinsic viscosity theory in two places. First, Eq. (28) no longer follows from Eq. (11); rather we obtain

$$\mathbf{u}_l = \sum_{\alpha,\beta=1}^{2n+4} \frac{\partial \mathbf{R}_{0l}}{\partial q^\beta} \frac{D^{\alpha\beta}}{kT} \left[\sum_{\gamma=1}^{6n+3} \zeta_{\alpha\gamma} v^{0\gamma} - kT \frac{\partial \ln f}{\partial q^\alpha} \right]. \tag{C.4}$$

In addition, the first order correction to the distribution function $\rho^{(1)}$ is seen, in view of Eq. (C.3) to depend upon this same expression in the unperturbed flow, $\mathbf{v}^0$.

The latter can be expressed in terms of the eigenvalues and eigenvectors of the tensor $\boldsymbol{\tau}$, Eq. (24), whence we obtain

$$\begin{aligned}
G &= H^{(0)} - H^{(1)} + H^{(2)}, \\
H^{(0)} &= \sum_j \sum_{l,k} \left\langle \frac{\alpha_{jl}\alpha_{jk}}{\sigma_j} (\mathbf{R}_{0l} \cdot \mathbf{e}_y)(\mathbf{R}_{0k} \cdot \mathbf{e}_y) \right\rangle_0, \\
H^{(1)} &= \sum_{j,j'} \sum_{l,k,s,t} \sum_{\alpha,\beta} \left\langle \frac{\alpha_{jl}\alpha_{j'k}}{\sigma_j \sigma_{j'}} \frac{D^{\alpha\beta}}{kT} (\mathbf{R}_{0l} \cdot \mathbf{e}_y)(\mathbf{R}_{0k} \cdot \mathbf{e}_y) \right. \\
&\qquad \left. \left(\frac{\partial \mathbf{R}_{0s}}{\partial q^\alpha} \cdot \boldsymbol{\varphi}_{js} \right) \left(\frac{\partial \mathbf{R}_{0t}}{\partial q^\beta} \cdot \boldsymbol{\varphi}_{j't} \right) \right\rangle_0, \\
H^{(2)} &= \frac{\zeta}{kT} \sum_\lambda \frac{V_\lambda V_\lambda^*}{\lambda + i\omega}, \\
V &= \sum_j \sum_{l,k} \sum_{\alpha,\beta} \frac{1}{g^{\frac{1}{2}}} \frac{\partial g^{\frac{1}{2}}}{\partial q^\beta} \left[\frac{\alpha_{jl}}{\sigma_j} D^{\alpha\beta} (\mathbf{R}_{0l} \cdot \mathbf{e}_y) \left(\frac{\partial \mathbf{R}_{0k}}{\partial q^\alpha} \cdot \boldsymbol{\varphi}_{jk} \right) \right].
\end{aligned} \tag{C.5}$$

With regard to the calculation of other transport properties, it should be noted that even though the perturbation Q is for zero flow field the same as the Kirkwood expression, the diffusion tensor is altered. In general, then, the inclusion of the hydrodynamic interactions from outside of chain space affects every transport property.

On an Approximate Theory of Transport in Dense Media

STUART A. RICE,* *Department of Chemistry and Institute for the Study of Metals University of Chicago, Chicago 37, Illinois*

AND

JOHN G. KIRKWOOD, *Department of Chemistry, Yale University, New Haven, Connecticut*

(Received April 6, 1959)

A new approximate theory of transport is presented which starts from the general statistical mechanical theory of heat flux and the stress tensor and uses three principal approximations. These are (a) the expansion of the gradient of the pair interaction potential between molecules at time $t + s$ about the gradient at time t and the neglect of all terms higher than the second, (b) the use of a local equilibrium distribution function in pair-space, and (c) the approximation of the pair diffusion tensor as the direct sum of singlet diffusion tensors. The intermolecular force contributions to the shear viscosity, bulk viscosity, and thermal conductivity are related to equilibrium properties of the fluid and, respectively, to other coefficients of the set of transport coefficients. Absolute calculations for liquid argon are within a factor of two of experiment. A semiempirical calculation suggested by the theory and using the observed diffusion coefficient is in exact agreement with experiment. The validity of the three approximations is discussed.

I. INTRODUCTION

One of the major concerns of the statistical theory of transport processes is the prediction of the stress tensor and heat flux from the properties of the molecules in the system. For the dilute gas, the distribution function in μ-space can be obtained as an expansion about the equilibrium distribution function. The perturbation of the equilibrium distribution function is considered to be small and is itself developed in powers of $\lambda\nabla$, where λ is of the order of a mean-free-path and the gradient operator acts upon the macroscopic variables specifying the state of the system. The success of such an expansion depends upon the density being sufficiently low so that individual molecules are far apart and hence essentially free. Under these conditions, molecules interact only when undergoing binary collisions, and the stress tensor and heat flux can be analyzed solely in terms of these binary encounters. In contrast to the low-density case, at liquid densities any given molecule is in essentially continuous interaction with its neighbors and the concept of binary encounters loses precision. To compute the transport of momentum and energy in a dense medium a significantly different approach must be adopted.

In the theory of Kirkwood,[1] the motion of an individual molecule is analyzed with the aid of analogies from the theory of Brownian motion. The

---

* Alfred P. Sloan Fellow.

[1] J. G. Kirkwood, *J. Chem. Phys.* **14**, 180 (1946).

evolution of the distribution functions in phase-space is described by generalized Fokker-Planck equations, and the correlation between the forces acting on a given molecule at separated instants of time is used to define a frictional coefficient which is then specified in terms of the gradient of the potential energy of a pair of molecules and suitable averages over the entire ensemble. To reduce this and other equations to tractable form it is necessary to make several physical approximations, the effects of which have not been estimated. The practical application of this theory requires still further purely mathematical approximations before explicit comparison with experiment can be made.[2] Though the molecular mechanisms involved in transport phenomena have been considerably clarified, and the qualitative agreement with experiment is excellent, the labor involved in making calculations is sufficiently great that the examination of different approximations than those previously employed seems warranted.

In this communication we shall present approximate calculations of the transport coefficients in dense fluids. Starting from the exact statistical mechanical equations of transport,[3] we will assume that: (a) the gradient of the pair interaction potential between molecules at time $t + s$ can be expanded in a Taylor series about the gradient at time t and terms higher than the second may be neglected, (b) the distribution function in pair-space may be approximated as the product of the local equilibrium radial distribution function in coordinate space and the zeroth-order distribution function in momentum-space, and (c) the diffusion tensor in pair-space may be approximated as the direct sum of the diffusion tensors (diagonal) in singlet-space.

These approximations will suffice to reduce the exact expressions to tractable analytical forms. Three virtues of the present treatment are that it demonstrates explicitly the role of time-smoothing in determining the transport coefficients in the fluid, that it relates the coefficients of thermal conductivity and shear viscosity to the diffusion coefficient and the thermodynamic properties of the system, and that all calculations can be performed very simply.

II. THE COEFFICIENT OF SELF-DIFFUSION

We shall first apply the theory to the determination of the coefficient of self-diffusion, D, in a pure liquid. For this purpose we use the well-known Einstein relation

$$D = kT/\zeta, \tag{1}$$

where ζ is the frictional coefficient. In order to calculate ζ it is expedient to consider a pseudo two-component system consisting of two molecular species, 1 and 2, interacting with potentials of intermolecular force V_{11}, V_{12}, and V_{22}, which in a pure fluid will all become identical and equal to $V(R)$. Suppose that the number of molecules of type 1 is N_1 and that of type 2 is N_2. The second species, 2, may be regarded as isotopically tagged molecules of type 1. Finally, we shall let the number N_2 of the tagged species approach zero.

The dynamical state of the N body system will be specified by the distribution function of $f^{(N)}(\mathbf{R}^{(N)}\mathbf{p}^{(N)}; t)$ in the $6N$ dimensional phase-space of the

---

[2] Kirkwood, Buff, and Green, *J. Chem. Phys.* **17**, 988 (1949); Zwanzig, Kirkwood, Stripp, and Oppenheim, *J. Chem. Phys.* **21**, 2050 (1953); Zwanzig, Kirkwood, Oppenheim, and Alder, *J. Chem. Phys.* **22**, 783 (1954).

[3] J. H. Irving and J. G. Kirkwood, *J. Chem. Phys.* **18**, 817 (1950).

centers of mass of the molecules, where $\mathbf{R}^{(N)}$ and $\mathbf{p}^{(N)}$ represent the N position vectors $\mathbf{R}_1, \mathbf{R}_2, \cdots, \mathbf{R}_N$ and the N momentum vectors, $\mathbf{p}_1, \mathbf{p}_2, \cdots, \mathbf{p}_N$. This distribution function satisfies Liouville's equation. If a time-smoothed distribution function $\bar{f}^{(N)}(\mathbf{R}^{(N)}\mathbf{p}^{(N)}; t)$ is defined by the relation[1] (τ is the interval of coarse-graining),

$$\bar{f}^{(N)}(\mathbf{R}^{(N)}\mathbf{p}^{(N)}; t) = (1/\tau) \int_0^\tau f^{(N)}(\mathbf{R}^{(N)}, \mathbf{p}^{(N)}; t + s) ds, \tag{2}$$

then the fundamental feature of the statistical theory of transport can be stated as follows: we identify any observable quantity with the ensemble average of the time average of the corresponding microscopic quantity.[1] This identification clearly corresponds to the usual experimental procedure of observing the behavior in time of a single system and then repeating the observations on many other single systems selected from some initial ensemble. It may readily be shown that when averaging a dynamical function, α, the order of integration of $\alpha(\mathbf{R}^{(N)}\mathbf{p}^{(N)})\bar{f}^{(N)}(\mathbf{R}^{(N)}\mathbf{p}^{(N)}; t)$ over phase-space and time may be commuted. This is not possible for the lower-order distribution functions since they do not satisfy a Liouville equation but rather an extended Boltzmann equation in their subphase-space. According to Bearman and Kirkwood[4,5] the mean frictional force acting on species α at the point $\mathbf{R}$ in a fluid mixture of γ components is given by

$$C_\alpha \bar{\mathbf{F}}_\alpha^{(1)*} = \langle \mathbf{F}_\alpha, \bar{f}^{(N)} \rangle, \tag{3}$$

where

$$\mathbf{F}_\alpha = - \sum_{\alpha=1}^{\gamma} \sum_{\beta=1}^{\gamma} \sum_{j=1}^{N_\alpha} \sum_{k=1}^{N_\beta} [\nabla_{R_{\alpha j}} V_{\alpha\beta}(|\mathbf{R}_{\beta k} - \mathbf{R}_{\alpha j}|) \delta(\mathbf{R}_{\alpha j} - \mathbf{R}) - \nabla_{R_{\beta k}} V_{\alpha\beta}(|\mathbf{R}_{\beta k} - \mathbf{R}_{\alpha j}|) \delta(\mathbf{R}_{\beta k} - \mathbf{R})], \tag{4}$$

and where the convenient notation,

$$\langle \mathbf{F}_\alpha, \bar{f}^{(N)} = \int \cdots \int \mathbf{F}_\alpha \bar{f}^{(N)}(\mathbf{R}^{(N)}\mathbf{p}^{(N)}) d\mathbf{R}^{(N)} d\mathbf{p}^{(N)}, \tag{5}$$

has been used. Note that for Eqs. (3), (4), and (5), it is the time coarse-grained distribution function in the phase-space of all molecules which appears. For a system of two components, the perturbation in $\bar{f}^{(N)}$ from equilibrium caused by diffusion leads to the result[4]

$$\bar{\mathbf{F}}_1^{(1)*} = \zeta(\mathbf{u}_2 - \mathbf{u}_1), \tag{6}$$

where ζ is, as before, the frictional coefficient and $\mathbf{u}_2$ and $\mathbf{u}_1$ are the mean diffusion velocities of the two components. Our procedure for determining ζ involves the transformation[1]

$$\langle \mathbf{F}_\alpha, \bar{f}^{(N)} \rangle = \langle \bar{\mathbf{F}}_\alpha, f^{(N)} \rangle, \tag{7}$$

where

$$\bar{\mathbf{F}}_\alpha = (1/\tau) \int_0^\tau \mathbf{F}_\alpha(t + s) ds, \tag{8}$$

---

[4] Bearman, Kirkwood, and Fixman, *Progress in Statistical Mechanics* (Academic Press, New York, 1958), Vol. I.

[5] R. Bearman and J. G. Kirkwood, *J. Chem. Phys.* **28**, 136 (1958).

and where $f^{(N)}$ is the fine-grained distribution function at time t. As defined by Eq. (8), $\bar{\mathbf{F}}_\alpha$ is the time average of $\mathbf{F}_\alpha$ over an interval τ, long on the molecular scale and short on the macroscopic scale.

We shall now proceed to calculate the average intermolecular force, $\langle \mathbf{F}_1 \rangle$, acting on a representative molecule 1 of the system moving with a mean velocity $\mathbf{u}$ under the action of an external force $\mathbf{X}$. When the total potential energy of interaction can be regarded as the sum of pair potentials, the instantaneous force acting on molecule 1 due to the $N - 1$ other molecules in the system is

$$\mathbf{F}_1(\mathbf{R}_1{}^0) = \sum_{j=2}^{N} \nabla_{R_{1j}} V(R_{1j}). \tag{9}$$

As usual, R_{ij} is the distance between molecules i and j. Following the prescription for obtaining the average of any quantity, the average force on molecule one of subset one is now easily seen to be

$$(1/v)\,\langle \mathbf{F}_1 \rangle = \int \Big[\int \cdots \int (1/\tau) \int_0^\tau \sum_{j=2}^{N} \nabla_{R_{1j}} V(R_{1j}(t+s))$$

$$\cdot f^{(N)}(t)\,\delta(\mathbf{R}_1{}^0 - \mathbf{R}_1)\,\delta(\mathbf{R}_j{}^0 - \mathbf{R}_j)\, ds\, d\mathbf{R}^{(N)} d\mathbf{p}^{(N)} \Big] d\mathbf{R}_j{}^0, \tag{10}$$

where v is the volume per molecule and where the position of molecule 1 is $\mathbf{R}_1{}^0$. The averaging process indicated in Eq. (10) has been explicitly divided into two steps. In the first integration over phase-space both molecules 1 and j are held fixed, giving the average force on molecule 1 due to molecule j at a fixed distance $\mathbf{R}_{1j}$ when the positions of the remaining $N - 2$ molecules are unspecified. The second integration is over the position coordinates of molecule j to obtain the average force at $\mathbf{R}_1{}^0$ when the positions of all the other molecules are unspecified. Equation (10) may be considerably simplified by recognizing that all $N - 1$ molecules make the same contribution to the average force at $\mathbf{R}_1{}^0$ so that

$$\langle \mathbf{F}_1 \rangle = \frac{(N-1)v}{\tau} \int \Big[\int \cdots \int \int_0^\tau \nabla_{R_{12}} V(R_{12}(t+s)) f^{(N)}(t)$$

$$\cdot\, \delta(\mathbf{R}_1{}^0 - \mathbf{R}_1)\,\delta(\mathbf{R}_2{}^0 - \mathbf{R}_2)\, ds\, d\mathbf{R}^{(N)} d\mathbf{p}^{(N)} \Big] d\mathbf{R}_2{}^0. \tag{11}$$

The potential energy is not an explicit function of the time, t, but depends on it only through the change in intermolecular separation with time. Expanding the gradient of the pair interaction potential in a Taylor series and retaining only the first two terms leads to

$$\nabla_{R_{12}} V(R_{12}(t+s)) = \nabla_{\mathrm{R}_{12}} V(R_{12}(t))$$

$$+ \Delta\mathbf{R}_{12}(s)\, \nabla_{R_{12}} \nabla_{R_{12}} V(R_{12}(t)) + \cdots, \tag{12}$$

where

$$\mathbf{R}_{12}(t+s) = \mathbf{R}_{12}(t) + \Delta\mathbf{R}_{12}(s), \tag{13}$$

with $\Delta\mathbf{R}_{12}(s)$ the increment in $\mathbf{R}_{12}$ in the time interval s. To compute the average indicated in Eq. (11), an explicit distribution function must be introduced and cognizance taken of the constraints imposed by the specification of the positions of selected molecules. In general, the probability density, $f^{(N)}$, may be related to the reduced distribution functions $f^{(n)}$ by

$$f^{(N)}(\mathbf{R}^{(n)}\mathbf{p}^{(n)}\mathbf{R}^{(N-n)}\mathbf{p}^{(N-n)}, t)$$
$$= f^{(n)}(\mathbf{R}^{(n)}\mathbf{p}^{(n)}; t) f^{(n/N-n)}(\mathbf{R}^{(N-n)}\mathbf{p}^{(N-n)}; t), \tag{14}$$

which defines $f^{(n/N-n)}$ as the relative probability density in the subspace $\mathbf{R}^{(N-n)}\mathbf{p}^{(N-n)}$ given that particles $1, \cdots, n$ have specified coordinates. For the particular case of a pair of particles with specified positions, it will be assumed that $f^{(2)}$ can be approximated as the product of the local equilibrium configurational distribution functions multiplied by a momentum distribution function which is Maxwellian with a first-order perturbation due to the mean velocity. The explicit form of $f^{(2)}$ used is, then,

$$f^{(2)} = \frac{g_0^{(2)}(R_{12})}{v^2} \frac{\exp(-p_{12}^2/mkT)}{(\pi mkT)^{\frac{3}{2}}} \left(1 + \frac{\mathbf{p}_{12} \cdot \mathbf{u}_{12}}{kT}\right), \tag{15}$$

where $\mathbf{p}_{12}$ is the relative momentum of molecule one of subset and molecule two of subset two, and

$$\mathbf{u}_{12} = \mathbf{u}_2(\mathbf{R}_1) - \mathbf{u}_1(\mathbf{R}_1) + O(\nabla\mathbf{u}), \tag{16}$$

neglecting terms of order $\nabla\mathbf{u}$, is the difference in mean velocities of molecule 1 of subset 1 at the point $\mathbf{R}_1$ and molecule 2, also at the point $\mathbf{R}_1$. It is important to note that to define a frictional coefficient or a diffusion tensor it is necessary to consider a system containing at least two (possibly hypothetical) species. Moreover, for the case of the self-diffusion coefficient, the $\nabla\mathbf{u}$ term can be exactly neglected because the flux of matter is defined in terms of the difference $\mathbf{u}_2(\mathbf{R}_1) - \mathbf{u}_1(\mathbf{R}_1)$. As usual, $g_0^{(2)}(R_{12})$ is the pair-correlation function, the subscript zero indicating that it is to be evaluated under the assumption of local equilibrium in configuration space. The other symbols in Eq. (15) are: m, the mass of a molecule and v, the volume per molecule. When Eqs. (12) and (14) are substituted into Eq. (10), four terms are obtained. The two terms resulting from the product of the local equilibrium part of $f^{(2)}$ and the expansion of the gradient of the potential energy vanish, since the average force acting on a molecule at equilibrium is zero. The integral of the product of $\mathbf{p}_{12}$ and the first term in the expansion of Eq. (12) vanish because $\nabla_{R_{12}}V(R_{12})$ is independent of $\mathbf{p}_{12}$, and the integrand is then an odd function integrated over an even interval. The result obtained, after integration over angles, assumes the form

$$\langle \mathbf{F}_1 \rangle = \frac{(N-1)v}{3kT\tau} \iint_0^\tau \nabla_{\mathbf{R}_{12}}{}^2 V(R_{12})\mathbf{u}_{12}$$
$$\cdot \langle \mathbf{p}_{12}\Delta\mathbf{R}_{12}(s)\rangle^{1,2} f_0{}^{(2)} ds\, d\mathbf{p}_1 d\mathbf{p}_2 d\mathbf{R}_{12}{}^0, \tag{17}$$

where

$$\langle \mathbf{p}_{12}\Delta\mathbf{R}_{12}(s)\rangle^{1,2} = \int \cdots \int \mathbf{p}_{12}\Delta\mathbf{R}_{12}(s) f^{(2/N-2)}(12/N-2)$$
$$\cdot\, d\mathbf{p}^{(N-2)} d\mathbf{R}^{(N-2)}, \tag{18}$$

with the relative probability density $f^{(2/N-2)}$ defined by Eq. (14). The argument

$(12/N-2)$ indicates that molecules 1 and 2 form the subset (2) chosen from the N molecules. Note that the only quantities in the integrand of Eq. (17) which depend upon s are $\mathbf{p}_{12}$ and $\Delta\mathbf{R}_{12}(s)$. With the identification of the frictional force defined in Eq. (6) and the mean force given in Eq. (17), it is found that the frictional coefficient is related to intermolecular forces by

$$\zeta = \frac{(N-1)v}{3kT\tau}\int\int_0^\tau \langle \mathbf{p}_{12}\Delta\mathbf{R}_{12}(s)\rangle^{1,2}\nabla_{\mathbf{R}_{12}}{}^2 V(R_{12})f_0{}^{(2)}\cdot d\mathbf{p}_1 d\mathbf{p}_2 d\mathbf{R}_{12}{}^0 ds. \quad (19)$$

It is expedient to note that

$$\mathbf{p}_{12}\{[d\Delta\mathbf{R}_{12}(s)]/ds\} = (2\mathbf{p}_{12}\mathbf{p}_{12})/m, \quad (20)$$

and by changing the variable of integration in Eq. (18) from ds to $d\Delta\mathbf{R}_{12}(s)$, it is found that

$$(1/\tau)\int_0^\tau \langle \mathbf{p}_{12}\Delta\mathbf{R}_{12}(s)\rangle^{1,2} ds = (m/2\tau)\int_0^\tau \mathbf{I}\cdot\langle\Delta\mathbf{R}_{12}(s)d\Delta\mathbf{R}_{12}(s)\rangle^{1,2}, \quad (21)$$

or

$$(m/2\tau)\langle\Delta\mathbf{R}_{12}(\tau)\Delta\mathbf{R}_{12}(\tau)\rangle^{1,2} = (m/2)\mathbf{D}^{(2)}, \quad (22)$$

where $\mathbf{D}^{(2)}$ is the diffusion tensor in pair-space, and we have used the relation $\mathbf{p}_{12}\mathbf{p}_{12}(\mathbf{p}_{12}\mathbf{p}_{12})^{-1} = \mathbf{I}$. At large interparticle separations, the pair-diffusion tensor has the simple form

$$\mathbf{D}^{(2)} = D_1\mathbf{I}_1 \oplus D_2\mathbf{I}_2, \quad (23)$$

where the symbol $\oplus$ indicates a direct sum. D_1 and D_2 are the singlet-space diffusion coefficients in the spaces of molecules 1 and 2, respectively. It is clear that the pair-diffusion tensor cannot have the form indicated at short distances since Eq. (23) implies that the molecules move independently of one another. At what intermolecular distance the deviations from Eq. (23) become significant is unknown. Ignorance of the true form of the pair-diffusion tensor forces us to effect closure in the calculation with the approximation that $\mathbf{D}^{(2)}$ is the direct sum of diffusion tensors (diagonal) in singlet-space for all intermolecular separations. On combining Eqs. (19) and (22) and introducing the approximation just described, we finally obtain

$$\zeta^2 = (Nm/3v)\int \nabla_{\mathbf{R}_{12}}{}^2 V(R_{12})g_0{}^{(2)}(R_{12})d^3R_{12}, \quad (24)$$

which defines the frictional coefficient in terms of the intermolecular potential and the local equilibrium pair correlation function.

III. THE STRESS TENSOR

In this section we shall discuss the derivation of the Newtonian form of the stress tensor and the subsequent identification of the coefficients of shear and bulk viscosity. We confine attention to the intermolecular force contribution to the stress tensor which may be written in the form,[3]

$$\boldsymbol{\sigma}_v = \tfrac{1}{2}\sum_{k\neq j}\sum \int\cdots\int (1/\tau)\int_0^\tau \mathbf{R}_{jk}\nabla_{R_{jk}}V(R_{jk})\delta(\mathbf{R}_j-\mathbf{R}_2)$$
$$\cdot\,\delta(\mathbf{R}_k-\mathbf{R}_1)f^{(N)}ds\,d\mathbf{R}^{(N)}d\mathbf{p}^{(N)}d\mathbf{R}_{12}, \quad (25)$$

and which, upon utilization of the general definition of an average quantity becomes

$$\boldsymbol{\sigma}_v = \frac{N^2}{2\tau}\int_0^\tau \int \langle \mathbf{R}_{12}\nabla_{R_{12}} V(R_{12})\rangle^{1,2} f^{(2)} d\mathbf{R}_{12} d\mathbf{p}_1 d\mathbf{p}_2 ds, \tag{26}$$

where, as before,

$$\langle \mathbf{R}_{12}\nabla_{R_{12}} V(R_{12})\rangle^{1,2} = \int \cdots \int \mathbf{R}_{12}\nabla_{R_{12}} V(R_{12}) \cdot f^{(2/N-2)}(12/N-2)\, d\mathbf{p}^{(N-2)} d\mathbf{R}^{(N-2)}. \tag{27}$$

As in the preceding section, the gradient of the potential energy may be expanded in a Taylor series retaining only the first two terms. This expansion, together with the distribution function given in Eq. (15), is substituted into Eq. (26) to give

$$\boldsymbol{\sigma}_v = \frac{N^2}{2\tau}\int_0^\tau \int \langle \mathbf{R}_{12}\nabla_{R_{12}} V(R_{12}) + \mathbf{R}_{12}\Delta\mathbf{R}_{12} \cdot \nabla_{R_{12}}\nabla_{R_{12}} V(R_{12})\rangle^{1,2} \cdot f_0^{(2)}\left[1 + \frac{\mathbf{p}_{12}\cdot\mathbf{u}_{12}}{kT}\right] d\mathbf{p}_1 d\mathbf{p}_2 d\mathbf{R}_{12} ds. \tag{28}$$

A word must be inserted at this point concerning the interpretation of the distribution function defined in Eq. (15). In the preceding section it was stated that $\mathbf{u}_{12}$ was the difference in mean velocities between molecules of species one and two both at the point $\mathbf{R}_1$. As stated in that section, it was necessary to introduce some means of identifying molecules to define a mutual diffusion coefficient and thereby a frictional coefficient. The calculation presented in the last section is valid with neglect of terms of order $\nabla\mathbf{u}$. In the present discussion it is unnecessary to be able to distinguish between the molecules, but it is important to retain all terms up to and including those of order $\nabla\mathbf{u}$. In fact, it is just these terms of order $\nabla\mathbf{u}$ which introduce the dissipative terms into the Newtonian stress tensor. The distribution function defined in Eq. (15) correctly involves the differences in mean velocities between molecules 1 and 2 located at the points $\mathbf{R}_1$ and $\mathbf{R}_2$. The interpretation presented in the preceding section corresponds to the Taylor series expansion

$$\mathbf{u}_2(\mathbf{R}_2) - \mathbf{u}_1(\mathbf{R}_1) = \mathbf{u}_2(\mathbf{R}_1) - \mathbf{u}_1(\mathbf{R}_1) + \mathbf{R}_{12}\cdot\nabla\mathbf{u} + \cdots, \tag{29}$$

where the term $\nabla\mathbf{u}$ was neglected. In the present section we shall retain this term.

The intermolecular force contribution to the hydrostatic pressure may be separated from the intermolecular force contribution to the nonequilibrium part of the stress tensor. The result is

$$\begin{aligned}\boldsymbol{\sigma}_v = \boldsymbol{\sigma}_v^{(\text{equil})} &+ \tfrac{1}{2}\left(\frac{N}{v}\right)^2 \frac{1}{kT}\int (1/\tau)\int_0^\tau [\langle \Delta\mathbf{R}_{12}\nabla_{R_{12}} V(R_{12})\mathbf{p}_{12}\cdot\mathbf{u}_{12}\rangle^{1,2} \\ &+ \langle \mathbf{R}_{12}\Delta\mathbf{R}_{12}\cdot\nabla_{R_{12}}\nabla_{R_{12}} V(R_{12})\mathbf{p}_{12}\cdot\mathbf{u}_{12}\rangle]^{1,2} \\ &\cdot g_0^{(2)}(R_{12}) d^3R_{12} ds + \int O(\Delta R_{12})^2 \cdots,\end{aligned} \tag{30}$$

where $\boldsymbol{\sigma}_v^{(\text{equil})}$ is the intermolecular force contribution to the hydrostatic pressure. We shall neglect the terms of order $(\Delta R_{12})^2$. With the use of the definition of the diffusion tensor, Eq. (22), and carrying out the differentiation explicitly, it is found that

$$\boldsymbol{\sigma}_v = \boldsymbol{\sigma}_v^{(\text{equil})} + \frac{mD}{2kT}\left(\frac{N}{v}\right)^2 \int [\mathbf{R}_{12}\mathbf{u}_{12} \cdot \nabla_{R_{12}}\nabla_{R_{12}}V + \mathbf{u}_{12}\nabla_{R_{12}}V] \cdot g_0^{(2)}(R_{12})d^3R_{12}. \quad (31)$$

The double gradient operator may be expanded in terms of unit vectors along $\mathbf{R}_{12}$ and the unit tensor, so that

$$\nabla_{R_{12}}\nabla_{R_{12}}V = \mathbf{R}_{12}\left[\mathbf{e}_{R_{12}}V'' - \mathbf{e}_{R_{12}}\frac{V'}{R_{12}}\right] + \frac{V'}{R_{12}}\mathbf{I}, \quad (32)$$

where the prime (′) refers to differentiation with respect to R_{12} and the unit vectors $\mathbf{e}_{R_{12}}$ point along $\mathbf{R}_{12}$. By substitution of Eq. (29), the relation, Eq. (31), is transformed to the form

$$\boldsymbol{\sigma}_v = \boldsymbol{\sigma}_v^{(\text{equil})} + \frac{mD}{2kT}\left(\frac{N}{v}\right)^2 \int \Bigg[\mathbf{R}_{12}\mathbf{R}_{12} \cdot \nabla\mathbf{u} \cdot \left\{\mathbf{e}_{R_{12}}\mathbf{e}_{R_{12}}\left(V'' - \frac{V'}{R_{12}}\right) + 2\mathbf{I}\frac{V'}{R_{12}}\right\}\Bigg] g_0^{(2)}(R_{12})d^3R_{12}. \quad (33)$$

The classical Newtonian stress tensor may be written as

$$\boldsymbol{\sigma} = -p\mathbf{I} + 2\eta[\boldsymbol{\epsilon} - \tfrac{1}{3}\nabla \cdot \mathbf{u}\mathbf{I}] + \phi\nabla \cdot \mathbf{u}\mathbf{I}, \quad (34)$$

where p is the hydrostatic pressure, η the coefficient of shear viscosity, ϕ the coefficient of dilatational viscosity and $\boldsymbol{\epsilon}$ is the rate of strain tensor defined as $\text{Sym}\nabla\mathbf{u}$. Equation (33) may be transformed into a form similar to Eq. (34) by writing $\mathbf{R}_{12}$, $\mathbf{e}_{R_{12}}$, and $\nabla\mathbf{u}$ in spherical polar coordinates and integrating over the polar and azimuthal angles. Identification of the coefficients in Eqs. (33) and (34) then leads to the relations

$$\eta_v = \frac{m}{30\zeta}\left(\frac{N}{v}\right)^2 \int R_{12}^2\left(V'' + \frac{4}{R_{12}}V'\right) g_0^{(2)}(R_{12})d^3R_{12}, \quad (35)$$

and

$$\phi_v = \frac{m}{18\zeta}\left(\frac{N}{v}\right)^2 \int R_{12}^2\left(V'' + \frac{V'}{R_{12}}\right) g_0^{(2)}(R_{12})d^3R_{12}, \quad (36)$$

for the coefficients of shear and dilatational viscosity. It is important to note that in the transition from Eq. (31) to Eq. (33) we have used the fact that for indistinguishable (identical) molecules, the term $\mathbf{u}_2(\mathbf{R}_1) - \mathbf{u}_1(\mathbf{R}_1)$ appearing in Eq. (29) vanishes. When the molecules are distinguishable, as in the case treated in Sec. II, this term is not zero.

IV. THERMAL CONDUCTIVITY

The intermolecular force contribution to the heat flux in a dense fluid system was shown by Irving and Kirkwood to have the form[3]

$$\mathbf{q}_v = \sum_{k \neq i}\sum \int \cdots \int \frac{1}{2\tau}\int_0^\tau \{[V(R_{12})\,\mathbf{I} - \mathbf{R}_{12}\nabla V]$$

$$\cdot\, [\langle(\mathbf{p}_k/m)\delta(\mathbf{R}_k - \mathbf{R}_1)\delta(\mathbf{R}_i - \mathbf{R}_2); f^{(N)}\rangle$$

$$- \mathbf{u}(\mathbf{R}_1; t)\langle\delta(\mathbf{R}_k - \mathbf{R}_1)\delta(\mathbf{R}_i - \mathbf{R}_2); f^{(N)}\rangle]\}\, ds\, d\mathbf{R}_{12}. \quad (37)$$

To evaluate the heat flux in a manner similar to the reduction of the stress tensor discussed in the last section, Eq. (37) is rewritten as

$$\mathbf{q}_v = \frac{N(N-1)}{2m}\int (1/\tau)\int_0^\tau \left\langle [V\mathbf{I} - \mathbf{R}_{12}\nabla V]\cdot \frac{\boldsymbol{\pi}_1 + \boldsymbol{\pi}_2}{2}\right\rangle^{1,2} f^{(2)}$$

$$\cdot\, d\mathbf{p}_{12}\, d\mathbf{R}_{12}\, ds, \quad (38)$$

where $(\boldsymbol{\pi}_1 + \boldsymbol{\pi}_2)/2$ is the peculiar momentum of the center of mass of the pair, i.e., the peculiar momentum at $\mathbf{R}_1$ when another molecule is present at $\mathbf{R}_2$. In a nonisothermal single-component system with no bulk matter flow, the distribution function in pair-space, $f^{(2)}$, may be expanded in powers of the gradient of the temperature. Starting with Eq. (15) for the pair distribution function, and terminating the Taylor series expansion after the term linear in the gradient operator, it is readily found that

$$f^{(2)}(\mathbf{R}_{12}, \mathbf{R}_1, \mathbf{p}_{12}, T) = f_0^{(2)} + \mathbf{R}_{12}\cdot\nabla_{R_{12}} f_0^{(2)} + \cdots,$$

$$\mathbf{R}_{12}\cdot\nabla_{R_{12}} f_0^{(2)} = \left(\frac{\partial f_0}{\partial T}\right)_p^{(2)} \mathbf{R}_{12}\cdot\nabla_{R_{12}} T, \quad (39)$$

so that the perturbed distribution function may be written in the form

$$f^{(2)}(\mathbf{R}_{12}, \mathbf{p}_{12}, T) = f_0^{(2)}(\mathbf{R}_{12}, \mathbf{p}_{12}, T)\left[1 + \frac{(p_{12}^2 - \frac{3}{2}mkT)}{mkT^2}\right.$$

$$\left.\cdot\, \mathbf{R}_{12}\cdot\nabla T + \frac{\partial \ln(g_0^{(2)}/v^2)_p}{\partial T}\mathbf{R}_{12}\cdot\nabla T\right], \quad (40)$$

where, as before, $f_0^{(2)}$ is the local equilibrium value of the pair distribution function. Using the expansion displayed in Eq. (12), the time-smoothed portion of the integrand of Eq. (38) becomes (neglecting terms which vanish on integration),

$$(1/\tau)\int_0^\tau \left\langle [\mathbf{I}V - \mathbf{R}_{12}\nabla V]\cdot \frac{\boldsymbol{\pi}_1 + \boldsymbol{\pi}_2}{2}\right\rangle^{1,2} ds$$

$$= \frac{mD}{2}[\mathbf{R}_{12}\cdot\nabla\nabla V + 2\nabla V], \quad (41)$$

and the right-hand side of Eq. (41) is readily rearranged to

$$\frac{mD}{2}\left[\mathbf{e}_{R_{12}}R_{12}V'' + 2\mathbf{e}_{R_{12}}V'\right] = \frac{mD}{2}R_{12}(\nabla_{R_{12}}{}^2 V)\mathbf{e}_{R_{12}}. \tag{42}$$

The substitution of Eqs. (40) and (42) into Eq. (38) and the expression of the vectors $\mathbf{R}_{12}$ and $\mathbf{e}_{R_{12}}$ in spherical polar coordinates, followed by integration over the polar and azimuthal angles and the relative momentum $\mathbf{p}_{12}$, leads to the expression

$$\mathbf{q}_v = \frac{N(N-1)D}{12}\int R_{12}{}^2\nabla^2 V\left(\frac{\partial(g_0{}^{(2)}/v^2)}{\partial T}\right)_p d^3R_{12}. \tag{43}$$

The coefficient of thermal conductivity is related to the heat flux by Fourier's law, i.e.,

$$\mathbf{q}_v = \kappa_v \nabla T, \tag{44}$$

and if the integral I is defined by the relation

$$I = -\frac{N(N-1)}{v^2}\int R_{12}{}^2\nabla^2 V g_0{}^{(2)}(R_{12})d^3R_{12}, \tag{45}$$

then it is easily seen that the intermolecular force contribution to the coefficient of thermal conductivity is

$$\kappa_v = (D/12)(\partial I/\partial T)_p, \tag{46}$$

a relation that will be used later.

V. EVALUATION OF COEFFICIENTS OF SHEAR VISCOSITY AND THERMAL CONDUCTIVITY FOR A PURE FLUID

In this section we shall implement the equations previously derived and evaluate the coefficients of shear viscosity and thermal conductivity in terms of the frictional coefficient and the thermodynamic properties of the fluid. We start by noting that the equation of state of an isotropic fluid is given by the well-known relation[6]

$$\frac{pv}{NkT} = 1 - \frac{N}{6vkT}\int R_{12}V'(R_{12})g_0{}^{(2)}(R_{12})d^3R_{12}, \tag{47}$$

so that the intermolecular force contribution to the coefficient of shear viscosity may be written

$$\eta_v = \frac{m}{30\zeta}\left[12\left(\frac{NkT}{v} - p\right) - I\right]. \tag{48}$$

In a similar manner, by using the relationship between κ_v and I and performing the differentiation explicitly, it may be shown that

$$\kappa_v = \frac{5k\eta_v}{m}\left(\frac{\partial \ln (D/T\eta_v)}{\partial \,\mathrm{ld}T}\right)_p + D\left(\frac{\partial(RT/v)}{\partial T}\right)_p. \tag{49}$$

To proceed further we note that the energy of the fluid, L, is related to the pair distribution function by[6]

$$L = -\frac{N^2}{2v}\int V(R_{12})g_0{}^{(2)}(R_{12})d^3R_{12}, \tag{50}$$

so that if we assume that the pair potential is of the well-known Lennard-Jones form,

$$V(R_{12}) = 4\epsilon\left[\left(\frac{a}{R_{12}}\right)^{12} - \left(\frac{a}{R_{12}}\right)^{6}\right], \tag{51}$$

then it is easy to see that

$$2L = B_6 - B_{12}, \tag{52}$$

where the integrals B_6 and B_{12} are defined as

$$B_6 = \frac{4\epsilon N^2}{v}\int\left(\frac{a}{R_{12}}\right)^6 g_0{}^{(2)}(R_{12})d^3R_{12}$$

and

$$B_{12} = \frac{4\epsilon N^2}{v}\int\left(\frac{a}{R_{12}}\right)^{12} g_0{}^{(2)}(R_{12})d^3R_{12}, \tag{53}$$

with ϵ, the depth of the potential well and a, the distance at which the repulsive core of the potential crosses the axis $V = 0$. A second relation between the integrals B_6 and B_{12} is easily obtained by the use of Eq. (51) in the equation of state, Eq. (47). The result, which involves the pressure and molar volume is,

$$RT - pv = B_6 - 2B_{12}. \tag{54}$$

The simultaneous solution of Eqs. (52) and (54) permits the evaluation of B_6 and B_{12} solely in terms of the thermodynamic properties of the fluid. The result is

$$B_{12} = 2L + pv - RT$$

and

$$B_6 = 4L + pv - RT. \tag{55}$$

By substitution of the pair potential, Eq. (51), into Eq. (35), the shear viscosity may be expressed in terms of B_6 and B_{12} which may in turn be eliminated in favor of thermodynamic properties of the fluid via Eq. (55). The result of these operations is

$$\eta_v = (mD/5kTv)[24L + 15pv - 15RT]. \tag{56}$$

In a similar manner, explicit differentiation of Eq. (56) leads to the following expression of κ_v:

$$\kappa_v = \frac{D}{v}[24\Delta C_p - 45R - 15pv\alpha] + \frac{5kT\eta_v\alpha}{m} + D\left[\frac{R}{v} - \frac{RT\alpha}{v}\right], \tag{57}$$

where ΔC_p is the difference in heat capacities between the gaseous and liquid phases and α is the coefficient of thermal expansion. The transport coefficients

[6] See, for example, T. L. Hill, *Statistical Mechanics* (McGraw-Hill Book Company, Inc., New York, 1956).

η_v and κ_v have thus been expressed in terms of D and thermodynamic functions only. As an example we compute the shear viscosity and thermal conductivity of liquid Argon at 90°K. To make a direct comparison with experiment it is necessary to estimate the kinetic contribution to the transport coefficients. We estimate these by using the values appropriate to a dense fluid of rigid spheres.[7] These contributions are

$$\eta_k = \frac{5kT}{8\Omega^{(2,2)}}\left[\frac{1}{g_0^{(2)}(a)} + \frac{4\pi a^3}{15v}\right], \tag{58}$$

$$\kappa_k = \frac{75k^2T}{32m\Omega^{(2,2)}}\left[\frac{1}{g_0^{(2)}(a)} + \frac{6\pi a^3}{15v}\right], \tag{59}$$

$$\Omega^{(2,2)} = \left(\frac{4\pi kT}{m}\right)^{\frac{1}{2}} a^2, \tag{60}$$

where a, the hard sphere diameter, is taken as 3.72 A and $g_0^{(2)}(a) = 2.75$; $(v/v_0) = 1.32$.[8] Assuming that the kinetic contributions estimated from Eqs. (58) and (59) are correct to order of magnitude, the computed transport coefficients are all within 50% of the experimental values, as can be seen in Table I.[9–12] It is especially interesting to note that the ratio of the computed coefficients of shear viscosity and thermal conductivity is the same as the ratio of the corresponding observed quantities to within one percent. This fact suggests that the general form of the equations derived is correct even if the numerical coefficients which affect an absolute calculation are numerically inaccurate. To pursue this line of thought somewhat further, we shall compute the thermal conductivity using the experimental values of the self-diffusion coefficient and the viscosity. Equation (57) refers only to the intermolecular force contribution to the viscosity. This contribution is estimated by subtracting from the experimental shear viscosity the kinetic contribution estimated for a dense fluid of rigid spheres. This "experimental" value of the intermolecular force contribution, together with the observed value of the self-diffusion coefficient, 2.07×10^{-5} cm^2/sec,[9] is substituted into Eq. (56), and the kinetic contribution (estimated again for a hard sphere fluid) added to give a total computed coefficient of thermal conductivity. As can be seen in Table I, this computed value is within one precent of the experimental value. This agreement is probably fortuitously good, but our general surmise that the semiempirical use of experimental data permits accurate prediction via the relations derived is certainly supported.

VI. DISCUSSION

In this communication we have presented a new approximate theory of transport in dense fluids based upon the three approximations stated in the introduction. We shall discuss these approximations in order.

---

[7] Rice, Kirkwood, Ross, and Zwanzig, *J. Chem. Phys.* **31**, 575 (1959).
[8] Kirkwood, Mann, and Alder, *J. Chem. Phys.* **18**, 1040 (1950).
[9] J. W. Corbett and J. H. Wang, *J. Chem. Phys.* **25**, 422 (1956).
[10] A. Uhlir, Jr., *J. Chem. Phys.* **20**, 463 (1952).
[11] N. S. Rudenko and L. W. Schubnikow, *Physik. Z. Sowjetunion* **6**, 470 (1934).
[12] International Critical Tables.

The effects of the neglect of third- and higher-order terms in the expansion of the gradient of the pair potential at time $t + s$ about the gradient at time t can only be rigorously assessed when an exact statistical theory of transport is developed. Nevertheless, some intuitive notions, while not rigorous, are worth discussing. First note that the expansion used is invalid for hard spheres. It is, in fact, useful only for soft collisions since it implies that the force changes linearly with time. In a liquid it is probable that most of the interactions are soft due to the continuous overlap of potential fields of neighbor molecules. The expansion used would, of course, be rigorously correct if the displacement of an atom obeyed Hooke's law. In that case, third- and higher-order derivatives are identically zero. The expansion used would also be accurate if the length of a diffusive motion, $\Delta R(s)$, was very small, since

TABLE I.[a] Transport coefficients for liquid argon at 90°K.

	$\eta \times 10^3$ (poise)	$K \times 10^4$ (cal/0)	$D \times 10^5$ (cm²/sec)
Computed, Eqs. (25), (57), (58)	1.18	1.42	2.60
Estimated kinetic contribution, Eqs. (59), (60)	0.15	0.22	
Semiempirical computation		2.87	
Experiment	2.39[11]	2.90[10]	2.07[9]

[a] The following data has been used[12]: $L = \Delta H_{vap} - RT = 1320$ cal/mole; $v = 29$ cc/mole; $p = 1$ atmos; $\Delta C_p = 2.5\ R$; and $\alpha = 4.65 \times 10^{-3}/o$.

then, the higher powers of $\Delta R(s)$ would annihilate any contribution from derivatives of the pair potential. We may cite the following physical inferences to support the proposition that both $\nabla^3 V$ and ΔR are small. It is important to note that these inferences are based on incorrect models and should not be considered as more than order of magnitude indications. If the self-diffusion coefficients of liquids are forced into the activated-state model of diffusion, and the effective jump frequency estimated via the specific heat, then the length of a diffusive displacement is of the order of magnitude of one-tenth a nearest neighbor distance for all the liquids studied.[13] Within the framework of the activated-state model, $\Delta R(s)$ cannot be large, or any consistency with thermodynamic properties is lost. In the same vein and in fact closely related, the cell model for liquids gives good agreement with the energy of a fluid, poor agreement with the entropy, while using essentially a harmonic oscillator model. The entropy disagreement can be largely removed by considering correlations in the motions of nearby atoms, even in the cell approximation.[14] This would tend to indicate that $\nabla^3 V$ is small relative to $\nabla^2 V$. While both the estimates of ΔR and $\nabla^3 V$ may be in considerable error, the above arguments point to the probability that the product $\frac{1}{2}(\Delta R)^2 \nabla^3 V$ is small relative to the terms retained.

The fact that the distribution function in pair-space is approximated as the product of the local equilibrium distribution function in configuration-space and the zeroth-order distribution function in momentum-space is probably the mildest of the approximations we have made. In the gaseous state, the zeroth-order contributions to the stress tensor and heat flux are dominant,

[13] See, for example, R. E. Meyer and N. H. Nachtrieb, *J. Chem. Phys.* **23**, 1851 (1955).
[14] J. DeBoer, *Physica* **20**, 655 (1954).

and the higher terms amount to small corrections of the order of magnitude of ten percent or less. It is planned to investigate the use of other distribution functions in a separate publication.

The diffusion tensor in pair-space can always be approximated as the direct sum of the diffusion tensors (diagonal) in singlet-space if the pair separation is large. How close a pair of molecules must be before this breaks down is unknown. It should be noted that this additivity approximation is equivalent to decoupling the molecules at all distances. This is very much like the approximations involved in the cell model and the activated-state model of diffusion already mentioned. Again, rigorous justification must await a more complete theory.

In a recent paper, Collins and Raffel[15] have presented calculations of the heat flux and stress tensor based on very different approximations from those used in this paper. It is notable that the detailed expressions found for the coefficients of thermal conductivity and shear viscosity are very similar in structure to those found herein and the two different computations of the self-diffusion coefficient lead to identical formulae for the frictional coefficient. The major difference in the final results is that the expressions of Collins and Raffel are for the squares of the coefficients of shear viscosity and thermal conductivity in contrast to the forms in Eqs. (35), (36), and (46).

The role of time-smoothing may be interpreted in several related ways. The interval of coarse-graining is in principle chosen to be of sufficient length to render the basic dynamical event independent of both prior and future events. In a gas, the basic dynamical event may be taken as the binary collision and in this case the interval of coarse-graining must be long compared to the duration of a collision but short compared to the time between collisions. In a liquid, the basic dynamical event is not so easily identified and it is convenient to reinterpret the interval of coarse-graining. We imagine the initial state of the system to be attained via a thermodynamic fluctuation. That is, the initial state of the system is one of local equilibrium. It then will require a finite interval of time for the steady state fluxes to arise, and an interval of time, τ, may be introduced for the purposes of linearly predicting the steady state fluxes from the initial conditions and extrapolating past the transient region.[16] With this interpretation it is clear that τ must be long enough to bridge the transient period in the development of the fluxes, but short compared to the time scale on which the fluxes are nonzero.

In this paper time-smoothing has been employed in the sense just indicated. Collins and Raffel, however, use a very different assumption in which it is presumed that the curvature of the decay trajectory in the steady-state region is equal and opposite in sign to the curvature at the origin of the time scale. The course of the decay of a dynamical variable such as the momentum of a particle which initially has a non-equilibrium value is thereby rendered essentially quadratic at the origin, and this gives rise to the formulae for the squares of the transport coefficients. Such an approximation to the initial curvature of the trajectory describing the return to equilibrium is not unreasonable, but its accuracy cannot be assessed and the methods required to develop higher-order approximations are not clearly definable in terms of the physical situation envisaged. In view of the agreement between the results of Collins and

---

[15] F. C. Collins and H. Raffel, *J. Chem. Phys.* **29**, 699 (1958).

[16] M. Fixman, *J. Chem. Phys.* **26**, 1421 (1957).

Raffel and those obtained in this investigation by totally different methods, a further and more extensive investigation of the molecular interpretation of Collins's approximation and its relation to the formal development of Kirkwood seems warranted.

VII. ACKNOWLEDGMENTS

We are indebted to Dr. Richard Bearman and Dr. William T. King for many helpful discussions. One of us (SAR) would also like to thank his colleagues at the University of Chicago for numerous helpful criticisms.

On the Kinetic Theory of Dense Fluids. VIII. Some Comments on the Formal Computation of the Non-equilibrium Distribution Function of a Fluid

STUART A. RICE*, JOHN G. KIRKWOOD† AND ROBERT A. HARRIS‡
Department of Theoretical Chemistry, University Chemical Laboratory, Cambridge, England

(Received 10.12.60).

Synopsis

In this paper we consider two problems:
(a) The formal cluster expansion of the integro-differential equation determining the non-equilibrium *n* body distribution function, and
(b) Methods of computing the phase space transformation function.
Two formal solutions for the phase space transformation function are presented, one exact for the case of weak interactions, and one approximate and connected closely with the concepts of local equilibrium and Brownian motion.

The cluster expansion leads to collision kerneis corresponding to multiple body encounters. The operators are so defined that at least one interaction must occur between a group of *m* molecules and a separate group of *n* molecules for there to be a non-vanishing contribution to the transport equation for the *m*th order distribution function. Interactions wholly within the group *m* or the group *n* make no contribution. To mitigate the difficulties in computing multiple body trajectories it is suggested that the approximate solutions for the transformation functions be used in the theory of dense fluids.

I. INTRODUCTION

There have been numerous attempts to derive the equations satisfied by non-equilibrium distribution functions from the first principles of statistical mechanics with the aid of some auxiliary nonmechanical conditions which relate to the introduction of the irreversibility.[1] The conditions referred to may be assumed, as in the use of stochastic interactions at the walls, or they may be derived in the limit as the number of molecules N and the volume v simultaneously tend to become indefinitely large with the ratio (N/v) remaining constant. It is not our purpose to discuss this aspect of the problem, but we here remark that the recent important work of Mayer[2] provides an elegant and abstract formulation of the relationship between the two approaches. For

---

* John Simon Guggenheim Fellow, 1960–1961.
Permanent address: Department of Chemistry and Institute for the Study of Metals, University of Chicago, Chicago 37, Illinois, U.S.A.
† Deceased.
‡ Junior Fellow, Society of Fellows, Harvard University.
[1] For a convenient review see Rice, S. A. and Frisch, H. L., *Ann. Rev. Phys. Chem.* **11** (1960) 187.
[2] Mayer, J. E., *J. chem. Phys.* **33**, 1484 (1960).

the case of the Boltzmann equation, descriptive of transport in the dilute gas, the conditions required to effect a derivation are basically three in number:[3] the truncation of the interaction sequence with neglect of interactions of complexity of a higher order than binary collisions, the condition of molecular chaos, and the assumption of slow secular variation of the singlet distribution function, $f^{(1)}$, in space. Of these considerations, it is the molecular chaos which is responsible for the irreversibility. In this paper we shall be primarily concerned with the development of an equation for the time rate of change of the singlet distribution function (and also higher order distribution functions) which is valid at high densities. We shall develop such a relation by the removal of the restriction that only binary collisions occur.

It is pertinent to consider briefly the nature of the time scale involved in the Boltzmann equation. In the analysis due to Kirkwood,[4] the singlet distribution function which satisfies the Boltzmann equation is smoothed or "coarse grained" over an interval of time long relative to the duration of a collision but short relative to the time between collisions. The molecular chaos assumption appears in the statement that the pair distribution function is a product of singlet distribution functions prior to the collision. This approximation can be rigorously justified if the correlation between the distribution functions is finite in the initial state, since then the correlation can be made to vanish if the coarse graining in time is long enough (but still restricted as above).[5]

Bogolubov[6] has presented a density expansion of the equation of transport based in part upon a classification of the relevant time scales descriptive of the approach to equilibrium. In particular, Bogolubov assumes that an arbitrary initial state relaxes to a state in which the time dependence of the higher order distribution functions is determined by the time dependence of the singlet distribution function. This state is assumed to be reached in a time of the order of the duration of a collision. On the scale of the time between collisions, the time dependence of the singlet distribution function is determined by the dependence of the local thermodynamic and hydrodynamic variables. Subsequent development of the higher order distribution functions leads to a virial expansion for the time rate of change of $f^{(1)}$.

There have been at least four other techniques used to develop a virial expansion of the type mentioned above. Green[7] has shown how an initial distribution washes out after a time which, for reasonable initial distributions, is small compared to the time required to reach equilibrium. This demonstration substantiates the assumption made by Bogolubov. Green also has developed a power series in the density for the time rate of change of the singlet distribution function and gives an excellent discussion of the various types and mechanical prerequisites of three body encounters. Brout[8] has given an analysis in which the effects of higher order interactions are displayed explicitly in the form of the number of particles involved in the collision and not as a density power series. The argument rests on the observation that many body collisions may be built up from closely spaced successive binary

---

[3] Grad, H., *Handbuch der Physik* **12,** 205 Springer/Verlag, Berlin (1958).

[4] Kirkwood, J. G., *J. chem. Phys.* **14** (1946) 180. *J. chem. Phys.* **15** (1947) 72.

[5] Kirkwood, J. G., and Ross, J., *Symposium on the Statistical Mechanics of Transport Processes*, p. 1., Interscience Publishers, New York, (1958).

[6] Bogolubov, N., *J. Phys.* (U.S.S.R.) **10** (1946) 265.

[7] Green, M., *J. chem. Phys.* **25** (1956) 836.

[8] Brout, R., **22** (1956) 509.

collisions. Such an analysis is exact for the case of a finite fluid of rigid spheres and, with suitable definitions, arbitrarily accurate for the case of short range soft potentials. The resultant transport equation is represented as a Master equation when recollision terms and closed cycles of collisions are neglected. Montroll and Ward[9] have developed a systematic cluster integral expansion by employing the Kubo[10] formalism for the expression of the transport coefficients as autocorrelation functions of suitable dynamical variables. The calculations are quite complex despite the simplifications introduced by using a diagram technique. Finally, Prigogine and Balescu[11] have studied the evolution in time of the Fourier components of the distribution function in Γ space, $f^{(N)}$. By the use of a diagrammatic classification of terms according to powers of the time, the density, and the magnitude of the potential energy of interaction, it is possible to derive an asymptotic equation for the time evolution of the distribution function. In the case of weak coupling the resultant transport equation is the same as the Master equation derived by Brout and Prigogine. In the case of strong interactions, a density expansion is made and it is found that the first higher density correction depends upon a restricted three body problem. Higher order terms are not explicitly displayed or evaluated.

The approach we shall employ in this paper is different from those cited above. First we shall develop a formal method for obtaining the non-equilibrium distribution function of arbitrary order by the use of Green's functions (phase space transformation functions). Following this we shall examine some methods for getting formal representations of the Green's functions for the case of small departures from equilibrium. In this paper we present only the formal results of calculations and do not treat explicit problems.

II. THE FORMAL CLUSTER EXPANSION

As in preceding work [4,5] we shall assume throughout the following analysis that it is possible to find a time interval τ such that a selected dynamical event which occurs in τ is stochastically independent of both prior and future events. If the n body distribution function, $f^{(n)}$, is averaged over the interval τ and use made of the definitions

$$\bar{f}^{(n)}(t) = \frac{1}{\tau}\int_0^\tau f^{(n)}(t+s)\mathrm{d}s$$

$$\frac{\partial \bar{f}^{(n)}}{\partial t} = \frac{f^{(n)}(t+\tau) - f^{(n)}(t)}{\tau} \tag{1}$$

then we can show that

$$\frac{\partial \bar{\bar{f}}^{(n)}}{\partial t} = \frac{1}{\tau}\int_0^\tau \frac{f^{(n)}(t+s+\tau) - f^{(n)}(t+s)}{\tau}\mathrm{d}s$$

$$= \frac{\partial \bar{f}^{(n)}}{\partial t} + \frac{1}{\tau^2}\int_0^\tau [f^{(n)}(t+s+\tau) + f^{(n)}(t) - f^{(n)}(t+\tau) - f^{(n)}(t+s)]\mathrm{d}s$$

$$= \frac{\partial \bar{f}^{(n)}}{\partial t} \tag{2}$$

---

[9] Montroll, E. and Ward, J., *Physica* **25** (1959) 423.
[10] Kubo, R., *J. phys. Soc.* Japan **12** (1957) 570, 1203.
[11] Prigogine, I. and Balescu, R., *Physica* **23** (1957) 555; *Physica* **25** (1959) 281.

because τ has been so chosen that $\bar{f}^{(n)}(t)$ is independent of the length of the smoothing with the restrictions stated. We shall find use for this result later in the analysis. The justification for the assumption that such a time interval τ can be defined is not to be found in our analysis, but must come from the more general theories of Mayer[2] and Prigogine and co-workers.[11,12] We merely note that time smoothing in itself does not introduce irreversibility. Rather, it is the assumption that events in successive intervals of length τ are uncorrelated which provides the directional flow. Thus, the introduction of time smoothing is to be considered as a technique for isolating the basic dynamical event, and not as a philosophical principle.[13]

We take as our starting points the definition embodied in Eq. (1) together with the definition of the Green's function $K^{(N)}(s)$,

$$f^{(N)}(\{\boldsymbol{N}\}; t+s) = \int K^{(N)}(\{\boldsymbol{N}\}/\{\boldsymbol{N}'\}; s) f^{(N)}(\{\boldsymbol{N}'\}; t)\, \mathrm{d}\{\boldsymbol{N}'\} \tag{3}$$

where, since we have no occasion to us unsymmetrical distribution functions the symbol $\{\boldsymbol{N}\}$ stands for *all momenta and coordinates* of the N molecules and $\mathrm{d}\{\boldsymbol{N}\}$ stands for the volume element $\prod_2^N \mathrm{d}\boldsymbol{p}_i\, \mathrm{d}\boldsymbol{R}_i$. For a single molecule we shall use the corresponding symbols $(\boldsymbol{k})$ and $\mathrm{d}(\boldsymbol{k})$. It is clear from Eq. (3) that $K^{(N)}(s)$ satisfies the Liouville equation,

$$\frac{\partial K^{(N)}}{\partial s} + L^{(N)} K^{(N)} = 0 \tag{4}$$

$$L^{(N)} = \sum_{i=1}^{N} \left[\frac{\mathbf{p}_i}{m} \cdot \nabla_{R_i} + \boldsymbol{F}_i \cdot \nabla_{pi} \right] \tag{5}$$

with $\boldsymbol{F}_i$ the force acting on molecule i, and $\boldsymbol{p}_i$, $\boldsymbol{R}_i$ and m its position, momentum and mass. From the definition of $K^{(N)}(s)$ as a conditional probability density we have the relation

$$f^{(n)}(\{\boldsymbol{n}\}; t+s) = \int K^{(n)}(\{\boldsymbol{n}\}/\{\boldsymbol{n}'\}; s) f^{(n)}(\{\boldsymbol{n}'\}; t)\, \mathrm{d}\{\boldsymbol{n}'\} \tag{6}$$

with

$$f^{(n)}(\{\boldsymbol{n}\}; t) = \frac{1}{(N-n)!} \int f^{(N)}(\{\boldsymbol{N}\}; t)\, \mathrm{d}\{\boldsymbol{N} - \boldsymbol{n}\} \tag{7}$$

and

$$K^{(n)}(\{\boldsymbol{n}\}/\{\boldsymbol{n}'\}; s) = \int K^{(N)}(\{\boldsymbol{N}\}/\{\boldsymbol{N}'\}; s) \frac{f^{(N)}(\{\boldsymbol{N}'\})}{f^{(n)}(\{\boldsymbol{n}'\})}\, \mathrm{d}\{\boldsymbol{N} - \boldsymbol{n}\}\, \mathrm{d}\{(\boldsymbol{N} - \boldsymbol{n})'\}. \tag{8}$$

We consider the sequence of Green's functions, $K_0^{(n)}$, which satisfy the n body Liouville equations

$$\frac{\partial K_0^{(n)}}{\partial s} + L^{(n)} K_0^{(n)} = 0 \tag{9}$$

---

[12] Resibois, P., *Physica* **25** (1959) 725.

[13] The reader should note that the equations developed will be valid for the description of transport processes, but not for the general description of the approach to equilibrium. This restriction arises from the use of Eq. (1) since as τ gets larger and larger in order to include more and more complex dynamical events, the time derivative $\partial \bar{f}/\partial t$ becomes ambiguous unless $\partial \bar{f}/\partial t$ is very small. This is the situation for the description of transport phenomena, but is not necessarily true in the approach to equilibrium.

and define cluster operators $B^{(n,v)}(\{\boldsymbol{n}+v\}/\{(\boldsymbol{n}+v)'\};\tau)$ by the relations

$$K_0{}^{(n+v)}(\{\boldsymbol{n}+v\};\tau) = \prod_{k=n+1}^{n+v} K_0{}^{(1)}(\boldsymbol{k})\, K_0{}^{(n)}(\{\boldsymbol{n}\};\tau)$$

$$+ \sum_{s=1}^{v} \sum_{\substack{i_1>i_2>\ldots i_s\\ =n+1}}^{n+v} \prod_{\substack{k=n+1\\ \neq i_1,\ldots i_s}}^{n+v} K_0{}^{(1)}(\boldsymbol{k}) B^{(n,s)}(\{\boldsymbol{n}\},\{\boldsymbol{i}_s\};\tau). \tag{10}$$

From Eq. (10) we find for $K^{(N)}$

$$K^{(N)}(\tau) = \prod_{k=n+1}^{N} K_0{}^{(1)}(\boldsymbol{k}) K_0{}^{(n)}(\{\boldsymbol{n}\};\tau)$$

$$+ \sum_{s=1}^{N-n} \sum_{\substack{i_1>i_2>\ldots i_s\\ =n+1}}^{N} \prod_{\substack{k=n+1\\ \neq i_1,\ldots i_s}}^{N} K_0{}^{(1)}(\boldsymbol{k}) B^{(n,s)}(\{\boldsymbol{n}\},\{\boldsymbol{i}_s\};\tau). \tag{11}$$

In the cluster expansions displayed the sets $\{n\}$ and $\{i_s\}$ contain the specific molecules 1, . . ., and $i_1, \ldots i_s$, respectively. The reader should also note that we have dropped the double notation $K^{(n)}(\{\boldsymbol{n}\}/\{\boldsymbol{n}'\};\tau)$ when no confusion can result. Equation (11) is a remarkable result since it represents a relation between the transformation function in the N body system and the transformation functions for smaller sub-systems of isolated molecules. The first few cluster operators are

$$B^{(1,1)}(1,2) = K_0{}^{(2)}(1,2) - K_0{}^{(1)}(1)K_0{}^{(1)}(2)$$

$$B^{(1,2)}(1,2,3) = K_0{}^{(3)}(1,2,3) - K_0{}^{(1)}(2)K_0{}^{(2)}(1,3) \tag{12}$$

$$- K_0{}^{(1)}(3)K_0{}^{(2)}(1,2) + K_0{}^{(1)}(1)K_0{}^{(1)}(2)K_0{}^{(1)}(3)$$

$$B^{(2,1)}(1,2,3) = K_0{}^{(3)}(1,2,3) - K_0{}^{(1)}(3)K_0{}^{(2)}(1,2)$$

with an obvious notation for the arguments of the functions. It should be noted that the normalization condition

$$\int K^{(n)}\, d\{\boldsymbol{n}\} = \int K_0{}^{(n)}\, d\{\boldsymbol{n}\} = 1 \tag{13}$$

is the same for both $K^{(n)}$ and $K_0{}^{(n)}$. Also, $K^{(n)}$ and $K_0{}^{(n)}$ have the same formal representation in terms of delta functions. In one case, the increments of momenta and coordinates are determined from the n body dynamics in the presence of $N-n$ other molecules. In the other case, the increments of momenta and coordinates are determined from the dynamics of an isolated n body system. The general relation defining the cluster operators in terms of the transformation functions is obtained by inverting Eq. (10). The result is

$$B^{(n+v)} = (-1)^v K_0{}^{(n)}(\{\boldsymbol{n}\}) \prod_{k=n+1}^{n+v} K_0{}^{(1)}(\boldsymbol{k})$$

$$+ \sum_{s=1}^{v} (-1)^{v-s} \sum_{\substack{i_1<\ldots<i_s\\ =n+1}}^{n+v} \prod_{\substack{k=n+1\\ \neq i_1\ldots i_s}}^{n+v} K_0{}^{(1)}(\boldsymbol{k})\, K_0{}^{(n+s)}(\{\boldsymbol{n}\},\{\boldsymbol{i}_s\}). \tag{14}$$

The introduction of the cluster operators serves, as in the equilibrium case, to classify events. Suppose that the $(n + v)^{th}$ molecule does not interact with the remaining molecules during the interval τ. Then during this time

$$K_0{}^{(n+s)}(\{\boldsymbol{n}\}, \{\boldsymbol{i}_{s-1}\}, \boldsymbol{n} + v) = K_0{}^{(n+s-1)}(\{\boldsymbol{n}\}, \{\boldsymbol{i}_{s-1}\})\, K_0{}^{(1)}(\boldsymbol{n} + v). \quad (15)$$

By algebraic rearrangement of Eq. (14) the second term on the right-hand side can be written in the form

$$\sum_{s=1}^{v-1} (-1)^{v-s} \left\{ \sum_{i_1<\dots<i_s}^{n+v-1} \prod_{\substack{k=1\\ \neq i_1\dots i_s'}}^{n+v} K_0{}^{(1)}(\boldsymbol{k}) K_0{}^{(n+s)}(\{\boldsymbol{n}\}, \{\boldsymbol{i}_s\}) \right.$$

$$\left. + \sum_{i_1<\dots<i_{s-1}}^{n+v-1} \prod_{\substack{k=1\\ \neq i_1\dots i_{s-1}}}^{n+v-1} K_0{}^{(1)}(\boldsymbol{k}) K_0{}^{(n+s)}(\{\boldsymbol{n}\}, \{\boldsymbol{i}_{s-1}\}, \boldsymbol{n} + v) \right\}$$

$$+ K_0{}^{(n+v)}(\{\boldsymbol{n}\}, \{v\}). \quad (16)$$

Thus, the substitution of Eq. (15) and the relation (16) into Eq. (14) gives, after putting $s' = s - 1$

$$B^{(n,v)} = K_0{}^{(1)}(\boldsymbol{n} + v) \left\{ - B^{(n,v-1)} \right.$$

$$\left. + \sum_{s'=0}^{v-1} (-1)^{v-1-s'} \sum_{i_1<\dots i_s'}^{n+v-1} \prod_{\substack{k=1\\ \neq i_1\dots i_s'}}^{n+v-1} K_0{}^{(1)}(\boldsymbol{k}) K_0{}^{(n+s')}(\{\boldsymbol{n}\}, \{\boldsymbol{i}_s'\}) \right\}$$

$$= K_0{}^{(1)}(\boldsymbol{n} + v)\{- B^{(n,v-1)} + B^{(n,v-1)}\}$$

$$= 0. \quad (17)$$

Thus, if other members of the set $\{v\}$ have not collided with molecule $n + v$ and member $n + v$ of set $\{v\}$ has not collided with set $\{n\}$, $B^{(n,v)} = 0$. Further if no member of the set $\{v\}$ has collided with any member of the set $\{n\}$, then

$$B^{(n,v)} = (-1)^v \prod_{k=n+1}^{n+v} K_0{}^{(1)}(\boldsymbol{k}) K_0{}^{(n)}(\{\boldsymbol{n}\})$$

$$+ \sum_{s=1}^{v} (-1)^{v-s} \sum_{\substack{i_1<\dots<i_s\\ =n+1}}^{n+v} \prod_{\substack{k=n+1\\ \neq i_1\dots i_s}}^{n+v} K_0{}^{(1)}(\boldsymbol{k}) K_0{}^{(n)}(\{\boldsymbol{n}\}) K_0{}^{(s)}(\{\boldsymbol{i}_s\}) \quad (18)$$

and since

$$\int K_0{}^{(s)}(\{\boldsymbol{i}_s\}/\{\boldsymbol{i}_s'\})\, d\{\boldsymbol{i}_s\} = 1, \quad i_1 \cdots i_s \subset \{v\} \quad (19)$$

we have by integration of Eq. (18)

$$\int B^{(n,v)}\, d\{\boldsymbol{i}_s\} = K_0{}^{(n)}(\{\boldsymbol{n}\}) \sum_{s=0}^{v} (-1)^{v-s} \frac{v!}{s!\,(v - s)!}$$

$$= K_0{}^{(n)}(\{\boldsymbol{n}\})(-1)^v[1 - 1]^v \quad (20)$$

$$= 0 \qquad i_1 \cdots i_s \subset \{v\}$$

regardless of internal collisions within either set $\{n\}$ or set $\{v\}$.

To derive an equation from which the distribution function $f^{(n)}$ may be determined, we now combine Eqs. (1), (3) and (11). This leads, after a second time smoothing, to the relation

$$\frac{\partial \bar{f}^{(n)}}{\partial t} + L^{(n)}\bar{f}^{(n)} = \sum_{s=1}^{N-n} \frac{N!}{s!(N-s)!} \int \frac{B^{(n,s)}(\{\boldsymbol{n}\},\{\boldsymbol{s}\})}{\tau} \bar{f}^{(n+s)}\{(\boldsymbol{n}+\boldsymbol{s})'\}\, \mathrm{d}\{(\boldsymbol{n}+\boldsymbol{s})'\}\, \mathrm{d}\{\boldsymbol{s}\} \tag{21}$$

where we have used the identity

$$L^{(n)}\bar{f}^{(n)} = -\int \frac{K_0{}^{(n)}(\{\boldsymbol{n}\}/\{\boldsymbol{n}'\};\tau) - K_0{}^{(n)}(\{\boldsymbol{n}\}/\{\boldsymbol{n}'\};0)}{\tau} \times \bar{f}^{(n)}(\{\boldsymbol{n}'\})\, \mathrm{d}\{\boldsymbol{n}'\}. \tag{22}$$

We note that, with the use of Eq. (2), Eq. (22) can be interpreted as a time smoothing along an isolated n body trajectory.

Let $\boldsymbol{R}_{0k}$ be the vector distance between molecule k and the centre of mass of the set $\{n\}$. Then in the limit as R_{0k} becomes indefinitely large,

$$\lim_{R_{0k}\to\infty} \bar{f}^{(n+1)}(\{\boldsymbol{n}\}, \boldsymbol{k}) = \bar{f}^{(n)}(\{\boldsymbol{n}\})\bar{f}^{(1)}(\boldsymbol{k}). \tag{23}$$

Similarly, if $\boldsymbol{R}_{mn}$ is the vector distance between the centres of mass of the sets $\{m\}$ and $\{n\}$, then

$$\lim_{R_{mn}\to\infty} \bar{f}^{(m+n)}(\{\boldsymbol{m}\}, \{\boldsymbol{n}\}) = \bar{f}^{(m)}(\{\boldsymbol{m}\})\bar{f}^{(n)}(\{\boldsymbol{n}\}). \tag{24}$$

Consider now the correlation integrals

$$\Theta_{n,\sigma} = \int B^{(n,s)}(\{\boldsymbol{n}\}, \{\boldsymbol{s}\})[\bar{f}^{(n+s)}(\{(\boldsymbol{n}+\boldsymbol{s})'\}) - \bar{f}^{(n+s-\sigma)}(\{(\boldsymbol{n}+\boldsymbol{s}-\boldsymbol{\sigma})'\})\bar{f}^{(\sigma)}(\{\boldsymbol{\sigma}'\})]\, \mathrm{d}\{(\boldsymbol{n}+\boldsymbol{s})'\}\, \mathrm{d}\{\boldsymbol{s}\}. \tag{25}$$

By addition and subtraction of the product form of the distribution function we find, in the limit that $\tau \gg \Theta_{n,\sigma}$

$$\begin{aligned}\frac{\partial \bar{f}^{(n)}}{\partial t} + L^{(n)}\bar{f}^{(n)} &= \sum_{s=1}^{N-n} \sum_{k=n+1}^{n+s} \frac{N!}{s!(N-s)!} \int \Big[\int B^{(n,s)}(\{\boldsymbol{n}\}, \{\boldsymbol{s}\}; \tau) \\ &\times \bar{f}^{(n+s-1)}(\{(\boldsymbol{n}+\boldsymbol{s}-\boldsymbol{1}_k)'\})\bar{f}^{(1)}(\boldsymbol{k}')\, \mathrm{d}\{(\boldsymbol{n}+\boldsymbol{s}-\boldsymbol{1}_k)'\}\, \mathrm{d}\{\boldsymbol{s}\} \Big] V_{k0}'\, \mathrm{d}A_k'\mathrm{d}^3p_k' \\ &+ \sum_{s=1}^{N-n} \sum_{k=n+1}^{n+s} \sum_{\substack{l=n+1\\ l\neq k}}^{n+s} \frac{N!}{s!(N-s)!} \int \Big[\int B^{(n,s)}(\{\boldsymbol{n}\}, \{\boldsymbol{s}\}; \tau) \\ &\times \bar{f}^{(n+s-2)}(\{(\boldsymbol{n}+\boldsymbol{s}-\boldsymbol{1}_k-\boldsymbol{1}_l)'\})\bar{f}^{(2)}(\boldsymbol{l}, \boldsymbol{k})\, \mathrm{d}\{(\boldsymbol{n}+\boldsymbol{s}-\boldsymbol{1}_k-\boldsymbol{1}_l)'\}\mathrm{d}\{\boldsymbol{s}\} \Big] \\ &\cdot V_{lk0}'\, \mathrm{d}A'_k\mathrm{d}^3p_k'\mathrm{d}^3p_l' \\ &+ \dots \end{aligned} \tag{26}$$

The pattern by which the higher order terms may be written down is clear. In Eq. (26) dA_k is the element of area of a plane containing the centre of mass of the set $\{n + s - 1\}$ molecules, excluding k, or the element of area of a plane containing the centre of mass of the set $\{n + s - 2\}$ molecules, excluding k and l, and so forth for each integral. Similarly, V_{k0} is the relative velocity of k and the centre of mass of the set $\{n + s - 1\}$ before interaction, V_{lk0} the relative velocity of the centre of mass of the pair k, l and the set $\{n + s - 2\}$ before interaction, ... We note that the integrations must be phased so that at least one molecule from the set $\{n\}$ has an interaction with the set $\{s\}$. This must occur during the time interval τ and, therefore, all the relevant integrals are independent of τ for sufficiently long τ.

Equation (26) may be transformed into a density expansion by suitable development of the distribution functions. Since the choice of development depends upon the problem to be considered we shall consider such a development in another paper.

As an example of the use of the cluster development we consider the transport equation for the singlet distribution function. Examination of Eq. (12) shows that the term $B^{(1,1)}$ introduces the usual Boltzmann kernel with molecular chaos before the collision automatically incorporated. As usual, the coordinates and momenta after the collision are computed from the mechanics of the two body encounter. These terms are so familiar that we shall not display them herein.

The three body collision term has an interesting structure which gives some physical insight into the formal cluster series. Consider the term $B^{(1,2)}$ corresponding to an encounter between one molecule and a pair of other molecules. This is given in Eq. (12). First we note that if molecules 2 and 3 have not interacted with molecule 1,

$$K_0^{(3)}(1, 2, 3) = K_0^{(1)}(1)K_0^{(2)}(2, 3)$$

whereupon

$$B^{(1,2)} = K_0^{(1)}(1)[K_0^{(2)}(2, 3) - K_0^{(1)}(2)K_0^{(1)}(3)]$$

the other terms cancelling. As shown in Eq. (20), this expression, when integrated, vanishes. In a similar manner the contribution when molecule 2 collides with one and three does not, or when molecule 3 collides with 1 and 2 does not, are easily shown to vanish. For, in the cases cited, the functions $K_0^{(3)}(1, 2, 3) \rightarrow K_0^{(1)}(3)\, K_0^{(2)}(1, 2)$; $K_0^{(1)}(2)\, K_0^{(1)}(1, 3)$ and $K_0^{(2)}(1, 3)$ or $K_0^{(2)}(1, 2)$ goes to the product $K_0^{(1)}(1)\, K_0^{(1)}(3)$ or $K_0^{(1)}(1)\, K_0^{(1)}(2)$ respectively. Simple substitution in Eq. (12) readily shows that $B^{(1,2)}$ vanishes. Thus, there is no triple interaction term unless both molecules 2 and 3 have interacted with molecule 1 in the time interval τ. It should be noted that we do not require that molecules 2 and 3 do or do not interact with each other, but only that they both interact with molecule 1.

An examination of the structure of the cluster operators $B^{(1,1)}$ shows that the collision kernel of the ordinary Boltzmann equation is generated from the difference between free particle trajectories and the pair trajectory, with the increments in momenta and coordinates determined from the two body dynamics. Similarly, the structure of $B^{(1,2)}$ leads to an interaction kernel corresponding to the differences between the three body trajectory, and the possible subdivisions of this into non-interacting pair and singlet or all singlet terms. We find, in particular, that

$$\int [\int B^{(1,2)}(1, 2, 3)\,\mathrm{d}(\mathbf{2})\bar{f}^{(2)}(1', 2')\bar{f}^{(1)}(3')\,\mathrm{d}(\mathbf{1}')\,\mathrm{d}(\mathbf{2}')]\,V_{30}\,\mathrm{d}A_3\,\mathrm{d}^3p_3$$
$$= \int [\bar{f}^{(2)}(1, 2; [123])\bar{f}^{(1)}(3; (123]) - \bar{f}^{(2)}(1; [12], 2; [2])\bar{f}^{(1)}(3; [13])$$
$$- \bar{f}^{(2)}(1; [12], 2;[12])\bar{f}^{(1)}(3; [3])$$
$$+ \bar{f}^{(2)}(1; [1], 2;[2])\bar{f}^{(1)}(3; [3])]\,V_{30}\,\mathrm{d}A_3\,\mathrm{d}^3p_3\,\mathrm{d}\Omega_{12} \tag{27}$$

with the volume elements $\mathrm{d}\Omega_{12} = 8\ \mathrm{d}^3p_{12}\ \mathrm{d}^3R_{12}$ and $\boldsymbol{p}_{12} = \frac{1}{2}(\boldsymbol{p}_2 - \boldsymbol{p}_1)$. In Eq. (27) the notation in the square bracket indicates the number and identity of molecules which must be considered in computing the particular increments of momentum and coordinate in question. To Eq. (27) must be added the other collision terms corresponding to alternative ways of selecting one molecule from a group of three. The sum of all such terms comprises the ternary interaction, as can be seen from the given formula given in Eq. (26).

Higher order collision kernels may be generated simply by the use of the relation embodied in Eq. (14). For the rate of change of $\bar{f}^{(1)}$ we must take all terms of the form $B^{(1,n)}$. Of course, in all cases other than simple binary encounters, the collision kernel depends upon the evaluation of $n(n > 2)$ body trajectories. For this reason we do not display the formulae herein but turn instead to methods of circumventing the difficulties in the mechanical n-body problem by seeking directly approximate solutions for the basic Green's functions defining $B^{(n,v)}$.

Before proceeding it is pertinent to point out that Eq. (27) is identical in form with the three body collision kernel derived by Green, who has also given an incisive analysis of the correlation, memory and phase relations in the ternary encounter. Green's technique is to expand directly the n body distribution function in powers of the number density.

In our study, we classify terms according to the number of interactions and use an expansion of the phase space transformation function. By using this particular expansion we hope to explore some approximate transport equations for dense fluids derived from the formal cluster expansion by making approximations to the transformation functions.

III. APPROXIMATE SOLUTIONS FOR THE GREEN'S FUNCTIONS

Just as the equilibrium form of the distribution function $\bar{f}^{(1)}$ is known, so also is the asymptotic time, momentum and displacement dependence of $K^{(1)}$. It is a direct consequence of the central limit theorem that for s sufficiently large[1]

$$\lim_{s\to\infty} K^{(1)}(1) = \frac{\mathrm{e}^{-(\Delta R_1)^2/4D^{(1)}s}}{(4\pi D^{(1)}s)^{\frac{3}{2}}}\cdot\frac{\mathrm{e}^{-(\Delta p_1)^2/4D_p^{(1)}s}}{(4\pi D_p{}^{(1)}s)^{\frac{3}{2}}} \tag{28}$$

with $D^{(1)}$ the ordinary diffusion coefficient and $D_p{}^{(1)}$ a "diffusion coefficient" in the momentum space of molecule one.[14] For very short times, on the other hand,

$$\lim_{s\to 0} K^{(1)}(1) = \delta(\boldsymbol{R}_1 - \boldsymbol{R}_1' - \Delta\boldsymbol{R}_1)\delta(\boldsymbol{p}_1 - \boldsymbol{p}_1' - \Delta\boldsymbol{p}_1) \tag{29}$$

---

[14] Kihara, T., *Symposium on the Statistical Mechanics of Transport Processes*, p. 180, Interscience Publishers New York (1958).

with the increments $\Delta \boldsymbol{R}_1$ and $\Delta \boldsymbol{p}_1$ in this case computed from the solution to the N body problem. Although the form displayed in Eq. (28) approaches a delta function as $s \to 0$, this delta function is characteristic of the scalar displacements ΔR_1 and Δp_1 in Eq. (28) and does not have the directional character implied by the vector displacements $\Delta \boldsymbol{R}_1$ and $\Delta \boldsymbol{p}_1$ in Eq. (29). The gap in the description of $K^{(1)}(s)$ corresponds to our inability to compute multipole collision trajectories.

To compute, at least formally, the Green's function $K^{(1)}(s)$ we start with the Liouville equation, Eq. (4), and rewrite it to make the operator self adjoint,

$$\tilde{L}^{(N)} f^{(N)} = i \frac{\partial f^{(N)}}{\partial t}$$

$$\tilde{L}^{(N)} \equiv i \sum_j \left[\frac{\boldsymbol{p}_j}{m} \cdot \nabla_{R_j} + \boldsymbol{F}_j \cdot \nabla_{pj} \right]. \tag{30}$$

Equation (30) may be formally integrated with the use of Eq. (7) to yield

$$\frac{\partial f^{(1)}}{\partial t} + \frac{\boldsymbol{p}_1}{m} \cdot \nabla_{R_1} f^{(1)} = - \int \boldsymbol{F}_{1j} \cdot \nabla_{p1} f^{(2)}(1, j)\, \mathrm{d}(\boldsymbol{j}) \tag{31}$$

If we introduce the pair correlation function $g^{(2)}(\boldsymbol{i}, \boldsymbol{j}; t)$ by the definition

$$g^{(2)}(\boldsymbol{i}, \boldsymbol{j}; t) f^{(1)}(\boldsymbol{i}; t) f^{(1)}(\boldsymbol{j}; t) = f^{(2)}(\boldsymbol{i}, \boldsymbol{j}; t) \tag{32}$$

then it is easily seen that

$$\tilde{L}^{(1)} f^{(1)} = - i \frac{\partial f^{(1)}}{\partial t}.$$

$$\tilde{L}^{(1)} = i \left[\frac{\boldsymbol{p}_1}{m} \cdot \nabla_{R_1} + \int \boldsymbol{F}_{1j} \cdot \nabla_{p_1} g^{(2)}(\boldsymbol{i}, \boldsymbol{j}; t) f^{(1)}(\boldsymbol{j}; t)\, \mathrm{d}(\boldsymbol{j}) \right]. \tag{33}$$

The eigenfunctions of the self-adjoint operator $\tilde{L}^{(1)}$ are determined by

$$\tilde{L}^{(1)} \phi_k = \Lambda_k \phi_k \tag{34}$$

so that the usual expansions yield

$$f^{(1)}(\boldsymbol{i}; t) = \sum_k C_k \phi_k(\boldsymbol{i}) \mathrm{e}^{-i\Lambda_k t}$$

$$C_k = \int \phi_k^*(\boldsymbol{i}) f^{(1)}(\boldsymbol{i}; t) \mathrm{e}^{i\Lambda_k t}\, \mathrm{d}(\boldsymbol{i}) \tag{35}$$

and all the Λ_k are real. Equation (6) provides a connexion between the distribution functions $f^{(1)}(\boldsymbol{i}; t + s)$ and $f^{(1)}(\boldsymbol{i}; t)$. Another connexion may be established by writing

$$f^{(1)}(\boldsymbol{i}; t + s) = \sum_k C_k \phi_k(t + s) \mathrm{e}^{-i\Lambda_k (t+s)} \tag{36}$$

from which we obtain

$$f^{(1)}(\boldsymbol{i}; t + s) = \int \sum_k \phi_k^*(t) f^{(1)}(\boldsymbol{i}; t)\, \phi_k(t + s)\, \mathrm{e}^{-i\Lambda_k s}\, \mathrm{d}(\boldsymbol{i}). \tag{37}$$

A comparison of Eqs. (6) and (37) then yields

$$K^{(1)}(\boldsymbol{i}/\boldsymbol{i}'; s) = \sum_k \phi_k^*(\boldsymbol{i}') \phi_k(\boldsymbol{i}) e^{-i\Lambda_k s} \tag{38}$$

It is convenient now to consider $K^{(1)}$ for times such that $s \geqslant 0$. For this purpose we introduce the unit step function with the properties

$$\begin{aligned} H(s) &= 1, \quad s \geqslant 0 \\ H(s) &= 0, \quad s < 0 \\ \frac{dH}{ds} &= \delta(s). \end{aligned} \tag{39}$$

The introduction of $H(s)$ into Eq. (38) as a multiplier allows us to find the differential equation satisfied by $K^{(1)}(s)$. For, by use of Eqs. (33) and (38) we find that

$$\tilde{L}^{(1)} K^{(1)}(s) + i \frac{\partial K^{(1)}}{\partial s} = i\delta(s)\, \delta(\boldsymbol{p}_i - \boldsymbol{p}_i')\, \delta(\boldsymbol{R}_i - \boldsymbol{R}_i'). \tag{40}$$

The necessary condition that

$$\lim_{s \to 0} K^{(1)}(\boldsymbol{i}/\boldsymbol{i}'; s) = \delta(\boldsymbol{p}_i - \boldsymbol{p}_i')\, \delta(\boldsymbol{R}_i - \boldsymbol{R}_i') \tag{41}$$

is easily seen to follow when the definition embodied in Eq. (30) is employed.

We now seek a solution of Eq. (40) for the case of weak interactions. By setting

$$K^{(1)}(s) = K_0^{(1)}(s) + K_1^{(1)}(s) + \ldots \tag{42}$$

and substitution into Eq. (40) we find

$$\begin{aligned} \frac{\partial K_0^{(1)}}{\partial s} + \frac{\mathbf{p}_1}{m} \cdot \nabla_{R_1} K_0^{(1)}(s) &= \delta(s)\, \delta(\boldsymbol{p}_1 - \boldsymbol{p}_1')\, \delta(\boldsymbol{R}_1 - \boldsymbol{R}_1') \\ \frac{\partial K_n^{(1)}}{\partial s} + \frac{\boldsymbol{p}_1}{m} \cdot \nabla_{R_1} K_n^{(1)}(s) &= -\, J K_n^{(1)}(s); \ n \geqslant 1 \\ J = \int \boldsymbol{F}_{1j} \cdot \nabla_{p_1} & g^{(2)}(\mathit{1},\boldsymbol{j}) f^{(1)}(\boldsymbol{j})\, d(\boldsymbol{j}). \end{aligned} \tag{43}$$

In conformity with our previous notation, the subscript zero indicates a free particle trajectory. The solution is, therefore,

$$K_0^{(1)}(s) = H(s)\, \delta\left(\boldsymbol{R}_1 - \boldsymbol{R}_1' - \frac{\boldsymbol{p}_1'}{m} s\right) \delta(\boldsymbol{p}_1 - \boldsymbol{p}_1'). \tag{44}$$

For $K_n^{(1)}(s)$ one finds the corresponding relation

$$K_n^{(1)}(s) = -\int dt''\, d(\boldsymbol{i}'') K_0^{(1)}(\boldsymbol{i}/\boldsymbol{i}''; s - t'')\, J(\boldsymbol{i}'') K_{n-1}^{(1)}(\boldsymbol{i}''/\boldsymbol{i}'; t'') \tag{45}$$

and the successive application of this iterative relation using Eq. (44) as the basic solution leads to a solution for $K_n^{(1)}(s)$ in terms of positions and momenta at various retarded points in the interval of time s. The solution is cumbersome and will not be displayed herein. We merely note that for the case of weak interactions, when the interated solution may be expected to converge rapidly, it is convenient to use a diagram technique to solve specific problems. Diagrams of the required type have been considered by Von Roos[15] in a development of the scattering operator for the N body Green's function. These may be adapted to the case considered in this paper.

When the interaction between molecules is strong, the iterated solution built from a basis function corresponding to free molecules does not converge rapidly. To consider the case of strong interaction we turn to an analysis more closely allied to the concept of local equilibrium and make use of the known asymptotic behavior.

We proceed by considering an interval of time s during which there occurs a dynamical event which is independent of both prior and future events. We again consider the model dense fluid studied by Rice and Allnatt,[16] consisting of spherical molecules interacting pairwise through a rigid core and an attraction. The dynamical event will be taken to be a rigid core collision followed by a quasi-Brownian motion in the fluctuating attractive field of the close neighbours. Consistent with this physical description we may write for the singlet Green's function

$$K^{(1)}(s) = K_R{}^{(1)}(s)[1 - H(s - (+0))] + K_s{}^{(1)}(s)\, H(s - (+0)) \tag{46}$$

with the first term corresponding to the impulsive rigid core interaction and the second term to the diffusive motion. We now divide the force $\boldsymbol{F}_{1j}$ into two parts, $\boldsymbol{F}_{1j}{}^{(R)}$ and $\boldsymbol{F}_{1j}{}^{(s)}$ in analogous manner. In the limit as $s \to +0$ we may take $\boldsymbol{F}_{1j}{}^{(s)} \approx 0$ (see Rice and Allnatt[16] for a discussion of this assumption) whereupon we find

$$K_R{}^{(1)}(s) = \delta(\boldsymbol{p}_1 - \boldsymbol{p}_1' - \Delta \boldsymbol{p}_1)\delta(\boldsymbol{R}_1 - \boldsymbol{R}_1' - \Delta \boldsymbol{R}_1); \quad 0 \leqslant s \leqslant +0 \tag{47}$$

with $\Delta\boldsymbol{p}_1$ and $\Delta\boldsymbol{R}_1$ determined from the dynamics of the two body encounter in the time $+\,0$. For the remainder of the interval we have

$$\tilde{L}_s{}^{(1)} K_s{}^{(1)}(s) + i\frac{\partial K_s{}^{(1)}}{\partial s} = i\delta(s)\delta(\boldsymbol{p}_1 - \boldsymbol{p}_1')\delta(\boldsymbol{R}_1 - \boldsymbol{R}_1'); \quad +0 \leqslant s \leqslant \tau \tag{48}$$

where the subscript s again means that the force acting arises only from the attractive region of the pair potential. For many fluids, the attractive region of the potential is weak and therefore Eq. (48) may be solved by the methods already described. It is important to note that because of the assumptions inherent in the physical description no cross terms appear in this expansion. The presence of the unit step functions in Eq. (46) insure that the contribution to the Green's function $K^{(1)}(s)$ of $K_R{}^{(1)}(s)$ vanishes outside the interval of length $+\,0$, and the contribution to $K^{(1)}(s)$ of $K_s{}^{(1)}(s)$ vanishes within the interval of length $+\,0$. It is clear that the spatial dependence of $K_s{}^{(1)}(s)$ is given in the limit as s gets large by the form (see Eq. (28))

$$\lim_{s \text{ large}} K_s{}^{(1)}(s) = \frac{e^{-\zeta_s(\Delta R_1)^2/4kTs}}{(4\pi D_s{}^{(1)} s)^{\frac{3}{2}}}\, F(p, s) \tag{49}$$

---

[15] Von Roos, O., *J. math. Phys.* **1** (1960) 107. The development discussed in our paper was made independently of the work of Von Roos.

[16] Rice, S. A. and Allnatt, A. R., *J. chem. Phys.*, **34** (1961) 2144.

with $F(p, s)$ a function of the momentum change and time interval, and

$$\zeta_s = \frac{kT}{D_s{}^{(1)}} \tag{50}$$

is the frictional coefficient corresponding to the attractive region of the potential, i.e., ζ_s is determined by the autocorrelation function of the attractive forces. An explicit formula for ζ_s is given in the paper of Rice and Allnatt[16] cited above. In view of the known asymptotic dependence on ΔR, Δp and s of $K^{(1)}(s)$, an alternative method of determining $K_s{}^{(1)}(s)$ would be to assume the function to be only slightly different from the asymptotic form and derive a differential equation which the function must satisfy. This program can be carried out by the methods introduced by Kirkwood.[4] If the Liouville equation, Eq. (4), is reduced to a differential equation for $\bar{K}_s{}^{(1)}(s)$, where $\bar{K}_s{}^{(1)}(s)$ is the averaged transition probability density defined by

$$\bar{K}_s{}^{(1)}(s) = \frac{1}{\tau}\int_0^\tau K_s{}^{(1)}(s+s')\,\mathrm{d}s'. \tag{51}$$

Then it is found that

$$\frac{\partial \bar{K}_s{}^{(1)}}{\partial s} + \frac{\boldsymbol{p}_1}{m}\cdot\nabla_R \bar{K}_s{}^{(1)} = \nabla_{p_1}\cdot\boldsymbol{\Omega}_s; \quad +0 \leqslant s \leqslant \tau \tag{52}$$

$$\boldsymbol{\Omega}_s = -\frac{1}{\tau}\int_0^\tau \int \boldsymbol{F}_1{}^{(s)}(t+s')K_s{}^{(N)}(s+s')\left[\frac{f^{(N)}(t+s')}{f^{(1)}(t+s')}\right] \times \mathrm{d}\{\boldsymbol{N}-\boldsymbol{1}\}\,\mathrm{d}\{(\boldsymbol{N}-\boldsymbol{1})'\}\,\mathrm{d}s'. \tag{53}$$

We shall find it convenient to define

$$K_s{}^{(1/N-1)}(s) = K_s{}^{(N)}(s)/K_s{}^{(1)}(s). \tag{54}$$

In the integrand of Eq. (53) we now substitute Eq. (54). To develop the integrand further we assume that $K_s{}^{(1/N-1)}$ may be approximated by its asymptotic form $K^{(1/N-1)}_{\infty,s}$ and that $f^{(1/N-1)}$ may be approximated by its value at local equilibrium $f_0{}^{(1/N-1)}$. Let $\Delta R(s)$ and $\Delta p(s)$ be the magnitudes of the increments in position and momentum in time s. By a Taylor's expansion

$$K_s{}^{(1)}(s+s', \Delta R(s), \Delta p(s)) = K_s{}^{(1)}(s+s', \Delta R(s+s'), \Delta p(s+s')) \times\left[1 - \Delta R(s')\frac{\partial \ln K_s{}^{(1)}}{\partial R_1} - \Delta p(s')\frac{\partial \ln K_s{}^{(1)}}{\partial p_1} + \cdots\right] \tag{55}$$

and using the relations

$$\Delta R(s') = s'\Delta p(s')$$

$$\Delta p(s') = \int_s^{s+s'} \boldsymbol{F}_1{}^{(s)}(t+s'')\,\mathrm{d}s'' \tag{56}$$

as well as Eq. (28), we are led, by direct substitution, to the equation

$$\boldsymbol{\Omega}_s = \frac{K_s{}^{(1)}(s+s', \Delta R(s+s'), \Delta p(s+s'))}{\tau} \int_0^\tau \int \boldsymbol{F}_1{}^{(s)}(t+s') K_{\infty,s}^{(1/N-1)} f_0{}^{(1/N-1)}$$

$$\times \Bigg[-1 + s' \int_s^{s+s'} \boldsymbol{F}_1{}^{(s)}(t+s'')\,\mathrm{d}s'' \left\{ \frac{\partial \ln K_s{}^{(1)}}{\partial R_1} - \frac{1}{2D_s{}^{(1)}s'} \int_s^{s+s'} \boldsymbol{F}_1{}^{(s)}(t+s'')\,\mathrm{d}s'' \right\}$$

$$+ \int_s^{s+s'} \boldsymbol{F}_1{}^{(s)}(t+s)''\,\mathrm{d}s'' \left\{ \frac{\partial \ln K_s{}^{(1)}}{\partial p_1} - \frac{1}{2D_{p,s}{}^{(1)}s} \int_s^{s+s'} \boldsymbol{F}_1{}^{(s)}(t+s'')\,\mathrm{d}s'' \right\} \Bigg]$$

$$\cdot\, \mathrm{d}\{N -- \mathit{1}\}\mathrm{d}\{(N-\mathit{1})'\}\,\mathrm{d}s'. \tag{57}$$

With the definitions

$$\langle \boldsymbol{F}_1 \rangle^{(1/N-1)} = \frac{1}{\tau} \int_0^\tau \int \boldsymbol{F}_1{}^{(s)}(t+s') K_{\infty,s}^{(1/N-1)} f_0{}^{(1/N-1)}\,\mathrm{d}W \tag{58}$$

$$\zeta = \frac{1}{\tau} \int_0^\tau \int \boldsymbol{F}_1{}^{(s)}(t+s')\, \boldsymbol{F}_1{}^{(s)}(t+s'') K_{\infty,s}^{(1/N+1)} f_0{}^{(1/N-1)}\,\mathrm{d}W\,\mathrm{d}s'' \tag{59}$$

$$\gamma = \frac{1}{\tau} \int_0^\tau \int \frac{\boldsymbol{F}_1{}^{(s)}(t+s')\boldsymbol{F}_1{}^{(s)}(t+s'')\boldsymbol{F}_1{}^{(s)}(t+s''')}{s'}$$

$$K_{\infty,s}^{(1/N-1)} f_0{}^{(1/N-1)}\,\mathrm{d}W\mathrm{d}s''\mathrm{d}s''' \tag{60}$$

$$\Delta = \frac{1}{\tau} \int_0^\tau \int \boldsymbol{F}_1{}^{(s)}(t+s')s'\, \boldsymbol{F}_1{}^{(s)}(t+s'')\, K_{\infty,s}^{(1/N-1)} f_0{}^{(1/N-1)}\,\mathrm{d}W\mathrm{d}s'' \tag{61}$$

$$\Xi = \frac{1}{\tau} \int_0^\tau \int \boldsymbol{F}_1{}^{(s)}(t+s')\boldsymbol{F}_1{}^{(s)}(t+s'')\boldsymbol{F}_1{}^{(s)}(t+s''') K_{\infty,s}^{(1/N-1)} f^{(1/N-1)}\,\mathrm{d}W\mathrm{d}s''\mathrm{d}s'''$$

$$\mathrm{d}W = d\{N - \mathit{1}\}\mathrm{d}\{(N-\mathit{1})'\}\mathrm{d}s' \tag{62}$$

one finds the differential equation (after a second time smoothing)

$$\frac{\partial \bar{K}_s{}^{(1)}}{\partial s} + \frac{\mathbf{p}_1}{m} \cdot \nabla_{R_1} \bar{K}_s{}^{(1)} = -\nabla_{p_1} \cdot \left[\langle \boldsymbol{F}_1 \rangle^{(1/N-1)} + \frac{1}{2D_{p,s}{}^{(1)}} \gamma + \frac{1}{2D_s{}^{(1)}} \Xi \right] \bar{K}_s{}^{(1)}$$

$$+ \nabla_{p_1} \cdot \left[\zeta \frac{\partial \bar{K}_s{}^{(1)}}{\partial p_1} + \boldsymbol{\Delta} \frac{\partial \bar{K}_s{}^{(1)}}{\partial R_1} \right]. \tag{63}$$

It would be logical to seek solutions to Eq. (63) by introducing a perturbation and expanding the perturbation in Sonine polynomials with argument $(\Delta R)^2$ or $(\Delta p)^2$. This suggestion follows directly from the functional analogy between (38) and the Maxwellian velocity distribution.[17]

Rice and Allnatt have computed the singlet and pair distribution functions for the model fluid consisting of rigid spheres with an attractive potential. The methods used were rather different than those considered herein since no

[17] See for example Lebowitz, J. L., Frisch, H. L. and Helfand, E., *J. Phys. Fluids* **3** (1960) 325.

explicit form of the Green's function was sought. A perturbation solution of character similar to that described at the beginning of this section but in which the size of the coupling potential is the parameter was employed.[18] This approximation corresponds to taking the asymptotic form for the Green's function. If the methods suggested herein prove useful, it should be possible to improve the computed distribution functions.

ACKNOWLEDGMENT

We wish to thank the Alfred P. Sloan Foundation and the Petroleum Research Fund of the American Chemical Society for financial support.

---

[18] The method used was introduced by Ross, J., *J. chem. Phys.* **24** (1956) 375.

The Statistical Mechanical Basis of the Enskog Theory of Transport in Dense Gases

J. G. KIRKWOOD AND S. A. RICE, *Sterling Chemistry Laboratory, Yale University, New Haven, Connecticut*

The theory of transport in a dense fluid of rigid spheres is developed from Liouville's equation with the use of distribution functions coarse grained in time by methods employed by Ross and Kirkwood in the derivation of Maxwell-Boltzmann integro-differential equation for gases of low density. If the interval of time smoothing is chosen to be an arbitrarily small non-zero positive quantity, only binary encounters contribute to the collision term in the contracted Liouville equation satisfied by the probability density $f^{(1)}$ in μ-space (singlet phase space). When the collision term is evaluated under the assumption, which cannot be exact, that the correlation function $g^{(2)}(R_1, R_{12})$ pair space is independent of momentum, a modified Maxwell-Boltzmann equation is obtained, which differs only in minor respects from the intuitively derived Enskog equation.

The Enskog expressions for the stress tensor and heat flux are derived from first principles and the coefficients of shear viscosity and thermal conductivity are evaluated by means of the new theory. The shear viscosity turns out to be identical with that of Enskog, while the thermal conductivity exhibits minor differences.

The physical implications of short time coarse-graining are discussed. Due to the singular nature of the force between rigid spheres, the time smoothed distribution functions are never identical with the fine-grained distribution functions even when the interval of time smoothing becomes an arbitrarily small non-zero quantity. However, the identification of macroscopic observable with averages corresponding to distribution functions with short time smoothing is open to serious question.

The following expressions are obtained for the coefficient of shear viscosity η and the coefficient of thermal conductivity κ,

$$\eta = \frac{5kT}{8\Omega^{(2,2)}}\left[\frac{1}{g^{(a)}} + \frac{8\pi a^3}{15v} + \left(\frac{4}{25} + \frac{48}{25\pi}\right)\left(\frac{2\pi a^3}{3v}\right)^2\right.$$

$$\kappa = \frac{75k^2T}{32m\Omega^{(2,2)}}\left[\frac{1}{g^{(a)}} + \frac{11\pi a^3}{15v} + \left(\frac{36}{75} + \frac{192}{150\pi}\right)\left(\frac{2\pi a^3}{3v}\right)^2\right.$$

$$\Omega^{(2,2)} = \left(\frac{4\pi kT}{m}\right)^{\frac{1}{2}} a^2,$$

where v is the volume per molecule and a and m are the diameter and mass of the rigid spheres. $g^{(a)}$ is the equilibrium radial distribution function for a pair of spheres in contact.

INTERVENTI E DISCUSSIONI

G. Careri: What about the self-diffusion coefficient?

S. Ono: Recently we (S. Ono and T. Murakami) made the investigation on the mechanical basis of the Enskog-Chapmann. This is based on the variation principle just the same as Hirschfelder and Curtiss' one, and gives exactly the same as Enskog and Chapmann for viscosity and thermal conductivity. This is not the method based on the first principles of statistical mechanics. However, the result seems to have the relation to Prof. Kirkwood's results.

I. Prigogine: I would like to ask Prof. Kirkwood the following two questions:

(1) Is your result not identical to the lowest order in concentration to the result given by Bogoliubov in his book?

(2) I do not understand your method of expansion. I understand that one may expand in power of interaction constant or in power of concentration, but what is here the expansion parameter?

This is as more obscure for me because the recent derivations of the Boltzmann equations, especially the Bogoljubov derivation show clearly that the higher order terms in concentration are closely related to the "N body problem". I believe therefore that no two body theory can give reliable results for higher concentrations.

G. Uhlenbeck: If you develop your results in a virial expansion, up to which order is there agreement with the Enskog theory?

J. Kirkwood: This has not yet been done, but will be done in the near future.

M. Toda: I am trying to see if one can derive the Uhlenbeck and the Boltzmann equations using quantum mechanics and Bogoljubov's method. So far I am restricted to weak interactions. So I would like to ask Prof. Kirkwood if I can see easily the change in your calculation when you use well-potential instead of rigid sphere.

The Statistical-Mechanical Theory of Irreversible Processes* †

J. G. Kirkwood, *Pasadena, California*

I

The objectives of a statistical mechanical theory of irreversible processes are in broad outline the derivation of the macroscopic transport equations of hydrodynamics from the laws of molecular dynamics, the investigation of the limits of validity of the empirical laws of diffusion, heat conduction and viscous fluid flow, and the determination of the coefficients of diffusion, thermal conductivity, and viscosity in terms of molecular variables. The formulation of a general statistical mechanical theory with these objectives has been undertaken by the writer[1] in an article, which will be referred to as SMT I. An alternative approach is provided by the kinetic theory of liquids developed almost simultaneously with our own by Born and Green.[2] While the two theories parallel each other in many aspects, they differ in the manner in which thermodynamic dissipative effects are explicitly taken into account. Our theory leads to the Maxwell-Boltzmann integro-differential equation for gases of low density, and to a molecular theory of Brownian motion for liquids and liquid solutions. Differential equations of the Chandrasekhar[3] type for probability distribution functions in the phase space of sets of one, two, and three molecules of the liquid are derived from molecular considerations and serve as the basis of the theory of transport processes in liquid phases.

It is the purpose of the present article to review the applications of our theory to transport processes in pure liquids. The general aspects of the problems of viscous fluid flow and heat conduction will be treated and the coefficients of viscosity[4] and heat conductivity will be expressed in terms of the friction constant of theory of Brownian motion and integrals involving the potential of intermolecular force and perturbations in molecular distribution functions produced by departures from thermodynamic equilibrium.

The macroscopic equations of hydrodynamics, which it will be our task to interpret are the equations of continuity, motion, and energy transport,

$$\begin{aligned} &\frac{d\rho}{dt} + \nabla \cdot (\rho \vec{u}) = 0 \\ &\rho \frac{d\vec{u}}{dt} = \nabla \cdot \boldsymbol{\sigma}_m + \vec{X} \\ &\rho \frac{dE}{dt} + \nabla \cdot \vec{j}_q - \boldsymbol{\sigma} : \nabla \vec{u} = 0 \end{aligned} \qquad (1)$$

$$\frac{d}{dt} = \frac{\partial}{\partial t} + \vec{u} \cdot \nabla \qquad \boldsymbol{\sigma} : \nabla \vec{u} = \sum_{\alpha,\beta=1} \sigma_{\alpha\beta} \frac{\partial u_\alpha}{\partial x_\beta}$$

* Work supported by the United States Office of Naval Research.

† This paper was read on May 18th afternoon. [*Editor's note.*]

[1] J. G. Kirkwood: *Journ. Chem. Phys.* **14**, 180 (1946).

[2] M. Born and H. S. Green, *Proc. Roy. Soc.*, A **188**, 10 (1946); **190**, 455 (1947).

[3] S. Chandrasekhar, *Rev. Mod. Phys.* **15**, 1 (1943).

[4] J. G. Kirkwood, F. P. Buff, and M. S. Green, *Journ. Chem. Phys.*, in press.

where ρ is the density, $\vec{u}$ the particle velocity, $\vec{X}$ the external body force, $\boldsymbol{\sigma}$ the stress tensor, $\vec{j_q}$ the heat current density and E the specific internal energy of the fluid. The differential Eqs. (1) become determinant, subject to appropriate initial and boundary conditions, when supplemented by the phenomenological relations,

$$\begin{aligned}
\boldsymbol{\sigma} &= -\left[p + \left(\frac{2\eta}{3} - \varphi\right)\nabla \cdot \vec{u}\right]\mathbf{1} + 2\eta\dot{\boldsymbol{\epsilon}} \\
\dot{\boldsymbol{\epsilon}} &= \text{Sym}\,\nabla\vec{u} \\
\vec{j_q} &= -\,\mathfrak{H}\,\nabla T
\end{aligned} \tag{2}$$

where $\dot{\boldsymbol{\epsilon}}$ is the rate of strain tensor, p the equilibrium pressure of the fluid, determined by its equation of state, T is the temperature, η and φ the coefficients of shear and dilatation viscosity, and $\mathfrak{H}$ the coefficient of heat conductivity.

II

The macroscopic observables of a system of N molecules are to be put into correspondence with average values determined by probability densities $\bar{f}^{(n)}(p, q; t)$ in the phase space of subsets of n molecules,

$$\begin{aligned}
\bar{f}^{(n)}(p, q; t) &= \iint \bar{f}^{(n)}(p, q, P, Q; t)\, d\vec{P}\, d\vec{Q} \\
\bar{f}^{(N)}(p, q, P, Q; t) &= \frac{1}{\tau}\int_0^{\alpha} f^{(N)}(p, q, P, Q; t + s)ds
\end{aligned} \tag{3}$$

where (P, Q) is the phase space of the residual set of $N - n$ molecules and $f^{(N)}(p, q, P, Q; t)$ is the probability density in the complete phase space of an example of the appropriate statistical ensemble, from which the system is sampled in the process of its preparation at time t with specified values of the molar variables determining its macroscopic state. The interval τ is determined by the time resolution of the instruments employed in the measurement of the macroscopic observable. If the shortest period macroscopically resolved is long relative to the correlation time in Brownian motion, the description does not sensibly depend on the smoothing time τ, provided it is small relative to this shortest period and long relative to the correlation time.

For the representation of average values of the configuration coordinates along, it is convenient to define number densities $\rho^{(n)}(q, t)$ for subsets of n molecules by the relation,

$$\rho^{(n)}(q, t) = \frac{N!}{(N-n)!}\bar{f}^{(n)}(p, q; t)d\vec{p} \tag{4}$$

as well as average number current densities,

$$\vec{j}_{\alpha}^{(n)}(q, t) = \frac{N!}{(N-n)!}\int \frac{\vec{p}_{\alpha}}{m}\bar{f}^{(n)}(p, q; t)d\vec{p} \qquad (\alpha = 1, \ldots, n) \tag{5}$$

where $\vec{j}_\alpha^{(n)}$ is the projection of $\vec{j}^{(n)}$ on the 3-space of molecule α. Thus, a mass density ρ and the particle velocity $\vec{u}$ of three-dimensional hydrodynamic theory at a point R in a fluid are given by

$$\begin{aligned} \rho(\vec{R}) &= m\rho^{(1)}(\vec{R}) \\ \rho\,\vec{u} &= m\vec{j}^{(1)}(\vec{R}) \end{aligned} \tag{6}$$

where m is the molecular mass.

The probability density $f^{(N)}(p, q, P, Q; t)$ of classical statistical mechanics satisfies the Liouville equation

$$\frac{\partial f^{(N)}}{\partial t} + \sum_{\alpha=1}^{N} \left\{ \frac{\vec{p}_\alpha}{m_\alpha} \cdot \nabla_{q_\alpha} f^{(N)} + (\vec{X}_\alpha + \vec{F}_\alpha) \cdot \nabla_{p_\alpha} f^{(N)} \right\} = 0. \tag{7}$$

where $\vec{X}_\alpha$ is the external force and $\vec{F}_\alpha$ is the total intermolecular force acting on molecule α. In a system of molecules for which the potential of intermolecular force can be represented in the form,

$$V_N = \sum_{\alpha<\beta} V(R_{\alpha,\beta}) \tag{8}$$

where $V(R_{\alpha,\beta})$ is a function, say of the Lennard-Jones type of the distance between the molecular pair $(\alpha\beta)$, the average number and energy densities and the average current density at a point $\vec{R}$ in μ-configuration space of a system are given by,

$$\rho^{(1)} = \int \cdots \int \sum_{\alpha=1}^{N} \delta(\vec{R}_\alpha - \vec{R}) f^{(N)})p, q, P, Q; t)\, d\vec{p}\, d\vec{q}\, d\vec{P}\, d\vec{Q}$$

$$\vec{j}^{(1)} = \int \cdots \int \sum_{\alpha=1}^{N} \frac{\vec{p}_\alpha}{m} \delta(\vec{R}_\alpha - \vec{R}) f^{(N)}(p, q, P, Q; t) d\vec{p}\, d\vec{q}\, d\vec{P}\, d\vec{Q} \tag{9}$$

$$\rho\left(E + \frac{u^2}{2}\right) = \int \cdots \int \sum_{\alpha=1}^{N} \left[\frac{p_\alpha^2}{2m} + \frac{1}{2} \sum_{\beta=1}^{N} V(R_{\alpha\beta})\right]$$
$$\times\, \delta(\vec{R}_\alpha - \vec{R}) f^{(N)}(p, q, P, Q; t)\, d\vec{p}\, d\vec{q}\, d\vec{P}\, d\vec{Q}.$$

When both sides of the Liouville equation, Eq. (7), are multiplied by the respective operators defining the mean values of Eq. (9) and integrated over phase space with subsequent time smoothing, we obtain for a closed system after some simple transformations the equations of hydrodynamics, Eq. (6), if the stress tensor $\boldsymbol{\sigma}$ and the heat current density $\vec{j}_q$ are identified with the following expressions,

$$\boldsymbol{\sigma} = -\rho^{(1)}\left[\left\{\frac{\vec{p}\,\vec{p}}{m}\right\}_{\mathrm{Av}} - \vec{u}\,\vec{u}\right] + \frac{1}{2}\int \frac{\vec{R}_{12}\vec{R}_{12}}{R_{12}}\frac{dV}{dR_{12}}\rho^{(2)}(\vec{R}, \vec{R}_{12})dv_{12}$$

$$\rho^{(1)}\{\vec{p}\;\vec{p}\}_{\mathrm{Av}} = \int \vec{p}\;\vec{p}f^{(1)}(\vec{p}, \vec{R})\,d\vec{p} \tag{10}$$

$$\vec{j}_q = \frac{\rho^{(1)}}{2m^2}\{(\vec{p} - m\,\vec{u})\,(\vec{p} - m\,\vec{u})^2\}_{\mathrm{Av}}$$

$$-\frac{1}{2}\int\left\{\frac{\vec{R}_{12}\vec{R}_{12}}{R_{12}}\frac{dV}{dR_{12}} - V\mathbf{1}\right\}\left\{\vec{j}_1^{(2)}(\vec{R}, \vec{R}_{12}) - \rho^{(2)}\,\vec{u}\,(R)\right\}dv_{12},$$

where the integrals extend over the relative configuration space of a representative pair, one molecule of which is situated at point R, and the particle current density $\vec{j}_{\uparrow}^{(2)}$ in pair space is given by Eq. (5). In a fluid in thermodynamic equilibrium, the stress reduces to a uniform pressure, $-p\mathbf{1}$ where

$$\begin{aligned} p &= \rho^{(1)}kT - \frac{2\pi\rho^{(1)2}}{3}\int_0^\infty R_{12}^3\frac{dV}{dR_{12}}g_0^{(2)}(R_{12})dR_{12} \\ \rho^{(2)}(\vec{R}, \vec{R}_{12}) &= \rho^{(1)}(\vec{R})\rho^{(2)}(\vec{R} + \vec{R}_{12})g^{(2)}(\vec{R}, \vec{R}_{12}), \end{aligned} \tag{11}$$

where the equilibrium correlation function $g_0^{(2)}(R_{12})$ is the radial distribution function of the theory of the liquid state, accessible to experimental determination from the angular distribution of scattered X-rays.

III

In order to determine the influence of departures from thermodynamic equilibrium on the stress tensor and heat current, it is necessary to investigate the perturbations in the distribution function $f^{(1)}$ and $\rho^{(1)}$ and the particle current density $\vec{j}^{(2)}$ produced by such departures. For this purpose we employ the generalized Chandrasekhar equations, SMT I, Eqs. (59). After introducing the pair correlation function, $g^{(2)}, (\vec{R}_1\,\vec{E}_{12})$ defined by the relation,

$$\rho^{(2)}(\vec{R}_1, \vec{R}_2) = \rho^{(1)}(\vec{R}_1)\rho^{(1)}(\vec{R}_2)g^{(2)}(\vec{R}_1, \vec{R}_{12})$$

$$g^{(2)}(\vec{R}_1, \vec{R}_{12}) = g_0^{(2)}(\vec{R}_{12}, T_1, p_1) + g_1^{(2)})$$

where $g_0^{(2)}$ is the equilibrium radial distribution function at temperature and pressure prevailing at the point of location of the member of the pair situated at R_1, we find that the perturbation $g_1^{(2)}$, arising from convective and thermal departures from equilibrium, satisfies the partial differential equation,

$$\nabla_R \cdot [\nabla_R\, g_1^{(2)} - g_1^{(2)}\, \nabla_R \log g_1^{(2)}] - \frac{\zeta}{2kT}\frac{\partial g_1^{(2)}}{\partial t}$$

$$= -\frac{\zeta}{2kT}\frac{\vec{R}\cdot\dot{\boldsymbol{\epsilon}}\cdot\vec{R}}{R}\frac{dg_0^{(2)}}{dR} \qquad (12)$$

$$+\frac{1}{2}\nabla_R\cdot\left\{g_0^{(2)}\,\nabla_R\left[(\vec{R}\cdot\nabla T)\left(\frac{\partial\log g_0^{(2)}}{\partial T}\right)_p\right]\right\},$$

$$D = kT/\zeta, \qquad \vec{R} = \vec{R}_{12}$$

with the neglect of non-linear terms in the rate of strain $\dot{\boldsymbol{\epsilon}}$ and the temperature gradient. Here ζ is the friction constant of the theory of Brownian motion, and D is the coefficient of self diffusion related to the intermolecular forces acting in the system in the manner prescribed in SMT I. Equation (12) involve the following approximations

$$\boldsymbol{\zeta}^{(2)} = \zeta(T_1)\,\mathbf{1}^{(1)} + \zeta(T_2)\,\mathbf{1}^{(2)}$$

$$\left\{\frac{\vec{p}_\alpha\vec{p}_\alpha}{m}\right\}_{\mathrm{Av}} = kT(\vec{R}_\alpha)\,\mathbf{1}^{(\alpha)}; \qquad \alpha = 1, 2 \qquad (13)$$

where $\mathbf{1}^{(\alpha)}$ is unit tensor in the 3-space of molecule α, $\boldsymbol{\zeta}^{(2)}$ is the friction tensor in pair space and ζ is the scalar magnitude of the components of the isotropic friction tensor in singlet space. The current density in pair space projected on the 3-space of molecule 1 is given by

$$\vec{j}_1^{(2)} - \rho^{(2)}\,\vec{u}_1 = \rho^{(1)2}\frac{kT}{\zeta}\left\{\nabla_R g_1^{(2)} - g_1^{(2)}\,\nabla_R \log g_0^{(2)} - \frac{1}{2}\left(\frac{\partial g_0^{(2)}}{\partial T}\right)_p \nabla T\right\} \qquad (14)$$

$$\vec{j}_{12}^{(2)} = (\vec{j}_2^{(2)} - \rho^{(2)}\,\vec{u}_2) - (\vec{j}_1^{(2)} - \rho^{(2)}\,\vec{u}_1)$$

and Eq. (12) is subject to the boundary conditions that the relative excess pair current $\vec{j}_{12}^{(2)}$ vanishes at $R = \infty$ and no sources or sinks at $R = 0$.

Solutions of Eq. (12) satisfying the boundary conditions may be constructed in the form,

$$g_1^{(2)} = g_0^{(2)}(R)\left\{1 + \frac{\zeta}{2kT}\left[\frac{\vec{R}_1\dot{\boldsymbol{\epsilon}}\cdot\vec{R}}{R^2} - \frac{1}{3}\nabla\cdot\vec{u}\right]\psi_2(R)\right.$$

$$\left. + \frac{\zeta}{6kT}(\nabla, \vec{u})\psi_0(R) + (\vec{R}\cdot\nabla T)\chi_1(R)\right\} \qquad (15)$$

$$\chi_1(R) = \frac{1}{2}\left(\frac{\partial\log g_0^{(2)}}{\partial T}\right)_p$$

where the function ψ_2, determining the shear components of the stress satisfies the ordinary differential equation,

$$\frac{d}{dR}\left(R^2 g_0^{(2)} \frac{d\psi_2}{dR}\right) - 6g_0^{(2)}\psi_2 - R^3 \frac{dg_0^{(2)}}{dR} \tag{16}$$

$$\lim_{R\to\infty} \psi_2(R) \to 0; \qquad \lim_{R\to 0} R^2 g_0^{(2)} \frac{d\psi_2}{dR} \to 0.$$

The momentum transport contribution to the stress and kinetic energy transport contribution to the heat current, Eq. (10) are of minor importance in liquids. When they are evaluated by methods described by Kirkwood, Buff and Green,[4] and when Eqs. (14) and (15) are employed in the evaluation of the dominant contributions arising from intermolecular forces represented by the second term of Eq. (10), $\boldsymbol{\sigma}$ and $\vec{j_q}$ assume the phenomenological forms of Eq. (2). The coefficients of viscosity η and φ and the heat conductivity $\mathfrak{H}$ are then determined by

$$\eta = \frac{\rho kT}{2\zeta} + \frac{\pi\zeta\rho^{(1)2}}{15kT}\int_0^\infty R^3 \frac{dV}{dR}\psi_2(R)g_0^{(2)}(R)dR$$

$$\varphi = + \frac{\pi\zeta\rho^{(1)2}}{9kT}\int_0^\infty R^3 \frac{dV}{dR}\psi_0(R)g_0^{(2)}(R)dR \tag{17}$$

$$\mathfrak{H} = \left(\frac{\rho^1 kT}{\zeta}\middle|\frac{5k}{6}\right) + \pi\rho^{(1)}\int_0^\infty R^5 g_0^{(2)} \frac{d(V/R)}{dR}\frac{d}{dR}\left(\frac{d\log g_0^{(2)}}{dT}\right)_p dR.$$

Equation (17) provides the desired relations between the transport parameters η, φ, $\mathfrak{H}$, and molecular variables, the potential of intermolecular force and the equilibrium radial distribution function of the liquid.

In order to complete the theory, the determination of the friction constant ζ in terms of molecular variables is necessary. Work is in progress on this difficult task, based on the theory of SMT I. A preliminary estimate, correct at least in order of magnitude is provided by the relation

$$\zeta^2 = \frac{4\pi\rho}{3}\int_0^\infty R^2\left[\frac{d^2V}{dR^2} + \frac{2}{R}\frac{dV}{dR}\right]g_0^{(2)}(R)dR. \tag{18}$$

Calculations of the shear viscosity η of liquid argon at 89°K have been carried out by Kirkwood, Buff and Green[4] with the use of Eqs. (17) and (18), the Lennard-Jones potential of intermolecular force and the experimental radial distribution function of Eisenstein and Gingrich. The result 1.3×10^{-3} poise is in moderately good agreement with the experimental value 2.4×10^{-3} poise. Calculations of the dilatational viscosity φ and the heat conductivity $\mathfrak{H}$ have not yet been completed.

The Statistical Mechanical Basis of the Boltzmann Equation

John G. Kirkwood, *Sterling Chemistry Laboratory, Yale University, New Haven, Connecticut*

John Ross, *Metcalf Chemical Laboratories, Brown University, Providence, Rhode Island*

The statistical mechanical basis of the Maxwell-Boltzmann integro-differential equation of transport has been the subject of a number of recent investigations.[1–5] In the analysis of Kirkwood,[2] the Boltzmann equation is derived in the limit of zero density from the first principles of statistical mechanics for a coarse-grained single particle distribution function in μ-space, the coarse-grained function being defined as an average over an interval of time τ long relative to the representative duration of a binary collision.[6] It is the purpose of the present article to refine the derivation of Kirkwood by means of a more precise formulation of the binary collision mechanism, depending upon the use of phase space transformation functions. More detailed attention is given to the spatial dependence of the distribution functions and to the conditions for the existence of the integral of the pair correlation function in the collision term. The formalism based upon the phase space transformation functions will be applied in a future investigation to the generalization of the Boltzmann equation to higher densities and to the development of cluster expansions of the distribution functions.

We shall denote by $f^{(N)}(\mathbf{R}, \mathbf{p}; t)$ the probability density in phase space in a statistical ensemble of identical systems of N molecules. This function satisfies the Liouville equation,

$$\frac{\partial f^{(N)}}{\partial t} + \sum_{j=1}^{N} \left\{ \frac{\mathbf{p}_j}{m_j} \cdot \nabla_{\mathbf{R}_j} f^{(N)} + (\mathbf{X}_j + \mathbf{F}_j) \cdot \nabla_{\mathbf{p}_j} f^{(N)} \right\} = 0, \tag{1}$$

subject to arbitrary initial conditions.

The external forces on particle j are designated by $\mathbf{X}_j$ and the intermolecular forces by $\mathbf{F}_j$; the latter are assumed to be decomposable into central symmetric pair forces,

$$\mathbf{F}_j = \sum_{j \neq i=1}^{N} \mathbf{F}_{ij}(|\mathbf{R}_j - \mathbf{R}_i|). \tag{2}$$

Integration of the distribution function $f^{(N)}$ over the coordinates and momenta

---

[1] J. Yvon, *Actualités Scientifiques et Industrielles*, Hermann, Paris, 1935.
[2] J. G. Kirkwood, *J. Chem. Phys.* **15**, 72 (1947).
[3] M. Born and H. S. Green, *A General Kinetic Theory of Liquids*, Cambridge Univ. Press, London, 1949.
[4] N. Bogolyubov, *J. Phys.* (*U.S.S.R.*), **10**, 265 (1946).
[5] H. L. Frisch, *J. Chem. Phys.* **22**, 1713 (1954).
[6] J. G. Kirkwood, *J. Chem. Phys.* **14**, 180 (1946).
[7] S. Chapman and T. G. Cowling, *The Mathematical Theory of Non-Uniform Gases*, Cambridge Univ. Press, London, 1952.

of a subset of the N particles yields a reduced distribution function for the remaining set of particles. Integration of any distribution function over an interval of time τ leads to a time-smoothed function defined as

$$\bar{f}^{(n)}(\mathbf{r}, \mathbf{p}; t) = \frac{1}{\tau}\int_0^\tau f^{(n)}(\mathbf{r}, \mathbf{p}; t + s)\, ds. \tag{3}$$

Thus the equation for the time-smoothed singlet distribution function, in terms of which the derived Boltzmann equation will be expressed, is obtained from Eq. (1) by integration over the phase space of the complementary set of $N - 1$ molecules,

$$\frac{\partial \bar{f}^{(1)}}{\partial t} + \frac{\mathbf{p}_1}{m_1} \cdot \nabla_{\mathbf{R}_1} \bar{f}^{(1)} + \mathbf{X}_1 \cdot \nabla_{\mathbf{p}_1} \bar{f}^{(1)}$$
$$= -\frac{(N-1)}{\tau}\int_0^\tau \cdots \int \mathbf{F}_{12} \cdot \nabla_{\mathbf{p}_1} f^{(2)}(\mathbf{R}_1\mathbf{R}_2\mathbf{p}_1\mathbf{p}_2; t + s)\, d\mathbf{R}_2 d\mathbf{p}_2 ds. \tag{4}$$

Before proceeding with the further development of Eq. (4) we turn to a consideration of phase space transformation functions.[8] The integral equation

$$f^{(N)}(\mathbf{Rp}; t + s) = \int \cdots \int K^{(N)}(\mathbf{Rp}|\mathbf{R}'\mathbf{p}'; s) f^{(N)}(\mathbf{R}'\mathbf{p}'; t)\, d\mathbf{R}' d\mathbf{p}' \tag{5}$$

defines the transformation function $K^{(N)}$, which is a conditional probability density of finding the N-particle system at $[\mathbf{R}, \mathbf{p}]$ in phase space at time $(t + s)$ if the system was at $[\mathbf{R}'\ \mathbf{p}']$ at time t. $K^{(N)}$ obeys Liouville's equation

$$\frac{\partial K^{(N)}}{\partial s} + \sum_{j=1}^{N} \left\{ \frac{\mathbf{p}_j}{m_j} \cdot \nabla_{\mathbf{R}_j} K^{(N)} + (\mathbf{X}_j + \mathbf{F}_j) \cdot \nabla_{\mathbf{p}_j} K^{(N)} \right\} = 0 \tag{6}$$

with the initial condition

$$K^{(N)}(\mathbf{Rp}|\mathbf{R}'\mathbf{p}'; 0) = \prod_{j=1}^{N} \delta(\mathbf{R}_j - \mathbf{R}_j')\delta(\mathbf{p}_j - \mathbf{p}_j'). \tag{7}$$

The formal solution of Eq. (6) for the transformation function can be expressed as follows

$$K^{(N)}(\mathbf{Rp}|\mathbf{R}'\mathbf{p}'; s) = \prod_{j=1}^{N} \delta[\mathbf{R}_j - \mathbf{R}_j' - \Delta\mathbf{R}_j(s)]\delta[\mathbf{p}_j - \mathbf{p}_j' - \Delta\mathbf{p}_j(s)]$$

where $\Delta\mathbf{R}_j(s)$ and $\Delta\mathbf{p}_j(s)$ are the changes in coordinates and momenta of particle j determined from a solution of the equation of motion of the N-particle system.

Reduced transformation functions can be formed from the defining Eq. (5) by integration. Consider first the reduced distribution $f^{(n)}(\mathbf{r}, \mathbf{p}; t + s)$ which is given by the expression,

$$f^{(n)}(\mathbf{r}, \mathbf{p}; t + s) = \int \cdots \int f^{(N)}(\mathbf{rpQP}; t + s)\, d\mathbf{P} d\mathbf{Q}, \tag{8}$$

[8] These functions have been discussed by J. E. Moyal, *Proc. Cambridge Phil. Soc.*, **45**, 99 (1949), in connection with quantum statistical problems. The theory has been further developed by J. Ross and J. G. Kirkwood, *J. Chem. Phys.* **22**, 1094 (1954), and applied to a derivation of the analog of the Boltzmann equation of transport for quantum mechanical systems. For an application of these functions in classical statistical mechanics see J. Ross, *J. Chem. Phys.* **24**, 375 (1956), "Contribution to the Theory of Brownian Motion."

where $[\mathbf{r}, \mathbf{p}]$ are the phase space coordinates of the subset of n particles and $[\mathbf{Q}, \mathbf{P}]$ the coordinates of the remaining set. The two functions $f^{(n)}$ and $f^{(N)}$ are also related by the equation

$$f^{(N)}(\mathbf{rpQP}; t+s) = f^{(n)}(\mathbf{rp}; t+s) f^{(n|N-n)}(\mathbf{rp}|\mathbf{QP}; t+s), \tag{9}$$

which defines the relative probability density $f^{(n/N-n)}$. Substitution of Eq. (5) into Eq. (8) shows that the reduced transformation function $K^{(n)}$ which fulfills the relation

$$f^{(n)}(\mathbf{rp}; t+s) = \int \cdots \int K^{(n)}(\mathbf{rp}|\mathbf{r}'\mathbf{p}'; s) f^{(n)}(\mathbf{r}'\mathbf{p}'; t) d\mathbf{r}' d\mathbf{p}' \tag{10}$$

is given by

$$K^{(n)}(\mathbf{rp}|\mathbf{r}'\mathbf{p}'; s) = \int \cdots \int K^{(N)}(\mathbf{rpQP}|\mathbf{r}'\mathbf{p}'\mathbf{Q}'\mathbf{P}'; s) \times f^{(n|N-n)}(\mathbf{r}'\mathbf{p}'|\mathbf{Q}'\mathbf{P}'; t) d\mathbf{P} d\mathbf{Q} d\mathbf{P}' d\mathbf{Q}'. \tag{11}$$

We return now to Eq. (4) to introduce the pair transformation function

$$\frac{\partial f^{(1)}}{\partial t} + \frac{\mathbf{p}_1}{m_1} \cdot \nabla_{\mathbf{R}_1} f^{(1)} + \mathbf{X}_1 \cdot \nabla_{\mathbf{p}_1} f^{(1)} = -\frac{(N-1)}{\tau} \int_0^\tau \cdots \int \mathbf{F}_{12} \cdot \nabla_{\mathbf{p}_1} K^{(2)}(s) f^{(2)}(t) d\mathbf{R}_2 d\mathbf{p}_2 ds d\mathbf{R}_1' d\mathbf{R}_2' d\mathbf{p}_1' d\mathbf{p}_2' \tag{12}$$

and relate the pair distribution function to singlet distribution functions by the equation

$$f^{(2)}(\mathbf{R}_1'\mathbf{R}_2'\mathbf{p}_1'\mathbf{p}_2'; t) = g(\mathbf{R}_1'\mathbf{R}_2'\mathbf{p}_1'\mathbf{p}_2'; t) f^{(1)}(\mathbf{R}_1'\mathbf{p}_1'; t) f^{(1)}(\mathbf{R}_2'\mathbf{p}_2'; t), \tag{13}$$

which defines the pair correlation function g, so that we obtain

$$\frac{\partial f^{(1)}}{\partial t} + \frac{\mathbf{p}_1}{m_1} \cdot \nabla_{\mathbf{R}_1} f^{(1)} + \mathbf{X}_1 \cdot \nabla_{\mathbf{p}_1} f^{(1)} = (N-1)\left[\Omega + \frac{\Theta}{\tau}\right], \tag{14}$$

where

$$\Omega = -\frac{1}{\tau} \int_0^\tau \cdots \int \mathbf{F}_{12} \cdot \nabla_{\mathbf{p}_1} K^{(2)}(s) f^{(1)}(t) f^{(1)}(t) d\mathbf{R}_2 d\mathbf{p}_2 ds d\mathbf{R}_1' d\mathbf{R}_2' d\mathbf{p}_1' d\mathbf{p}_2',$$

$$\Theta = +\int_0^\tau \cdots \int \mathbf{F}_{12} \cdot \nabla_{\mathbf{p}_1} K^{(2)}(s) \{[1 - g^{(2)}(t)] f^{(1)}(t) f^{(1)}(t)\} \times d\mathbf{R}_2 d\mathbf{p}_2 ds d\mathbf{R}_1' d\mathbf{R}_2' d\mathbf{p}_1' s\mathbf{p}_2'. \tag{15}$$

We require that the correlation integral, which is the integral of the deviation of the pair correlation function from unity over relative configuration space, be finite at a given initial time and denote this condition a part of the assumption of molecular chaos. Furthermore, it can be shown in the limit of zero density that if the correlation integral is finite at one time it will remain finite at future times. Thus the contribution of the term (Θ/τ) can be made as small as desired for sufficiently large τ.

The integro-differential equation satisfied by $K^{(2)}$ is derived from Liouville's equation for $K^{(N)}$ by multiplication of that equation by $f^{(2/N-2)}\mathbf{R}(_1'\mathbf{R}_2'\mathbf{p}_1'\mathbf{p}_2'/\mathbf{P}'\mathbf{Q}';t)$ from the right and integration over $d\mathbf{P}d\mathbf{Q}d\mathbf{P}'d\mathbf{Q}'$; this leads to

$$\frac{\partial K^{(2)}}{\partial s}+\frac{\mathbf{p}_1}{m_1}\cdot\nabla_{\mathbf{R}_1}K^{(2)}+\frac{\mathbf{p}_2}{m_2}\cdot\nabla_{\mathbf{R}_2}K^{(2)}$$
$$+(\mathbf{X}_1+\mathbf{F}_{12})\cdot\nabla_{\mathbf{p}_1}K^{(2)}+(\mathbf{X}_2+\mathbf{F}_{21})\cdot\nabla_{\mathbf{p}_2}K^{(2)}$$
$$=-\sum_{j=3}^{N}\int\cdots\int[\mathbf{F}_{1j}\cdot\nabla_{\mathbf{p}_1}+\mathbf{F}_{2j}\cdot\nabla_{\mathbf{p}_2}]K^{(N)}(s)f^{(2/N-2)} \tag{16}$$
$$(\mathbf{R}_1'\mathbf{R}_2'\mathbf{p}_1'\mathbf{p}_2'|\mathbf{Q}'\mathbf{P}';t)d\mathbf{P}d\mathbf{Q}d\mathbf{P}'d\mathbf{Q}',$$

where $d\mathbf{P}=d\mathbf{p}_3\ldots d\mathbf{p}_N$, $d\mathbf{Q}=d\mathbf{R}_3\ldots d\mathbf{R}_N$, etc. Eq. (13) is applicable to a description of the behavior of two particles in a system at arbitrary density. In the limit of zero density the triple collision terms on the right-hand side of Eq. (16) obviously vanish and $K^{(2)}$ approaches $K_0^{(2)}$ which obeys the equation

$$\frac{\partial K_0^{(2)}}{\partial s}+\frac{\mathbf{p}_1}{m_1}\cdot\nabla_{\mathbf{R}_1}K_0^{(2)}+\frac{\mathbf{p}_2}{m_2}\cdot\nabla_{\mathbf{R}_2}K_0^{(2)}+(\mathbf{X}_1+\mathbf{F}_{12})\cdot\nabla_{\mathbf{p}_1}K_0^{(2)}$$
$$+(\mathbf{X}_2+\mathbf{F}_{12})\cdot\nabla_{\mathbf{p}_2}K_0^{(2)}=0. \tag{17}$$

The solution for $K_0^{(2)}$ is determined with the additional approximation that the external forces are sufficiently slowly varying so as not to affect significantly a binary encounter. With this simplification $K_0^{(2)}$ becomes

$$K_0^{(2)}(\mathbf{R}_1\mathbf{p}_1\mathbf{R}_2\mathbf{p}_2|\mathbf{R}_1'\mathbf{p}_1'\mathbf{R}_2'\mathbf{p}_2';s)$$
$$=\delta[\mathbf{R}_1-\mathbf{R}_1'-\Delta\mathbf{R}_1(s)]\delta[\mathbf{R}_2-\mathbf{R}_2'-\Delta\mathbf{R}_2(s)]\delta[\mathbf{p}_1-\mathbf{p}_1'-\Delta\mathbf{p}_1(s)]$$
$$\delta[\mathbf{p}_2-\mathbf{p}_2'-\Delta\mathbf{p}_2(s)], \tag{18}$$

where now $\Delta\mathbf{p}_1$, $\Delta\mathbf{p}_2$, $\Delta\mathbf{R}_1$, and $\Delta\mathbf{R}_2$ are the increments, in the time interval s, in the momenta and radius vectors of a pair of molecules undergoing a binary collision with initial coordinates $\mathbf{p}_1'\mathbf{R}_1'\mathbf{p}_2'\mathbf{R}_2'$. We take Eqs. (17) and (18) to be the analytic formulation of the binary collision mechanism in the limit of zero density.

Substitution of Eq. (17) into the function Ω Eq. (15), leads to

$$\Omega=\frac{1}{\tau}\int\cdots\int_0^{\tau}\left\{\frac{\partial K^{(2)}}{\partial s}+\frac{\mathbf{p}_1}{m_1}\cdot\nabla_{\mathbf{R}_1}K_0^{(2)}+\frac{\mathbf{p}_2}{m_2}\cdot\nabla_{\mathbf{R}_2}K_0^{(2)}\right\}$$
$$\times f^{(1)}(\mathbf{R}_1'\mathbf{p}_1';t)f^{(1)}(\mathbf{R}_2'\mathbf{p}_2';t)d\mathbf{R}_2d\mathbf{p}_2dsd\mathbf{R}_1'd\mathbf{R}_2'd\mathbf{p}_1'd\mathbf{p}_2', \tag{19}$$

which, with the aid of Eq. (18), can be altered to read

$$\Omega=\frac{1}{\tau}\int\cdots\int_0^{\tau}\{\delta(\mathbf{R}_1-\mathbf{R}_1'-\Delta\mathbf{R}_1)\delta(\mathbf{R}_2-\mathbf{R}_2'-\Delta\mathbf{R}_2)$$
$$\frac{\partial}{\partial s}[\delta(\mathbf{p}_1-\mathbf{p}_1'-\Delta\mathbf{p}_1)\delta(\mathbf{p}_2-\mathbf{p}_2'-\Delta\mathbf{p}_2)]\}$$
$$\times f^{(1)}(\mathbf{R}_1'\mathbf{p}_1';t)f^{(1)}(\mathbf{R}_2'\mathbf{p}_2';t)d\mathbf{R}_2d\mathbf{p}_2dsd\mathbf{R}'d\mathbf{R}_2'd\mathbf{p}_1'd\mathbf{p}_2'. \tag{20}$$

We denote the difference between this last expression and

$$\Omega' = \frac{1}{\tau}\int_0^{\tau}\cdots\int \{\delta(\mathbf{R}_1 - \mathbf{R}_1')\delta(\mathbf{R}_2 - \mathbf{R}_2')\frac{\partial}{\partial s}[\delta(\mathbf{p}_1 - \mathbf{p}_1' - \Delta\mathbf{p}_1)$$

$$\delta(\mathbf{p}_2 - \mathbf{p}_2' - \Delta\mathbf{p}_2)]\}$$

$$\times f^{(1)}(\mathbf{R}_1'\mathbf{p}_1'; t)f^{(1)}(\mathbf{R}_1'\mathbf{p}_2'; t)\, d\mathbf{R}_2 d\mathbf{p}_2 ds d\mathbf{R}_1' d\mathbf{R}_2' d\mathbf{p}_1' d\mathbf{p}_2' \qquad (21)$$

by $(\Delta\Omega|\tau)$, i.e., $\Omega = \Omega' + (\Delta\Omega|\tau)$. The expansion of the δ-functions in Taylor series leads to the following expression for $[\Delta\Omega|\tau]$ to first order in configuration space gradients

$$\frac{\Delta\Omega}{\tau} = -\frac{1}{\tau^2}\int\cdots\int_0^{\tau}\{\delta(\mathbf{R}_1 - \mathbf{R}_1')[\Delta\mathbf{R}_2\cdot\nabla_{\mathbf{R}_2}\delta(\mathbf{R}_2 - \mathbf{R}_2') - \delta(\mathbf{R}_2 - \mathbf{R}_2')$$

$$\mathbf{R}'\cdot\nabla_{\mathbf{R}_1}] + \delta(\mathbf{R}_2 - \mathbf{R}_2')\Delta\mathbf{R}_1\cdot\nabla_{\mathbf{R}_1}\delta(\mathbf{R}_1 - \mathbf{R}_1')\}$$

$$\times\left\{\frac{\partial}{\partial s}[\delta(\mathbf{p}_1 - \mathbf{p}_1' - \Delta\mathbf{p}_1)\delta(\mathbf{p}_2 - \mathbf{p}_2' - \Delta\mathbf{p}_2)]\right\}$$

$$f^{(1)}(\mathbf{R}_1'\mathbf{p}_1'; t)f^{(1)}(\mathbf{R}_1'\mathbf{p}_2'; t)d\mathbf{R}_2 d\mathbf{p}_2 ds d\mathbf{R}_1' d\mathbf{R}_2' d\mathbf{p}_1' d\mathbf{p}_2'.$$

The term $[\Delta\Omega|\tau]$ is independent of τ for sufficiently large values of τ and therefore is in general a constituent of the Boltzmann equation. An estimate of the average extent of $\Delta\mathbf{R}(s)$ yields a distance L_τ which is much larger than the range of the intermolecular forces but much smaller than the mean free path. If the application of the equation of transport is restricted to systems in which the distribution functions and therefore the macroscopic properties do not vary significantly over a distance L_τ, then the term $[\Delta\Omega|\tau]$ becomes a small correction which is usually neglected.

The integration over s, $\mathbf{R}_1'$, $\mathbf{R}_2'$ in Eq. (21) is simple and Ω' becomes

$$\Omega' = \int\cdots\int\frac{1}{\tau}\{\delta[\mathbf{p}_1 - \mathbf{p}_1' - \Delta\mathbf{p}_1(\tau)]\delta[\mathbf{p}_2 - \mathbf{p}_2' - \Delta\mathbf{p}_2(\tau)] - \delta[\mathbf{p}_1 - \mathbf{p}_1']$$

$$\delta[\mathbf{p}_2 - \mathbf{p}_2']\}\times f^{(1)}(\mathbf{R}_1\mathbf{p}_1'; t)f^{(1)}(\mathbf{R}_1\mathbf{p}_2'; t)d\mathbf{R}d\mathbf{p}_2 d\mathbf{p}_1' d\mathbf{p}_2', \qquad (22)$$

where $d\mathbf{R}_2$ has been replaced by $d\mathbf{R}$, $\mathbf{R} = \mathbf{R}_2 - \mathbf{R}_1$. At this point the remainder of the derivation is identical with that of Kirkwood and will be outlined only briefly. The integration over the relative configuration space is accomplished in a cylindrical coordinate system (z, b, ϵ) with origin on molecule 1 and z-axis antiparallel to the initial relative momentum vector. The regions of this relative Lagrange configuration space for which complete collisions occur in the interval τ consist of filaments of volume

$$\frac{\mathbf{p}_{12}}{m_{12}}\tau b\, db\, d\epsilon,$$

where $\mathbf{p}_{12}$ is the magnitude of the initial relative momentum and m_{12} is the reduced mass. Incomplete collisions or motion in multiply periodic orbits arise from regions of relative configuration space of finite volume elements independent of τ so that their contribution becomes inconsequential for sufficiently large τ. For all other regions of relative configuration space the bracket in Eq. (21) vanishes since the increments in momenta of particles 1 and 2 are zero. These considerations and use of Eqs. (14) and (22) lead to an expression which, upon additional time smoothing, finally yields the Boltzmann equation,

$$\frac{\partial \bar{f}^{(1)}}{\partial t} + \frac{\mathbf{p}_1}{m_1} \cdot \nabla_{\mathbf{R}_1} \bar{f}^{(1)} + \mathbf{X}_1 \cdot \nabla_{\mathbf{p}_1} \bar{f}^{(1)}$$

$$= (N-1) \int \cdots \int \frac{\mathbf{p}_{12}}{m_{12}} \{ \bar{f}^{(1)}[\mathbf{R}_1, \mathbf{p}_1 - \Delta\mathbf{p}_1; t] \bar{f}^{(1)}[\mathbf{R}_1, \mathbf{p}_2 - \Delta\mathbf{p}_2; t]$$

$$- \bar{f}^{(1)}(\mathbf{R}_1 \mathbf{p}_1; t) \bar{f}^{(1)}(\mathbf{R}_1 \mathbf{p}_2; t) \} b\,db\,d\epsilon\,d\mathbf{p}_2, \qquad (23)$$

provided the function $\overline{f^{(1)} f^{(1)}}$ can be replaced by $\bar{f}^{(1)} \bar{f}^{(1)}$, a procedure which can be justified for distributions close to equilibrium.

One of the authors (J.R.) wishes to acknowledge that this work was supported in part by a grant from the National Science Foundation.